U.S. LITERATURE ORDER FORM

NAME: ______________________ TITLE: ____________

COMPANY: ______________________

ADDRESS: ______________________

CITY: ______________ STATE: ________ ZIP: ________

COUNTRY: ______________________

PHONE NO.: (   ) ______________________

ORDER NO.	TITLE	QTY.		PRICE		TOTAL
☐☐☐☐☐☐-☐☐☐	________	____	×	____	=	____
☐☐☐☐☐☐-☐☐☐	________	____	×	____	=	____
☐☐☐☐☐☐-☐☐☐	________	____	×	____	=	____
☐☐☐☐☐☐-☐☐☐	________	____	×	____	=	____
☐☐☐☐☐☐-☐☐☐	________	____	×	____	=	____
☐☐☐☐☐☐-☐☐☐	________	____	×	____	=	____

Subtotal ____________

Your Local Sales Tax ____________

POSTAGE AND HANDLING:
Add appropriate postage and handling to subtotal
10% U.S.
20% Canada
→ ____________

Allow 4–6 weeks for delivery

Total ____________

Pay by Visa, MasterCard, Check or Money Order, payable to Intel Literature. Purchase Orders have a $50.00 minimum.

☐ Visa
☐ MasterCard

Account No. ______________________ Expiration Date ________

Signature: ______________________

Mail To: Intel Literature Distribution
Mail Stop SC6-714
3065 Bowers Avenue
Santa Clara, CA 95051.

Customers outside the U.S. and Canada should contact the local Intel Sales Office or Distributor listed in the back of this book.

For information on quantity discounts, call the 800 number below:

TOLL-FREE NUMBER: (800) 548-4725

Prices good until 12/31/85.

Source HB

Cut Along Dotted Line

Mail To: Intel Literature Distribution
Mail Stop SC6-714
3065 Bowers Avenue
Santa Clara, CA 95051.

iAPX 86/88, 186/188 User's Manual

Hardware Reference

1985

Intel Corporation makes no warranty for the use of its products and assumes no responsibility for any errors which may appear in this document nor does it make a commitment to update the information contained herein.

Intel retains the right to make changes to these specifications at any time, without notice.

Contact your local sales office to obtain the latest specifications before placing your order.

The following are trademarks of Intel Corporation and may only be used to identify Intel Products:

Additional copies of this manual or other Intel literature may be obtained from:

Intel Corporation
Literature Department
Mail Stop SC6-714
3065 Bowers Avenue
Santa Clara, CA 95051

Table of Contents

Chapter 1
8086/8088 CPU

Chapter 2
80186/80188 CPU

Chapter 3
8087 Numeric Processor Extension

Chapter 4
8089 Input/Output Processor

TABLE OF CONTENTS

Tables

TABLE OF CONTENTS

Figures

TABLE OF CONTENTS

TABLE OF CONTENTS

TABLE OF CONTENTS

TABLE OF CONTENTS

TABLE OF CONTENTS

8086/8088 CPU

1

CHAPTER 1
8086/8088 CPU

1.1 INTRODUCTION

This chapter contains specific hardware design information on the operation and functions of INTEL's 8086/8088 Central Processing Units (CPUs). This information consists of a component overview of the 8086/88 microprocessors presenting architectural and software considerations, individual device pin functional and electrical signal definitions, a detailed description of the minimum and maximum operating modes, detailed descriptions of the operation of the address and data buses, an explanation of the protocols supported for local bus transfers to other devices, and a detailed description of interrupt operation. In addition, descriptions of the various 8086/88 family support circuits and their circuit functions appear at the end of the chapter. For more specific information of any of the 8086 family support circuits, refer to the Microsystem Components Handbook (Order Number: 230843-002).

1.2 COMPONENT OVERVIEW

The 8086 and 8088 are closely related third-generation microprocessors. Both CPU's contain a 20-bit address bus (1 mega-byte of address space) and utilize an identical instruction/function format. Differences between the two devices consist essentially of their respective data bus widths. The 8088 is designed with an 8-bit external data path to memory and I/O, while the 8086 can transfer 16 bits at a time. In almost every other respect the processors are identical; software written for one CPU will execute on the other without alteration. Both chips are contained in standard 40-pin dual in-line packages and operate from a single +5V power source. Except where expressly noted, the descriptions contained in this chapter are applicable to both microprocessors.

The 8086 and 8088 Microprocessors can be used for a wide spectrum of microcomputer applications. This flexibility is one of their most outstanding characteristics. Systems can range from small uniprocessor minimal-memory designs implemented with a few chips (see Figure 1-1), to multiprocessor systems with up to a megabyte of memory (see Figure 1-2).

Both the 8086 and 8088 microprocessors use a combined, or "time-multiplexed", address and data bus that permits several of the device pins to serve dual functions. Some microprocessor control pins also serve dual functions. These pins are defined according to the strapping of a single input pin (the MN/MX* pin). This feature provides configuration of the CPU's in either "minimum mode" or "maximum mode" circuits.

In the "minimum mode," the CPU is configured for small, single-processor systems. In this configuration all control signals are provided by the CPU and the dual function pins transfer signals directly to memory and input/output devices.

In the "maximum mode" these same pins take on different functions that are helpful in medium to large systems, especially systems with multiple processors. An Intel 8288 Bus Controller is used to provide the control signal outputs. This allows several of the device pins previously delegated to these control functions to be redefined in order to support multiprocessing applications. A detailed description of this feature is presented later in the chapter.

The 8086 and 8088 Microprocessors are designed to operate with the 8089 Input/Output Processor (IOP) and other processors in multiprocessing and distributed processing systems. When used in conjunction with one or more 8089s, the 8086 and 8088 expand the applicability of microprocessors into I/O-intensive data processing systems. Built-in coordinating signals and instructions, and electrical compatibility with Intel's MULTIBUS® shared bus architecture, simplify and reduce the cost of developing multiple-processor designs.

Both the 8086 and 8088 are substantually more powerful than any microprocessor previously offered by Intel. Actual performance, of course, varies from application to application, but comparisons to the industry standard 2-MHz 8080A are instructive. The 8088 is from four to six times more powerful than the 8080A; the 8086 provides seven to ten times the 8080A's performance.

The 8086's advantage over the 8088 is the result of the 8086's 16-bit external data bus. In applications that manipulate 8-bit quantities extensively, or that are execution-bound, the 8088 can approach to within 10% of the 8086's processing throughput.

The improved performance of the 8086 and 8088 is accomplished by combining a 16-bit internal data path with a pipelined architecture that allows instructions to be prefetched during spare bus cycles. In addition, a compact instruction format that enables more instructions to be fetched in a given amount of time contributes to this high performance.

Software for 8086 and 8088 systems does not need to be written in assembly language. The CPUs are designed to provide direct hardware support for programs written in high-level languages such as Intel's PL/M-86. Most high-level languages store variables in memory; the 8086/8088 symmetrical instruction set supports direct operation on memory operands, including operands on the

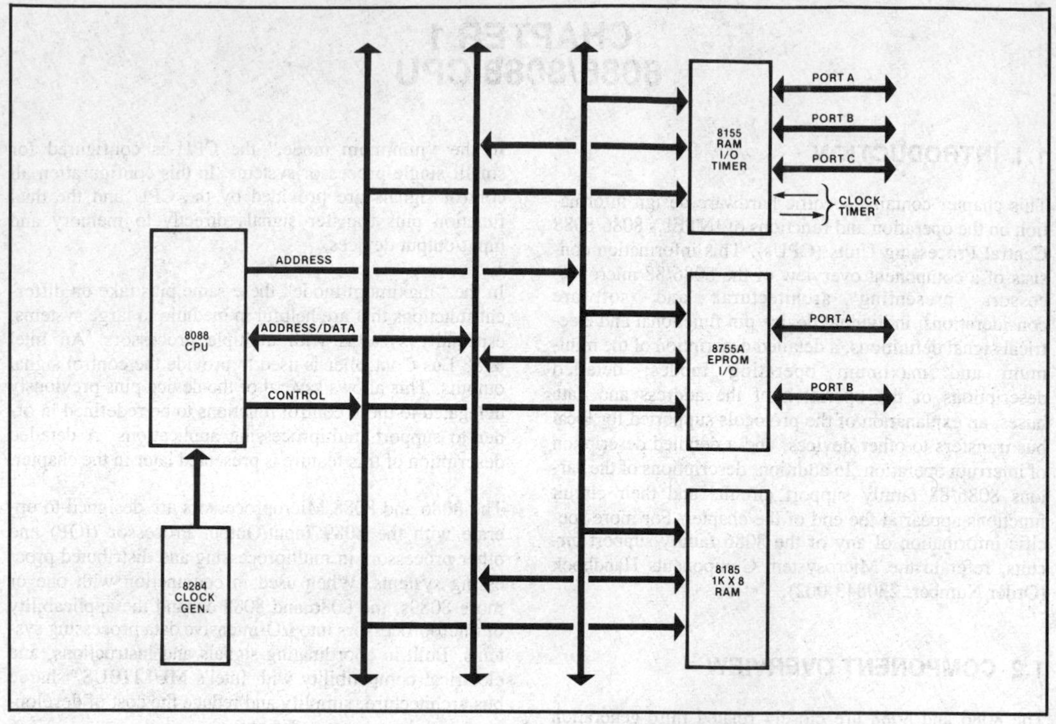

Figure 1-1 Small 8088-Based System

stack. The hardware addressing modes provide efficient, straightforward implementations of based variables, arrays, arrays of structures and other high-level language data constructs. A powerful set of memory-to-memory string operations is available for efficient character data manipulation. Finally, routines with critical performance requirements that cannot be met with PL/M-86 may be written in ASM-86 (the 8086/8088 assembly language) and linked with PL/M-86 code.

Although the 8086 and 8088 Microprocessors are totally new designs, they make the most of user's existing investments in systems designed around the 8080/8085 microprocessors. Many of the standard Intel memory, peripheral control and communication chips are compatible with the 8086 and the 8088. Software is developed in the familiar Intellec Microcomputer Development System environment, and most existing programs, whether written in ASM-80 or PL/M-80, can be directly converted to run on the 8086 and 8088.

1.2.1 Architectural Overview

Both the 8086 and 8088 microprocessors incorporate two separate processing units (see Figures 1-3 and 1-4). These are the Execution Unit (EU) and the Bus Interface Unit (BIU). Both microprocessors contain identical EU's. In the 8086 the BIU incorporates a 16-bit data bus and a 6-byte instruction queue. In the 8088 the BIU incorporates an 8-bit data bus and a 4-byte instruction queue.

The EU executes instructions and the BIU fetches instructions, reads operands and writes results. The two units can operate independently of one another and are able, under most circumstances, to extensively overlap instruction fetch with execution. The result is that, in most cases, the time normally required to fetch instructions "disappears" because the EU executes instructions that have already been fetched by the BIU. Figure 1-5 illustrates this overlap and compares it with traditional microprocessor operation. In the example, overlapping reduces the elapsed time required to execute three instructions, and allows two additional instructions to be prefetched as well.

In the 8086 CPU, when two or more bytes of the 6-byte instruction queue are empty and the EU does not require the BIU to perform a bus cycle, the BIU executes instruction fetch cycles to refill the queue. In the 8088 CPU, when one byte of the 4-byte instruction queue is empty, the BIU executes an instruction fetch cycle. Note that since the 8086 CPU has a 16-bit data bus, it can access *two* instruction object code bytes in a single bus cycle. Since the 8088 CPU has an 8-bit data bus, it accesses *one* instruction object code byte per bus cycle. If the EU

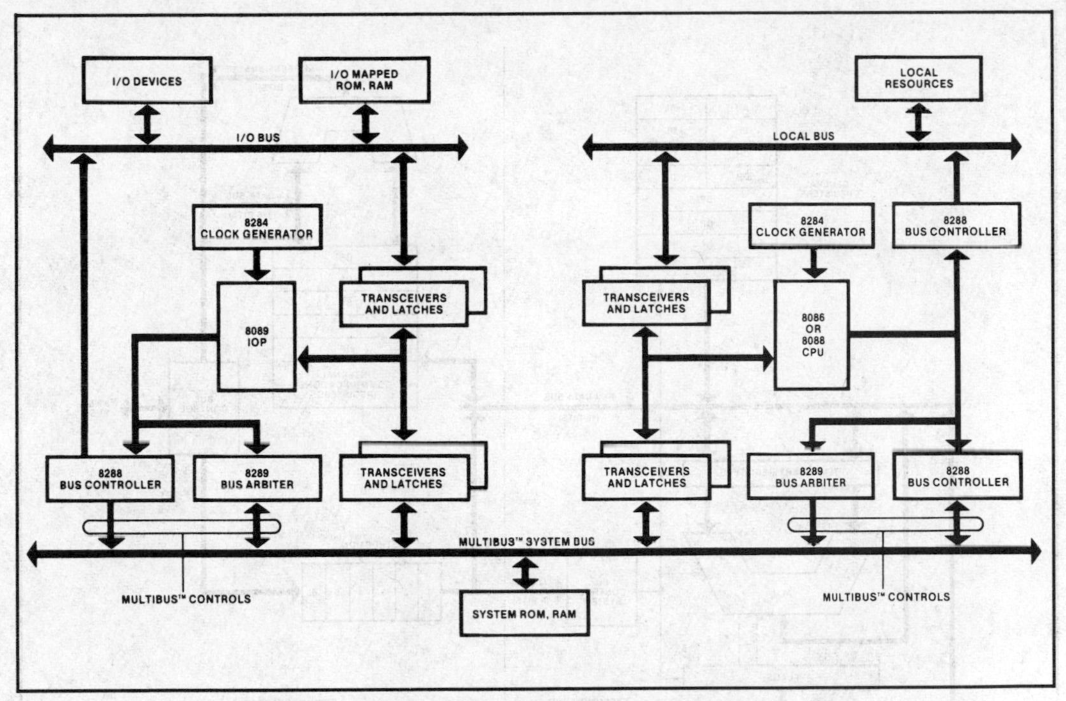

Figure 1-2 8086/8088/8089 Multiprocessing System

issues a request for bus access while the BIU is in the process of an instruction fetch bus cycle, the BIU completes the cycle before honoring the EU's request.

EXECUTION UNIT

The execution units (EU's) of the 8086 and 8088 are identical (see Figures 1-3 and 1-4). The EU is responsible for the execution of all instructions, for providing data and addresses to the BIU, and for manipulating the general registers and the flag register. A 16-bit arithmetic/logic unit (ALU) in the EU maintains the CPU status and control flags, and manipulates the general registers and instruction operands. All registers and data paths in the EU are 16 bits wide for fast internal transfers.

The EU has no connection to the system bus, the "outside world." It obtains instructions from a queue maintained by the BIU. Likewise, when an instruction requires access to memory or to a peripheral device, the EU requests the BIU to obtain and store the data. All addresses manipulated by the EU are 16 bits wide. The BIU, however, performs an address relocation that gives the EU access to the full megabyte of memory space.

When the EU is ready to execute an instruction, it fetches the instruction object code byte from the BIU's instruction queue and then executes the instruction. If the queue is empty when the EU is ready to fetch an instruction byte, the EU waits for the instruction byte to be fetched. If a memory location or I/O port must be accessed during the execution of an instruction, the EU requests the BIU to perform the required bus cycle.

BUS INTERFACE UNIT

The 8086 and 8088 BIU's are functionally identical, but are implemented differently to match the structure and performance characteristics of their respective buses. Data is transferred between the CPU and memory or I/O devices upon demand from the EU. The BIU executes all external bus cycles. This unit consists of the segment and communications registers, the instruction pointer and the instruction object code queue. The BIU combines segment and offset values in a dedicated adder to derive 20-bit addresses, transfers data to and from the EU on the ALU data bus and loads or "prefetches" instructions into the queue. These "prefetched" instructions can then be fetched by the EU with a minimum of wait.

During periods when the EU is busy executing instructions, the BIU "looks ahead" and fetches more instructions from memory. These instructions are stored in an internal RAM array called the instruction stream queue. The 8088 instruction queue holds up to four bytes of the instruction stream, while the 8086 queue can store up to

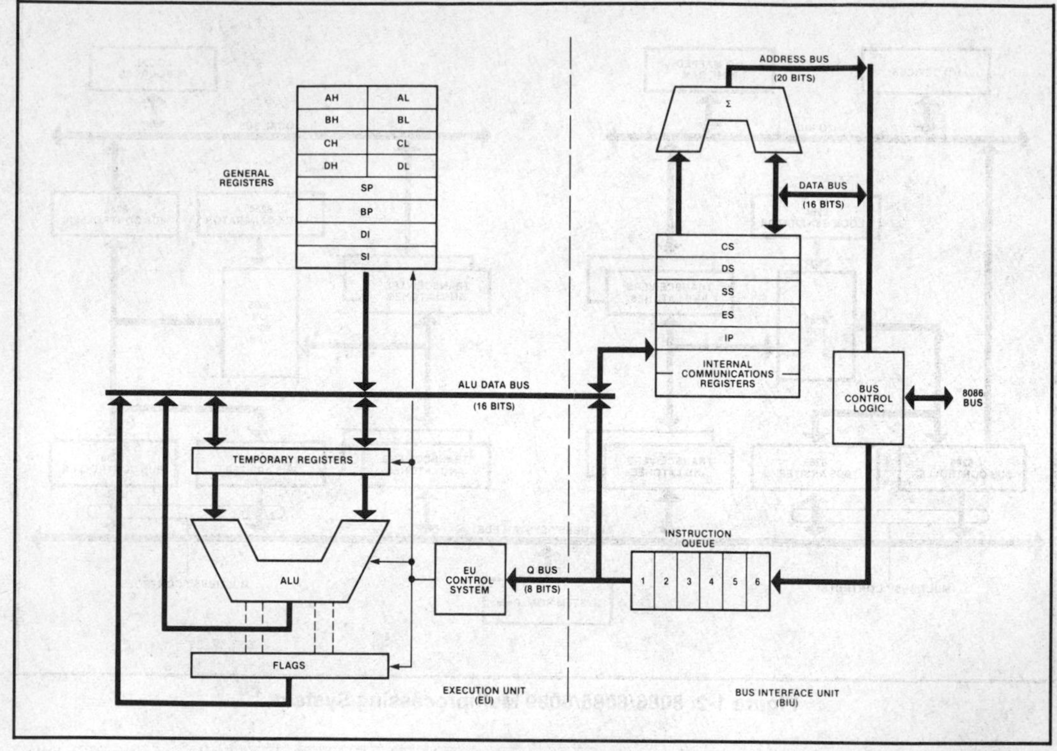

Figure 1-3 8086 Simplified Functional Block Diagram

six instruction bytes. These queue sizes allow the BIU to keep the EU supplied with prefetched instructions under most conditions without monopolizing the system bus. The 8088 BIU fetches another instruction byte whenever one byte in its queue is empty and there is no active request for bus access from the EU. The 8086 BIU operates similarly except that it does not initiate a fetch until there are two empty bytes in its queue. The 8086 BIU normally obtains two instruction bytes per fetch. If a program transfer forces fetching from an odd address, the 8086 automatically reads one byte from the odd address and then resumes fetching two-byte words from the subsequent even addresses.

In most circumstances the queues contain at least one byte of the instruction stream and the EU does not have to wait for instructions to be fetched. The instructions in the queue are those stored in memory locations immediately adjacent to and higher than the instruction currently being executed. That is, they are the next logical instructions so long as execution proceeds serially. If the EU executes an instruction that transfers control to another location, the BIU resets the queue, fetches the instruction from the new address, passes it immediately to the EU, and then begins refilling the queue from the new location. In addition, the BIU suspends instruction fetching whenever the EU requests a memory or I/O read or write (except that a fetch already in progress is completed before executing the EU's bus request).

GENERAL REGISTERS

Both CPU's have the same complement of eight 16-bit general registers (see Figure 1-6). The general registers are subdivided into two sets of four registers each. These are the data registers (sometimes called the H & L group for "high" and "low"), and the pointer and index registers (sometimes called the P & I group).

The data registers are unique in that their upper (high) and lower halves are separately addressable. This means that each data register can be used interchangeably as a 16-bit register, or as a two 8-bit registers. The other CPU registers are always accessed as 16-bit only. The data registers can be used without constraint in most arithmetic and logic operations. In addition, some instructions use certain registers implicitly (see Table 1-1), therefore allowing compact yet powerful encoding.

The pointer and index registers can also be used in most arithmetic and logic operations. All eight general registers fit the definition of an "accumulator" as defined in

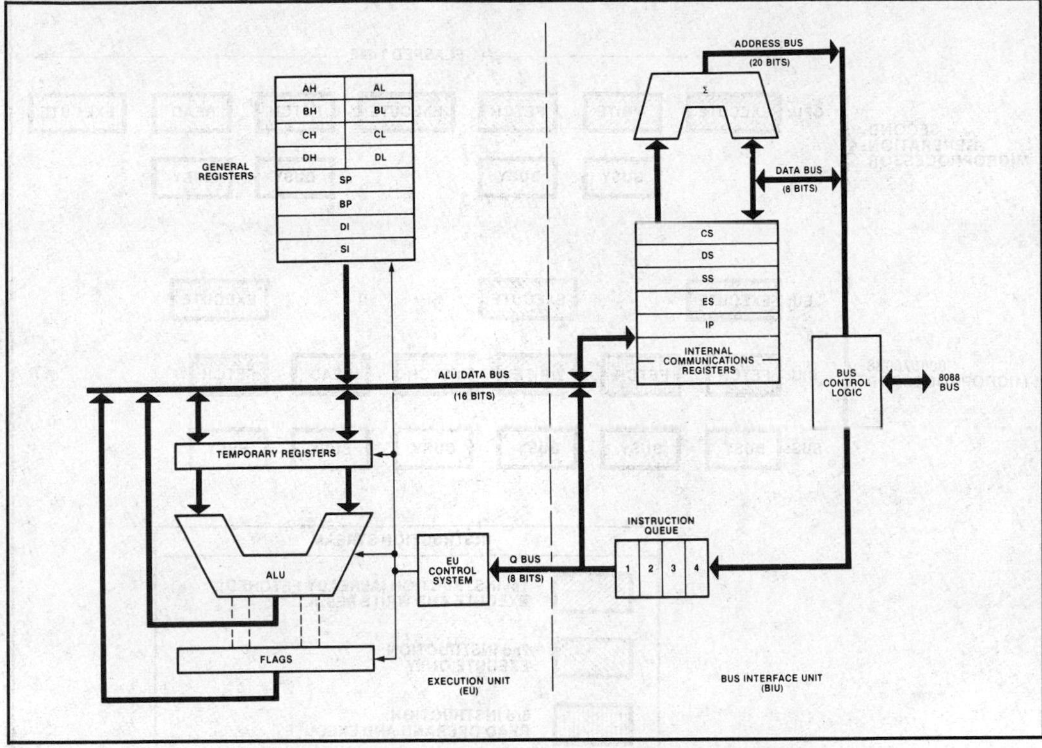

Figure 1-4 8088 Simplified Functional Block Diagram

first and second generation microprocessors. The P & I registers (except for BP) are also used implicitly in some instructions (see Table 1-1).

SEGMENT REGISTERS

The 8086 and 8088 memory space (up to one megabyte) is divided into logical segments of up to 64k bytes each. The CPU has direct access to four segments at a time. The base addresses (starting locations) of these memory segments are contained in the segment registers (see Figure 1-7). The CS register points to the current code segment. Instructions are fetched from the CS segment. The SS register points to the current stack segment. Stack operations are performed on locations in the SS segment. The DS register points to the current data segment. The DS register generally contains program variables. The ES register points to the current extra segment, which also is typically used for data storage.

The segment registers are accessable to programs and can be manipulated with several instructions. Good programming practice and consideration of compatibility with future Intel hardware and software products dictate that the segment registers be used in a disciplined fashion.

INSTRUCTION POINTER

The 16-bit instruction pointer (IP) is similar to the program counter (PC) in the 8080/8085 CPUs. The instruction pointer is updated by the BIU so that it contains the offset (distance in bytes) of the next instruction from the beginning of the current code segment; i.e., IP points to the next instruction. During normal execution, IP contains the offset of the next instruction to be *fetched* by the BIU. Whenever IP is saved on the stack, however, it is first automatically adjusted to point to the next instruction to be *executed*. Programs do not have direct access to the instruction pointer, but instructions cause it to change and to be saved on and restored from the stack.

FLAGS

The 8086 and 8088 have six 1-bit status flags (see Figure 1-8) that the EU posts to reflect certain properties of the result of an arithmetic or logic operation. A group of instructions is available that allows a program to alter its execution depending on the state of these flags, i.e., on the result of a prior operation. Different instructions affect the status flags differently; in general, however, the flags reflect the following conditions:

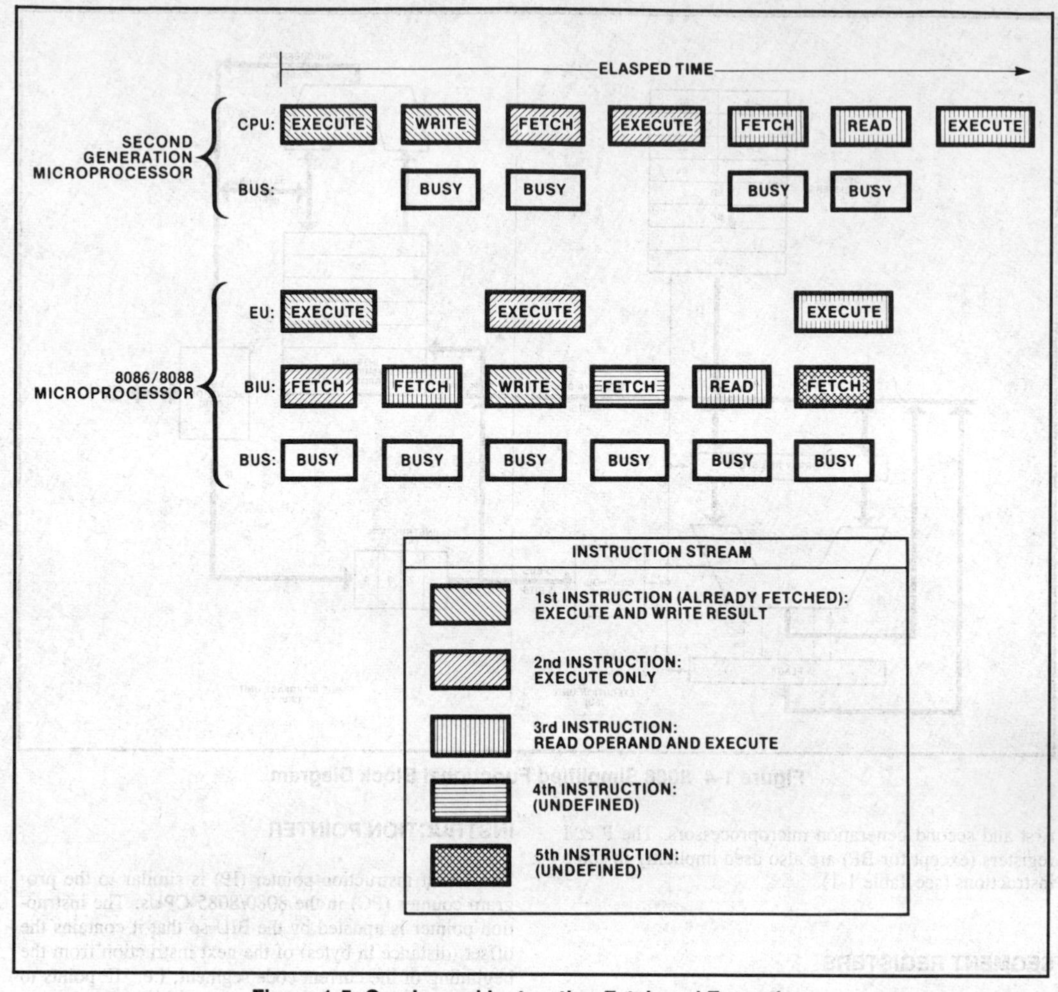

Figure 1-5 Overlapped Instruction Fetch and Execution

1. If AF (the auxiliary flag) is set, there has been a carry out of the low nibble into the high nibble or a borrow from the high from the high nibble into the low nibble of an 8-bit quantity (low-order byte of a 16-bit quantity). This flag is used by decimal arithmetic instructions.

2. If CF (the carry flag) is set, there has been a carry out of, or a borrow into, the high-order bit of the result (8-or 16- bit). The flag is used by instructions that add and subtract multibyte numbers. Rotate instructions can also isolate a bit in memory or a register by placing it in the carry flag.

3. If OF (the overflow flag) is set, an arithmetic overflow has occurred; that is, a significant digit has been lost because the size of the result exceeded the capacity of its destination location. An Interrupt On Overflow instruction is available that will generate an interrupt in this situation.

4. If SF (the sign flag) is set, the high-order bit of the result is a 1. Since negative binary numbers are represented in the 8086 and 8088 in standard two's complement notation, SF indicates the sign of the result (0 = positive, 1 = negative).

5. If the PF (the parity flag) is set, the result has even parity, an even number of 1-bits. This flag can be used to check for data transmission errors.

6. If ZF (the zero flag) is set, the result of the operation is 0.

Three additional control flags (see Figure 1-8) can be set and cleared by programs to alter processor operations:

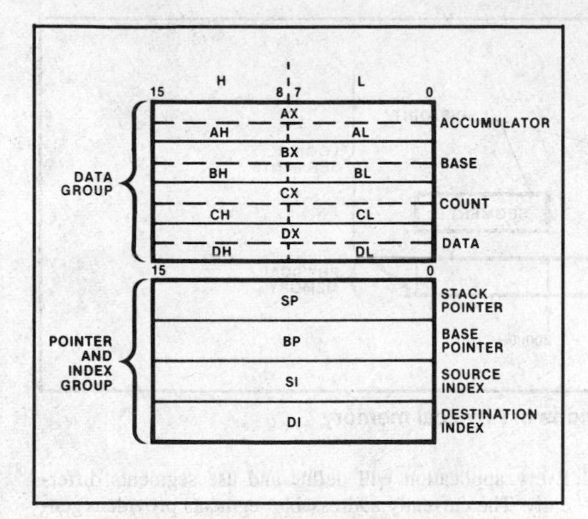

Figure 1-6 General Registers

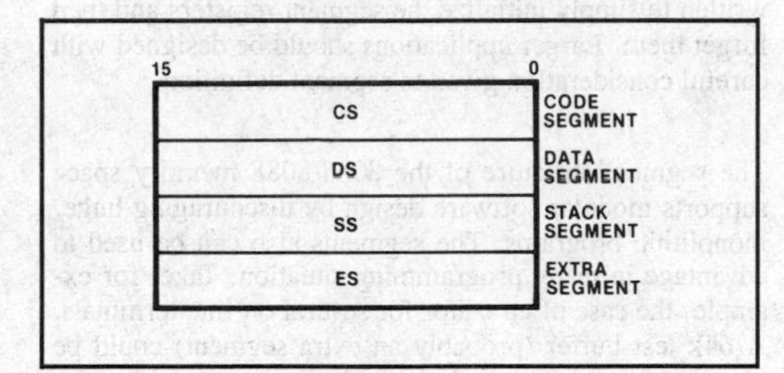

Figure 1-7 Segment Registers

Table 1-1 Implicit Use of General Registers

REGISTER	OPERATIONS
AX	Word Multiply, Word Divide, Word I/O
AL	Byte Multiply, Byte Divide, Byte I/O, Translate, Decimal Arithmetic
AH	Byte Multiply, Byte Divide
BX	Translate
CX	String Operations, Loops
CL	Variable Shift and Rotate
DX	Word Multiply, Word Divide, Indirect I/O
SP	Stack Operations
SI	String Operations
DI	String Operations

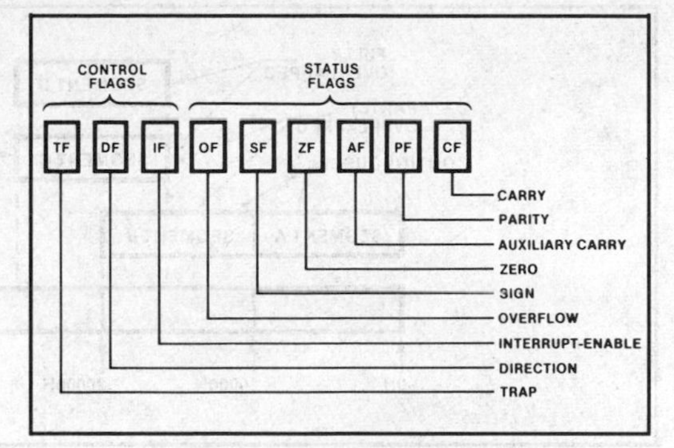

Figure 1-8 Status Flags

1. Setting DF (the direction flag) causes string instructions to auto-decrement; that is, to process strings from the high address to the low address, or from "right to left." Clearing DF causes string instructions to auto-increment, or process strings from "left to right."
2. Setting IF (the interrupt-enable flag) allows the CPU to recognize external (maskable) interrupt requests. Clearing IF disables these interrupts. IF has no affect on either non- maskable external or internally generated interrupts.
3. Setting TF (the trap flag) puts the processor into single-step mode for debugging. In this mode, the CPU automatically generates an internal interrupt after each instruction, allowing a program to be inspected as it executes instruction by instruction.

MODE SELECTION

Each of the processors has a strap pin (MN/MX*) that defines the function of eight CPU pins in the 8086 and nine pins in the 8088. Connecting MN/MX* to +5V places the CPU in minimum mode. This configuration is designed for small systems (roughly one or two boards) and the CPU provides bus control signals needed by memory and peripherals. When MN/MX* is strapped to ground, the CPU is configured in maximum mode. In this configuration the CPU encodes control signals on three lines. An 8288 Bus Controller is added to decode the signals for the rest of the system. The CPU uses the remaining free lines for a new set of signals designed to help coordinate the activities of other processors in the system.

SEGMENTATION

Programs for the 8086 and 8088 "view" the memory space (one megabyte) as a group of segments that are defined by application. A segment is a logical unit of memory that may be up to 64k bytes long. Each segment is made up of contiguous memory locations and is an independent, separately-addressable unit. Every segment is

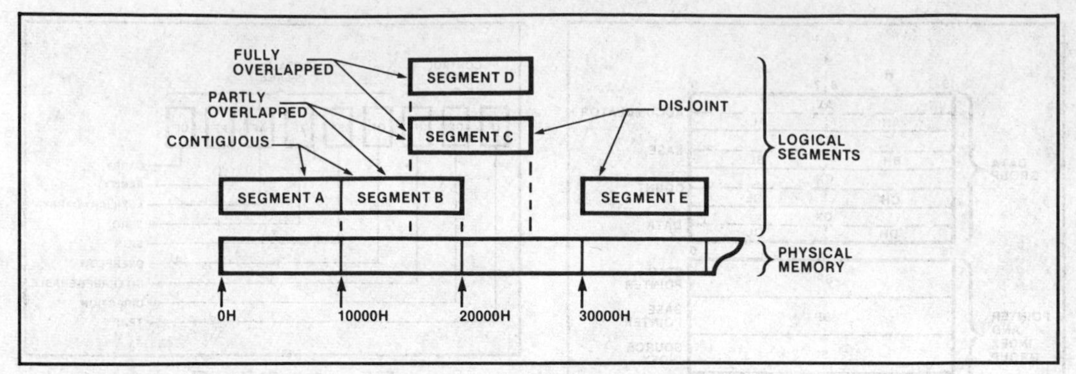

Figure 1-9 Segment Locations in Physical memory

assigned (by software) a base address, which is its starting location in the memory space. All segments begin on 16-byte memory boundaries. There are no other restrictions on segment locations. Segments may be adjacent, disjoint, partially overlapped, or fully overlapped (see Figure 1-9). A physical memory location may be mapped into (contained in) one or more logical segments.

The segment registers point to (contain the base address values of) the four currently addressable segments (see Figure 1-10). Programs obtain access to code and data in other segments by changing the segment registers to point to the desired segments.

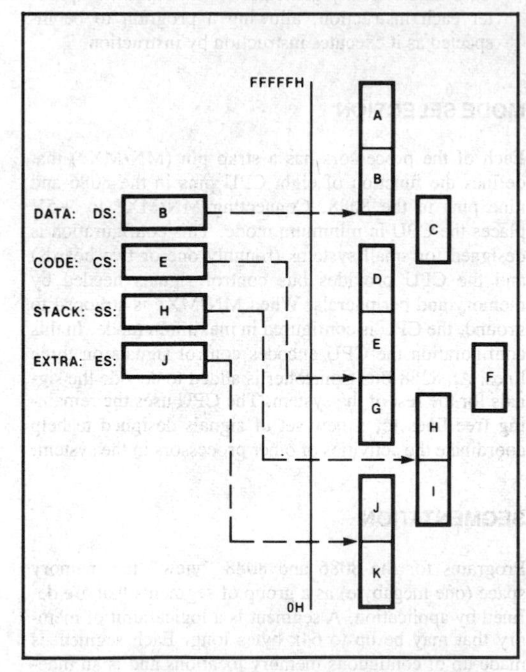

Figure 1-10 Currently Addressable Segments

Every application will define and use segments differently. The currently addressable segments provide a generous work space; 64k bytes for code, a 64k byte stack and 128k bytes of data storage. Many applications can be written to simply initialize the segment registers and then forget them. Larger applications should be designed with careful consideration given to segment definition.

The segment structure of the 8086/8088 memory space supports modular software design by discouraging huge, monolithic programs. The segments also can be used to advantage in many programming situation. Take, for example, the case of an editor for several on-line terminals. A 64k test buffer (probably an extra segment) could be assigned to each terminal. A single program could maintain all the buffers by simply changing register ES to point to the buffer of the terminal requiring service.

PHYSICAL ADDRESS GENERATION

In theory, it is useful to think of every memory location as having two kinds of addresses, physical and logical. A physical address is the 20-bit value that uniquely identifies each byte location in the megabyte memory space. Physical addresses range from 0H to FFFFFH. All exchanges between the CPU and memory components use this physical address.

Programs deal with logical, rather than physical addresses and allow code to be developed without prior knowledge of where the code is to be located in memory an facilitate dynamic management of memory resources. A logical address consists of a segment base value and an offset value. For any given memory location, the segment base value locates the first byte of the containing segment and the offset value is the distance, in bytes, of the target location from the beginning of the segment. Segment base and offset values are unsigned 16-bit quantities. The lowest-addressed byte in a segment has an offset of 0. Many different logical addresses can map to the same

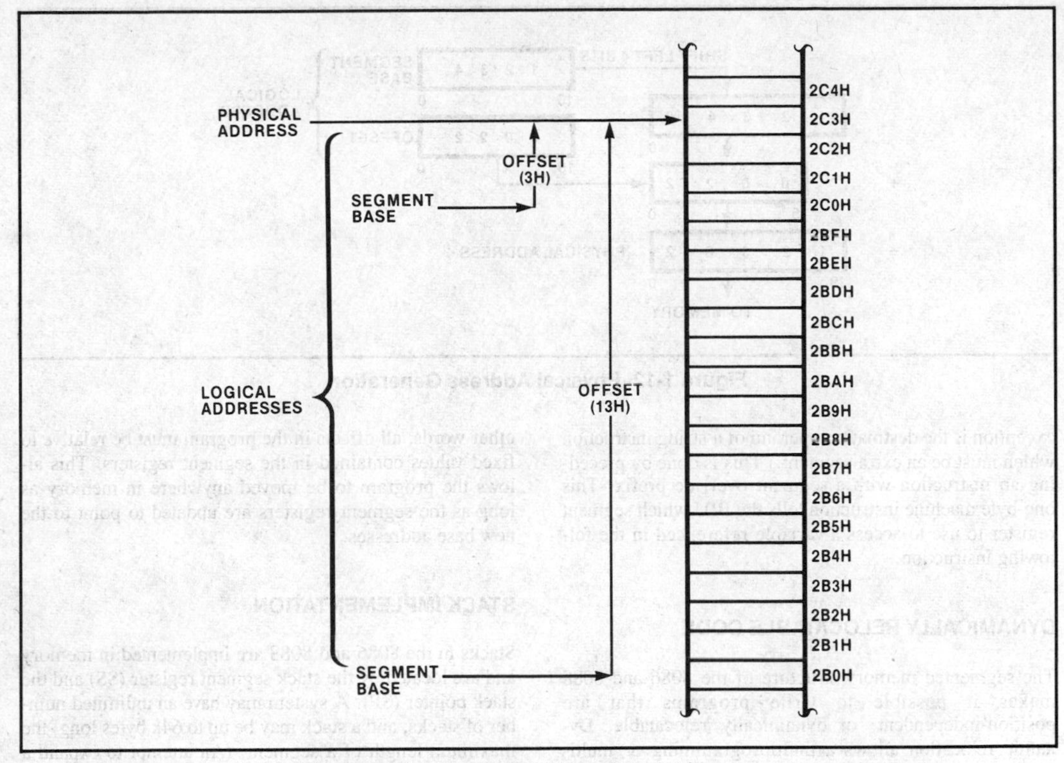

Figure 1-11 Logical and Physical Addresses

physical location. In the example (see Figure 1-11) physical memory location 2C3H is contained in two different overlapping segments, one beginning at 2B0H and the other at 2C0H.

Whenever the BIU accesses memory -to fetch an instruction or to obtain or store a variable -it generates a physical address from a logical address. This is done by shifting the segment base value four bit positions and adding the offset as illustrated in Figure 1-12. Note that this addition process provides for modulo 64k addressing (addresses wrap around from the end of a segment to the beginning of the same segment).

The BIU obtains the logical address of a memory location from different sources, depending on the type of reference that is being made (see Table 1-2). Instructions are always fetched from the current code segment; IP contains the offset of the target instruction from the beginning of the segment. Stack instructions always operate on the current stack segment; SP contains the offset of the top of the stack. Most variables (memory operands) are assumed to reside in the current data segment, although a program can instruct the BIU to access a variable in one of the other currently addressable segments. The offset of a memory variable is calculated by the EU. This calculation is based on the addressing mode specified in the instruction; the result is called the operand's effective address (EA).

Strings are addressed differently than other variables. The source operand of a string instruction is assumed to lie in the current data segment, but another currently addressable segment may be specified. Its offset is taken from register SI, the source index register. The destination operand of a string instruction always resides in the current extra segment; its offset is taken from DI, the destination index register. The string instructions automatically adjust SI and DI as they process the strings one byte or word at a time.

When register BP, the base pointer register, is designated as a base register in an instruction, the variable is assumed to reside in the current stack segment. Therefore, register BP provides a convenient way to address data on the stack. However, BP can also be used to access data in any of the other currently addressable segments.

The BIU's segment assumptions are a convenience to programmers in most cases. However, it is possible for a programmer to explicitly direct the BIU to access a variable in any of the currently addressable segments. (The only

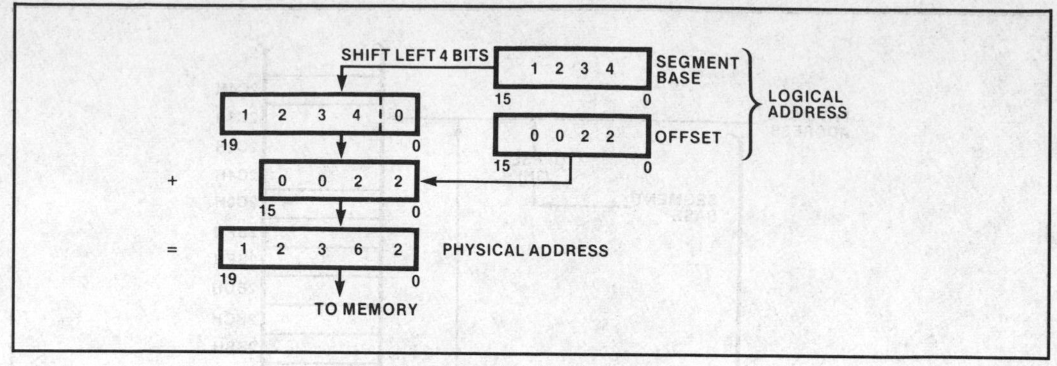

Figure 1-12 Physical Address Generation

exception is the destination operand of a string instruction which must be an extra segment.) This is done by preceding an instruction with a segment override prefix. This one-byte machine instruction tells the BIU which segment register to use to access a variable referenced in the following instruction.

DYNAMICALLY RELOCATABLE CODE

The segmented memory structure of the 8086 and 8088 makes it possible to write programs that are position-independent, or dynamically relocatable. Dynamic relocation allows a multiprogramming or multitasking system to make particularly effective use of available memory. Inactive programs can be written to disk and the space they occupied allocated programs. If a disk-resident program is needed later, it can be read back into any available memory location and restarted. Similarly, if a program needs a large contiguous block of storage, and the total amount is only available in non-adjacent fragments, other program segments can be compacted to free up a continuous space. This process is illustrated graphically in Figure 1-13.

To be dynamically relocatable, a program must not load or alter its segment registers and must not transfer directly to a location outside the current code segment. In other words, all offsets in the program must be relative to fixed values contained in the segment registers. This allows the program to be moved anywhere in memory as long as the segment registers are updated to point to the new base addresses.

STACK IMPLEMENTATION

Stacks in the 8086 and 8088 are implemented in memory and are located by the stack segment register (SS) and the stack pointer (SP). A system may have an unlimited number of stacks, and a stack may be up to 64k bytes long, the maximum length of a segment. (An attempt to expand a stack beyond 64k bytes overwrites the beginning of the segment.) One stack is directly addressable at a time; this is the current stack, often referred to simply as "the" stack. SS contains the base address of the current stack and SP points to the top of stack (TOS). In other words, SP contains the offset of the top of the stack from the stack segment's base address. However, the stack's base address (contained in SS) is not the "bottom" of the stack.

Stacks in the 8086 and 8088 are 16 bits wide; instructions that operate on a stack add and remove stack items one word at a time. An item is pushed onto the stack (see Figure 1-14) by *decrementing* SP by 2 and writing the item at a new TOS. An item is popped off the stack by

Table 1-2 Logical Addresses Sources

TYPE OF MEMORY REFERENCE	DEFAULT SEGMENT BASE	ALTERNATE SEGMENT BASE	OFFSET
Instruction Fetch	CS	NONE	IP
Stack Operation	SS	NONE	SP
Variable (except following)	DS	CS,ES,SS	Effective Address
String Source	DS	CS,ES,SS	SI
String Destination	ES	NONE	DI
BP Used As Base Register	SS	CS,DS,ES	Effective Address

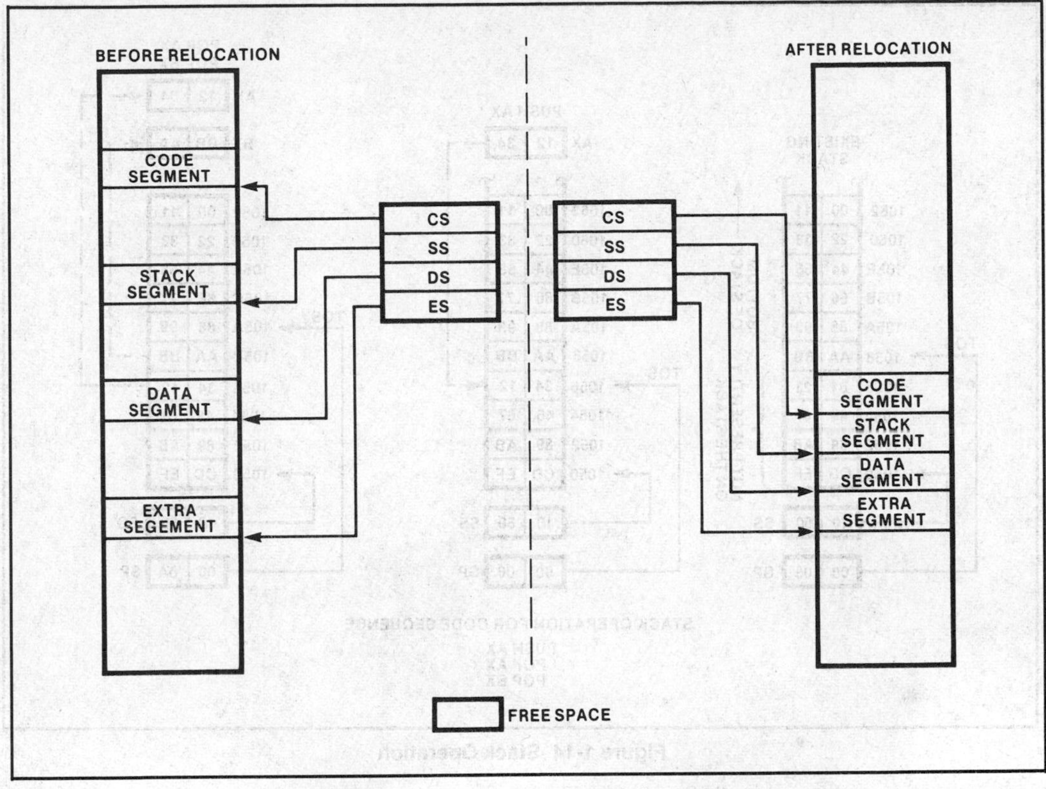

Figure 1-13 Dynamic Code Relocation

copying it from TOS and the *incrementing* SP by 2. In other words, the stack goes *down* in memory toward its base address. Stack operations never move items on the stack, nor do they erase them. The top of the stack changes only as a result of updating the stack pointer.

RESERVED MEMORY

Two areas in extreme low and high memory (see Figure 1-15) are dedicated to specific processor functions or are reserved by Intel Corporation for use by Intel hardware and software products. The locations are 0H through 7FH (128 bytes) and FFFF0H through FFFFFH (16 bytes). These areas are used for interrupt and system reset processing. 8086 and 8088 application systems do not use these areas for any other purpose. Doing so may make these systems incompatible with future Intel products.

8086/8088 MEMORY ACCESS DIFFERENCES

The 8086 can access either 8 or 16 bits of memory at a time. If an instruction refers to a word variable and that variable is located at an even-numbered address, the 8086 accesses the complete word in one bus cycle. If the word is located at an odd-numbered address, the 8086 accesses the word one byte at a time in two consecutive bus cycles.

To maximize throughput in 8086-based systems, 16-bit data should be stored at even addresses (should be word-aligned). This is particularly true of stacks. Unaligned stacks can slow a system's response to interrupts. Nevertheless, except for the performance penalty, word alignment is totally transparent to software. This allows maximum data packing where memory space is constrained.

The 8086 always fetches the instruction stream in words from even addresses except that the first fetch after a program transfer to an odd address obtains a byte. The instruction stream is disassembled inside the processor and instruction alignment will not materially affect the performance of most systems.

The 8088 always accesses memory in bytes. Word operands are accessed in two bus cycles regardless of their alignment. Instructions are also fetched one byte at a time. Although alignment of word operands does not

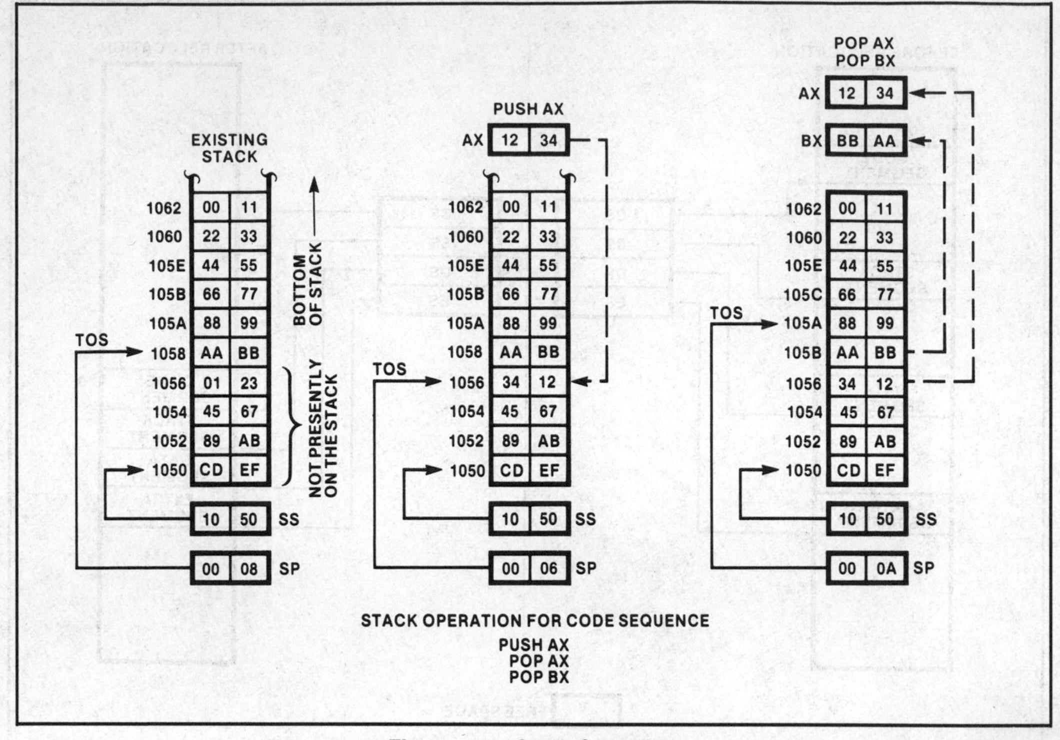

Figure 1-14 Stack Operation

affect the performance of 8088, locating 16-bit data on even addresses will insure maximum throughput if the system is ever transferred to an 8086.

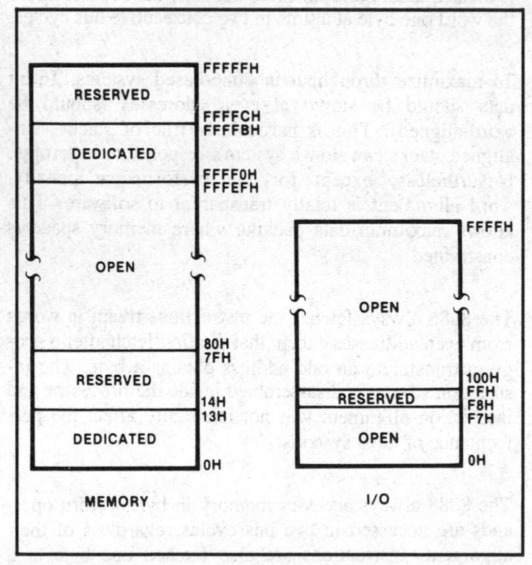

Figure 1-15 Reserved Memory and I/O Locations

1.2.2 Software Overview

The 8086 and 8088 execute exactly the same instructions. This instruction set includes equivalents to the instructions typically found in previous microprocessors, such as the 8080/8085. Significant new operations include:

- multiplication and division of signed and unsigned binary numbers as well as unpacked decimal numbers,
- move, scan and compare operations for strings up to 64k bytes in length,
- non-destructive bit testing,
- byte translation from one code to another,
- software generated interrupts,
- a group of instructions that can help coordinate the activities of multiprocessing systems.

The following paragraphs provide a description of the instructions by category and a detailed discussion of the various operand addressing modes. In addition, a complete instruction set summary is provided in tabular form which recaps each device instruction by category, and provides timing cycles for each instruction. Information is also described on how to encode and decode machine instructions for any given assembly code instruction.

8086/8088 INSTRUCTION SET

The 8086/8088 instructions treat different types of operands uniformly. Nearly every instruction can operate on either byte or word data. Register, memory and immediate operands may be specified interchangeably in most instructions. The exception to this is that immediate values serve as "source" and not "destination" operands. In particular, memory variables may be added to, subtracted from, shifted, compared, and so on, in place, without moving them in and out of registers. This saves instructions, registers, and execution time in assembly language programs. In high-level languages, where most variables are memory based, compilers can produce faster and shorter object programs.

The 8086/8088 instruction set can be viewed as existing on two levels. One is the assembly level and the other is the machine level. To the assembly language programmer, the 8086/8088 appear to have a repertoire of about 100 instructions. One MOV (move) instruction, for example, transfers a byte or a word from a register or a memory location or an immediate value to either a register or a memory location. The 8086/8088 CPU's, however, recognize 28 different MOV machine instructions ("move byte register to memory," move word immediate to register," etc.).

The two levels of instruction set address two different requirements: efficiency and simplicity. The approximately 300 forms of machine-level instructions make very efficient use of storage. For example, the machine instructions that increments a memory operand is three or four bytes long because the address of the operand must be encoded in the instruction. To increment a register, however, does not require as much information, so the instruction can be shorter. The 8086/88 have eight different machine-level instructions that increment a different 16-bit register. Each of these instructions are only one byte long.

The assembly level instructions simplify the programmers view of the instruction set. The programmer writes one form of an INC (increment) instruction and the ASM-86 assembler examines the operand to determine which machine level instruction to generate. The following paragraphs provide a functional description of the assembly-level instructions.

Data Transfer Instructions

The 8086/8088 instruction set contains 14 data transfer instructions. These instructions move single bytes and words between memory and registers, and also move single bytes and words between the AL or AX registers and I/O ports. Table 1-3 lists the four types of data transfer instructions and their functions.

Table 1-3 Data Transfer Instructions

GENERAL PURPOSE	
MOV	Move byte or word
PUSH	Push word onto stack
POP	Pop word off stack
XCHG	Exchange byte or word
XLAT	Translate byte
INPUT/OUTPUT	
IN	Input byte or word
OUT	Output byte or word
ADDRESS OBJECT	
LEA	Load effective address
LDS	Load pointer using DS
LES	Load pointer using ES
FLAG TRANSFER	
LAHF	Load AH register from flags
SAHF	Store AH register in flags
PUSHF	Push flags onto stack
POPF	Pop flags off stack

Data transfer instructions are categorized into four types: 1) general purpose; 2) input/output; 3) address object; and 4) flag transfer. The stack manipulation instructions, which are used for transferring flag contents, and the instructions for loading segment registers are also included in this group. Figure 1-16 shows the flag storage formats. These formats are used primarily by the LAHF instruction

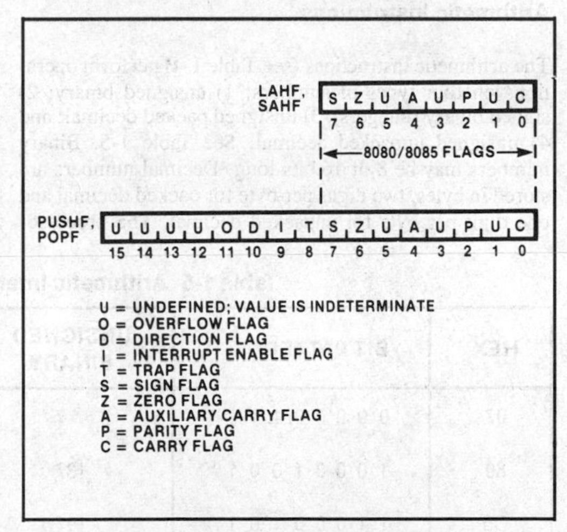

Figure 1-16 Flag Storage Formats

Table 1-4 Arithmetic Instructions

ADDITION	
ADD	Add byte or word
ADC	Add byte or word with carry
INC	Increment byte or word by 1
AAA	ASCII adjust for addition
DAA	Decimal adjust for addition
SUBTRACTION	
SUB	Subtract byte or word
SBB	Subtract byte or word with borrow
DEC	Decrement byte or word by 1
NEG	Negate byte or word
CMP	Compare byte or word
AAS	ASCII adjust for subtraction
DAS	Decimal adjust for subtraction
MULTIPLICATION	
MUL	Multiply byte or word unsigned
IMUL	Integer multiply byte or word
AAM	ASCII adjust for multiply
DIVISION	
DIV	Divide byte or word unsigned
IDIV	Integer divide byte or word
AAD	ASCII adjust for division
CBW	Convert byte to word
CWD	Convert word to doubleword

when converting 8080/8085 assembly language programs to run on the 8086 or 8088. The address object instructions manipulate the addresses of variables instead of the contents of values of the variables. This is useful for list processing, based variable and string operations.

Arithmetic Instructions

The arithmetic instructions (see Table 1-4) perform operations on four types of numbers: 1) unsigned binary; 2) signed binary (integers); 3) unsigned packed decimal; and 4) unsigned unpacked decimal. See Table 1-5. Binary numbers may be 8 or 16 bits long. Decimal numbers are stored in bytes, two digits per byte for packed decimal and one digit per byte for unpacked decimal. The processor always assumes that the operands specified in arithmetic instructions contain data that represents valid numbers for the type of instruction being performed. Invalid data may produce unpredictable results.

Arithmetic instructions post certain characteristics of the result of an operation to six flags. Refer to Chapter 3 in the iAPX 86/88,186/188 User's Manual Programmers Reference for a detailed description of the arithmetic instructions and flags.

Bit Manipulation Instructions

The 8086 and 8088 CPU's provide three groups of instructions for manipulating bits within both bytes and word. These three groups are logicals, shifts and rotates. Table 1-6 lists these three groups of bit manipulation instructions with their functions.

a. Logical

The logical instructions include the boolean operators "not", "and", "inclusive or", and "exclusive or". A TEST instruction that sets the flags as a result of a boolean "and" operation, but does not alter either of its operands, is also included.

b. Shifts

The bits in bytes and words may be shifted arithmetically or logically. Up to 255 shifts may be performed, according to the value of the count operand coded in the instruction. The count may be specified as a constant 1, or register CL, allowing the shift count to be a variable supplied at execution time. Arithmetic shifts may be used to multiply and divide binary numbers by powers of two. Logical shifts can be used to isolate bits in bytes or words.

c. Rotates

Bits in bytes and words can also be rotated. Bits rotated out of an operand are not lost as in a shift, but are "circled" back into the other "end" of the operand. As in the shift instructions, the number of bits to be rotated is taken

Table 1-5 Arithmetic Interpretation of 8-Bit Numbers

HEX	BIT PATTERN	UNSIGNED BINARY	SIGNED BINARY	UNPACKED DECIMAL	PACKED DECIMAL
07	0 0 0 0 0 1 1 1	7	+7	7	7
89	1 0 0 0 1 0 0 1	137	−119	invalid	89
C5	1 1 0 0 0 1 0 1	197	−59	invalid	invalid

Table 1-6 Bit Manipulation Instructions

LOGICALS	
NOT	"Not" byte or word
AND	"And" byte or word
OR	"Inclusive or" byte or word
XOR	"Exclusive or" byte or word
TEST	"Test" byte or word
SHIFTS	
SHL/SAL	Shift logical/arithmetic left byte or word
SHR	Shift logical right byte or word
SAR	Shift arithmetic right byte or word
ROTATES	
ROL	Rotate left byte or word
ROR	Rotate right byte or word
RCL	Rotate through carry left byte or word
RCR	Rotate through carry right byte or word

from the count operand, which may specify either a constant of 1, or the CL register. The carry flag may act as an extension of the operand in two of the rotate instructions, allowing a bit to be isolated in CF and then tested by a JC (jump if carry) or JNC (jump if not carry) instruction.

String Instructions

Five basic string operations, called primitives, allow strings of bytes or words to be operated on, one element (byte or word) at a time. Strings of up to 64k bytes may be manipulated with these instructions. Instructions are available to move, compare and scan for a value, as well as moving string elements to and from the accumulator. Table 1-7 lists the string instructions. These basic operations may be preceded by a special one-byte prefix that causes the instruction to be repeated by the hardware, allowing long strings to be processed much faster than would be possible with a software loop. The repetitions can be terminated by a variety of conditions, and a repeated operation may be interrupted and resumed.

The string instructions operate similarly in many respects (refer to Table 1-8). A string instruction may have a source operand, a destination operand, or both. The hardware assumes that a source string resides in the current data segment. A segment prefix may be used to override this assumption. A destination string must be in the current extra segment. The assembler checks the attributes of the operands to determine if the elements of the strings are bytes or words. However, the assembler does not use the operand names to address strings. Instead, the contents of register SI (source index) is used as an offset to address the current element of the source string. Also, the contents of register DI (destination index) is taken as the offset of the current destination string element. These registers must be initialized to point to the source/destination strings before executing the string instructions. The LDS, LES and LEA instructions are useful in performing this function.

String instructions automatically update SI and/or DI in anticipation of processing the next string element. Setting DF (direction flag) determines whether the index registers are auto-incremented (DF = 0) or auto-decremented (DF = 1). If byte strings are being processed, SI and/or DI is adjusted by 1. The adjustment is 2 for word strings.

Table 1-7 String Instructions

REP	Repeat
REPE/REPZ	Repeat while equal/zero
REPNE/REPNZ	Repeat while not equal/not zero
MOVS	Move byte or word string
MOVSB/MOVSW	Move byte or word string
CMPS	Compare byte or word string
SCAS	Scan byte or word string
LODS	Load byte or word string
STOS	Store byte or word string

Table 1-8 String Instruction Register and Flag Use

SI	Index (offset) for source string
DI	Index (offset) for destination string
CX	Repetition counter
AL/AX	Scan value Destination for LODS Source for STOS
DF	0 = auto-increment SI, DI 1 = auto-decrement SI, DI
ZF	Scan/compare terminator

If a repeat prefix has been coded, then register CX (count register) is decremented by 1 after each repetition of the string instruction. CX must be initialized to the number of repetitions desired before the string instruction is executed. If CX is 0, the string instruction is not executed, and control goes to the following instruction.

Program Transfer Instructions

The sequence in which instructions are executed in the 8086/8088 is determined by the content of the code segment register (CS) and the instruction pointer (IP). The CS register contains the base address of the current code segment, the 64k portion of memory from which instructions are currently being fetched. The IP points to the memory location from which the next instruction is to be fetched. In most operating conditions, the next instruction to be executed will have already been fetched and is waiting in the CPU instruction queue. The program transfer instructions operate on the instruction pointer and on the CS register; changing the content of these causes normal sequential operation to be altered. When a program transfer occurs, the queue no longer contains the correct instruction. When the BIU obtains the next instruction from memory using the new IP and CS values, it passes the instruction directly to the EU and then begins refilling the queue from the new location.

Four groups of program transfers are available with the 8086/8088 CPU's. See Table 1-9. These are unconditional transfers, conditional transfers, iteration control instructions, and interrupt-related instructions.

a. Unconditional Transfers

The unconditional transfer instructions may transfer control to a target instruction within the current code segment (intrasegment transfer) or to a different code segment (intersegment transfer). The ASM-86 Assembler terms an intrasegment transfer SHORT or NEAR and an intersegment transfer FAR. The transfer is made unconditionally any time the instruction is executed.

b. Conditional Transfers

The conditional transfer instructions are jumps that may or may not transfer control depending on the state of the CPU flags at the time the instruction is executed. These 18 instructions (see Table 1-10) each test a different combination of flags for a condition. If the condition is "true" then control is transferred to the target specified in the instruction. If the condition is "false" then control passes to the instruction that follows the conditional jump. All conditional jumps are SHORT, that is, the target must be in the current code segment and within −128 to +127 bytes of the first byte of the next instruction (JMP 00H jumps to the first byte of the next instruction). Since

Table 1-9 Program Transfer Instructions

UNCONDITIONAL TRANSFERS	
CALL	Call procedure
RET	Return from procedure
JMP	Jump
CONDITIONAL TRANSFERS	
JA/JNBE	Jump if above/not below nor equal
JAE/JNB	Jump if above or equal/not below
JB/JNAE	Jump if below/not above nor equal
JBE/JNA	Jump if below or equal/not above
JC	Jump if carry
JE/JZ	Jump if equal/zero
JG/JNLE	Jump if greater/not less nor equal
JGE/JNL	Jump if greater or equal/not less
JL/JNGE	Jump if less/not greater nor equal
JLE/JNG	Jump if less or equal/not greater
JNC	Jump if not carry
JNE/JNZ	Jump if not equal/not zero
JNO	Jump if not overflow
JNP/JPO	Jump if not parity/parity odd
JNS	Jump if not sign
JO	Jump if overflow
JP/JPE	Jump if parity/parity even
JS	Jump if sign
ITERATION CONTROLS	
LOOP	Loop
LOOPE/LOOPZ	Loop if equal/zero
LOOPNE/LOOPNZ	Loop if not equal/not zero
JCXZ	Jump if register CX = 0
INTERRUPTS	
INT	Interrupt
INTO	Interrupt if overflow
IRET	Interrupt return

Table 1-10 Interpretation of Conditional Transfers

MNEMONIC	CONDITION TESTED	"JUMP IF ..."
JA/JNBE	(CF OR ZF)=0	above/not below nor equal
JAE/JNB	CF=0	above or equal/not below
JB/JNAE	CF=1	below/not above nor equal
JBE/JNA	(CF OR ZF)=1	below or equal/not above
JC	CF=1	carry
JE/JZ	ZF=1	equal/zero
JG/JNLE	((SF XOR OF) OR ZF)=0	greater/not less nor equal
JGE/JNL	(SF XOR OF)=0	greater or equal/not less
JL/JNGE	(SF XOR OF)=1	less/not greater nor equal
JLE/JNG	((SF XOR OF) OR ZF)=1	less or equal/not greater
JNC	CF=0	not carry
JNE/JNZ	ZF=0	not equal/not zero
JNO	OF=0	not overflow
JNP/JPO	PF=0	not parity/parity odd
JNS	SF=0	not sign
JO	OF=1	overflow
JP/JPE	PF=1	parity/parity equal
JS	SF=1	sign

Note: "above" and "below" refer to the relationship of two unsigned values; "greater" and "less" refer to the relationship of two signed values.

jumps are made by adding the relative displacement of the target to the instruction pointer, all conditional jumps are self-relative and are appropriate for position-independent routines.

c. Iteration Control

The iteration control instructions can be used to regulate the repetition of software loops. These instructions use the CX register as a counter. Like the conditional transfers, the iteration control instructions are self-relative and may only transfer to targets that are within −128 to +127 bytes of themselves, i.e., they are SHORT transfers.

d. Interrupt Instructions

The interrupt instructions allow interrupt service routines to be activated by programs as well as by external hardware devices. The effect of software interrupts is similar to hardware-initiated interrupts. However, the processor does not execute an interrupt acknowledge bus cycle if the interrupt originates in software or with an NMI.

Processor Control Instructions

The processor control instructions (see Table 1-11) allow programs to control various CPU functions. One group of instructions updates flags, and another group is used primarily for synchronizing the 8086 or 8088 to external events. A final instruction causes the CPU to do nothing. Except for the flag operations, none of the processor control instructions affect the flags.

OPERAND ADDRESSING MODES

The 8086 and 8088 access instruction operands in many different ways. Operands may be contained in registers, within the instruction itself, in memory, or at I/O ports. Also, the addresses of memory and I/O port operands can be calculated in several different ways. These addressing

Table 1-11 Processor Control Instructions

FLAG OPERATIONS	
STC	Set carry flag
CLC	Clear carry flag
CMC	Complement carry flag
STD	Set direction flag
CLD	Clear direction flag
STI	Set interrupt enable flag
CLI	Clear interrupt enable flag
EXTERNAL SYNCHRONIZATION	
HLT	Halt until interrupt or reset
WAIT	Wait for $\overline{TEST}$ pin active
ESC	Escape to external processor
LOCK	Lock bus during next instruction
NO OPERATION	
NOP	No operation

modes greatly extend the flexibility and convenience of the instruction set. The following paragraphs briefly describe the register and immediate modes of operand addressing, and then provide a detailed description of the memory and I/O addressing modes.

Register and Immediate Operands

Instructions that specify only register operands are generally the most compact and fastest executing of the operand addressing forms. This is because the register operand addresses are encoded in instructions in just a few bits, and because these operands are performed entirely within the CPU (no bus cycles are run). Registers may serve as source operands, destination operands, or both.

Immediate operands are constant data contained in an instruction. The data may be either 8 or 16 bits in length. Immediate operands can be accessed quickly because they are available directly from the instruction queue. Like the register operand, no bus cycles need to be run to obtain an immediate operand. The limitations on immediate operands are that they may only serve as source operands and that they are constant value.

Memory Addressing Modes

Although the EU has direct access to register and immediate operands, memory operands must be transferred to and from the CPU over the bus. When the EU needs to read or write a memory operand, it must pass an offset value to the BIU. The BIU adds the offset to the (shifted) content of a segment register producing a 20-bit physical address and then executes the bus cycle or cycles needed to access the operand.

a. The Effective Address

The offset that the EU calculates for a memory operand is called the operand's effective address or EA. This address is an unsigned 16-bit number that expresses the operand's distance in bytes from the beginning of the segment in which it resides. The EU can calculate the effective address in several different ways. Information encoded in the second byte of the instruction tells the EU how to calculate the effective address of each memory operand. A compiler or assembler derives this information from the statement or instruction written by the programmer. Assembly language programmers have access to all addressing modes.

The EU calculates the EA by summing a displacement, the content of a base register and the content of an index register (see Figure 1-17). Any combination of these three components may be present in a given instruction. This allows a variety of memory addressing modes.

The displacement element is an 8-or 16-bit number that is contained in the instruction. The displacement generally is derived from the position of the operand name (a variable or label) in the program. The programmer can also modify this value or explicitly specify the displacement.

A programmer may specify that either BX or BP is to serve as a base register whose content is to be used in the EA computation.

Similarly, either SI or DI may be specified as the index register. The displacement value is a constant. The contents of the base and index registers may change during execution. This allows one instruction to access different memory locations as determined by the current values in the base and/or index registers. Effective address calculations with the BP are made using the SS register, by default, Although either the DS or the ES registers may be specified instead.

b. Direct Addressing

Direct addressing is the simplest memory addressing mode (see Figure 1-18). No registers are involved and the EA is taken directly from the displacement of the instruction. Direct addressing is typically to access simple variables (scalars).

c. Register Indirect Addressing

The effective address of a memory operand may be taken directly from one of the base or index registers (see Figure 1-19). One instruction can operate on many different memory locations if the value in the base or index register is updated appropriately. Any 16-bit general register may be used for register indirect addressing with the JMP or CALL instructions.

d. Based Addressing

In based addressing (see Figure 1-20), the effective address is the sum of a displacement value and the content of register BX or BP. Specifying register BP as a base register directs the BIU to obtain the operand from the current stack segment (unless a segment override prefix is present). This makes based addressing with BP a very convenient way to access stack data.

Based addressing also provides a simple way to address structures which may be located at different places in memory (see Figure 1-21). A base register can be pointed at the base of the structure and elements of the structure can be addressed by their displacement from the structure base. Different copies of the same structure can be accessed by simply changing the base register.

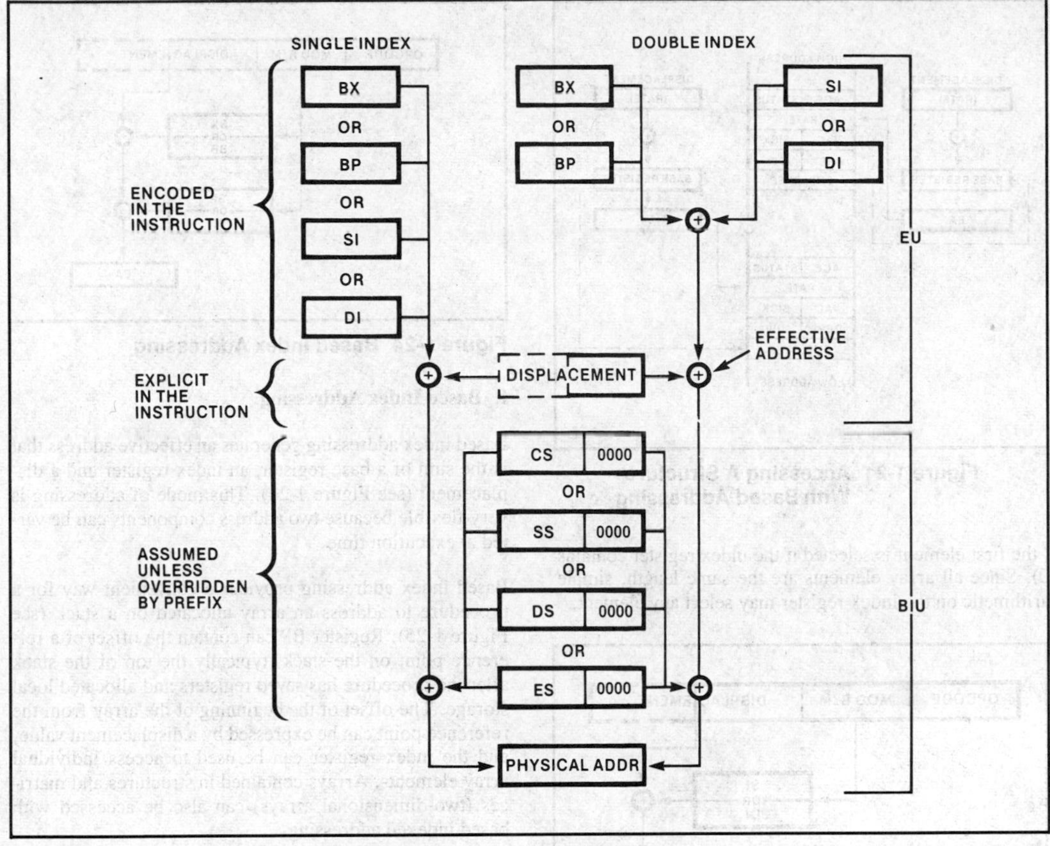

Figure 1-17 Memory Address Computation

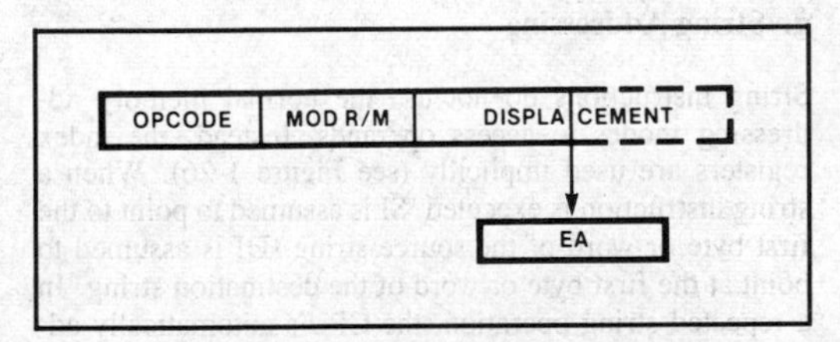

Figure 1-18 Direct Addressing

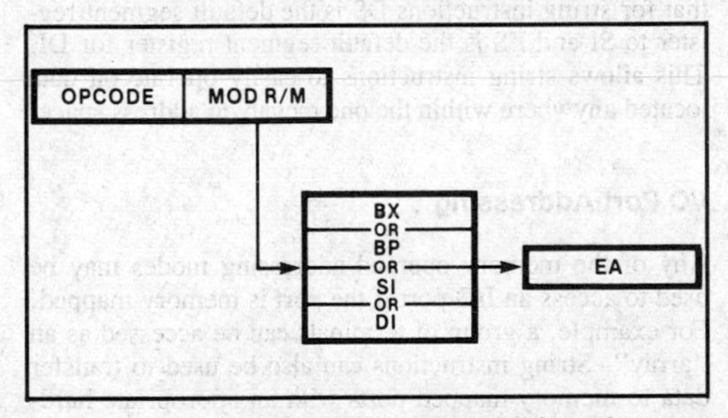

Figure 1-19 Register Indirect Addressing

e. Indexed Addressing

The effective address is calculated from the sum of a displacement plus the content of an index register (SI or DI) in index addressing (see Figure 1-22). Indexed address is often used to access elements in an array (see Figure 1-23). The displacement locates the beginning of the array, and the value of the index register selects one element

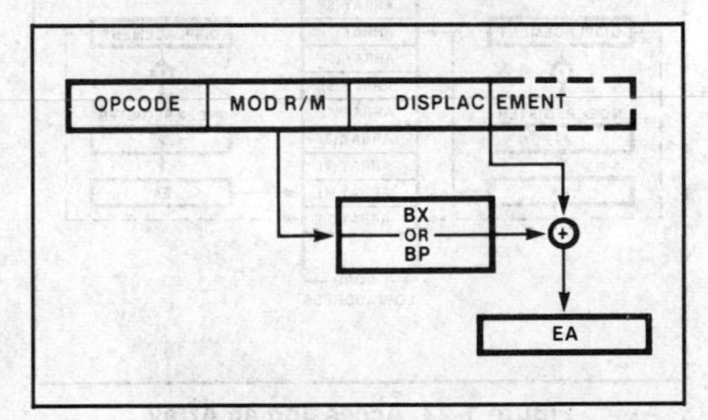

Figure 1-20 Based Addressing

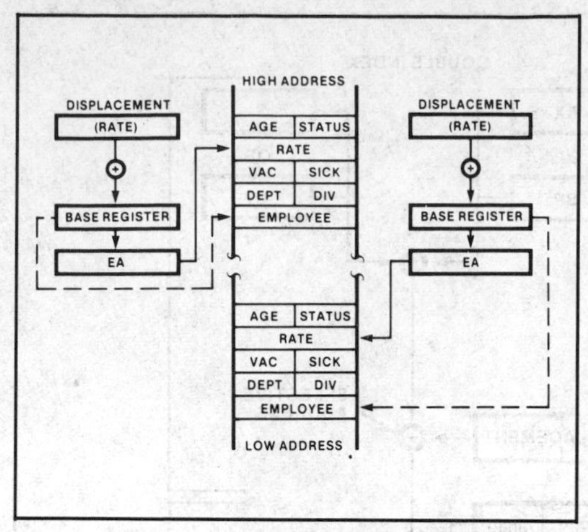

Figure 1-21 Accessing A Structure With Based Addressing

(the first element is selected if the index register contains 0). Since all array elements are the same length, simple arithmetic on the index register may select any element.

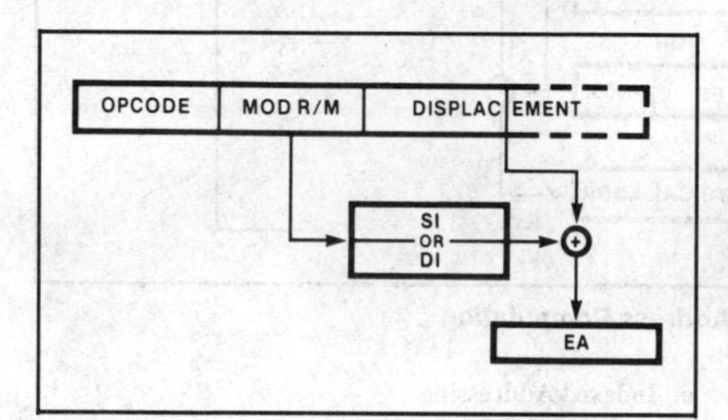

Figure 1-22 Indexed Addressing

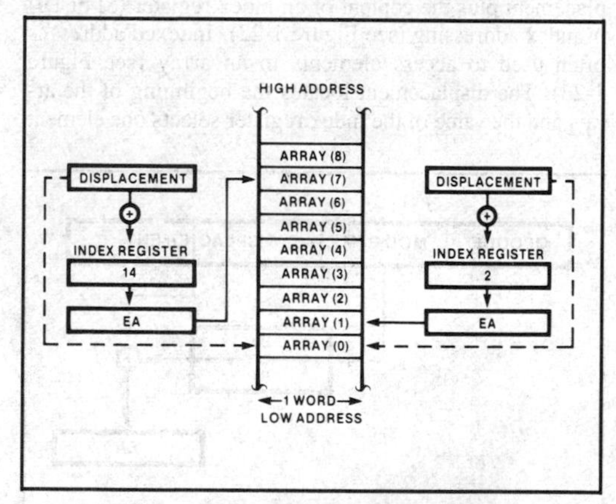

Figure 1-23 Accessing an Array With Indexed Addressing

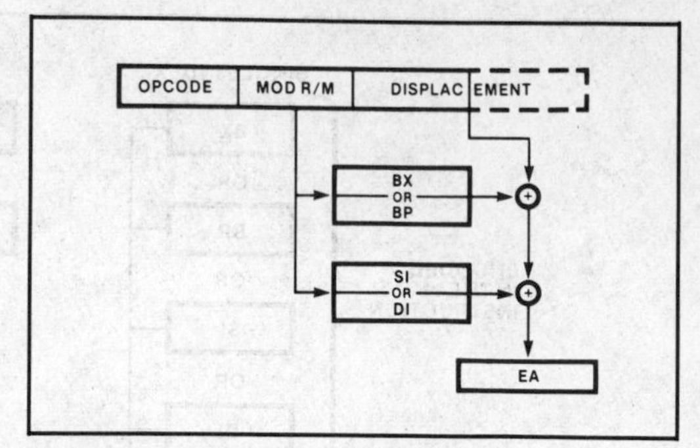

Figure 1-24 Based Index Addressing

f. Based Index Addressing

Based index addressing generates an effective address that is the sum of a base register, an index register and a displacement (see Figure 1-24). This mode of addressing is very flexible because two address components can be varied at execution time.

Based index addressing provides a convenient way for a procedure to address an array allocated on a stack (see Figure 1-25). Register BP can contain the offset of a reference point on the stack, typically the top of the stack after the procedure has saved registers and allocated local storage. The offset of the beginning of the array from the reference point can be expressed by a displacement value, and the index register can be used to access individual array elements. Arrays contained in structures and matrices (two-dimensional arrays) can also be accessed with based indexed addressing.

g. String Addressing

String instructions do not use the normal memory addressing modes to access operands. Instead, the index registers are used implicitly (see Figure 1-26). When a string instruction is executed, SI is assumed to point to the first byte or word of the source string. DI is assumed to point at the first byte or word of the destination string. In a repeated string operation, the CPU's automatically adjust SI and DI to obtain subsequent bytes or words. Note that for string instructions DS is the default segment register to SI and ES is the default segment register for DI. This allows string instructions to easily operate on data located anywhere within the one megabyte address space.

I/O Port Addressing

Any of the memory operand addressing modes may be used to access an I/O port if the port is memory mapped, For example, a group of terminals can be accessed as an "array". String instructions can also be used to transfer data to memory-mapped ports with an appropriate hardware interface.

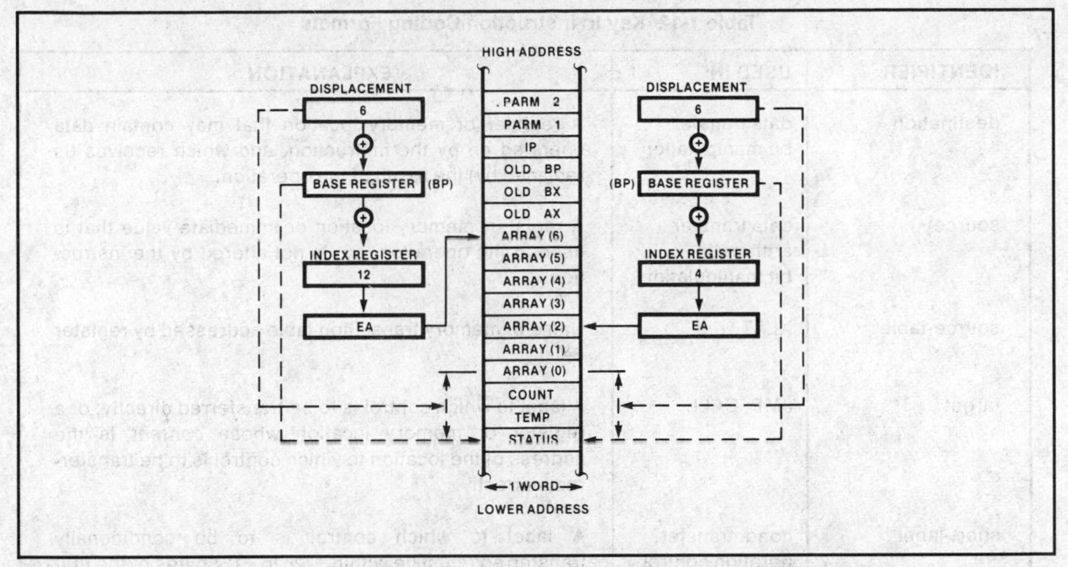

Figure 1-25 Accessing a Stacked Array with Based Index Addressing

Two different addressing modes can be used to access ports located in the I/O space (see Figure 1-27). The port number is an 8-bit immediate operand for direct addressing. This allow fixed access to ports numbered 0–255. Indirect I/O port addressing is similar to register indirect addressing of memory operands. The port number is taken from register DX and can range from 0 to 65,535. By previously adjusting the content of register DX, one instruction can access any port in the I/O space. A group of adjacent ports can be accessed using a simple software loop that adjusts the value of DX.

INSTRUCTION SET SUMMARY

The following paragraphs, and tables, provide detailed information for the 8086/8088 instruction set. Tables 1-12, 1-13 and 1-14 explain the symbols that are used in Table 1-16, the instruction set reference data table. Machine language instruction encoding and decoding information is provided in the paragraphs immediately following the instruction set summary.

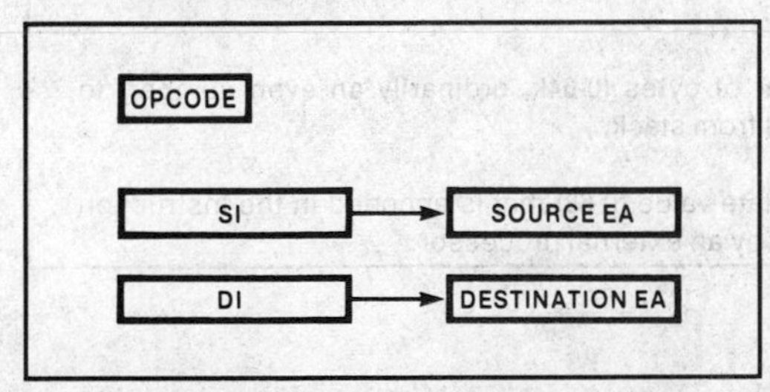

Figure 1-26 String Operand Addressing

Instruction timings are presented as the number of clock periods required to execute a particular form of the instruction (register-to-register, immediate-to-memory, etc.). If the system is running with a 5 MHz maximum clock, the maximum clock period is 200ns; at 8MHz, the clock period is 125ns. When memory operands are used, "+EA" indicates a variable number of additional clock periods needed to calculate the operand's effective address. Table 1-15 lists all effective address calculation times.

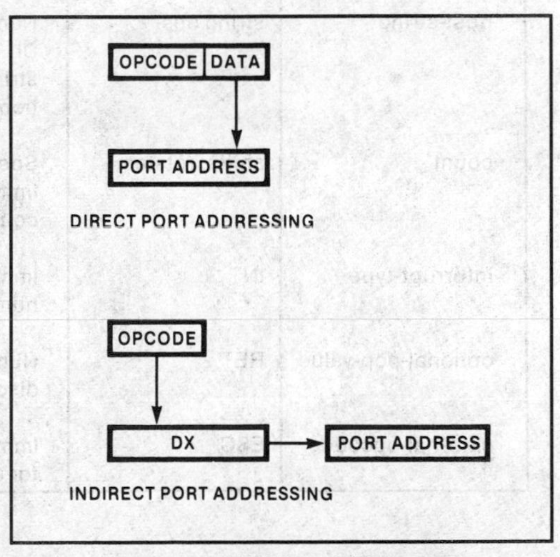

Figure 1-27 I/O Port Addressing

Table 1-12 Key to Instruction Coding Formats

IDENTIFIER	USED IN	EXPLANATION
destination	data transfer, bit manipulation	A register or memory location that may contain data operated on by the instruction, and which receives (is replaced by) the result of the operation.
source	data transfer, arithmetic, bit manipulation	A register, memory location or immediate value that is used in the operation, but is not altered by the instruction.
source-table	XLAT	Name of memory translation table addressed by register BX.
target	JMP, CALL	A label to which control is to be transferred directly, or a register or memory location whose *content* is the address of the location to which control is to be transferred indirectly.
short-label	cond. transfer, iteration control	A label to which control is to be conditionally transferred; must lie within −128 to +127 bytes of the first byte of the next instruction.
accumulator	IN, OUT	Register AX for word transfers, AL for bytes.
port	IN, OUT	An I/O port number; specified as an immediate value of 0-255, or register DX (which contains port number in range 0-64k).
source-string	string ops.	Name of a string in memory that is addressed by register SI; used only to identify string as byte or word and specify segment override, if any. This string is used in the operation, but is not altered.
dest-string	string ops.	Name of string in memory that is addressed by register DI; used only to identify string as byte or word. This string receives (is replaced by) the result of the operation.
count	shifts, rotates	Specifies number of bits to shift or rotate; written as immediate value 1 or register CL (which contains the count in the range 0-255).
interrupt-type	INT	Immediate value of 0-255 identifying interrupt pointer number.
optional-pop-value	RET	Number of bytes (0-64k, ordinarily an even number) to discard from stack.
external-opcode	ESC	Immediate value (0-63) that is encoded in the instruction for use by an external processor.

Table 1-13 Key to Flag Effects

IDENTIFIER	EXPLANATION
(blank)	not altered
0	cleared to 0
1	set to 1
X	set or cleared according to result
U	undefined—contains no reliable value
R	restored from previously-saved value

The timings given for control transfer instructions include any additional clocks required to reinitialize the instruction queue as well as the time required to fetch the target instructions. For instructions executing on an 8086, four clocks should be added for each instruction reference to a word operand located at an odd memory address to reflect any additional operand bus cycles required. Also, for instructions executing on an 8088, four clocks should be added to each instruction reference to a 16-bit memory operand. This includes stack operations. The required number of data references is listed for each instruction in Table 1-16 to aid in this calculation.

All of the instruction times given are of the form "n(m)", where "n" is the number of clocks required for the 8086 to execute the given instruction, and "m" is the number of clocks required by the 80186 for the same instruction. The number of clocks required for the 8088 will be n for 8-bit operations and n + (4 * transfers) for 16-bit operations. For the 80188, the number of clocks will be m for 8-bit operations and m + (4 * transfers) for 16 bit operations.

For instructions which repeat a specified number of times, the values m and n each consist of two parts in the relation "x + y/rep", where x is the initial number of clocks required to start the instruction, and y is the number of clocks corresponding to the number of iterations specified. For 16-bit repeated instructions on the 8088 and 80188, when the expression "(4 * transfers)" has to be added to m or n, it should be added to the y part of the expression before it is multiplied by the number of repetitions.

Several additional factors can alter the actual execution time from the figures shown in Table 1-16. The time provided assumes that the instruction has already been prefetched and that it is waiting in the instruction queue. This assumption is valid under most, but not all, operating conditions. A series of fast executing (fewer than two clocks per opcode byte) instructions can drain the queue and increase execution time. Execution time is also slightly

Table 1-14 Key to Operand Types

IDENTIFIER	EXPLANATION
(no operands)	No operands are written
register	An 8- or 16-bit general register
reg 16	A 16-bit general register
seg-reg	A segment register
accumulator	Register AX or AL
immediate	A constant in the range 0-FFFFH
immed8	A constant in the range 0-FFH
memory	An 8- or 16-bit memory location[(1)]
mem8	An 8-bit memory location[(1)]
mem16	A 16-bit memory location[(1)]
source-table	Name of 256-byte translate table
source-string	Name of string addressed by register SI
dest-string	Name of string addressed by register DI
DX	Register DX
short-label	A label within −128 to +127 bytes of the end of the instruction
near-label	A label in current code segment
far-label	A label in another code segment
near-proc	A procedure in current code segment
far-proc	A procedure in another code segment
memptr16	A word containing the offset of the location in the current code segment to which control is to be transferred[(1)]
memptr32	A doubleword containing the offset and the segment base address of the location in another code segment to which control is to be transferred[(1)]
regptr16	A 16-bit general register containing the offset of the location in the current code segment to which control is to be transferred
repeat	A string instruction repeat prefix

[(1)]Any addressing mode—direct, register indirect, based, indexed, or based indexed—may be used

Table 1-15 Effective Address Calculation Time

EA COMPONENTS		CLOCKS*
Displacement Only		6
Base or Index Only	(BX,BP,SI,DI)	5
Displacement + Base or Index	(BX,BP,SI,DI)	9
Base + Index	BP + DI, BX + SI	7
	BP + SI, BX + DI	8
Displacement + Base + Index	BP + DI + DISP BX + SI + DISP	11
	BP + SI + DISP BX + DI + DISP	12

*Add 2 clocks for segment override

effected by the interaction of the EU and BIU when memory operands must be read or written. If the EU needs access to memory, it may have to wait for up to one clock if the BIU has already started an instruction fetch bus cycle. (The EU can detect the need for a memory operand and post a bus request far enough in advance of its need for this operand to avoid waiting a full 4-clock bus cycle). If the queue is full the EU does not have to wait because the BIU is idle. (This assumes the BIU can obtain the bus on demand and no other processors are competing for the bus).

With typical instruction mixes, the time actually required to execute a sequence of instructions will be within 5 – 10% of the sum of the individual timings provided in Table 1-16. Cases can be constructed, however, in which execution time may be much higher than the sum of the figures provided in the table. The execution time for a given sequence of instructions is always repeatable, assuming comparable external conditions (interrupts, coprocessor activity, etc.). If the execution time for a given series of instructions must be determined exactly, the instructions should be run on an execution vehicle such as the iSBC 88/25 or 86/30 board.

MACHINE INSTRUCTION ENCODING AND DECODING

Machine instruction encoding and decoding is primarily the concern of the programmer. It is presented here for the hardware designer since such encoding and decoding

Table 1-16 Instruction Set Reference Data

AAA — **AAA** (no operands) ASCII adjust for addition

Flags	O	D	I	T	S	Z	A	P	C
	U				U	U	X	U	X

Operands	Clocks	Transfers*	Bytes	Coding Example
(no operands)	8(8)	—	1	AAA

AAD — **AAD** (no operands) ASCII adjust for division

Flags	O	D	I	T	S	Z	A	P	C
	U				X	X	U	X	U

Operands	Clocks	Transfers*	Bytes	Coding Example
(no operands)	60(15)	—	2	ADD

AAM — **AAM** (no operands) ASCII adjust for multiply

Flags	O	D	I	T	S	Z	A	P	C
	U				X	X	U	X	U

Operands	Clocks	Transfers*	Bytes	Coding Example
(no operands)	83(19)	—	2	AAM

AAS — **AAS** (no operands) ASCII adjust for subtraction

Flags	O	D	I	T	S	Z	A	P	C
	U				U	U	X	U	X

Operands	Clocks	Transfers*	Bytes	Coding Example
(no operands)	8(7)	—	1	AAS

*For the 8086 (80186) add four clocks for each 16-bit word transfer with an odd address. For the 8088 (80188) add four clocks for each 16-bit word transfer.

Table 1-16 Instruction Set Reference Data (continued)

ADC — **ADC** destination, source / Add with carry

Flags: O D I T S Z A P C — X . . . X X X X X

Operands	Clocks	Transfers*	Bytes	Coding Example
register, register	3(3)	—	2	ADC AX, SI
register, memory	9(10)+EA	1	2-4	ADC CX, BETA [SI]
memory, register	16(10)+EA	2	2-4	ADC ALPHA [BX] [SI], DI
register, immediate	4(4)	—	3-4	ADC BX, 256
memory, immediate	17(16)+EA	2	3-6	ADC GAMMA, 30H
accumulator, immediate	4(3-4)	—	2-3	ADC AL, 5

ADD — **ADD** destination, source / Addition

Flags: O D I T S Z A P C — X . . . X X X X X

Operands	Clocks	Transfers*	Bytes	Coding Example
register, register	3(3)	—	2	ADD CX, DX
register, memory	9(10)+EA	1	2-4	ADD DI, [BX],ALPHA
memory, register	16(10)+EA	2	2-4	ADD TEMP, CL
register, immediate	4(4)	—	3-4	ADD CL, 2
memory, immediate	17(16)+EA	2	3-6	ADD ALPHA, 2
accumulator, immediate	4(3-4)	—	2-3	ADD AX, 200

AND — **AND** destination, source / Logical and

Flags: O D I T S Z A P C — O . . . X X U X O

Operands	Clocks	Transfers*	Bytes	Coding Example
register, register	3(3)	—	2	AND AL, BL
register, memory	9(10)+EA	1	2-4	AND CX, FLAB WORD
memory, register	16(10)+EA	2	2-4	AND ASCII [DI], AL
register, immediate	4(4)	—	3-4	AND CX, 0F0H
memory, immediate	17(16)+EA	2	3-6	AND BETA, 01H
accumulator, immediate	4(3-4)	—	2-3	AND AX, 01010000B

BOUND — **BOUND** destination, source / Array bounds check

Flags: O D I T S Z A P C

Operands	Clocks	Transfers*	Bytes	Coding Example
register, memory	(35)	2	2	BOUND AX, ALPHA

CALL — **CALL** target / Call a procedure

Flags: O D I T S Z A P C — X . . . X X X X X

Operands	Clocks	Transfers*	Bytes	Coding Example
near-proc	19(14)	1	3	CALL NEAR__PROC
far-proc	28(23)	2	5	CALL FOR__PROC
memptr 16	21(19)+EA	2	2-4	CALL PROC__TABLE [SI]
regptr 16	16(13)	1	2	CALL AX
memptr 32	37(38)+EA	4	2-4	CALL [BX].TASK [SI]

CBW — **CBW** (no operands) / Convert byte to word

Flags: O D I T S Z A P C — U . . . U U X U X

Operands	Clocks	Transfers*	Bytes	Coding Example
(no operands)	2(2)	—	1	CBW

*For the 8086 (80186) add four clocks for each 16-bit word transfer with an odd address. For the 8088 (80188) add four clocks for each 16-bit word transfer.

Table 1-16 Instruction Set Reference Data (continued)

CLC

CLC (no operands)
Clear carry flag

Flags	O	D	I	T	S	Z	A	P	C
									O

Operands	Clocks	Transfers*	Bytes	Coding Example
(no operands)	2(2)	—	1	CLC

CLD

CLD (no operands)
Clear direction flag

Flags	O	D	I	T	S	Z	A	P	C
		O							

Operands	Clocks	Transfers*	Bytes	Coding Example
(no operands)	2(2)	—	1	CLD

CLI

CLI (no operands)
Clear interrupt flag

Flags	O	D	I	T	S	Z	A	P	C
		O							

Operands	Clocks	Transfers*	Bytes	Coding Example
(no operands)	2(2)	—	1	CLI

CMC

CMC (no operands)
Complement carry flag

Flags	O	D	I	T	S	Z	A	P	C
									X

Operands	Clocks	Transfers*	Bytes	Coding Example
(no operands)	2(2)	—	1	CMC

CMP

CMP destination, source
Compare destination to source

Flags	O	D	I	T	S	Z	A	P	C
	X				X	X	X	X	X

Operands	Clocks	Transfers*	Bytes	Coding Example
register, register	3(3)	—	2	CMP BX, CX
register, memory	9(10)+EA	1	2-4	CMP DH, ALPHA
memory, register	9(10)+EA	1	2-4	CMP [BP+2], SI
register, immediate	4(3)+EA	—	3-4	CMP BL, 02H
memory, immediate	10(10)+EA	1	3-6	CMP [BX].RADAR [DI], 3420H
accumulator, immediate	4(3-4)	—	2-3	CMP AL, 00010000B

CMPS

CMPS des-string, source-string
Compare string

Flags	O	D	I	T	S	Z	A	P	C
	X				X	X	X	X	X

Operands	Clocks	Transfers*	Bytes	Coding Example
dest-string, source-string	22(22)	2	1	CMPS BUSS1, BUFF2
(repeat) dest-string, source-string	9+22/rep (5+22/rep)	2/rep	1	REPE CMPS ID, KEY

CWD

CWD (no operands)
Convert word to doubleword

Flags	O	D	I	T	S	Z	A	P	C

Operands	Clocks	Transfers*	Bytes	Coding Example
(no operands)	5(4)	—	1	CWD

DAA

DAA (no operands)
Decimal adjust for addition

Flags	O	D	I	T	S	Z	A	P	C
	X				X	X	X	X	X

Operands	Clocks	Transfers*	Bytes	Coding Example
(no operands)	4(4)	—	1	DAA

*For the 8086 (80186) add four clocks for each 16-bit word transfer with an odd address. For the 8088 (80188) add four clocks for each 16-bit word transfer.

Table 1-16 Instruction Set Reference Data (continued)

DAS

DAS (no operands)
Decimal adjust for subtraction

Flags	O	D	I	T	S	Z	A	P	C
	U				X	X	X	X	X

Operands	Clocks	Transfers*	Bytes	Coding Example
(no operands)	4(4)	—	1	DAS

DEC

DEC destination
Decrement by 1

Flags	O	D	I	T	S	Z	A	P	C
	X				X	X	X	X	

Operands	Clocks	Transfers*	Bytes	Coding Example
reg 16	3(3)	—	1	DEC AX
reg8	3(3)	—	2	DEC AL
memory	15(15) + EA	2	2-4	DEC ARRAY [SI]

DIV

DIV source
Division, unsigned

Flags	O	D	I	T	S	Z	A	P	C
	U				U	U	U	U	U

Operands	Clocks	Transfers*	Bytes	Coding Example
reg 8	80-90(29)	—	2	DIV CL
reg 16	144-162(38)	—	2	DIV BX
mem 8	86-96 + EA (35)	1	2-4	DIV ALPHA
mem 16	150-168 + EA(94)	1	2-4	DIV TABLE [SI]

ENTER

ENTER
Procedure entry

Flags	O	D	I	T	S	Z	A	P	C

Operands	Clocks	Transfers*	Bytes	Coding Example
locals, level	L = 0(15) L = 1(25) L > 1 (22 + 16(n − 1))	—	4	ENTER 28, 3

ESC

ESC external-opcode, source
Escape

Flags	O	D	I	T	S	Z	A	P	C

Operands	Clocks	Transfers*	Bytes	Coding Example
immediate, memory	8(6) + EA	1	2-4	ESC 6.ARRAY [SI]
immediate, register	2(2)	—	2	ESC 20, AL

HLT

HLT (no operands)
Halt

Flags	O	D	I	T	S	Z	A	P	C

Operands	Clocks	Transfers*	Bytes	Coding Example
(no operands)	2(2)	—	1	HLT

*For the 8086 (80186) add four clocks for each 16-bit word transfer with an odd address. For the 8088 (80188) add four clocks for each 16-bit word transfer.

Table 1-16 Instruction Set Reference Data (continued)

IDIV	**IDIV** source Integer division			Flags O D I T S Z A P C U U U U U U
Operands	**Clocks**	**Transfers***	**Bytes**	**Coding Example**
reg 8	101-112 (44-52)	—	2	IDIV BL
reg 16	165-184 (53-61)	—	2	IDIV CX
mem 8	107-118+ EA(50-58)	1	2-4	IDIV DIVISOR_BYTE [SI]
mem 16	171-190+ EA(58-67)	1	2-4	IDIV [BX].DIVISOR_WORD

IMUL	**IMUL** source Integer multiplication			Flags O D I T S Z A P C X U U U U X
Operands	**Clocks**	**Transfers***	**Bytes**	**Coding Example**
immed 8	(22-24)	—	3	IMUL 6
immed 16	(29-32)	—	4	IMUL 20
reg 8	80-98 (25-28)	—	2	IMUL CL
reg 16	128-154 (34-37)	—	2	IMUL BX
mem 8	86-104+ EA(31-34)	1	2-4	IMUL RATE_BYTE
mem 16	134-160+ EA(40-43)	1	2-4	IMUL RATE_WORD [BP] [DI]

IN	**IN** accumulator, port Input byte or word			Flags O D I T S Z A P C
Operands	**Clocks**	**Transfers***	**Bytes**	**Coding Example**
accumulator, immed 8	10(10)	1	2	IN AL, 0FFEAH
accumulator, DX	8(8)	1	1	IN AX, DX

INC	**INC** destination Increment by 1			Flags O D I T S Z A P C X X X X X
Operands	**Clocks**	**Transfers***	**Bytes**	**Coding Example**
reg 16	3(3)	—	1	INC CX
reg 8	3(3)	—	2	INC BL
memory	15(15)+EA	2	2-4	INC ALPHA [DI] [BX]

INS	**INS** source-string, port Input string			Flags O D I T S Z A P C
Operands	**Clocks**	**Transfers***	**Bytes**	**Coding Example**
dest-string, port	(14)	2	1	INS BUFF1, USART D
(repeat) dest-string, port	(9+8/rep)	2/rep	1	REP INS BUFF1, USART D

*For the 8086 (80186) add four clocks for each 16-bit word transfer with an odd address. For the 8088 (80188) add four clocks for each 16-bit word transfer.

Table 1-16 Instruction Set Reference Data (continued)

INT	**INT** interrupt-type Interrupt			**Flags** O D I T S Z A P C O O
Operands	**Clocks**	**Transfers***	**Bytes**	**Coding Example**
mmed 8 (type = 3) immed 8 (type ≠ 3)	52(45) 52(47)	5 5	1 2	INT 3 INT 67

INTR†	**INTR** (external maskable interrupt) Interrupt if INTER and IF = 1			**Flags** O D I T S Z A P C O O
Operands	**Clocks**	**Transfers***	**Bytes**	**Coding Example**
(no operands)	61	7	N/A	N/A

INTO	**INTO** (no operands) Interrupt if overflow			**Flags** O D I T S Z A P C O O
Operands	**Clocks**	**Transfers***	**Bytes**	**Coding Example**
(no operands)	53 or 4(48 or 4)	5	1	INTO

IRET	**IRET** (no operands) Interrupt Return			**Flags** O D I T S Z A P C R R R R R R R R R
Operands	**Clocks**	**Transfers***	**Bytes**	**Coding Example**
(no operands)	32(28)	3	1	IRET

JA/JNBE	**JA/JNBE** short-label Jump if above/Jump if not below nor equal			**Flags** O D I T S Z A P C
Operands	**Clocks**	**Transfers***	**Bytes**	**Coding Example**
Short-label	16 or 4(13 or 4)	—	2	JA ABOVE

JAE/JNB	**JAE/JNB** short-label Jump if above or equal/Jump if not below			**Flags** O D I T S Z A P C
Operands	**Clocks**	**Transfers***	**Bytes**	**Coding Example**
short-label	16 or 4(13 or 4)	—	2	JAE ABOVE_EQUAL

JB/JNAE	**JB/JNAE** Jump if below/Jump if not above nor equal			**Flags** O D I T S Z A P C
Operands	**Clocks**	**Transfers***	**Bytes**	**Coding Example**
short-label	16 or 4(13 or 4)	—	2	JB BELOW

JBE/JNA	**JBE/JNA** short-label Jump if below or equal/Jump if not above			**Flags** O D I T S Z A P C
Operands	**Clocks**	**Transfers***	**Bytes**	**Coding Example**
short-label	16 or 4(13 or 4)	—	2	JNA NOT_ABOVE

*For the 8086 (80186) add four clocks for each 16-bit word transfer with an odd address. For the 8088 (80188) add four clocks for each 16-bit word transfer.

†INTR is not an instruction, it is included in table 1-16 only for timing information.

Table 1-16 Instruction Set Reference Data (continued)

JC	**JC** short-label Jump if carry			**Flags** O D I T S Z A P C
Operands	**Clocks**	**Transfers***	**Bytes**	**Coding Example**
short-label	16 or 4(13 or 4)	—	2	JC CARRY__SET

JCXZ	**JCXZ** short-label Jump if CX is zero			**Flags** O D I T S Z A P C
Operands	**Clocks**	**Transfers***	**Bytes**	**Coding Example**
short-label	16 or 4(16 or 5)	—	2	JCXZ COUNT__DONE

JE/JZ	**JE/JZ** short-label Jump if equal/Jump if zero			**Flags** O D I T S Z A P C
Operands	**Clocks**	**Transfers***	**Bytes**	**Coding Example**
short-label	16 or 4(13 or 4)	—	2	JZ ZERO

JG/JNLE	**JG/JNLE** short-label Jump if greater/Jump if not less nor equal			**Flags** O D I T S Z A P C
Operands	**Clocks**	**Transfers***	**Bytes**	**Coding Example**
short-label	16 or 4(13 or 4)	—	2	JG GREATER

JGE/JNL	**JGE/JNL** short-label Jump if greater or equal/Jump if not less			**Flags** O D I T S Z A P C
Operands	**Clocks**	**Transfers***	**Bytes**	**Coding Example**
short-label	16 or 4(13 or 4)	—	2	JGE GREATER__EQUAL

JL/JNGE	**JL/JNGE** short-label Jump if less/Jump if not greater nor equal			**Flags** O D I T S Z A P C
Operands	**Clocks**	**Transfers***	**Bytes**	**Coding Example**
short-label	16 or 4(13 or 4)	—	2	JL LESS

JLE/JNG	**JLE/JNG** short-label Jump if less or equal/Jump if not greater			**Flags** O D I T S Z A P C
Operands	**Clocks**	**Transfers***	**Bytes**	**Coding Example**
short-label	16 or 4(13 or 4)	—	2	JNG NOT__GREATER

*For the 8086 (80186) add four clocks for each 16-bit word transfer with an odd address. For the 8088 (80188) add four clocks for each 16-bit word transfer.

Table 1-16 Instruction Set Reference Data (continued)

JMP

JMP target
Jump

Flags: O D I T S Z A P C

Operands	Clocks	Transfers*	Bytes	Coding Example
short-label	15(13)	—	2	JMP SHORT
near-label	15(13)	—	3	JMP WITHIN__SEGMENT
far-label	15(13)	—	5	JMP FAR__LABEL
memptr 16	18(17)+EA	1	2-4	JMP [BX].TARGET
regptr 16	11(11)	—	2	JMP CX
memptr 32	24(26)+EA	2	2-4	JMP OTHER.SEG [SI]

JNC

JNC short-label
Jump if not carry

Flags: O D I T S Z A P C

Operands	Clocks	Transfers*	Bytes	Coding Example
short-label	16 or 4(13 or 4)	—	2	JNC NOT__CARRY

JNE/JNZ

JNE/JNZ short-label
Jump if not equal/Jump if not zero

Flags: O D I T S Z A P C

Operands	Clocks	Transfers*	Bytes	Coding Example
short-label	16 or 4(13 or 4)	—	2	JNE NOT__EQUAL

JNO

JNO short-label
Jump if not overflow

Flags: O D I T S Z A P C

Operands	Clocks	Transfers*	Bytes	Coding Example
short-label	16 or 4(13 or 4)	—	2	JNO NO__OVERLOW

JNP/JPO

JNP/JPO short-label
Jump if not parity/Jump if parity odd

Flags: O D I T S Z A P C

Operands	Clocks	Transfers*	Bytes	Coding Example
short-label	16 or 4(13 or 4)	—	2	JPO ODD__PARITY

JNS

JNS short-label
Jump if not sign

Flags: O D I T S Z A P C

Operands	Clocks	Transfers*	Bytes	Coding Example
short-label	16 or 4(13 or 4)	—	2	JNS POSITIVE

JO

JO short-label
Jump if overflow

Flags: O D I T S Z A P C

Operands	Clocks	Transfers*	Bytes	Coding Example
short-label	16 or 4(13 or 4)	—	2	JO SIGNED__OVRFLW

*For the 8086 (80186) add four clocks for each 16-bit word transfer with an odd address. For the 8088 (80188) add four clocks for each 16-bit word transfer.

Table 1-16 Instruction Set Reference Data (continued)

JP/JPE	**JP/JPE** short-label Jump if parity/Jump if parity even			Flags O D I T S Z A P C
Operands	**Clocks**	**Transfers***	**Bytes**	**Coding Example**
short-label	16 or 4(13 or 4)	—	2	JPE EVEN_PARITY

JS	**JS** short-label Jump if sign			Flags O D I T S Z A P C
Operands	**Clocks**	**Transfers***	**Bytes**	**Coding Example**
short-label	16 or 4(13 or 4)	—	2	JS NEGATIVE

LAHF	**LAHF** (no operands) Load AH from flags			Flags O D I T S Z A P C
Operands	**Clocks**	**Transfers***	**Bytes**	**Coding Example**
(no operands)	4(2)	—	1	LAHF

LDS	**LDS** destination, source Load pointer using DS			Flags O D I T S Z A P C
Operands	**Clocks**	**Transfers***	**Bytes**	**Coding Example**
reg 16, mem 16	16(18)+EA	2	2-4	LDS SI, DATA, SEG [DI]

LEA	**LEA** destination, source Load effective address			Flags O D I T S Z A P C
Operands	**Clocks**	**Transfers***	**Bytes**	**Coding Example**
reg 16, mem 16	2(6)+EA	—	2-4	LEA BX, [BP] [DI]

LEAVE	**LEAVE** (no operand) Restore stack for procedure exit			Flags O D I T S Z A P C U U X U X
Operands	**Clocks**	**Transfers***	**Bytes**	**Coding Example**
(no operands)	(8)	1	1	LEAVE

LES	**LES** destination, source Load pointer using ES			Flags O D I T S Z A P C
Operands	**Clocks**	**Transfers***	**Bytes**	**Coding Example**
reg 16, mem 32	16(18)+EA	2	2-4	LES DI, [BX], TXT_BUFF

LOCK	**LOCK** (no operands) Lock bus			Flags O D I T S Z A P C
Operands	**Clocks**	**Transfers***	**Bytes**	**Coding Example**
(no operands)	2(2)	—	1	LOCK XCHG FLAG, AL

*For the 8086 (80186) add four clocks for each 16-bit word transfer with an odd address. For the 8088 (80188) add four clocks for each 16-bit word transfer.

Table 1-16 Instruction Set Reference Data (continued)

LODS	**LODS** source-string Load string			**Flags** O D I T S Z A P C
Operands	**Clocks**	**Transfers***	**Bytes**	**Coding Example**
source-string (repeat) source-string	12(10) 9+13/rep (6+11/rep)	1 1/rep	1 1	LODS CUSTOMER_NAME REP LODS NAME

LOOP	**LOOP** short-label Loop			**Flags** O D I T S Z A P C
Operands	**Clocks**	**Transfers***	**Bytes**	**Coding Example**
short label	17/5(15/5)	—	2	LOOP AGAIN

LOOPE/LOOPZ	**LOOPE/LOOPZ** short label Loop if equal/Loop if zero			**Flags** O D I T S Z A P C
Operands	**Clocks**	**Transfers***	**Bytes**	**Coding Example**
short label	18 or 6(16 or 6)	—	2	LOOPE AGAIN

LOOPNE/LOOPNZ	**LOOPNE/LOOPNZ** short label Loop if not equal/Loop if not zero			**Flags** O D I T S Z A P C
Operands	**Clocks**	**Transfers***	**Bytes**	**Coding Example**
short label	19 or 5(16 or 5)	—	2	LOOPNE AGAIN

NMI†	**NMI** (external nonmaskable interrupt) Interrupt if NMI = 1			**Flags** O D I T S Z A P C O O
Operands	**Clocks**	**Transfers***	**Bytes**	**Coding Example**
(no operands)	50	5	N/A	N/A

MOV	**MOV** destination, source Move			**Flags** O D I T S Z A P C
Operands	**Clocks**	**Transfers***	**Bytes**	**Coding Example**
memory, accumulator	10(9)	1	3	MOV ARRAY [SI], AL
accumulator, memory	10(8)	1	3	MOV AX, TEMP_RESULT
register, register	2(2)	—	2	MOV AX, CX
register, memory	8(12)+EA	1	2-4	MOV BP, STACK_TOP
memory, register	9(9)+EA	1	2-4	MOV COUNT [DI], CX
register, immediate	4(3-4)	—	2-3	MOV CL, 2
memory, immediate	10(12-13) +EA	1	3-6	MOV MASK [BX] [SI], 2CH
seg-reg, reg 16	2(2)	—	2	MOV ES, CX
seg-reg, mem 16	8(9)+EA	1	2-4	MOV DS, SEGMENT_BASE
reg 16, seg-reg	2(2)	—	2	MOV BP, SS
memory, seg-reg	9(11)+EA	1	2-4	MOV [BX], SEG_SAVE, CS

*For the 8086 (80186) add four clocks for each 16-bit word transfer with an odd address. For the 8088 (80188) add four clocks for each 16-bit word transfer.

†NMI is not an instruction, it is included in table 1-16 only for timing information.

Table 1-16 Instruction Set Reference Data (continued)

MOVS	**MOVS** dest-string, source-string Move string			Flags	O D I T S Z A P C
Operands	**Clocks**	**Transfers***	**Bytes**	**Coding Example**	
dest-string, source-string	18(9)	2	1	MOVS LINE EDIT__DATA	
(repeat) dest-string, source-string	9+17/rep (8+8/rep)	2/rep	1	REP MOVS SCREEN, BUFFER	

MOVSB/MOVSW	**MOVSB/MOVSW** (no operands) Move string (byte/word)			Flags	O D I T S Z A P C
Operands	**Clocks**	**Transfers***	**Bytes**	**Coding Example**	
(no operands)	18(9)	2	1	MOVSB	
(repeat) (no operands)	9+17/rep (8+8/rep)	2/rep	1	REP MOVSW	

MUL	**MUL** source Multiplication, unsigned			Flags	O D I T S Z A P C X U U U U X
Operands	**Clocks**	**Transfers***	**Bytes**	**Coding Example**	
reg 8	70-77 (26-28)	—	2	MUL BL	
reg 16	118-133 (35-37)	—	2	MUL CX	
mem 8	76-83+ EA(32-34)	1	2-4	MUL MONTH [SI]	
mem 16	124-139+ EA(41-43)	1	2-4	MUL BAUD__RATE	

NEG	**NEG** destination Negate			Flags	O D I T S Z A P C
Operands	**Clocks**	**Transfers***	**Bytes**	**Coding Example**	
register	3(3)	—	2	NEG AL	
memory *0 if destination is 0	16(3)+EA	2	2-4	NEG MULTIPLIER	

NOP	**NOP** (no operands) No Operation			Flags	O D I T S Z A P C
Operands	**Clocks**	**Transfers***	**Bytes**	**Coding Example**	
(no operands)	3(3)	—	1	NOP	

NOT	**NOT** destination Logical not			Flags	O D I T S Z A P C
Operands	**Clocks**	**Transfers***	**Bytes**	**Coding Example**	
register	3(3)	—	2	NOT AX	
memory	16(3)+EA	2	2-4	NOT CHARACTER	

*For the 8086 (80186) add four clocks for each 16-bit word transfer with an odd address. For the 8088 (80188) add four clocks for each 16-bit word transfer.

Table 1-16 Instruction Set Reference Data (continued)

OR	**OR** destination, source Logical inclusive or			Flags: O D I T S Z A P C O X X U X O
Operands	**Clocks**	**Transfers***	**Bytes**	**Coding Example**
register, register	3(3)	—	2	OR AL, BL
register, memory	9(10)+EA	1	2-4	OR DX, PORT__ID [DI]
memory, register	16(10)+EA	2	2-4	OR FLAG__BYTE, CL
accumulator, immediate	4(3-4)	—	2-3	OR AL, 011011008
register, immediate	4(4)	—	3-4	OR CX, 01H
memory, immediate	17(16)+EA	2	3-6	OR [BX], CMD__WORD, 0CFH

OUT	**OUT** port, accumulator Output byte or word			Flags: O D I T S Z A P C
Operands	**Clocks**	**Transfers***	**Bytes**	**Coding Example**
immed 8, accumulator	10(9)	1	2	OUT 44, AX
DX, accumulator	8(7)	1	1	OUT DX, AL

OUTS	**OUTS** port, source-string Output string			Flags: O D I T S Z A P C
Operands	**Clocks**	**Transfers***	**Bytes**	**Coding Example**
port, source-string	(14)	2	1	OUTS PORT2, BUFF2
(repeat) port, source-string	(8)+8/rep	2/rep	1	REP OUTS PORT2, BUFF2

POP	**POP** destination Pop word off stack			Flags: O D I T S Z A P C
Operands	**Clocks**	**Transfers***	**Bytes**	**Coding Example**
register	8(10)	1	1	POP DX
seg-reg (CS illegal)	8(8)	1	1	POP DS
memory	17(20)+EA	2	2-4	POP PARAMETER

POPA	**POPA** (no operands) Pop all registers			Flags: O D I T S Z A P C
Operands	**Clocks**	**Transfers***	**Bytes**	**Coding Example**
(no operands)	(51)	8	1	POPA

POPF	**POPF** (no operands) Pop all registers			Flags: O D I T S Z A P C R R R R R R R R R
Operands	**Clocks**	**Transfers***	**Bytes**	**Coding Example**
(no operands)	8(8)	1	1	POPF

PUSH	**PUSH** source Push word onto stack			Flags: O D I T S Z A P C
Operands	**Clocks**	**Transfers***	**Bytes**	**Coding Example**
register	11(10)	1	1	PUSH SI
seg-reg (CS legal)	10(9)	1	1	PUSH ES
memory	16(16)+EA	2	2-4	PUSH DRETURN__CODE [SI]

*For the 8086 (80186) add four clocks for each 16-bit word transfer with an odd address. For the 8088 (80188) add four clocks for each 16-bit word transfer.

Table 1-16 Instruction Set Reference Data (continued)

PUSHA

PUSHA (no operands)
Push all registers

Flags: O D I T S Z A P C

Operands	Clocks	Transfers*	Bytes	Coding Example
(no operands)	(36)	8	4	PUSHA

PUSHF

PUSHF (no operands)
Push flags onto stack

Flags: O D I T S Z A P C

Operands	Clocks	Transfers*	Bytes	Coding Example
(no operands)	10(9)	1	1	PUSHF

RCL

RCL destination, count
Rotate left through carry

Flags: O D I T S Z A P C
X C

Operands	Clocks	Transfers*	Bytes	Coding Example
register, 1	2(2)	—	2	RCL CX, 1
register, CL	8+4/ bit(5+1/bit)	—	2	RCL AL, CL
memory, 1	15(15)+EA	2	2-4	RCL ALPHA, 1
memory CL	20+4/ bit(17+ 1/bit)+EA	2	2-4	RCL [BP], PARM, CL
register, n	(5+1/bit)	—	3	RCL CX, 5
memory, n	(17+1/bit)	2	3-5	RCL ALPHA, 5

RCR

RCR destination, count
Rotate right through carry

Flags: O D I T S Z A P C
X C

Operands	Clocks	Transfers*	Bytes	Coding Example
register, 1	2(2)	—	2	RCR BX, 1
register, CL	8+4/ bit(5+1/bit)	—	2	RCR BL, CL
memory, 1	15(15)+EA	2	2-4	RCR [BX], STATUS, 1
memory CL	20+4/ bit(17+ 1/bit)+EA	2	2-4	RCR ARRAY, [DI], CL
register, n	(5+1/bit)	—	3	RCR BX, 5
memory, n	(17+1/bit)	2	3-5	RCR ALPHA, 5

REP

REP (no operands)
Repeat string operation

Flags: O D I T S Z A P C

Operands	Clocks	Transfers*	Bytes	Coding Example
(no operands)	2(2)	—	1	REP MOVS DEST, SRCE

REPE/REPZ

REPE/REPZ (no operands)
Repeat string operation while equal/ while zero

Flags: O D I T S Z A P C

Operands	Clocks	Transfers*	Bytes	Coding Example
(no operands)	2(2)	—	1	REPE CMPS DATA, KEY

*For the 8086 (80186) add four clocks for each 16-bit word transfer with an odd address. For the 8088 (80188) add four clocks for each 16-bit word transfer.

210912-001

Table 1-16 Instruction Set Reference Data (continued)

REPNE/REPNZ

REPNE/REPNZ (no operands)
Repeat string operation while not equal/not zero

Flags	O	D	I	T	S	Z	A	P	C
	U				U	U	X	U	X

Operands	Clocks	Transfers*	Bytes	Coding Example
(no operands)	2(2)	—	1	REPNE SCAS INPUT_LINE

RET

RET optional-pop-value
Return from procedure

Flags	O	D	I	T	S	Z	A	P	C

Operands	Clocks	Transfers*	Bytes	Coding Example
(intra-segment, no pop)	16(16)	1	1	RET
(intra-segment, pop)	20(18)	1	3	RET 4
(inter-segment, no pop)	26(22)	2	1	RET
(inter-segment, pop)	25(25)	2	3	RET 2

ROL

ROL destination, count
Rotate left

Flags	O	D	I	T	S	Z	A	P	C
	X								X

Operands	Clocks	Transfers*	Bytes	Coding Example
register, 1	2(2)	—	2	ROL BX, 1
register, CL	8+4/bit(5+1/bit)	—	2	ROL DI, CL
memory, 1	15(15)+EA	2	2-4	ROL FLAG_BYTE [DI],1
memory CL	20+4/bit(17+1/bit)+EA	2	2-4	ROL ALPHA, CL
register, n	(5+1/bit)	—	3	ROL BX, 5
memory, n	(17+1/bit)	2	3-5	ROL BETA, 5

ROR

ROR destination, count
Rotate right

Flags	O	D	I	T	S	Z	A	P	C
	X								X

Operands	Clocks	Transfers*	Bytes	Coding Example
register, 1	2(2)	—	2	ROR BX, 1
register, CL	8+4/bit(5+1/bit)	—	2	ROR BX, CL
memory, 1	15(15)+EA	2	2-4	ROR PORT_STATUS, 1
memory CL	20+4/bit(17+1/bit)+EA	2	2-4	ROR CMD_WORD, CL
register, n	(5+1/bit)	—	3	ROR BX, 5
memory, n	(17+1/bit)	2	3-5	ROR BETA, 5

SAHF

SAHF (no operands)
Store AH into flags

Flags	O	D	I	T	S	Z	A	P	C
					R	R	R	R	R

Operands	Clocks	Transfers*	Bytes	Coding Example
(no operands)	4(3)	—	1	SAHF

*For the 8086 (80186) add four clocks for each 16-bit word transfer with an odd address. For the 8088 (80188) add four clocks for each 16-bit word transfer.

Table 1-16 Instruction Set Reference Data (continued)

SAL/SHL

SAL/SHL destination
Shift arithmetic left/Shift logical left

Flags	O	D	I	T	S	Z	A	P	C
	X								X

Operands	Clocks	Transfers*	Bytes	Coding Example
register, 1	2(2)	—	2	SAL AL, 1
register, CL	8+4/ bit(5+1/bit)	—	2	SAL DI, CL
memory, 1	15(15)+EA	2	2-4	SAL [BX], OVERDRAW, 1
memory, CL	20+4/ bit(17+ 1/bit)+EA	2	2-4	SAL STORE_COUNT, CL
register, n	(5+1/bit)	—	3	SAL AH, 5
memory, n	(17+1/bit)	2	3-5	SAL ALPHA, 5

SAR

SAR destination, source
Shift arithmetic right

Flags	O	D	I	T	S	Z	A	P	C
	X				X	X	U	X	X

Operands	Clocks	Transfers*	Bytes	Coding Example
register, 1	2(2)	—	2	SAR DX, 1
register, CL	8+4/ bit(5+1/bit)	—	2	SAR DI, CL
memory, 1	15(15)+EA	2	2-4	SAR N_BLOCKS, 1
memory CL	20+4/ bit(17+ 1/bit)+EA	2	2-4	SAR N_BLOCKS, CL
register, n	(5+1/bit)	—	3	SAR DX, 5
memory, n	(17+1/bit)	2	3-5	SAR DGLTH, 5

SBB

SBB destination, source
Subtract with borrow

Flags	O	D	I	T	S	Z	A	P	C
	X				X	X	X	X	X

Operands	Clocks	Transfers*	Bytes	Coding Example
register, register	3(3)	—	2	SBB BX, CX
register, memory	9(10)+EA	1	2-4	SBB DI, [BX], PAYMENT
memory, register	16(10)+EA	2	2-4	SBB BALANCE, AX
accumulator, immediate	4(3-4)	—	2-3	SBB AX, 2
register, immediate	4(4)	—	3-4	SBB CL, 1
memory, immediate	17(16)+EA	2	3-6	SBB COUNT, [SI], 10

SCAS

SCAS dest-string
Scan string

Flags	O	D	I	T	S	Z	A	P	C
	X				X	X	X	X	X

Operands	Clocks	Transfers*	Bytes	Coding Example
dest-string	15(15)	1	1	SCAS INPUT_LINE
(repeat) dest-string	9+15/rep (5+15/rep)	1/rep	1	REPNE SCAS BUFFER

*For the 8086 (80186) add four clocks for each 16-bit word transfer with an odd address. For the 8088 (80188) add four clocks for each 16-bit word transfer.

Table 1-16 Instruction Set Reference Data (continued)

SEGMENT†

SEGMENT override prefix
Override to specified segment

Flags	O	D	I	T	S	Z	A	P	C

Operands	Clocks	Transfers*	Bytes	Coding Example
(no operands)	2(2)	—	1	MOV SS:PARAMETER AX

SHR

SHR destination, count
Shift logical right

Flags	O	D	I	T	S	Z	A	P	C
	X								X

Operands	Clocks	Transfers*	Bytes	Coding Example
register, 1	2(2)	—	2	SHR SI, 1
register, CL	8+4/ bit(5+1/bit)	—	2	SHR SI, CL
memory, 1	15(15)+EA	2	2-4	SHR ID__BYTE [SI] [BX], 1
memory CL	20+4/ bit(17+ 1/bit)+EA	2	2-4	SHR INPUT__WORD, CL
register, n	(5+1/bit)	—	3	SHR SI, 5
memory, n	(17+1/bit)	2	3-5	SHR ALPHA, 5

SINGLE STEP†

SINGLE STEP (Trap flag interrupt)
Interrupt if TF=1

Flags	O	D	I	T	S	Z	A	P	C
			O	O					

Operands	Clocks	Transfers*	Bytes	Coding Example
(no operands)	50	5	N/A	N/A

STC

STC (no operands)
Set carry flag

Flags	O	D	I	T	S	Z	A	P	C
									C

Operands	Clocks	Transfers*	Bytes	Coding Example
(no operands)	2(2)	—	1	STC

STD

STD (no operands)
Set direction flag

Flags	O	D	I	T	S	Z	A	P	C
		1							

Operands	Clocks	Transfers*	Bytes	Coding Example
(no operands)	2(2)	—	1	STD

STI

STI (no operands)
Set interrupt enable flag

Flags	O	D	I	T	S	Z	A	P	C
			1						

Operands	Clocks	Transfers*	Bytes	Coding Example
(no operands)	2(2)	—	1	STI

*For the 8086 (80186) add four clocks for each 16-bit word transfer with an odd address. For the 8088 (80188) add four clocks for each 16-bit word transfer.

†ASM-86 incorporates the segment override prefix into the operand specification and not as a separate instruction. SEGMENT is included in table 1-16 only for timing information.

†SINGLE STEP is not an instruction, it is included in table 1-16 only for timing information.

Table 1-16 Instruction Set Reference Data (continued)

STOS

STOS dest-string
Store byte or word string

Flags	O	D	I	T	S	Z	A	P	C

Operands	Clocks	Transfers*	Bytes	Coding Example
dest-string	11(10)	1	1	STOS PRINT__LINE
(repeat) dest-string	9+10/rep (6+9/rep)	1/rep	1	REP STOS DISPLAY

SUB

SUB destination, source
Subtraction

Flags	O	D	I	T	S	Z	A	P	C
	X				X	X	X	X	X

Operands	Clocks	Transfers*	Bytes	Coding Example
register, register	3(3)		2	SUB CX, BX
register, memory	9(10)+EA	1	2-4	SUB DX, MATH__TOTAL [S1]
memory, register	16(10)+EA	2	2-4	SUB [BP+2], CL
accumulator, immediate	4(3-4)	—	2-3	SUB AL, 10
register, immediate	4(4)	—	3-4	SUB SI, 5280
memory, immediate	17(16)+EA	2	3-6	SUB [BP], BALANCE, 1000

TEST

TEST destination, source
Test or non-destructive logical and

Flags	O	D	I	T	S	Z	A	P	C
	O				X	X	U	X	O

Operands	Clocks	Transfers*	Bytes	Coding Example
register, register	3(3)	—	2	TEST SI, DI
register, memory	9(10)+EA	1	2-4	TEST SI, END__COUNT
accumulator, immediate	4(3-4)	—	2-3	TEST AL, 001000008
register, immediate	5(4)	—	3-4	TEST BX, 0CC4H
memory, immediate	11(10)+EA	—	3-6	TEST RETURN__COUNT, 01H

WAIT

WAIT (no operands)
Wait while TEST pin not asserted

Flags	O	D	I	T	S	Z	A	P	C

Operands	Clocks	Transfers*	Bytes	Coding Example
(no operands)	4+5(6)n	—	1	WAIT

XCHG

XCHG destination, source
Exchange

Flags	O	D	I	T	S	Z	A	P	C

Operands	Clocks	Transfers*	Bytes	Coding Example
accumulator, reg 16	3(3)	—	1	XCHG AX, BX
memory, register	17(17)+EA	2	2-4	XCHG SEMAPHORE, AX
register, register	4(4)	—	2	XCHG AL, BL

XLAT

XLAT source-table
Translate

Flags	O	D	I	T	S	Z	A	P	C

Operands	Clocks	Transfers*	Bytes	Coding Example
source-table	11(11)	1	1	XLAT ASCII__TAB

*For the 8086 (80186) add four clocks for each 16-bit word transfer with an odd address. For the 8088 (80188) add four clocks for each 16-bit word transfer.

Table 1-16 Instruction Set Reference Data (continued)

XOR	**XOR** destination, source Logical exclusive or			**Flags** O D I T S Z A P C O X X U X O
Operands	**Clocks**	**Transfers***	**Bytes**	**Coding Example**
register, register	3(3)	—	2	XOR CX, BX
register, memory	9(10)+EA	1	2-4	XOR CL, MASK_BYTE
memory, register	16(10)+EA	2	2-4	XOR ALPHA [SI], DX
accumulator, immediate	4(3-4)	—	2-3	XOR AL, 010000108
register, immediate	4(4)	—	3-4	XOR SI, 00C2H
memory, immediate	17(16)+EA	2	3-6	XOR RETURN_CODE, 0D2H

*For the 8086 (80186) add four clocks for each 16-bit word transfer with an odd address. For the 8088 (80188) add four clocks for each 16-bit word transfer.

directly affects bus activity. As an example of the encoding and decoding process, consider writing a MOV instruction in ASM-86 in the form:

MOV destination,source

This will cause the assembler to generate 1 of 28 possible forms of the MOV machine instruction. A programmer rarely needs to know the details of machine instruction formats or encoding. An exception may occur during debugging when it may be necessary to monitor instructions fetched on the bus, read unformatted memory dumps, etc. This section provides the information necessary to translate or decode an 8086 or 8088 machine instruction.

To pack instructions into memory as densely as possible, the 8086 and 8088 CPUs utilize an efficient coding technique. Machine instructions vary from one to six bytes in length. One-byte instructions, which generally operate on single registers or flags, are simple to identify; the keys to decoding longer instructions are in the first two bytes. The format of these bytes can vary, but most instructions follow the format shown in Figure 1-28.

The first six bits of a multibyte instruction generally contain an opcode that identifies the basic instruction type: ADD, XOR, etc. The following bit, called the D field, generally specifies the "direction" of the operation: 1 = the REG field in the second byte identifies the destination operand, 0 = the REG field identifies the source operand. The W field distinguishes between byte and word operations: 0 = byte, 1 = word.

One of three additional single-bit fields, S, V or Z, appears in some instruction formats (refer to Table 1-17). S, in conjunction with W, indicates the sign extension of immediate fields in arithmetic instructions. V distinguishes between single-and variable-bit shifts and rotates. Z is a compare bit with the zero flag in conditional repeat and loop instructions.

The second byte of the instruction usually identifies the instruction's operands. The MOD (mode) field indicates whether one of the operands is in memory or whether both operands are registers (refer to Table 1-18). The REG (register) field identifies a register that is one of the instruction operands (refer to Table 1-19). In a number of instructions, particularly the immediate-to-memory variety, REG is used as an extension of the opcode to identify the type of operation. The encoding of the R/M (register/memory) field (refer to Table 1-20) depends on how the mode field is set. If MOD = 11

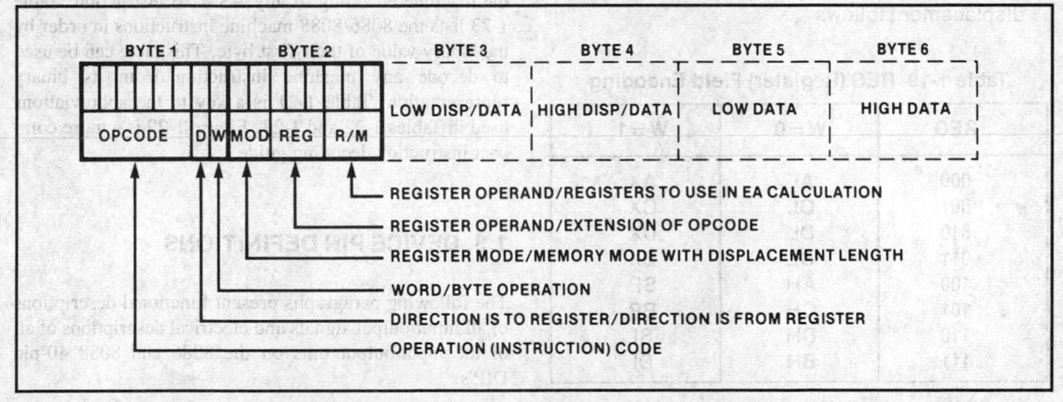

Figure 1-28 Typical 8086/88 Machine Instruction Format

Table 1-17 Single-Bit Field Encoding

Field	Value	Function
S	0	No sign extension
	1	Sign extend 8-bit immediate data to 16 bits if W=1
W	0	Instruction operates on byte data
	1	Instruction operates on word data
D	0	Instruction source is specified in REG field
	1	Instruction destination is specified in REG field
V	0	Shift/rotate count is one
	1	Shift/rotate count is specified in CL register
Z	0	Repeat/loop while zero flag is clear
	1	Repeat/loop while zero flag is set

(register-to-register mode), then R/M identifies the second register operand. If MOD selects memory mode, then R/M indicates how the effective address of the memory operand is to be calculated.

Table 1-18 Mode (MOD) Field Encoding

CODE	EXPLANATION
00	Memory Mode, no displacement follows*
01	Memory Mode, 8-bit displacement follows
10	Memory Mode, 16-bit displacement follows
11	Register Mode (no displacement)

*Except when R/M = 110, then 16-bit displacement follows

Table 1-19 REG (Register) Field Encoding

REG	W=0	W=1
000	AL	AX
001	CL	CX
010	DL	DX
011	BL	BX
100	AH	SP
101	CH	BP
110	DH	SI
111	BH	DI

Bytes 3 through 6 of an instruction are optional fields that usually contain the displacement value of a memory operand and/or the actual value of an immediate constant operand.

The displacement value may contain one or two bytes; the language translators generate one byte whenever possible. The MOD field indicates how many displacement bytes are present. Following Intel convention, if the displacement is two bytes, the most-significant byte is stored second in the instruction. If the displacement is only a single byte, the 8086 or 8088 automatically sign-extends this quantity to 16-bits before using the information in further address calculations. Immediate values always follow any displacement values that may be present. The second byte of a two-byte immediate value is the most significant.

Table 1-22 lists the instruction encodings for all 8086/8088 instructions. This table can be used to predict the machine encoding of any ASM-86 instruction. Table 1-23 lists the 8086/8088 machine instructions in order by the binary value of their first byte. This table can be used to decode any machine instruction from its binary representation. Table 1-21 is a key to the abbreviations used in Tables 1-22 and 1-23. Figure 1-29 is a more compact instruction decoding guide.

1.3 DEVICE PIN DEFINITIONS

The following paragraphs present functional descriptions of all input/output signals and electrical descriptions of all of the input/output pins on the 8086 and 8088 40-pin DIP's.

Table 1-20 Register/Memory Field Encoding

MOD = 11			EFFECTIVE ADDRESS CALCULATION			
R/M	W = 0	W = 1	R/M	MOD = 00	MOD = 01	MOD = 10
000	AL	AX	000	(BX) + (SI)	(BX) + (SI) + D8	(BX) + (SI) + D16
001	CL	CX	001	(BX) + (DI)	(BX) + (DI) + D8	(BX) + (DI) + D16
010	DL	DX	010	(BP) + (SI)	(BP) + (SI) + D8	(BP) + (SI) + D16
011	BL	BX	011	(BP) + (DI)	(BP) + (DI) + D8	(BP) + (DI) + D16
100	AH	SP	100	(SI)	(SI) + D8	(SI) + D16
101	CH	BP	101	(DI)	(DI) + D8	(DI) + D16
110	DH	SI	110	DIRECT ADDRESS	(BP) + D8	(BP) + D16
111	BH	DI	111	(BX)	(BX) + D8	(BX) + D16

1.3.1 Functional Description of All Signals

Figure 1-30 shows the 8086/8088 DIP pin assignments and Table 1-24 provides a complete functional description of each device pin signal and correlates the description to the pin number and associated signal symbol.

1.3.2 Electrical Description of Pins

The absolute maximum ratings for the 8086/8088 device are as follows.

ABSOLUTE MAXIMUM RATINGS

Ambient Temperature Under Bias	0°C to 70°C
Storage Temperature	−65°C to +150°C
Voltage on Any Pin with Respect to GND	−1.0 to +7V
Power Dissipation	2.5 Watt

Stresses above those listed above may cause permanent damage to the device. These values present stress ratings only and functional operation of the device at these or any other conditions above those indicated in the operational sections of the device specifications is not implied. Exposure to absolute maximum conditions for extended periods of time may affect the device reliability.

Table 1-25 presents the D.C. voltage characteristics of the 8086/8088 CPU's. Table 1-26 lists the A.C. characteristics timing requirements and timing responses for minimum complexity systems, and Table 1-27 lists the A.C. characteristics timing requirements and timing responses for maximum complexity systems (using 8288 bus controller). Figure 1-31 and Figure 1-32 presents waveforms for the minimum mode and maximum mode operation related to the preceding A.C. characteristics tables.

1.3.3 OPERATING MODES

One of the unique features the 8086 and 8088 CPU's allow the user is the ability to select between two functional definitions of a subset of the 8086/8088 outputs. This enables the user to tailor the intended CPU system environment. This "system tailoring" is accomplished by strapping the CPU's MN/MX* (minimum/maximum) input pin. Table 1-28 defines the 8086 and 8088 pin assignments for both the minimum and maximum modes of operation.

In the minimum mode, the CPU's support small systems by strapping the MN/MX* pin to +5V. In this mode of operation, the 8086/8088 CPU generates all bus control signals (DT/R*, DEN*, ALE and either M/IO* or IO/M*) and the command output signals (RD*, WR* or INTA*). The CPU also provides a mechanism for requesting bus access (HOLD/HLDA) that is compatible with bus master type controllers (e.g., the Intel 8237A DMA Controller).

When a bus master requires bus access in the minimum mode, it activates the HOLD input to the CPU through its request logic. In response to the "hold" request, The CPU activates HLDA as an acknowledgement to the bus master, requesting the bus, and simultaneously floats the system bus and control lines. Since a bus request is asynchronous, the CPU samples the HOLD input on the positive transition of each CLK signal and activates HLDA at the end of either the current bus cycle (if a bus cycle is in progress) or idle clock period. The CPU maintains the hold state until the bus master inactivates the HOLD input. At that time the CPU regains control of the system bus. Note that during a "hold" state, the CPU continues to execute instructions until a bus cycle is required.

In the minimum mode, the I/O-memory control line for the 8088 CPU is the reverse of the corresponding control line for the 8086 CPU (M/IO* on the 8086 and IO/M* on the 8088). Since the 8088 CPU is an 8-bit device, this conditioning provides compatibility with existing MCS®-85 systems specific MCS-85 family devices (e.g., the Intel 8155/56).

Hi \ Lo	0	1	2	3	4	5	6	7	8	9	A	B	C	D	E	F
0	ADD b.f.r/m	ADD w.f.r/m	ADD b.t.r/m	ADD w.t.r/m	ADD b.ia	ADD w.ia	PUSH ES	POP ES	OR b.f.r/m	OR w.f.r/m	OR b.t.r/m	OR w.t.r/m	OR b.i	OR w.i	PUSH CS	
1	ADC b.f.r/m	ADC w.f.r/m	ADC b.t.r/m	ADC w.t.r/m	ADC b.i	ADC w.i	PUSH SS	POP SS	SBB b.f.r/m	SBB w.f.r/m	SBB b.t.r/m	SBB w.t.r/m	SBB b.i	SBB w.i	PUSH DS	POP DS
2	AND b.f.r/m	AND w.f.r/m	AND b.t.r/m	AND w.t.r/m	AND b.i	AND w.i	SEG =ES	DAA	SUB b.f.r/m	SUB w.f.r/m	SUB b.t.r/m	SUB w.t.r/m	SUB b.i	SUB w.i	SEG CS	DAS
3	XOR b.f.r/m	XOR w.f.r/m	XOR b.t.r/m	XOR w.t.r/m	XOR b.i	XOR w.i	SEG =SS	AAA	CMP b.f.r/m	CMP w.f.r/m	CMP b.t.r/m	CMP w.t.r/m	CMP b.i	CMP w.i	SEG DS	AAS
4	INC AX	INC CX	INC DX	INC BX	INC SP	INC BP	INC SI	INC DI	DEC AX	DEC CX	DEC DX	DEC BX	DEC SP	DEC BP	DEC SI	DEC DI
5	PUSH AX	PUSH CX	PUSH DX	PUSH BX	PUSH SP	PUSH BP	PUSH SI	PUSH DI	POP AX	POP CX	POP DX	POP BX	POP SP	POP BP	POP SI	POP DI
6																
7	JO	JNO	JB/ JNAE	JNB/ JAE	JE/ JZ	JNE/ JNZ	JBE/ JNA	JNBE/ JA	JS	JNS	JP/ JPE	JNP/ JPO	JL/ JNGE	JNL/ JGE	JLE/ JNG	JNLE/ JG
8	Immed b.r/m	Immed w.r/m	Immed b.r/m	Immed is.r/m	TEST b.r/m	TEST w.r/m	XCHG b.r/m	XCHG w.r/m	MOV b.f.r/m	MOV w.f.r/m	MOV b.t.r/m	MOV w.t.r/m	MOV sr.f.r/m	LEA	MOV sr.t.r/m	POP r/m
9	XCHG AX	XCHG CX	XCHG DX	XCHG BX	XCHG SP	XCHG BP	XCHG SI	XCHG DI	CBW	CWD	CALL l.d	WAIT	PUSHF	POPF	SAHF	LAHF
A	MOV m → AL	MOV m → AX	MOV AL → m	MOV AX → m	MOVS	MOVS	CMPS	CMPS	TEST b.i.a	TEST w.i.a	STOS	STOS	LODS	LODS	SCAS	SCAS
B	MOV i → AL	MOV i → CL	MOV i → DL	MOV i → BL	MOV i → AH	MOV i → CH	MOV i → DH	MOV i → BH	MOV i → AX	MOV i → CX	MOV i → DX	MOV i → BX	MOV i → SP	MOV i → BP	MOV i → SI	MOV i → DI
C			RET. (i+SP)	RET	LES	LDS	MOV b.i.r/m	MOV w.i.r/m			RET. l.(i+SP)	RET l	INT Type 3	INT (Any)	INTO	IRET
D	Shift b	Shift w	Shift b.v	Shift w.v	AAM	AAD		XLAT	ESC 0	ESC 1	ESC 2	ESC 3	ESC 4	ESC 5	ESC 6	ESC 7
E	LOOPNZ/ LOOPNE	LOOPZ/ LOOPE	LOOP	JCXZ	IN b	IN w	OUT b	OUT w	CALL d	JMP d	JMP l.d	JMP si.d	IN v.b	IN v.w	OUT v.b	OUT v.w
F	LOCK		REP	REP z	HLT	CMC	Grp 1 b.r/m	Grp 1 w.r/m	CLC	STC	CLI	STI	CLD	STD	Grp 2 b.r/m	Grp 2 w.r/m

where:

mod□r/m	000	001	010	011	100	101	110	111
Immed	ADD	OR	ADC	SBB	AND	SUB	XOR	CMP
Shift	ROL	ROR	RCL	RCR	SHL/SAL	SHR	—	SAR
Grp 1	TEST	—	NOT	NEG	MUL	IMUL	DIV	IDIV
Grp 2	INC	DEC	CALL id	CALL l.id	JMP id	JMP l.id	PUSH	—

b = byte operation
d = direct
f = from CPU reg
i = immediate
ia = immed. to accum.
id = indirect
is = immed. byte, sign ext.
l = long ie. intersegment

m = memory
r/m = EA is second byte
si = short intrasegment
sr = segment register
t = to CPU reg
v = variable
w = word operation
z = zero

Figure 1-29 Machine Instruction Encoding Matrix

In the maximum mode (MN/MX* pin strapped to ground), the Intel 8288 Bus controller is added to provide sophisticated bus control functions and compatibility with the MULTIBUS architecture. (Combining an Intel 8289 Arbiter with the 8288 permits the CPU to support multiple processors on the system bus.) The bus controller, instead of the CPU (see Figure 1-33), provides all bus control and command outputs. This allows the pins previously delegated to these functions to be redefined to support multiprocessing functions.

1.3.4 Minimum Mode System Overview/Description

The minimum mode 8086 (see Figure 1-34) is optimized

Table 1-21 Key to Machine Instruction Encoding and Decoding

IDENTIFIER	EXPLANATION
MOD	Mode field; described in this chapter.
REG	Register field; described in this chapter.
R/M	Register/Memory field; described in this chapter.
SR	Segment register code: 00=ES, 01=CS, 10=SS, 11=DS.
W, S, D, V, Z	Single-bit instruction fields; described in this chapter.
DATA-8	8-bit immediate constant.
DATA-SX	8-bit immediate value that is automatically sign-extended to 16-bits before use.
DATA-LO	Low-order byte of 16-bit immediate constant.
DATA-HI	High-order byte of 16-bit immediate constant.
(DISP-LO)	Low-order byte of optional 8- or 16-bit unsigned displacement; MOD indicates if present.
(DISP-HI)	High-order byte of optional 16-bit unsigned displacement; MOD indicates if present.
IP-LO	Low-order byte of new IP value.
IP-HI	High-order byte of new IP value
CS-LO	Low-order byte of new CS value.
CS-HI	High-order byte of new CS value.
IP-INC8	8-bit signed increment to instruction pointer.
IP-INC-LO	Low-order byte of signed 16-bit instruction pointer increment.
IP-INC-HI	High-order byte of signed 16-bit instruction pointer increment.
ADDR-LO	Low-order byte of direct address (offset) of memory operand; EA not calculated.
ADDR-HI	High-order byte of direct address (offset) of memory operand; EA not calculated.
——	Bits may contain any value.
XXX	First 3 bits of ESC opcode.
YYY	Second 3 bits of ESC opcode.
REG8	8-bit general register operand.
REG16	16-bit general register operand.
MEM8	8-bit memory operand (any addressing mode).
MEM16	16-bit memory operand (any addressing mode).
IMMED8	8-bit immediate operand.
IMMED16	16-bit immediate operand.
SEGREG	Segment register operand.
DEST-STR8	Byte string addressed by DI.

Table 1-21 Key to Machine Instruction Encoding and Decoding (continued)

IDENTIFIER	EXPLANATION
SRC-STR8	Byte string addressed by SI.
DEST-STR16	Word string addressed by DI.
SRC-STR16	Word string addressed by SI.
SHORT-LABEL	Label within ±127 bytes of instruction.
NEAR-PROC	Procedure in current code segment.
FAR-PROC	Procedure in another code segment.
NEAR-LABEL	Label in current code segment but farther than −128 to +127 bytes from instruction.
FAR-LABEL	Label in another code segment.
SOURCE-TABLE	XLAT translation table addressed by BX.
OPCODE	ESC opcode operand.
SOURCE	ESC register or memory operand.

for small to medium (one or two boards), single CPU systems. Minimum mode system architecture is directed at satisfying requirements of the lower to middle segment of high performance 16-bit applications. The CPU maintains the full megabyte memory space, 64K-byte I/O space and 16-bit data path. The CPU directly provides all bus control (DT/R*, DEN*, ALE, M/IO*), commands (RD*, WR*, INTA*) and a simple CPU preemption mechanism

Table 1-22 8086/88 Instruction Encoding

DATA TRANSFER

MOV = Move:	7 6 5 4 3 2 1 0	7 6 5 4 3 2 1 0	7 6 5 4 3 2 1 0	7 6 5 4 3 2 1 0	7 6 5 4 3 2 1 0	7 6 5 4 3 2 1 0
Register/memory to/from register	1 0 0 0 1 0 d w	mod reg r/m	(DISP-LO)	(DISP-HI)		
Immediate to register/memory	1 1 0 0 0 1 1 w	mod 0 0 0 r/m	(DISP-LO)	(DISP-HI)	data	data if w = 1
Immediate to register	1 0 1 1 w reg	data	data if w = 1			
Memory to accumulator	1 0 1 0 0 0 0 w	addr-lo	addr-hi			
Accumulator to memory	1 0 1 0 0 0 1 w	addr-lo	addr-hi			
Register/memory to segment register	1 0 0 0 1 1 1 0	mod 0 SR r/m	(DISP-LO)	(DISP-HI)		
Segment register to register/memory	1 0 0 0 1 1 0 0	mod 0 SR r/m	(DISP-LO)	(DISP-HI)		

PUSH = Push:				
Register/memory	1 1 1 1 1 1 1 1	mod 1 1 0 r/m	(DISP-LO)	(DISP-HI)
Register	0 1 0 1 0 reg			
Segment register	0 0 0 reg 1 1 0			

POP = Pop:				
Register/memory	1 0 0 0 1 1 1 1	mod 0 0 0 r/m	(DISP-LO)	(DISP-HI)
Register	0 1 0 1 1 reg			
Segment register	0 0 0 reg 1 1 1			

Table 1-22 8086/88 Instruction Encoding (continued)

DATA TRANSFER (Cont'd.)						
XCHG = Exchange:	7 6 5 4 3 2 1 0	7 6 5 4 3 2 1 0	7 6 5 4 3 2 1 0	7 6 5 4 3 2 1 0	7 6 5 4 3 2 1 0	7 6 5 4 3 2 1 0
Register/memory with register	1 0 0 0 0 1 1 w	mod reg r/m	(DISP-LO)	(DISP-HI)		
Register with accumulator	1 0 0 1 0 reg					
IN = Input from:						
Fixed port	1 1 1 0 0 1 0 w	DATA-8				
Variable port	1 1 1 0 1 1 0 w					
OUT = Output to:						
Fixed port	1 1 1 0 0 1 1 w	DATA-8				
Variable port	1 1 1 0 1 1 1 w					
XLAT = Translate byte to AL	1 1 0 1 0 1 1 1					
LEA = Load EA to register	1 0 0 0 1 1 0 1	mod reg r/m	(DISP-LO)	(DISP-HI)		
LDS = Load pointer to DS	1 1 0 0 0 1 0 1	mod reg r/m	(DISP-LO)	(DISP-HI)		
LES = Load pointer to ES	1 1 0 0 0 1 0 0	mod reg r/m	(DISP-LO)	(DISP-HI)		
LAHF = Load AH with flags	1 0 0 1 1 1 1 1					
SAHF = Store AH into flags	1 0 0 1 1 1 1 0					
PUSHF = Push flags	1 0 0 1 1 1 0 0					
POPF = Pop flags	1 0 0 1 1 1 0 1					

ARITHMETIC						
ADD = Add:						
Reg/memory with register to either	0 0 0 0 0 0 d w	mod reg r/m	(DISP-LO)	(DISP-HI)		
Immediate to register/memory	1 0 0 0 0 0 s w	mod 0 0 0 r/m	(DISP-LO)	(DISP-HI)	data	data if s: w=01
Immediate to accumulator	0 0 0 0 0 1 0 w	data	data if w=1			
ADC = Add with carry:						
Reg/memory with register to either	0 0 0 1 0 0 d w	mod reg r/m	(DISP-LO)	(DISP-HI)		
Immediate to register/memory	1 0 0 0 0 0 s w	mod 0 1 0 r/m	(DISP-LO)	(DISP-HI)	data	data if s: w=01
Immediate to accumulator	0 0 0 1 0 1 0 w	data	data if w=1			
INC = Increment:						
Register/memory	1 1 1 1 1 1 1 w	mod 0 0 0 r/m	(DISP-LO)	(DISP-HI)		
Register	0 1 0 0 0 reg					
AAA = ASCII adjust for add	0 0 1 1 0 1 1 1					
DAA = Decimal adjust for add	0 0 1 0 0 1 1 1					

Table 1-22 8086/88 Instruction Encoding (continued)

ARITHMETIC (Cont'd.)

Instruction	7 6 5 4 3 2 1 0	7 6 5 4 3 2 1 0	7 6 5 4 3 2 1 0	7 6 5 4 3 2 1 0	7 6 5 4 3 2 1 0	7 6 5 4 3 2 1 0
SUB = Subtract:						
Reg/memory and register to either	0 0 1 0 1 0 d w	mod reg r/m	(DISP-LO)	(DISP-HI)		
Immediate from register/memory	1 0 0 0 0 0 s w	mod 1 0 1 r/m	(DISP-LO)	(DISP-HI)	data	data if s: w=01
Immediate from accumulator	0 0 1 0 1 1 0 w	data	data if w=1			
SBB = Subtract with borrow:						
Reg/memory and register to either	0 0 0 1 1 0 d w	mod reg r/m	(DISP-LO)	(DISP-HI)		
Immediate from register/memory	1 0 0 0 0 0 s w	mod 0 1 1 r/m	(DISP-LO)	(DISP-HI)	data	data if s: w=01
Immediate from accumulator	0 0 0 1 1 1 0 w	data	data if w=1			
DEC Decrement:						
Register/memory	1 1 1 1 1 1 1 w	mod 0 0 1 r/m	(DISP-LO)	(DISP-HI)		
Register	0 1 0 0 1 reg					
NEG Change sign	1 1 1 1 0 1 1 w	mod 0 1 1 r/m	(DISP-LO)	(DISP-HI)		
CMP = Compare:						
Register/memory and register	0 0 1 1 1 0 d w	mod reg r/m	(DISP-LO)	(DISP-HI)		
Immediate with register/memory	1 0 0 0 0 0 s w	mod 1 1 1 r/m	(DISP-LO)	(DISP-HI)	data	data if s: w=1
Immediate with accumulator	0 0 1 1 1 1 0 w	data				
AAS ASCII adjust for subtract	0 0 1 1 1 1 1 1					
DAS Decimal adjust for subtract	0 0 1 0 1 1 1 1					
MUL Multiply (unsigned)	1 1 1 1 0 1 1 w	mod 1 0 0 r/m	(DISP-LO)	(DISP-HI)		
IMUL Integer multiply (signed)	1 1 1 1 0 1 1 w	mod 1 0 1 r/m	(DISP-LO)	(DISP-HI)		
AAM ASCII adjust for multiply	1 1 0 1 0 1 0 0	0 0 0 0 1 0 1 0	(DISP-LO)	(DISP-HI)		
DIV Divide (unsigned)	1 1 1 1 0 1 1 w	mod 1 1 0 r/m	(DISP-LO)	(DISP-HI)		
IDIV Integer divide (signed)	1 1 1 1 0 1 1 w	mod 1 1 1 r/m	(DISP-LO)	(DISP-HI)		
AAD ASCII adjust for divide	1 1 0 1 0 1 0 1	0 0 0 0 1 0 1 0	(DISP-LO)	(DISP-HI)		
CBW Convert byte to word	1 0 0 1 1 0 0 0					
CWD Convert word to double word	1 0 0 1 1 0 0 1					

LOGIC

Instruction	7 6 5 4 3 2 1 0	7 6 5 4 3 2 1 0	7 6 5 4 3 2 1 0	7 6 5 4 3 2 1 0
NOT Invert	1 1 1 1 0 1 1 w	mod 0 1 0 r/m	(DISP-LO)	(DISP-HI)
SHL/SAL Shift logical/arithmetic left	1 1 0 1 0 0 v w	mod 1 0 0 r/m	(DISP-LO)	(DISP-HI)
SHR Shift logical right	1 1 0 1 0 0 v w	mod 1 0 1 r/m	(DISP-LO)	(DISP-HI)
SAR Shift arithmetic right	1 1 0 1 0 0 v w	mod 1 1 1 r/m	(DISP-LO)	(DISP-HI)
ROL Rotate left	1 1 0 1 0 0 v w	mod 0 0 0 r/m	(DISP-LO)	(DISP-HI)

Table 1-22 8086/88 Instruction Encoding (continued)

LOGIC (Cont'd.)	7 6 5 4 3 2 1 0	7 6 5 4 3 2 1 0	7 6 5 4 3 2 1 0	7 6 5 4 3 2 1 0	7 6 5 4 3 2 1 0	7 6 5 4 3 2 1 0
ROR Rotate right	1 1 0 1 0 0 v w	mod 0 0 1 r/m	(DISP-LO)	(DISP-HI)		
RCL Rotate through carry flag left	1 1 0 1 0 0 v w	mod 0 1 0 r/m	(DISP-LO)	(DISP-HI)		
RCR Rotate through carry right	1 1 0 1 0 0 v w	mod 0 1 1 r/m	(DISP-LO)	(DISP-HI)		
AND = And:						
Reg/memory with register to either	0 0 1 0 0 0 d w	mod reg r/m	(DISP-LO)	(DISP-HI)		
Immediate to register/memory	1 0 0 0 0 0 0 w	mod 1 0 0 r/m	(DISP-LO)	(DISP-HI)	data	data if w=1
Immediate to accumulator	0 0 1 0 0 1 0 w	data	data if w=1			
TEST = And function to flags no result:						
Register/memory and register	0 0 0 1 0 0 d w	mod reg r/m	(DISP-LO)	(DISP-HI)		
Immediate data and register/memory	1 1 1 1 0 1 1 w	mod 0 0 0 r/m	(DISP-LO)	(DISP-HI)	data	data if w=1
Immediate data and accumulator	1 0 1 0 1 0 0 w	data				
OR = Or:						
Reg/memory and register to either	0 0 0 0 1 0 d w	mod reg r/m	(DISP-LO)	(DISP-HI)		
Immediate to register/memory	1 0 0 0 0 0 0 w	mod 0 0 1 r/m	(DISP-LO)	(DISP-HI)	data	data if w=1
Immediate to accumulator	0 0 0 0 1 1 0 w	data	data if w=1			
XOR = Exclusive or:						
Reg/memory and register to either	0 0 1 1 0 0 d w	mod reg r/m	(DISP-LO)	(DISP-HI)		
Immediate to register/memory	0 0 1 1 0 1 0 w	data	(DISP-LO)	(DISP-HI)	data	data if w=1
Immediate to accumulator	0 0 1 1 0 1 0 w	data	data if w=1			
STRING MANIPULATION						
REP = Repeat	1 1 1 1 0 0 1 z					
MOVS = Move byte/word	1 0 1 0 0 1 0 w					
CMPS = Compare byte/word	1 0 1 0 0 1 1 w					
SCAS = Scan byte/word	1 0 1 0 1 1 1 w					
LODS = Load byte/wd to AL/AX	1 0 1 0 1 1 0 w					
STDS = Stor byte/wd from AL/A	1 0 1 0 1 0 1 w					

Table 1-22 8086/88 Instruction Encoding (continued)

CONTROL TRANSFER

CALL = Call:	7 6 5 4 3 2 1 0	7 6 5 4 3 2 1 0	7 6 5 4 3 2 1 0	7 6 5 4 3 2 1 0	7 6 5 4 3 2 1 0	7 6 5 4 3 2 1 0
Direct within segment	1 1 1 0 1 0 0 0	IP-INC-LO	IP-INC-HI			
Indirect within segment	1 1 1 1 1 1 1 1	mod 0 1 0 r/m	(DISP-LO)	(DISP-HI)		
Direct intersegment	1 0 0 1 1 0 1 0	IP-lo	IP-hi			
		CS-lo	CS-hi			
Indirect intersegment	1 1 1 1 1 1 1 1	mod 0 1 1 r/m	(DISP-LO)	(DISP-HI)		
JMP = Unconditional Jump:						
Direct within segment	1 1 1 0 1 0 0 1	IP-INC-LO	IP-INC-HI			
Direct within segment-short	1 1 1 0 1 0 1 1	IP-INC8				
Indirect within segment	1 1 1 1 1 1 1 1	mod 1 0 0 r/m	(DISP-LO)	(DISP-HI)		
Direct intersegment	1 1 1 0 1 0 1 0	IP-lo	IP-hi			
		CS-lo	CS-hi			
Indirect intersegment	1 1 1 1 1 1 1 1	mod 1 0 1 r/m	(DISP-LO)	(DISP-HI)		
RET = Return from CALL:						
Within segment	1 1 0 0 0 0 1 1					
Within seg adding immed to SP	1 1 0 0 0 0 1 0	data-lo	data-hi			
Intersegment	1 1 0 0 1 0 1 1					
Intersegment adding immediate to SP	1 1 0 0 1 0 1 0	data-lo	data-hi			
JE/JZ = Jump on equal/zero	0 1 1 1 0 1 0 0	IP-INC8				
JL/JNGE = Jump on less/not greater or equal	0 1 1 1 1 1 0 0	IP-INC8				
JLE/JNG = Jump on less or equal/not greater	0 1 1 1 1 1 1 0	IP-INC8				
JB/JNAE = Jump on below/not above or equal	0 1 1 1 0 0 1 0	IP-INC8				
JBE/JNA = Jump on below or equal/not above	0 1 1 1 0 1 1 0	IP-INC8				
JP/JPE = Jump on parity/parity even	0 1 1 1 1 0 1 0	IP-INC8				
JO = Jump on overflow	0 1 1 1 0 0 0 0	IP-INC8				
JS = Jump on sign	0 1 1 1 1 0 0 0	IP-INC8				
JNE/JNZ = Jump on not equal/not zer0	0 1 1 1 0 1 0 1	IP-INC8				
JNL/JGE = Jump on not less/greater or equal	0 1 1 1 1 1 0 1	IP-INC8				
JNLE/JG = Jump on not less or equal/greater	0 1 1 1 1 1 1 1	IP-INC8				
JNB/JAE = Jump on not below/above or equal	0 1 1 1 0 0 1 1	IP-INC8				
JNBE/JA = Jump on not below or equal/above	0 1 1 1 0 1 1 1	IP-INC8				
JNP/JPO = Jump on not par/par odd	0 1 1 1 1 0 1 1	IP-INC8				
JNO = Jump on not overflow	0 1 1 1 0 0 0 1	IP-INC8				

210912-001

Table 1-22 8086/88 Instruction Encoding (continued)

Instruction	7 6 5 4 3 2 1 0	7 6 5 4 3 2 1 0	7 6 5 4 3 2 1 0	7 6 5 4 3 2 1 0	7 6 5 4 3 2 1 0	7 6 5 4 3 2 1 0
CONTROL TRANSFER (Cont'd.)						
RET = Return from CALL:						
JNS = Jump on not sign	0 1 1 1 1 0 0 1	IP-INC8				
LOOP = Loop CX times	1 1 1 0 0 0 1 0	IP-INC8				
LOOPZ/LOOPE = Loop while zero/equal	1 1 1 0 0 0 0 1	IP-INC8				
LOOPNZ/LOOPNE = Loop while not zero/equal	1 1 1 0 0 0 0 0	IP-INC8				
JCXZ = Jump on CX zero	1 1 1 0 0 0 1 1	IP-INC8				
INT = Interrupt:						
Type specified	1 1 0 0 1 1 0 1	DATA-8				
Type 3	1 1 0 0 1 1 0 0					
INTO = Interrupt on overflow	1 1 0 0 1 1 1 0					
IRET = Interrupt return	1 1 0 0 1 1 1 1					
PROCESSOR CONTROL						
CLC = Clear carry	1 1 1 1 1 0 0 0					
CMC = Complement carry	1 1 1 1 0 1 0 1					
STC = Set carry	1 1 1 1 1 0 0 1					
CLD = Clear direction	1 1 1 1 1 1 0 0					
STD = Set direction	1 1 1 1 1 1 0 1					
CLI = Clear interrupt	1 1 1 1 1 0 1 0					
STI = Set interrupt	1 1 1 1 1 0 1 1					
HLT = Halt	1 1 1 1 0 1 0 0					
WAIT = Wait	1 0 0 1 1 0 1 1					
ESC = Escape (to external device)	1 1 0 1 1 x x x	m o d y y y r / m	(DISP-LO)	(DISP-HI)		
LOCK = Bus lock prefix	1 1 1 1 0 0 0 0					
SEGMENT = Override prefix	0 0 1 reg 1 1 0					

(HOLD, HLDA) compatible with existing DMA controllers (e.g., 8259A Interrupt Controller).

In the minimum mode the 8088 CPU provides an SSO status output. This output is equivalent to S0 in the maximum mode and can be decoded with DT/R* and −IO/M*, which are equivalent to S1* and S2* respectively, to provide the same CPU cycle status information (see Table 1-29). This type of decoding could be used in a minimum mode 8088-based system to allow dynamic RAM refresh during passive CPU cycle.

1.3.5 Maximum Mode System Overview/Description

The maximum mode (see Figure 1-35) extends the system architecture to support multiprocessor configurations and local instruction set extension processors (coprocessors). By adding the 8288 bipolar bus controller, the 8086 outputs assigned to bus control and commands in the minimum mode are redefined to allow these extensions and enhance general system performance. Specifically, (1) two prioritized levels of processor preemption (RQ*/GT0*, RQ*/GT1*) allow multiple processors to reside on the 8086's local bus and share its interface to the system bus, (2) Queue status (QS0, QS1) is available to allow external devices like ICE™-86 or special instruction set extension co-processors (such as the 8087 Numeric Co-processor) to track the CPU instruction execution, (3) access control to shared resources in multiprocessor systems is supported by a hardware bus lock mechanism and (4) system command and configuration options are expanded via devices like the 8288 bus controller and 8289 bus arbiter.

QUEUE STATUS

The queue status indicates what information is being removed from the internal queue and when the queue is being reset due to a transfer of control (Table 1-30). By monitoring the S0*, S1*, S2* status lines for instructions entering the 8086 (1, 0, 0 indicates code access while A0 and BHE* indicate word or byte) and QS0, QS1 for instructions leaving the 8086's internal queue, it is possible to track the instruction execution. Since instructions are executed from the 8086's internal queue, the queue status is presented each CPU clock cycle and is not related to the bus cycle activity. This mechanism (1) allows a co-processor to detect execution of an ESCAPE instruction which directs the co-processor to perform a specific task and (2) allows ICE™-86 to trap execution of a specific memory location.

An example of a circuit used by ICE is given in Figure 1-36. The first up down counter tracks the depth of the queue while the second captures the queue depth on a match. The second counter decrements on further fetches from the queue until the queue is flushed or the count goes to zero indicating execution of the match address. The first counter decrements on fetch from the queue (QS0 = 1) and increments on code fetches into the queue. Note that a normal code fetch will transfer two bytes into the queue so two clock increments are given to the counter (T201 and T301) unless a single byte is loaded over the upper half of the bus (A0-P is high). Since the execution unit (EU) is not synchronized to the bus interface unit (BIU), a fetch from the queue can occur simultaneously with a transfer into the queue. The Exclusive-OR gate driving the ENP input of the first counter allows these simultaneous operations to cancel each other and not modify the queue depth.

HARDWARE LOCK

To address the problem of controlling access to shared resources, the maximum mode 8086 provides a hardware LOCK* output. The LOCK* output is activated through the instruction stream by execution of the LOCK prefix instruction. The LOCK* output goes active in the first CPU clock cycle following execution of the prefix and remains active until the clock following the completion of the instruction following the LOCK prefix. To provide bus access control in multiprocessor systems, the LOCK* signal should be incorporated into the system bus arbitration logic resident to the CPU.

Table 1-23 Machine Instruction Decoding Guide

1ST BYTE		2ND BYTE	BYTES 3, 4, 5, 6	ASM-86 INSTRUCTION FORMAT	
HEX	BINARY				
00	0000 0000	MOD REG R/M	(DISP-LO),(DISP-HI)	ADD	REG8/MEM8,REG8
01	0000 0001	MOD REG R/M	(DISP-LO),(DISP-HI)	ADD	REG16/MEM16,REG16
02	0000 0010	MOD REG R/M	(DISP-LO),(DISP-HI)	ADD	REG8,REG8/MEM8
03	0000 0011	MOD REG R/M	(DISP-LO),(DISP-HI)	ADD	REG16,REG16/MEM16
04	0000 0100	DATA-8		ADD	AL,IMMED8
05	0000 0101	DATA-LO	DATA-HI	ADD	AX,IMMED16
06	0000 0110			PUSH	ES
07	0000 0111			POP	ES

Table 1-23 Machine Instruction Decoding Guide (continued)

1ST BYTE		2ND BYTE	BYTES 3,4,5,6	ASM-86 INSTRUCTION FORMAT	
HEX	BINARY				
08	0000 1000	MOD REG R/M	(DISP-LO),(DISP-HI)	OR	REG8/MEM8,REG8
09	0000 1001	MOD REG R/M	(DISP-LO),(DISP-HI)	OR	REG16/MEM16,REG16
0A	0000 1010	MOD REG R/M	(DISP-LO),(DISP-HI)	OR	REG8,REG8/MEM8
0B	0000 1011	MOD REG R/M	(DISP-LO),(DISP-HI)	OR	REG16,REG16/MEM16
0C	0000 1100	DATA-8		OR	AL,IMMED8
0D	0000 1101	DATA-LO	DATA-HI	OR	AX,IMMED16
0E	0000 1110			PUSH	CS
0F	0000 1111			(not used)	
10	0001 0000	MOD REG R/M	(DISP-LO),(DISP-HI)	ADC	REG8/MEM8,REG8
11	0001 0001	MOD REG R/M	(DISP-LO),(DISP-HI)	ADC	REG16/MEM16,REG16
12	0001 0010	MOD REG R/M	(DISP-LO),(DISP-HI)	ADC	REG8,REG8/MEM8
13	0001 0011	MOD REG R/M	(DISP-LO),(DISP-HI)	ADC	REG16,REG16/MEM16
14	0001 0100	DATA-8		ADC	AL,IMMED8
15	0001 0101	DATA-LO	DATA-HI	ADC	AX,IMMED16
16	0001 0110			PUSH	SS
17	0001 0111			POP	SS
18	0001 1000	MOD REG R/M	(DISP-LO),(DISP-HI)	SBB	REG8/MEM8,REG8
19	0001 1001	MOD REG R/M	(DISP-LO),(DISP-HI)	SBB	REG16/MEM16,REG16
1A	0001 1010	MOD REG R/M	(DISP-LO),(DISP-HI)	SBB	REG8,REG8/MEM8
1B	0001 1011	MOD REG R/M	(DISP-LO),(DISP-HI)	SBB	REG16,REG16/MEM16
1C	0001 1100	DATA-8		SBB	AL,IMMED8
1D	0001 1101	DATA-LO	DATA-HI	SBB	AX,IMMED16
1E	0001 1110			PUSH	DS
1F	0001 1111			POP	DS
20	0010 0000	MOD REG R/M	(DISP-LO),(DISP-HI)	AND	REG8/MEM8,REG8
21	0010 0001	MOD REG R/M	(DISP-LO),(DISP-HI)	AND	REG16/MEM16,REG16
22	0010 0010	MOD REG R/M	(DISP-LO),(DISP-HI)	AND	REG8,REG8/MEM8
23	0010 0011	MOD REG R/M	(DISP-LO),(DISP-HI)	AND	REG16,REG16/MEM16
24	0010 0100	DATA-8		AND	AL,IMMED8
25	0010 0101	DATA-LO	DATA-HI	AND	AX,IMMED16
26	0010 0110			ES:	(segment override prefix)
27	0010 0111			DAA	
28	0010 1000	MOD REG R/M	(DISP-LO),(DISP-HI)	SUB	REG8/MEM8,REG8
29	0010 1001	MOD REG R/M	(DISP-LO),(DISP-HI)	SUB	REG16/MEM16,REG16
2A	0010 1010	MOD REG R/M	(DISP-LO),(DISP-HI)	SUB	REG8,REG8/MEM8
2B	0010 1011	MOD REG R/M	(DISP-LO,(DISP-HI)	SUB	REG16,REG16/MEM16
2C	0010 1100	DATA-8		SUB	AL,IMMED8
2D	0010 1101	DATA-LO	DATA-HI	SUB	AX,IMMED16
2E	0010 1110			CS:	(segment override prefix)
2F	0010 1111			DAS	
30	0011 0000	MOD REG R/M	(DISP-LO),(DISP-HI)	XOR	REG8/MEM8,REG8
31	0011 0001	MOD REG R/M	(DISP-LO),(DISP-HI)	XOR	REG16/MEM16,REG16
32	0011 0010	MOD REG R/M	(DISP-LO),(DISP-HI)	XOR	REG8,REG8/MEM8
33	0011 0011	MOD REG R/M	(DISP-LO),(DISP-HI)	XOR	REG16,REG16/MEM16
34	0011 0100	DATA-8		XOR	AL,IMMED8
35	0011 0101	DATA-LO	DATA-HI	XOR	AX,IMMED16
36	0011 0110			SS:	(segment override prefix)

Table 1-23 Machine Instruction Decoding Guide (continued)

1ST BYTE		2ND BYTE	BYTES 3,4,5,6	ASM-86 INSTRUCTION FORMAT	
HEX	BINARY				
37	0011 0110			AAA	
38	0011 1000	MOD REG R/M	(DISP-LO),(DISP-HI)	CMP	REG8/MEM8,REG8
39	0011 1001	MOD REG R/M	(DISP-LO),(DISP-HI)	CMP	REG16/MEM16,REG16
3A	0011 1010	MOD REG R/M	(DISP-LO),(DISP-HI)	CMP	REG8,REG8/MEM8
3B	0011 1011	MOD REG R/M	(DISP-LO),(DISP-HI)	CMP	REG16,REG16/MEM16
3C	0011 1100	DATA-8		CMP	AL,IMMED8
3D	0011 1101	DATA-LO	DATA-HI	CMP	AX,IMMED16
3E	0011 1110			DS:	(segment override prefix)
3F	0011 1111			AAS	
40	0100 0000			INC	AX
41	0100 0001			INC	CX
42	0100 0010			INC	DX
43	0100 0011			INC	BX
44	0100 0100			INC	SP
45	0100 0101			INC	BP
46	0100 0110			INC	SI
47	0100 0111			INC	DI
48	0100 1000			DEC	AX
49	0100 1001			DEC	CX
4A	0100 1010			DEC	DX
4B	0100 1011			DEC	BX
4C	0100 1100			DEC	SP
4D	0100 1101			DEC	BP
4E	0100 1110			DEC	SI
4F	0100 1111			DEC	DI
50	0101 0000			PUSH	AX
51	0101 0001			PUSH	CX
52	0101 0010			PUSH	DX
53	0101 0011			PUSH	BX
54	0101 0100			PUSH	SP
55	0101 0101			PUSH	BP
56	0101 0110			PUSH	SI
57	0101 0111			PUSH	DI
58	0101 1000			POP	AX
59	0101 1001			POP	CX
5A	0101 1010			POP	DX
5B	0101 1011			POP	BX
5C	0101 1100			POP	SP
5D	0101 1101			POP	BP
5E	0101 1110			POP	SI
5F	0101 1111			POP	DI
60	0110 0000			(not used)	
61	0110 0001			(not used)	
62	0110 0010			(not used)	
63	0110 0011			(not used)	
64	0110 0100			(not used)	
65	0110 0101			(not used)	
66	0110 0110			(not used)	
67	0110 0111			(not used)	

210912-001

Table 1-23 Machine Instruction Decoding Guide (continued)

1ST BYTE HEX	1ST BYTE BINARY	2ND BYTE	BYTES 3,4,5,6	ASM-86 INSTRUCTION FORMAT	
68	0110 1000			(not used)	
69	0110 1001			(not used)	
6A	0110 1010			(not used)	
6B	0110 1011			(not used)	
6C	0110 1100			(not used)	
6D	0110 1101			(not used)	
6E	0110 1110			(not used)	
6F	0110 1111			(not used)	
70	0111 0000	IP-INC8		JO	SHORT-LABEL
71	0111 0001	IP-INC8		JNO	SHORT-LABEL
72	0111 0010	IP-INC8		JB/JNAE/ JC	SHORT-LABEL
73	0111 0011	IP-INC8		JNB/JAE/ JNC	SHORT-LABEL
74	0111 0100	IP-INC8		JE/JZ	SHORT-LABEL
75	0111 0101	IP-INC8		JNE/JNZ	SHORT-LABEL
76	0111 0110	IP-INC8		JBE/JNA	SHORT-LABEL
77	0111 0111	IP-INC8		JNBE/JA	SHORT-LABEL
78	0111 1000	IP-INC8		JS	SHORT-LABEL
79	0111 1001	IP-INC8		JNS	SHORT-LABEL
7A	0111 1010	IP-INC8		JP/JPE	SHORT-LABEL
7B	0111 1011	IP-INC8		JNP/JPO	SHORT-LABEL
7C	0111 1100	IP-INC8		JL/JNGE	SHORT-LABEL
7D	0111 1101	IP-INC8		JNL/JGE	SHORT-LABEL
7E	0111 1110	IP-INC8		JLE/JNG	SHORT-LABEL
7F	0111 1111	IP-INC8		JNLE/JG	SHORT-LABEL
80	1000 0000	MOD 000 R/M	(DISP-LO),(DISP-HI), DATA-8	ADD	REG8/MEM8,IMMED8
80	1000 0000	MOD 001 R/M	(DISP-LO),(DISP-HI), DATA-8	OR	REG8/MEM8,IMMED8
80	1000 0000	MOD 010 R/M	(DISP-LO),(DISP-HI), DATA-8	ADC	REG8/MEM8,IMMED8
80	1000 0000	MOD 011 R/M	(DISP-LO),(DISP-HI), DATA-8	SBB	REG8/MEM8,IMMED8
80	1000 0000	MOD 100 R/M	(DISP-LO),(DISP-HI), DATA-8	AND	REG8/MEM8,IMMED8
80	1000 0000	MOD 101 R/M	(DISP-LO),(DISP-HI), DATA-8	SUB	REG8/MEM8,IMMED8
80	1000 0000	MOD 110 R/M	(DISP-LO),(DISP-HI), DATA-8	XOR	REG8/MEM8,IMMED8
80	1000 0000	MOD 111 R/M	(DISP-LO),(DISP-HI), DATA-8	CMP	REG8/MEM8,IMMED8
81	1000 0001	MOD 000 R/M	(DISP-LO),(DISP-HI), DATA-LO,DATA-HI	ADD	REG16/MEM16,IMMED16
81	1000 0001	MOD 001 R/M	(DISP-LO),(DISP-HI), DATA-LO,DATA-HI	OR	REG16/MEM16,IMMED16
81	1000 0001	MOD 010 R/M	(DISP-LO),(DISP-HI), DATA-LO,DATA-HI	ADC	REG16/MEM16,IMMED16
81	1000 0001	MOD 011 R/M	(DISP-LO),(DISP-HI), DATA-LO,DATA-HI	SBB	REG16/MEM16,IMMED16

Table 1-23 Machine Instruction Decoding Guide (continued)

1ST BYTE		2ND BYTE	BYTES 3,4,5,6	ASM-86 INSTRUCTION FORMAT	
HEX	BINARY				
81	1000 0001	MOD 100 R/M	(DISP-LO),(DISP-HI), DATA-LO,DATA-HI	AND	REG16/MEM16,IMMED16
81	1000 0001	MOD 101 R/M	(DISP-LO),(DISP-HI), DATA-LO,DATA-HI	SUB	REG16/MEM16,IMMED16
81	1000 0001	MOD 110 R/M	(DISP-LO),(DISP-HI), DATA-LO,DATA-HI	XOR	REG16/MEM16,IMMED16
81	1000 0001	MOD 111 R/M	(DISP-LO),(DISP-HI), DATA-LO,DATA-HI	CMP	REG16/MEM16,IMMED16
82	1000 0010	MOD 000 R/M	(DISP-LO),(DISP-HI), DATA-8	ADD	REG8/MEM8,IMMED8
82	1000 0010	MOD 001 R/M		(not used)	
82	1000 0010	MOD 010 R/M	(DISP-LO),(DISP-HI), DATA-8	ADC	REG8/MEM8,IMMED8
82	1000 0010	MOD 011 R/M	(DISP-LO),(DISP-HI), DATA-8	SBB	REG8/MEM8,IMMED8
82	1000 0010	MOD 100 R/M		(not used)	
82	1000 0010	MOD 101 R/M	(DISP-LO),(DISP-HI), DATA-8	SUB	REG8/MEM8,IMMED8
82	1000 0010	MOD 110 R/M		(not used)	
82	1000 0010	MOD 111 R/M	(DISP-LO),(DISP-HI), DATA-8	CMP	REG8/MEM8,IMMED8
83	1000 0011	MOD 000 R/M	(DISP-LO),(DISP-HI), DATA-SX	ADD	REG16/MEM16, IMMED8
83	1000 0011	MOD 001 R/M		(not used)	
83	1000 0011	MOD 010 R/M	(DISP-LO), (DISP-HI), DATA-SX	ADC	REG16/MEM16,IMMED8
83	1000 0011	MOD 011 R/M	(DISP-LO),(DISP-HI), DATA-SX	SBB	REG16/MEM16,IMMED8
83	1000 0011	MOD 100 R/M		(not used)	
83	1000 0011	MOD 101 R/M	(DISP-LO),(DISP-HI), DATA-SX	SUB	REG16/MEM16,IMMED8
83	1000 0011	MOD 110 R/M		(not used)	
83	1000 0011	MOD 111 R/M	(DISP-LO),(DISP-HI), DATA-SX	CMP	REG16/MEM16,IMMED8
84	1000 0100	MOD REG R/M	(DISP-LO),(DISP-HI)	TEST	REG8/MEM8,REG8
85	1000 0101	MOD REG R/M	(DISP-LO),(DISP-HI)	TEST	REG16/MEM16,REG16
86	1000 0110	MOD REG R/M	(DISP-LO),(DISP-HI)	XCHG	REG8,REG8/MEM8
87	1000 0111	MOD REG R/M	(DISP-LO),(DISP-HI)	XCHG	REG16,REG16/MEM16
88	1000 1000	MOD REG R/M	(DISP-LO),(DISP-HI)	MOV	REG8/MEM8,REG8
89	1000 1001	MOD REG R/M	(DISP-LO),(DISP-HI)	MOV	REG16/MEM16/REG16
8A	1000 1010	MOD REG R/M	(DISP-LO),(DISP-HI)	MOV	REG8,REG8/MEM8
8B	1000 1011	MOD REG R/M	(DISP-LO),(DISP-HI)	MOV	REG16,REG16/MEM16
8C	1000 1100	MOD 0SR R/M	(DISP-LO),(DISP-HI)	MOV	REG16/MEM16,SEGREG
8C	1000 1100	MOD 1-- R/M		(not used)	
8D	1000 1101	MOD REG R/M	(DISP-LO),(DISP-HI)	LEA	REG16,MEM16
8E	1000 1110	MOD 0SR R/M	(DISP-LO),(DISP-HI)	MOV	SEGREG,REG16/MEM16
8E	1000 1110	MOD 1-- R/M		(not used)	
8F	1000 1111	MOD 000 R/M	(DISP-LO),(DISP-HI)	POP	REG16/MEM16
8F	1000 1111	MOD 001 R/M		(not used)	
8F	1000 1111	MOD 010 R/M		(not used)	

Table 1-23 Machine Instruction Decoding Guide (continued)

1ST BYTE		2ND BYTE	BYTES 3,4,5,6	ASM-86 INSTRUCTION FORMAT	
HEX	BINARY				
8F	1000 1111	MOD 011 R/M		(not used)	
8F	1000 1111	MOD 100 R/M		(not used)	
8F	1000 1111	MOD 101 R/M		(not used)	
8F	1000 1111	MOD 110 R/M		(not used)	
8F	1000 1111	MOD 111 R/M		(not used)	
90	1001 0000			NOP	(exchange AX,AX)
91	1001 0001			XCHG	AX,CX
92	1001 0010			XCHG	AX,DX
93	1001 0011			XCHG	AX,BX
94	1001 0100			XCHG	AX,SP
95	1001 0101			XCHG	AX,BP
96	1001 0110			XCHG	AX,SI
97	1001 0111			XCHG	AX,DI
98	1001 1000			CBW	
99	1001 1001			CWD	
9A	1001 1010	DISP-LO	DISP-HI,SEG-LO, SEG-HI	CALL	FAR_PROC
9B	1001 1011			WAIT	
9C	1001 1100			PUSHF	
9D	1001 1101			POPF	
9E	1001 1110			SAHF	
9F	1001 1111			LAHF	
A0	1010 0000	ADDR-LO	ADDR-HI	MOV	AL,MEM8
A1	1010 0001	ADDR-LO	ADDR-HI	MOV	AX,MEM16
A2	1010 0010	ADDR-LO	ADDR-HI	MOV	MEM8,AL
A3	1010 0011	ADDR-LO	ADDR-HI	MOV	MEM16,AL
A4	1010 0100			MOVS	DEST-STR8,SRC-STR8
A5	1010 0101			MOVS	DEST-STR16,SRC-STR16
A6	1010 0110			CMPS	DEST-STR8,SRC-STR8
A7	1010 0111			CMPS	DEST-STR16,SRC-STR16
A8	1010 1000	DATA-8		TEST	AL,IMMED8
A9	1010 1001	DATA-LO	DATA-HI	TEST	AX,IMMED16
AA	1010 1010			STOS	DEST-STR8
AB	1010 1011			STOS	DEST-STR16
AC	1010 1100			LODS	SRC-STR8
AD	1010 1101			LODS	SRC-STR16
AE	1010 1110			SCAS	DEST-STR8
AF	1010 1111			SCAS	DEST-STR16
B0	1011 0000	DATA-8		MOV	AL,IMMED8
B1	1011 0001	DATA-8		MOV	CL,IMMED8
B2	1011 0010	DATA-8		MOV	DL,IMMED8
B3	1011 1011	DATA-8		MOV	BL,IMMED8
B4	1011 0100	DATA-8		MOV	AH,IMMED8
B5	1011 0101	DATA-8		MOV	CH,IMMED8
B6	1011 0110	DATA-8		MOV	DH,IMMED8
B7	1011 0111	DATA-8		MOV	BH,IMMED8
B8	1011 1000	DATA-LO	DATA-HI	MOV	AX,IMMED16
B9	1011 1001	DATA-LO	DATA-HI	MOV	CX,IMMED16
BA	1011 1010	DATA-LO	DATA-HI	MOV	DX,IMMED16
BB	1011 1011	DATA-LO	DATA-HI	MOV	BX,IMMED16

Table 1-23 Machine Instruction Decoding Guide (continued)

1ST BYTE		2ND BYTE	BYTES 3,4,5,6	ASM-86 INSTRUCTION FORMAT	
HEX	BINARY				
BC	1011 1100	DATA-LO	DATA-HI	MOV	SP,IMMED16
BD	1011 1101	DATA-LO	DATA-HI	MOV	BP,IMMED16
BE	1011 1110	DATA-LO	DATA-HI	MOV	SI,IMMED16
BF	1011 1111	DATA-LO	DATA-HI	MOV	DI,IMMED16
C0	1100 0000			(not used)	
C1	1100 0001			(not used)	
C2	1100 0010	DATA-LO	DATA-HI	RET	IMMED16 (intraseg)
C3	1100 0011			RET	(intrasegment)
C4	1100 0100	MOD REG R/M	(DISP-LO),(DISP-HI)	LES	REG16,MEM16
C5	1100 0101	MOD REG R/M	(DISP-LO),(DISP-HI)	LDS	REG16,MEM16
C6	1100 0110	MOD 000 R/M	(DISP-LO),(DISP-HI), DATA-8	MOV	MEM8,IMMED8
C6	1100 0110	MOD 001 R/M		(not used)	
C6	1100 0110	MOD 010 R/M		(not used)	
C6	1100 0110	MOD 011 R/M		(not used)	
C6	1100 0110	MOD 100 R/M		(not used)	
C6	1100 0110	MOD 101 R/M		(not used)	
C6	1100 0110	MOD 110 R/M		(not used)	
C6	1100 0110	MOD 111 R/M		(not used)	
C7	1100 0111	MOD 000 R/M	(DISP-LO),(DISP-HI), DATA-LO,DATA-HI	MOV	MEM16,IMMED16
C7	1100 0111	MOD 001 R/M		(not used)	
C7	1100 0111	MOD 010 R/M		(not used)	
C7	1100 0111	MOD 011 R/M		(not used)	
C7	1100 0111	MOD 100 R/M		(not used)	
C7	1100 0111	MOD 101 R/M		(not used)	
C7	1100 0111	MOD 110 R/M		(not used)	
C7	1100 0111	MOD 111 R/M		(not used	
C8	1100 1000			(not used)	
C9	1100 1001			(not used)	
CA	1100 1010	DATA-LO	DATA-HI	RET	IMMED16 (intersegment)
CB	1100 1011			RET	(intersegment)
CC	1100 1100			INT	3
CD	1100 1101	DATA-8		INT	IMMED8
CE	1100 1110			INTO	
CF	1100 1111			IRET	
D0	1101 0000	MOD 000 R/M	(DISP-LO),(DISP-HI)	ROL	REG8/MEM8,1
D0	1101 0000	MOD 001 R/M	(DISP-LO),(DISP-HI)	ROR	REG8/MEM8,1
D0	1101 0000	MOD 010 R/M	(DISP-LO),(DISP-HI)	RCL	REG8/MEM8,1
D0	1101 0000	MOD 011 R/M	(DISP-LO),(DISP-HI)	RCR	REG8/MEM8,1
D0	1101 0000	MOD 100 R/M	(DISP-LO),(DISP-HI)	SAL/SHL	REG8/MEM8,1
D0	1101 0000	MOD 101 R/M	(DISP-LO),(DISP-HI)	SHR	REG8/MEM8,1
D0	1101 0000	MOD 110 R/M		(not used)	
D0	1101 0000	MOD 111 R/M	(DISP-LO),(DISP-HI)	SAR	REG8/MEM8,1
D1	1101 0001	MOD 000 R/M	(DISP-LO),(DISP-HI)	ROL	REG16/MEM16,1
D1	1101 0001	MOD 001 R/M	(DISP-LO),(DISP-HI)	ROR	REG16/MEM16,1
D1	1101 0001	MOD 010 R/M	(DISP-LO),(DISP-HI)	RCL	REG16/MEM16,1
D1	1101 0001	MOD 011 R/M	(DISP-LO),(DISP-HI)	RCR	REG16/MEM16,1
D1	1101 0001	MOD 100 R/M	(DISP-LO),(DISP-HI)	SAL/SHL	REG16/MEM16,1

Table 1-23 Machine Instruction Decoding Guide (continued)

1ST BYTE		2ND BYTE	BYTES 3,4,5,6	ASM-86 INSTRUCTION FORMAT	
HEX	BINARY				
D1	1101 0001	MOD 101 R/M	(DISP-LO),(DISP-HI)	SHR	REG16/MEM16,1
D1	1101 0001	MOD 110 R/M		(not used)	
D1	1101 0001	MOD 111 R/M	(DISP-LO),(DISP-HI)	SAR	REG16/MEM16,1
D2	1101 0010	MOD 000 R/M	(DISP-LO),(DISP-HI)	ROL	REG8/MEM8,CL
D2	1101 0010	MOD 001 R/M	(DISP-LO),(DISP-HI)	ROR	REG8/MEM8,CL
D2	1101 0010	MOD 010 R/M	(DISP-LO),(DISP-HI)	RCL	REG8/MEM8,CL
D2	1101 0010	MOD 011 R/M	(DISP-LO),(DISP-HI)	RCR	REG8/MEM8,CL
D2	1101 0010	MOD 100 R/M	(DISP-LO),(DISP-HI)	SAL/SHL	REG8/MEM8,CL
D2	1101 0010	MOD 101 R/M	(DISP-LO),(DISP-HI)	SHR	REG8/MEM8,CL
D2	1101 0010	MOD 110 R/M		(not used)	
D2	1101 0010	MOD 111 R/M	(DISP-LO),(DISP-HI)	SAR	REG8/MEM8,CL
D3	1101 0011	MOD 000 R/M	(DISP-LO),(DISP-HI)	ROL	REG16/MEM16,CL
D3	1101 0011	MOD 001 R/M	(DISP-LO),(DISP-HI)	ROR	REG16/MEM16,CL
D3	1101 0011	MOD 010 R/M	(DISP-LO),(DISP-HI)	RCL	REG16/MEM16,CL
D3	1101 0011	MOD 011 R/M	(DISP-LO),(DISP-HI)	RCR	REG16/MEM16,CL
D3	1101 0011	MOD 100 R/M	(DISP-LO),(DISP-HI)	SAL/SHL	REG16/MEM16,CL
D3	1101 0011	MOD 101 R/M	(DISP-LO),(DISP-HI)	SHR	REG16/MEM16,CL
D3	1101 0011	MOD 110 R/M		(not used)	
D3	1101 0011	MOD 111 R/M	(DISP-LO),(DISP-HI)	SAR	REG16/MEM16,CL
D4	1101 0100	00001010		AAM	
D5	1101 0101	00001010		AAD	
D6	1101 0110			(not used)	
D7	1101 0111			XLAT	SOURCE-TABLE
D8	1101 1000	MOD 000 R/M			
	1XXX	MOD YYY R/M	(DISP-LO), (DISP-HI)	ESC	OPCODE,SOURCE
DF	1101 1111	MOD 111 R/M			
E0	1110 0000	IP-INC-8		LOOPNE/ LOOPNZ	SHORT-LABEL
E1	1110 0001	IP-INC-8		LOOPE/ LOOPZ	SHORT-LABEL
E2	1110 0010	IP-INC-8		LOOP	SHORT-LABEL
E3	1110 0011	IP-INC-8		JCXZ	SHORT-LABEL
E4	1110 0100	DATA-8		IN	AL,IMMED8
E5	1110 0101	DATA-8		IN	AX,IMMED8
E6	1110 0110	DATA-8		OUT	AL,IMMED8
E7	1110 0111	DATA-8		OUT	AX,IMMED8
E8	1110 1000	IP-INC-LO	IP-INC-HI	CALL	NEAR-PROC
E9	1110 1001	IP-INC-LO	IP-INC-HI	JMP	NEAR-LABEL
EA	1110 1010	IP-LO	IP-HI,CS-LO,CS-HI	JMP	FAR-LABEL
EB	1110 1011	IP-INC8		JMP	SHORT-LABEL
EC	1110 1100			IN	AL,DX
ED	1110 1101			IN	AX,DX
EE	1110 1110			OUT	AL,DX
EF	1110 1111			OUT	AX,DX
F0	1111 0000			LOCK	(prefix)
F1	1111 0001			(not used)	
F2	1111 0010			REPNE/REPNZ	
F3	1111 0011			REP/REPE/REPZ	
F4	1111 0100			HLT	
F5	1111 0101			CMC	

Table 1-23 Machine Instruction Decoding Guide (continued)

1ST BYTE		2ND BYTE	BYTES 3,4,5,6	ASM-86 INSTRUCTION FORMAT	
HEX	BINARY				
F6	1111 0110	MOD 000 R/M	(DISP-LO),(DISP-HI), DATA-8	TEST	REG8/MEM8,IMMED8
F6	1111 0110	MOD 001 R/M		(not used)	
F6	1111 0110	MOD 010 R/M	(DISP-LO),(DISP-HI)	NOT	REG8/MEM8
F6	1111 0110	MOD 011 R/M	(DISP-LO),(DISP-HI)	NEG	REG8/MEM8
F6	1111 0110	MOD 100 R/M	(DISP-LO),(DISP-HI)	MUL	REG8/MEM8
F6	1111 0110	MOD 101 R/M	(DISP-LO),(DISP-HI)	IMUL	REG8/MEM8
F6	1111 0110	MOD 110 R/M	(DISP-LO),(DISP-HI)	DIV	REG8/MEM8
F6	1111 0110	MOD 111 R/M	(DISP-LO),(DISP-HI)	IDIV	REG8/MEM8
F7	1111 0111	MOD 000 R/M	(DISP-LO),(DISP-HI), DATA-LO,DATA-HI	TEST	REG16/MEM16,IMMED16
F7	1111 0111	MOD 001 R/M		(not used)	
F7	1111 0111	MOD 010 R/M	(DISP-LO),(DISP-HI)	NOT	REG16/MEM16
F7	1111 0111	MOD 011 R/M	(DISP-LO),(DISP-HI)	NEG	REG16/MEM16
F7	1111 0111	MOD 100 R/M	(DISP-LO),(DISP-HI)	MUL	REG16/MEM16
F7	1111 0111	MOD 101 R/M	(DISP-LO),(DISP-HI)	IMUL	REG16/MEM16
F7	1111 0111	MOD 110 R/M	(DISP-LO),(DISP-HI)	DIV	REG16/MEM16
F7	1111 0111	MOD 111 R/M	(DISP-LO),(DISP-HI)	IDIV	REG16/MEM16
F8	1111 1000			CLC	
F9	1111 1001			STC	
FA	1111 1010			CLI	
FB	1111 1011			STI	
FC	1111 1100			CLD	
FD	1111 1101			STD	
FE	1111 1110	MOD 000 R/M	(DISP-LO),(DISP-HI)	INC	REG8/MEM8
FE	1111 1110	MOD 001 R/M	(DISP-LO),(DISP-HI)	DEC	REG8/MEM8
FE	1111 1110	MOD 010 R/M		(not used)	
FE	1111 1110	MOD 011 R/M		(not used)	
FE	1111 1110	MOD 100 R/M		(not used)	
FE	1111 1110	MOD 101 R/M		(not used)	
FE	1111 1110	MOD 110 R/M		(not used)	
FE	1111 1110	MOD 111 R/M		(not used)	
FF	1111 1111	MOD 000 R/M	(DISP-LO),(DISP-HI)	INC	MEM16
FF	1111 1111	MOD 001 R/M	(DISP-LO),(DISP-HI)	DEC	MEM16
FF	1111 1111	MOD 010 R/M	(DISP-LO),(DISP-HI)	CALL	REG16/MEM16 (intra)
FF	1111 1111	MOD 011 R/M	(DISP-LO),(DISP-HI)	CALL	MEM16 (intersegment)
FF	1111 1111	MOD 100 R/M	(DISP-LO),(DISP-HI)	JMP	REG16/MEM16 (intra)
FF	1111 1111	MOD 101 R/M	(DISP-LO),(DISP-HI)	JMP	MEM16 (intersegment)
FF	1111 1111	MOD 110 R/M	(DISP-LO),(DISP-HI)	PUSH	MEM16
FF	1111 1111	MOD 111 R/M		(not used)	

Table 1-24 8086/8088 Device Pin Descriptions

The following pin function descriptions are for iAPX 86 systems in either minimum or maximum mode. The "Local Bus" in these descriptions is the direct multiplexed bus interface connection to the 8086 (without regard to additional bus buffers).

<table>
<tr><th>Symbol</th><th>Pin No.</th><th>Type</th><th>Name and Function</th></tr>
<tr><td>AD_{15}-AD_0</td><td>2-16, 39</td><td>I/O</td><td>Address Data Bus: These lines constitute the time multiplexed memory/IO address (T_1) and data (T_2, T_3, T_W, T_4) bus. A_0 is analogous to $\overline{BHE}$ for the lower byte of the data bus, pins D_7-D_0. It is LOW during T_1 when a byte is to be transferred on the lower portion of the bus in memory or I/O operations. Eight-bit oriented devices tied to the lower half would normally use A_0 to condition chip select functions. (See $\overline{BHE}$.) These lines are active HIGH and float to 3-state OFF during interrupt acknowledge and local bus "hold acknowledge."</td></tr>
<tr><td>A_{19}/S_6,
A_{18}/S_5,
A_{17}/S_4,
A_{16}/S_3</td><td>35-38</td><td>O</td><td>Address/Status: During T_1 these are the four most significant address lines for memory operations. During I/O operations these lines are LOW. During memory and I/O operations, status information is available on these lines during T_2, T_3, T_W, and T_4. The status of the interrupt enable FLAG bit (S_5) is updated at the beginning of each CLK cycle. A_{17}/S_4 and A_{16}/S_3 are encoded as shown.
<table>
<tr><th>A_{17}/S_4</th><th>A_{16}/S_3</th><th>Characteristics</th></tr>
<tr><td>0 (LOW)</td><td>0</td><td>Alternate Data</td></tr>
<tr><td>0</td><td>1</td><td>Stack</td></tr>
<tr><td>1 (HIGH)</td><td>0</td><td>Code or None</td></tr>
<tr><td>1</td><td>1</td><td>Data</td></tr>
<tr><td>S_6 is 0 (LOW)</td><td></td><td></td></tr>
</table>
This information indicates which relocation register is presently being used for data accessing.

These lines float to 3-state OFF during local bus "hold acknowledge."</td></tr>
<tr><td>$\overline{BHE}/S_7$</td><td>34</td><td>O</td><td>Bus High Enable/Status: During T_1 the bus high enable signal ($\overline{BHE}$) should be used to enable data onto the most significant half of the data bus, pins D_{15}-D_8. Eight-bit oriented devices tied to the upper half of the bus would normally use $\overline{BHE}$ to condition chip select functions. $\overline{BHE}$ is LOW during T_1 for read, write, and interrupt acknowledge cycles when a byte is to be transferred on the high portion of the bus. The S_7 status information is available during T_2, T_3, and T_4. The signal is active LOW, and floats to 3-state OFF in "hold." It is LOW during T_1 for the first interrupt acknowledge cycle.
<table>
<tr><th>$\overline{BHE}$</th><th>A_0</th><th>Characteristics</th></tr>
<tr><td>0</td><td>0</td><td>Whole word</td></tr>
<tr><td>0</td><td>1</td><td>Upper byte from/ to odd address</td></tr>
<tr><td>1</td><td>0</td><td>Lower byte from/ to even address</td></tr>
<tr><td>1</td><td>1</td><td>None</td></tr>
</table></td></tr>
<tr><td>$\overline{RD}$</td><td>32</td><td>O</td><td>Read: Read strobe indicates that the processor is performing a memory of I/O read cycle, depending on the state of the S_2 pin. This signal is used to read devices which reside on the 8086 local bus. $\overline{RD}$ is active LOW during T_2, T_3 and T_W of any read cycle, and is guaranteed to remain HIGH in T_2 until the 8086 local bus has floated.

This signal floats to 3-state OFF in "hold acknowledge."</td></tr>
<tr><td>READY</td><td>22</td><td>I</td><td>READY: is the acknowledgement from the addressed memory or I/O device that it will complete the data transfer. The READY signal from memory/IO is synchronized by the 8284A Clock Generator to form READY. This signal is active HIGH. The 8086 READY input is not synchronized. Correct operation is not guaranteed if the setup and hold times are not met.</td></tr>
<tr><td>INTR</td><td>18</td><td>I</td><td>Interrupt Request: is a level triggered input which is sampled during the last clock cycle of each instruction to determine if the processor should enter into an interrupt acknowledge operation. A subroutine is vectored to via an interrupt vector lookup table located in system memory. It can be internally masked by software resetting the interrupt enable bit. INTR is internally synchronized. This signal is active HIGH.</td></tr>
<tr><td>$\overline{TEST}$</td><td>23</td><td>I</td><td>$\overline{TEST}$: input is examined by the "Wait" instruction. If the $\overline{TEST}$ input is LOW execution continues, otherwise the processor waits in an "Idle" state. This input is synchronized internally during each clock cycle on the leading edge of CLK.</td></tr>
</table>

Table 1-24 8086/8088 Device Pin Descriptions (continued)

Symbol	Pin No.	Type	Name and Function
NMI	17	I	**Non-maskable interrupt:** an edge triggered input which causes a type 2 interrupt. A subroutine is vectored to via an interrupt vector lookup table located in system memory. NMI is not maskable internally by software. A transition from a LOW to HIGH initiates the interrupt at the end of the current instruction. This input is internally synchronized.
RESET	21	I	**Reset:** causes the processor to immediately terminate its present activity. The signal must be active HIGH for at least four clock cycles. It restarts execution, as described in the Instruction Set description, when RESET returns LOW. RESET is internally synchronized.
CLK	19	I	**Clock:** provides the basic timing for the processor and bus controller. It is asymmetric with a 33% duty cycle to provide optimized internal timing.
V_{CC}	40		**V_{CC}:** + 5V power supply pin.
GND	1, 20		**Ground**
MN/$\overline{MX}$	33	I	**Minimum/Maximum:** indicates what mode the processor is to operate in. The two modes are discussed in the following sections.

The following pin function descriptions are for the 8086/8288 system in maximum mode (i.e., MN/$\overline{MX}$ = V_{SS}). Only the pin functions which are unique to maximum mode are described; all other pin functions are as described above.

Symbol	Pin No.	Type	Name and Function
$\overline{S_2}$, $\overline{S_1}$, $\overline{S_0}$	26-28	O	**Status:** active during T_4, T_1, and T_2 and is returned to the passive state (1,1,1) during T_3 or during T_W when READY is HIGH. This status is used by the 8288 Bus Controller to generate all memory and I/O access control signals. Any change by $\overline{S_2}$, $\overline{S_1}$, or $\overline{S_0}$ during T_4 is used to indicate the beginning of a bus cycle, and the return to the passive state in T_3 or T_W is used to indicate the end of a bus cycle. These signals float to 3-state OFF in "hold acknowledge." These status lines are encoded as shown.
$\overline{RQ}/\overline{GT}_0$, $\overline{RQ}/\overline{GT}_1$	30, 31	I/O	**Request/Grant:** pins are used by other local bus masters to force the processor to release the local bus at the end of the processor's current bus cycle. Each pin is bidirectional with $\overline{RQ}/\overline{GT}_0$ having higher priority than $\overline{RQ}/\overline{GT}_1$. $\overline{RQ}/\overline{GT}$ has an internal pull-up resistor so may be left unconnected. The request/grant sequence is as follows (see Figure 9): 1. A pulse of 1 CLK wide from another local bus master indicates a local bus request ("hold") to the 8086 (pulse 1). 2. During a T_4 or T_I clock cycle, a pulse 1 CLK wide from the 8086 to the requesting master (pulse 2), indicates that the 8086 has allowed the local bus to float and that it will enter the "hold acknowledge" state at the next CLK. The CPU's bus interface unit is disconnected logically from the local bus during "hold acknowledge." 3. A pulse 1 CLK wide from the requesting master indicates to the 8086 (pulse 3) that the "hold" request is about to end and that the 8086 can reclaim the local bus at the next CLK. Each master-master exchange of the local bus is a sequence of 3 pulses. There must be one dead CLK cycle after each bus exchange. Pulses are active LOW. If the request is made while the CPU is performing a memory cycle, it will release the local bus during T_4 of the cycle when all the following conditions are met: 1. Request occurs on or before T_2. 2. Current cycle is not the low byte of a word (on an odd address). 3. Current cycle is not the first acknowledge of an interrupt acknowledge sequence. 4. A locked instruction is not currently executing.

$\overline{S_2}$	$\overline{S_1}$	$\overline{S_0}$	Characteristics
0 (LOW)	0	0	Interrupt Acknowledge
0	0	1	Read I/O Port
0	1	0	Write I/O Port
0	1	1	Halt
1 (HIGH)	0	0	Code Access
1	0	1	Read Memory
1	1	0	Write Memory
1	1	1	Passive

Table 1-24 8086/8088 Device Pin Descriptions (continued)

Symbol	Pin No.	Type	Name and Function
			If the local bus is idle when the request is made the two possible events will follow: 1. Local bus will be released during the next clock. 2. A memory cycle will start within 3 clocks. Now the four rules for a currently active memory cycle apply with condition number 1 already satisfied.
$\overline{LOCK}$	29	O	**LOCK:** output indicates that other system bus masters are not to gain control of the system bus while $\overline{LOCK}$ is active LOW. The $\overline{LOCK}$ signal is activated by the "LOCK" prefix instruction and remains active until the completion of the next instruction. This signal is active LOW, and floats to 3-state OFF in "hold acknowledge."
QS_1, QS_0	24, 25	O	**Queue Status:** The queue status is valid during the CLK cycle after which the queue operation is performed. QS_1 and QS_0 provide status to allow external tracking of the internal 8086 instruction queue. QS_1 / QS_0 / CHARACTERISTICS: 0 (LOW) / 0 / No Operation 0 / 1 / First Byte of Op Code from Queue 1 (HIGH) / 0 / Empty the Queue 1 / 1 / Subsequent Byte from Queue

The following pin function descriptions are for the 8086 in minimum mode (i.e., $MN/\overline{MX} = V_{CC}$). Only the pin functions which are unique to minimum mode are described; all other pin functions are as described above.

Symbol	Pin No.	Type	Name and Function
$M/\overline{IO}$	28	O	**Status line:** logically equivalent to S_2 in the maximum mode. It is used to distinguish a memory access from an I/O access. $M/\overline{IO}$ becomes valid in the T_4 preceding a bus cycle and remains valid until the final T_4 of the cycle (M = HIGH, IO = LOW). $M/\overline{IO}$ floats to 3-state OFF in local bus "hold acknowledge."
$\overline{WR}$	29	O	**Write:** indicates that the processor is performing a write memory or write I/O cycle, depending on the state of the $M/\overline{IO}$ signal. $\overline{WR}$ is active for T_2, T_3 and T_W of any write cycle. It is active LOW, and floats to 3-state OFF in local bus "hold acknowledge."
$\overline{INTA}$	24	O	$\overline{INTA}$ is used as a read strobe for interrupt acknowledge cycles. It is active LOW during T_2, T_3 and T_W of each interrupt acknowledge cycle.
ALE	25	O	**Address Latch Enable:** provided by the processor to latch the address into the 8282/8283 address latch. It is a HIGH pulse active during T_1 of any bus cycle. Note that ALE is never floated.
$DT/\overline{R}$	27	O	**Data Transmit/Receive:** needed in minimum system that desires to use an 8286/8287 data bus transceiver. It is used to control the direction of data flow through the transceiver. Logically $DT/\overline{R}$ is equivalent to $\overline{S_1}$ in the maximum mode, and its timing is the same as for $M/\overline{IO}$. (T = HIGH, R = LOW.) This signal floats to 3-state OFF in local bus "hold acknowledge."
$\overline{DEN}$	26	O	**Data Enable:** provided as an output enable for the 8286/8287 in a minimum system which uses the transceiver. $\overline{DEN}$ is active LOW during each memory and I/O access and for INTA cycles. For a read or $\overline{INTA}$ cycle it is active from the middle of T_2 until the middle of T_4, while for a write cycle it is active from the beginning of T_2 until the middle of T_4. $\overline{DEN}$ floats to 3-state OFF in local bus "hold acknowledge."
HOLD, HLDA	31, 30	I/O	**HOLD:** indicates that another master is requesting a local bus "hold." To be acknowledged, HOLD must be active HIGH. The processor receiving the "hold" request will issue HLDA (HIGH) as an acknowledgement in the middle of a T_1 clock cycle. Simultaneous with the issuance of HLDA the processor will float the local bus and control lines. After HOLD is detected as being LOW, the processor will LOWer the HLDA, and when the processor needs to run another cycle, it will again drive the local bus and control lines. The same rules as for $\overline{RQ}/\overline{GT}$ apply regarding when the local bus will be released. HOLD is not an asynchronous input. External synchronization should be provided if the system cannot otherwise guarantee the setup time.

During normal multiprocessor system operation, priority of the shared system bus is determined by the arbitration circuits on a cycle by cycle basis. As each CPU requires a transfer over the system bus, it request access to the bus via its resident bus arbitration logic. When the CPU gains priority (determined by the system bus arbitration scheme and any associated logic), it takes control of the bus, performs its bus cycle and either maintains bus control, voluntarily releases the bus or is forced off the bus by the loss of priority. The lock mechanism prevents the CPU from losing bus control (either voluntarily or by force) and guarantees a CPU the ability to execute multiple bus cycles (during execution of the locked instruction) without intervention and possible corruption of the data by another CPU. A classic use of the mechanism is the 'TEST and SET semaphore' during which a CPU must read from a shared memory location and return data to the location without allowing another CPU to reference the same location between the TEST operation (read) and the SET operation (write). In the 8086 this is accomplished with a locked exchange instruction (see Figure 1-37).

```
LOCK XCHG reg, MEMORY; reg is any register
                      ; MEMORY is the address
                      of the
                      ; semaphore
```

Another application of LOCK* for multiprocessor systems consists of a locked block move which allows high speed message transfer from one CPU's message buffer to another.

During the locked instruction, a request for processor preemption (RQ*/GT*) is recorded but not acknowledged until completion of the locked instruction. The LOCK* has no direct affect on interrupts. As an example, a locked HALT instruction will cause HOLD (or RQ*/GT*) requests to be ignored but will allow the CPU to exit the HALT state on an interrupt. In general, prefix bytes are considered extensions of the instructions they preceded. Therefore, interrupts that occur during execution of a prefix are not acknowledged (assuming interrupts are enabled) until completion of the instruction following the prefix (except for instructions which are servicing interrupts during their execution, i.e., HALT, WAIT and repeated string primitive). Note that multiple prefix bytes may precede an instruction. Another example is a 'string primitive' preceded by the repetition prefix (REP) which is interruptible after each execution of the string primitive. This holds even if the REP prefix is combined with the LOCK prefix. This prevents interrupts from being locked out during a block move or other repeated string operation. As long as the operation is not interrupted, LOCK* remains active. Further information on the operation of an interrupted string operation with multiple prefixes is presented in the section dealing with the 8086 interrupt structure.

1.3.6 General Design Considerations

Since the minimum mode 8086 has common read and write commands for memory and I/O, if the memory and I/O address spaces overlap, the chip selects must be qualified by M/IO* to determine which address space the devices are assigned. This restriction on chip select decoding can be removed if the I/O and memory addresses in the system do not overlap and are properly decoded, all I/O is memory mapped, or RD*, WR* and M/IO* are decoded to provide separate memory and I/O read/write commands (see Figure 1-38). The 8288 bus controller in the maximum mode 8086 system generates separate I/O and memory commands in place of a M/IO* signal. An I/O device is assigned to the I/O space or memory space (memory mapped I/O) by connection of either I/O or memory command lines to the command inputs of the device. To allow overlap of the memory and I/O address space, the device must not respond to chip select alone but must require a combination of chip select and a read or a write command.

Linear select techniques (see Figure 1-39) for I/O devices can only be used with devices that either reside in the I/O address space or require more than one active chip select (at least one low active and one high active). Devices with a single chip select input cannot use linear select if they are memory mapped because memory address space FFFF0H-FFFFFH is assigned to reset startup and memory space 00000H-003FFH is assigned to interrupt vectors.

1.4 BUS OPERATION

In order to understand the operation of a time-multiplexed bus, the BIU's bus cycle must be understood. A bus cycle is an asynchronous event that presents the address of an I/O peripheral or memory location. The address is followed by either a read control signal to capture or read data from the addressed device, or a write control signal and the associated data to transmit or write the data to the addressed device. The selected device (memory or I/O peripheral) accepts the data on the bus during a write cycle or places the requested data on the bus during a read cycle. On termination of the specified cycle, the device latches the data written or removes the data read.

1.4.1 Multiplexed Address and Data Bus

The 8086/88 has a combined address and data bus commonly referred to as a time multiplexed bus. Time multiplexing makes the most efficient use of pins on the processor while permitting the use of a standard 40-pin package. This "local bus" can be buffered directly and used throughout the system with address latching provided on memory and I/O modules. In addition, the bus

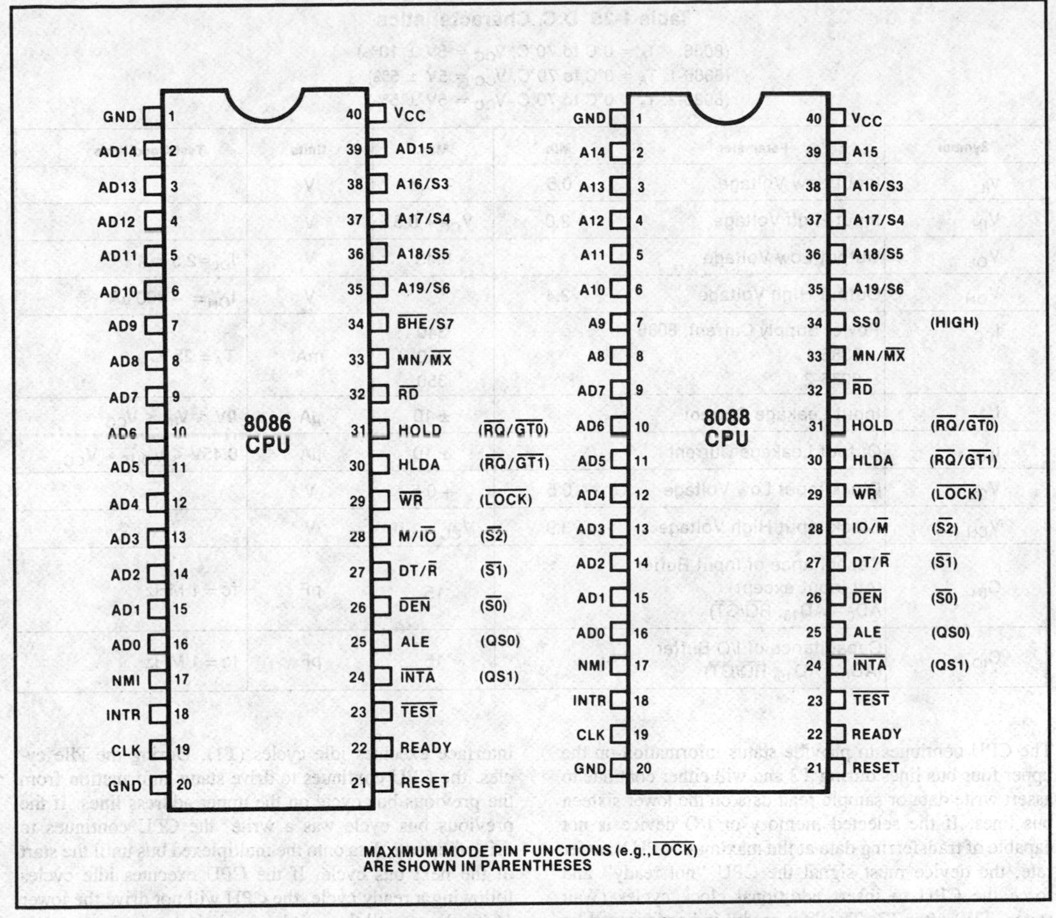

Figure 1-30 8086/8088 DIP Pin Assignments

can also be demultiplexed at the processor with a single set of address latches if a standard non-multiplexed bus is desired for the system.

1.4.2 Bus Cycle Definition

The 8086 is a true 16-bit microprocessor with 16-bit internal and external data paths, one megabyte of memory address space (2^{20}) and a separate 64K byte (2^{16}) I/O address space. The CPU communicates with its external environment via a twenty-bit time multiplexed address, status and data bus and a command bus. To transfer data or fetch instructions, the CPU executes a bus cycle (see Figure 1-40). The minimum bus cycle consists of four CPU clock cycles ("T") states. During the first T state (T1), the CPU asserts an address on the twenty-bit multiplexed address/data/ status bus. For the second T state (T2), the CPU removes the address from the bus and either tri-states its outputs on the lower sixteen bus lines in preparation for a ready cycle or asserts write data. Data bus transceivers are enabled in either T1 or T2 depending on the 8086 system configuration and the direction of the transfer (into or out of the CPU). Read, write or interrupt acknowledge commands are always enabled in T2. The maximum mode 8086 configuration also provides a write command enabled in T3 to guarantee time for data setup prior to command activation.

During T2, the upper four multiplexed bus lines switch from address (A19-A16) to bus cycle status (S6, S5, S4, S3). The status information (see Table 1-31) is available primarily for diagnostic monitoring. However, a decode of S3 and S4 could be used to select one of four banks of memory, one assigned to each segment register. This technique allows partitioning the memory by segment to expand the memory addressing beyond one megabyte. It also provides a degree of protection by preventing erroneous write operations to one segment from overlapping into, and destroying information, in another segment.

Table 1-25 D.C. Characteristics

(8086: T_A = 0°C to 70°C, V_{CC} = 5V ± 10%)
(8086-1: T_A = 0°C to 70°C, V_{CC} = 5V ± 5%)
(8086-2: T_A = 0°C to 70°C, V_{CC} = 5V ± 5%)

Symbol	Parameter	Min.	Max.	Units	Test Conditions
V_{IL}	Input Low Voltage	− 0.5	+ 0.8	V	
V_{IH}	Input High Voltage	2.0	V_{CC} + 0.5	V	
V_{OL}	Output Low Voltage		0.45	V	I_{OL} = 2.5 mA
V_{OH}	Output High Voltage	2.4		V	I_{OH} = − 400 μA
I_{CC}	Power Supply Current: 8086 8086-1 8086-2		340 360 350	mA	T_A = 25 °C
I_{LI}	Input Leakage Current		± 10	μA	0V ≤ V_{IN} ≤ V_{CC}
I_{LO}	Output Leakage Current		± 10	μA	0.45V ≤ V_{OUT} ≤ V_{CC}
V_{CL}	Clock Input Low Voltage	− 0.5	+ 0.6	V	
V_{CH}	Clock Input High Voltage	3.9	V_{CC} + 1.0	V	
C_{IN}	Capacitance of Input Buffer (All input except $AD_0 - AD_{15}$, $\overline{RQ}/\overline{GT}$)		15	pF	fc = 1 MHz
C_{IO}	Capacitance of I/O Buffer ($AD_0 - AD_{15}$, $\overline{RQ}/\overline{GT}$)		15	pF	fc = 1 MHz

The CPU continues to provide status information on the upper four bus lines during T3 and will either continue to assert write data or sample read data on the lower sixteen bus lines. If the selected memory or I/O device is not capable of transferring data at the maximum CPU transfer rate, the device must signal the CPU "not ready" and force the CPU to insert additional clock cycles (Wait states, TW) after T3. The 'not ready' indication must be presented to the CPU by the start of T3. Bus activity during TW is the same as T3. In a "normally not ready" system, when the selected device has had sufficient time to complete the transfer, it asserts "Ready" and allows the CPU to continue from the TW states. The CPU will latch the data on the bus during the last wait state or during T3 if no wait states are requested. The bus cycle is terminated in T4 (command lines are disabled and the selected external device releases the bus). To devices in the system, the bus cycle appears as an asynchronous event consisting of an address to select the device followed by a read strobe or data and a write strobe. The selected device accepts bus data during a write cycle and drives the desired data onto the bus during a read cycle. On termination of the command, the device latches write data or disables its bus drives. The only way the device controls the bus cycle is by inserting wait cycles.

The 8086 CPU only executes a bus cycle when instructions or operands must be transferred to or from memory or I/O devices. When not executing a bus cycle, the bus interface executes idle cycles (T1). During the idle cycles, the CPU continues to drive status information from the previous bus cycle on the upper address lines. If the previous bus cycle was a write, the CPU continues to drive the write data onto the multiplexed bus until the start of the next bus cycle. If the CPU executes idle cycles following a ready cycle, the CPU will not drive the lower 16 bus lines until the next bus cycle is required.

Since the CPU prefetches up to six bytes of the instruction stream for storage and execution from an internal instruction queue, the relationship may be skewed in time and separated by additional instruction fetch bus cycles. In general, if the BIU fetches an instruction into the 8086's internal instruction queue, it may also fetch several additional instructions before the EU removes the instruction from the queue and executes it. If the EU executes a jump or other control transfer instruction from the queue, it ignores any instructions remaining in the queue; the CPU discards these instructions with no effect on operation. The bus activity observed during execution of a specific instruction depends on the preceding instructions; the activity, however, may always be determined within a specific sequence.

1.4.3 Address and Data Bus Concepts

The programmer views the 8086 memory address space as a sequence of one million bytes in which any byte may contain an eight bit data element and any two consecutive bytes may contain a 16-bit data element. There is no constraint on byte or word addresses (i.e., boundaries). The address space is physically implemented on a 16-bit data bus by dividing the address space into two banks of up to 512K bytes (see Figure 1-41). One bank connects to the lower half of the 16-bit data bus (D7-0) and contains even addressed bytes (A0 = 0). The other bank connects to the upper half of the data bus (D15-8) and contains odd addressed bytes (A0 = 1). Address lines A19-A1 select a specific byte within each bank. To perform byte transfers to even addresses (Figure 1-42), the information is transferred over the lower half of the data bus (D7-0). A0 (active low) enables the bank connected to the lower half of the data bus to participate in the transfer. Another 8086 signal, Bus High Enable (BHE*), disables the bank on the upper half of the data bus to prevent its participation in the transfer. This action prevents a write operation to the lower bank from destroying data in the upper bank. Device pin 34 (refer to paragraph 1.3) is multiplexed between BHE* during T1 and S7 during T2 through T4. The current implementation of the 8086 equates BHE* to S7. That is, if BHE* is high during T1 then S7 will likewise be high during T2 through T4. Since BHE* is a multiplexed signal with timing identical to the A19-A16 address lines, it also should be latched during T1 with ALE to provide a stable signal during the bus cycle. To perform byte transfers to odd addresses (see Figure 1-42),

Table 1-26 A.C. Timing Requirements for Minimum Complexity System

(8086: T_A = 0°C to 70°C, V_{CC} = 5V ± 10%)
(8086-1: T_A = 0°C to 70°C, V_{CC} = 5V ± 5%)
(8086-2: T_A = 0°C to 70°C, V_{CC} = 5V ± 5%)

MINIMUM COMPLEXITY SYSTEM TIMING REQUIREMENTS

Symbol	Parameter	8086		8086-1 (Preliminary)		8086-2		Units	Test Conditions
		Min.	Max.	Min.	Max.	Min.	Max.		
TCLCL	CLK Cycle Period	200	500	100	500	125	500	ns	
TCLCH	CLK Low Time	118		53		68		ns	
TCHCL	CLK High Time	69		39		44		ns	
TCH1CH2	CLK Rise Time		10		10		10	ns	From 1.0V to 3.5V
TCL2CL1	CLK Fall Time		10		10		10	ns	From 3.5V to 1.0V
TDVCL	Data in Setup Time	30		5		20		ns	
TCLDX	Data in Hold Time	10		10		10		ns	
TR1VCL	RDY Setup Time into 8284A (See Notes 1, 2)	35		35		35		ns	
TCLR1X	RDY Hold Time into 8284A (See Notes 1, 2)	0		0		0		ns	
TRYHCH	READY Setup Time into 8086	118		53		68		ns	
TCHRYX	READY Hold Time into 8086	30		20		20		ns	
TRYLCL	READY Inactive to CLK (See Note 3)	−8		−10		−8		ns	
THVCH	HOLD Setup Time	35		20		20		ns	
TINVCH	INTR, NMI, $\overline{\text{TEST}}$ Setup Time (See Note 2)	30		15		15		ns	
TILIH	Input Rise Time (Except CLK)		20		20		20	ns	From 0.8V to 2.0V
TIHIL	Input Fall Time (Except CLK)		12		12		12	ns	From 2.0V to 0.8V

Table 1-26 A.C. Timing Requirements for Minimum Complexity System (continued)

TIMING RESPONSES

Symbol	Parameter	8086		8086-1 (Preliminary)		8086-2		Units	Test Conditions
		Min.	Max.	Min.	Max.	Min.	Max.		
TCLAV	Address Valid Delay	10	110	10	50	10	60	ns	
TCLAX	Address Hold Time	10		10		10		ns	
TCLAZ	Address Float Delay	TCLAX	80	10	40	TCLAX	50	ns	
TLHLL	ALE Width	TCLCH−20		TCLCH−10		TCLCH-10		ns	
TCLLH	ALE Active Delay		80		40		50	ns	
TCHLL	ALE Inactive Delay		85		45		55	ns	
TLLAX	Address Hold Time to ALE Inactive	TCHCL−10		TCHCL−10		TCHCL−10		ns	
TCLDV	Data Valid Delay	10	110	10	50	10	60	ns	*C_L = 20-100 pF for all 8086 Outputs (In addition to 8086 self-load)
TCHDX	Data Hold Time	10		10		10		ns	
TWHDX	Data Hold Time After WR	TCLCH−30		TCLCH−25		TCLCH−30		ns	
TCVCTV	Control Active Delay 1	10	110	10	50	10	70	ns	
TCHCTV	Control Active Delay 2	10	110	10	45	10	60	ns	
TCVCTX	Control Inactive Delay	10	110	10	50	10	70	ns	
TAZRL	Address Float to READ Active	0		0		0		ns	
TCLRL	$\overline{RD}$ Active Delay	10	165	10	70	10	100	ns	
TCLRH	$\overline{RD}$ Inactive Delay	10	150	10	60	10	80	ns	
TRHAV	$\overline{RD}$ Inactive to Next Address Active	TCLCL−45		TCLCL−35		TCLCL−40		ns	
TCLHAV	HLDA Valid Delay	10	160	10	60	10	100	ns	
TRLRH	$\overline{RD}$ Width	2TCLCL−75		2TCLCL−40		2TCLCL−50		ns	
TWLWH	$\overline{WR}$ Width	2TCLCL−60		2TCLCL−35		2TCLCL−40		ns	
TAVAL	Address Valid to ALE Low	TCLCH−60		TCLCH−35		TCLCH−40		ns	
TOLOH	Output Rise Time		20		20		20	ns	From 0.8V to 2.0V
TOHOL	Output Fall Time		12		12		12	ns	From 2.0V to 0.8V

NOTES:
1. Signal at 8284A shown for reference only.
2. Setup requirement for asynchronous signal only to guarantee recognition at next CLK.
3. Applies only to T2 state. (8 ns into T3).

the information is transferred over the upper half of the data bus (D15-D8). BHE* (active low) will enable the upper bank and A0 will disable the lower bank. Directing the data transfer to the appropriate half of the data bus and activation of S7 (BHE*) and A0 is performed by the 8086, transparent to the programmer. For example, consider loading a byte of data into the CX register (lower half of the CX register) from an odd addressed memory location (referenced over the upper half of the 16-bit data bus). The data is transferred into the 8086 over the upper 8 bits of the data bus, automatically redirected to the lower half of the 8086 internal 16-bit data path and stored in the CX register. This capability also allows byte I/O transfers with the AL register to be directed to I/O devices connected to either the upper or lower half of the 16-bit data bus.

To access even addressed 16-bit words (two consecutive bytes with the least significant byte at an even byte address), A19-A1 select the appropriate byte within each bank and A0 and BHE* (active low) enable both banks simultaneously (see Figure 1-43). To access an odd addressed 16-bit word (see Figure 1-43), the least significant byte (addressed by A19-A1) is first transferred over the upper half of the bus (odd addressed byte, upper bank, BHE* low active and A0-1). The most significant byte is accessed by incrementing the address (A19-A0) which allows A19-A1 to address the next physical word location (recall that A0 was high which indicates a word referenced from an odd byte boundary). A second bus cycle is then executed to perform the transfer of the most significant byte with the lower bank (A0 is now low and BHE* is high). The sequence is automatically executed by the 8086 whenever a word transfer is executed to an odd address. Directing the upper and lower bytes of the 8086's

Table 1-27 A.C. Timing Requirements for Maximum Complexity System

MAX MODE SYSTEM (USING 8288 BUS CONTROLLER)
TIMING REQUIREMENTS

Symbol	Parameter	8086		8086-1 (Preliminary)		8086-2 (Preliminary)		Units	Test Conditions
		Min.	Max.	Min.	Max.	Min.	Max.		
TCLCL	CLK Cycle Period	200	500	100	500	125	500	ns	
TCLCH	CLK Low Time	118		53		68		ns	
TCHCL	CLK High Time	69		39		44		ns	
TCH1CH2	CLK Rise Time		10		10		10	ns	From 1.0V to 3.5V
TCL2CL1	CLK Fall Time		10		10		10	ns	From 3.5V to 1.0V
TDVCL	Data in Setup Time	30		5		20		ns	
TCLDX	Data In Hold Time	10		10		10		ns	
TR1VCL	RDY Setup Time into 8284A (See Notes 1, 2)	35		35		35		ns	
TCLR1X	RDY Hold Time into 8284A (See Notes 1, 2)	0		0		0		ns	
TRYHCH	READY Setup Time into 8086	118		53		68		ns	
TCHRYX	READY Hold Time into 8086	30		20		20		ns	
TRYLCL	READY Inactive to CLK (See Note 4)	−8		−10		−8		ns	
TINVCH	Setup Time for Recognition (INTR, NMI, $\overline{TEST}$) (See Note 2)	30		15		15		ns	
TGVCH	$\overline{RQ}/\overline{GT}$ Setup Time	30		12		15		ns	
TCHGX	$\overline{RQ}$ Hold Time into 8086	40		20		30		ns	
TILIH	Input Rise Time (Except CLK)		20		20		20	ns	From 0.8V to 2.0V
TIHIL	Input Fall Time (Except CLK)		12		12		12	ns	From 2.0V to 0.8V

NOTES:

1. Signal at 8284A or 8288 shown for reference only.
2. Setup requirement for asynchronous signal only to guarantee recognition at next CLK.
3. Applies only to T3 and wait states.
4. Applies only to T2 state (8 ns into T3).

Table 1-27 A.C. Timing Requirements for Maximum Complexity System (continued)

TIMING RESPONSES

Symbol	Parameter	8086		8086-1 (Preliminary)		8086-2 (Preliminary)		Units	Test Conditions
		Min.	Max.	Min.	Max.	Min.	Max.		
TCLML	Command Active Delay (See Note 1)	10	35	10	35	10	35	ns	
TCLMH	Command Inactive Delay (See Note 1)	10	35	10	35	10	35	ns	
TRYHSH	READY Active to Status Passive (See Note 3)		110		45		65	ns	
TCHSV	Status Active Delay	10	110	10	45	10	60	ns	
TCLSH	Status Inactive Delay	10	130	10	55	10	70	ns	
TCLAV	Address Valid Delay	10	110	10	50	10	60	ns	
TCLAX	Address Hold Time	10		10		10		ns	
TCLAZ	Address Float Delay	TCLAX	80	10	40	TCLAX	50	ns	
TSVLH	Status Valid to ALE High (See Note 1)		15		15		15	ns	
TSVMCH	Status Valid to MCE High (See Note 1)		15		15		15	ns	
TCLLH	CLK Low to ALE Valid (See Note 1)		15		15		15	ns	
TCLMCH	CLK Low to MCE High (See Note 1)		15		15		15	ns	
TCHLL	ALE Inactive Delay (See Note 1)		15		15		15	ns	C_L = 20-100 pF for all 8086 Outputs (In addition to 8086 self-load)
TCLMCL	MCE Inactive Delay (See Note 1)		15		15		15	ns	
TCLDV	Data Valid Delay	10	110	10	50	10	60	ns	
TCHDX	Data Hold Time	10		10		10		ns	
TCVNV	Control Active Delay (See Note 1)	5	45	5	45	5	45	ns	
TCVNX	Control Inactive Delay (See Note 1)	10	45	10	45	10	45	ns	
TAZRL	Address Float to Read Active	0		0		0		ns	
TCLRL	RD Active Delay	10	165	10	70	10	100	ns	
TCLRH	RD Inactive Delay	10	150	10	60	10	80	ns	
TRHAV	RD Inactive to Next Address Active	TCLCL−45		TCLCL−35		TCLCL−40		ns	
TCHDTL	Direction Control Active Delay (See Note 1)		50		50		50	ns	
TCHDTH	Direction Control Inactive Delay (See Note 1)		30		30		30	ns	
TCLGL	GT Active Delay	0	85	0	45	0	50	ns	
TCLGH	GT Inactive Delay	0	85	0	45	0	50	ns	
TRLRH	RD Width	2TCLCL−75		2TCLCL−40		2TCLCL−50		ns	
TOLOH	Output Rise Time		20		20		20	ns	From 0.8V to 2.0V
TOHOL	Output Fall Time		12		12		12	ns	From 2.0V to 0.8V

Table 1-28 Minimum/Maximum Mode Pin Assignments

8086			8088		
Pin	Mode		Pin	Mode	
	Minimum	Maximum		Minimum	Maximum
31	HOLD	$\overline{RQ}/\overline{GT0}$	31	HOLD	$\overline{RQ}/\overline{GT0}$
30	HLDA	$\overline{RQ}/\overline{GT1}$	30	HLDA	$\overline{RQ}/\overline{GT1}$
29	$\overline{WR}$	$\overline{LOCK}$	29	$\overline{WR}$	$\overline{LOCK}$
28	M/$\overline{IO}$	$\overline{S2}$	28	IO/$\overline{M}$	$\overline{S2}$
27	DT/$\overline{R}$	$\overline{S1}$	27	DT/$\overline{R}$	$\overline{S1}$
26	$\overline{DEN}$	$\overline{S0}$	26	$\overline{DEN}$	$\overline{S0}$
25	ALE	QS0	25	ALE	QS0
24	$\overline{INTA}$	QS1	24	$\overline{INTA}$	QS1
			34	SS0	High State

Table 1-29 Status Bit Decoding

Status Inputs			CPU Cycle	8288 Command
$\overline{S2}$	$\overline{S1}$	$\overline{S0}$		
0	0	0	Interrupt Acknowledge	$\overline{INTA}$
0	0	1	Read I/O Port	$\overline{IORC}$
0	1	0	Write I/O Port	$\overline{IOWC}$, $\overline{AIOWC}$
0	1	1	Halt	None
1	0	0	Instruction Fetch	$\overline{MRDC}$
1	0	1	Read Memory	$\overline{MRDC}$
1	1	0	Write Memory	$\overline{MWTC}$, $\overline{AMWC}$
1	1	1	Passive	None

Table 1-30 Status Line Decoders

$\overline{S_2}$	$\overline{S_1}$	$\overline{S_0}$	
0 (LOW)	0	0	Interrupt Acknowledge
0	0	1	Read I/O Port
0	1	0	Write I/O Port
0	1	1	Halt
1 (HIGH)	0	0	Code Access
1	0	1	Read Memory
1	1	0	Write Memory
1	1	1	Passive

internal 16-bit registers to the appropriate halves of the data bus is also performed automatically by the 8086 and is transparent to the programmer.

During a byte read, the CPU floats the entire 16-bit data bus even though data is only expected on the upper or lower half of the data bus. As will be demonstrated later, this action simplifies the chip select decoding requirements for read only devices (ROM, EPROM). During a byte write operation, the 8086 will drive the entire 16-bit data bus. The information on the half of the data bus not transferring data is indeterminate. These concepts also apply to the I/O address space. Specific examples of I/O and memory interfacing are considered in the corresponding sections.

1.4.4 Memory and I/O Peripherals Interface

The 8086 and 8088 CPUs have a 20-bit address bus and are capable of accessing one megabyte of memory address space. The memory is organized as a linear array of up to 1 million bytes, addressed as 00000(H) to FFFFF(H). The memory is logically divided into code, data, extra data, and stack segments of up to 64 K bytes each, with each segment falling on 16-byte boundaries (see Figure 1-44).

All memory references are made relative to base addresses contained in high speed segment registers. The segment types were chosen based on the addressing needs of programs. The segment register to be selected is auto-

WAVEFORMS

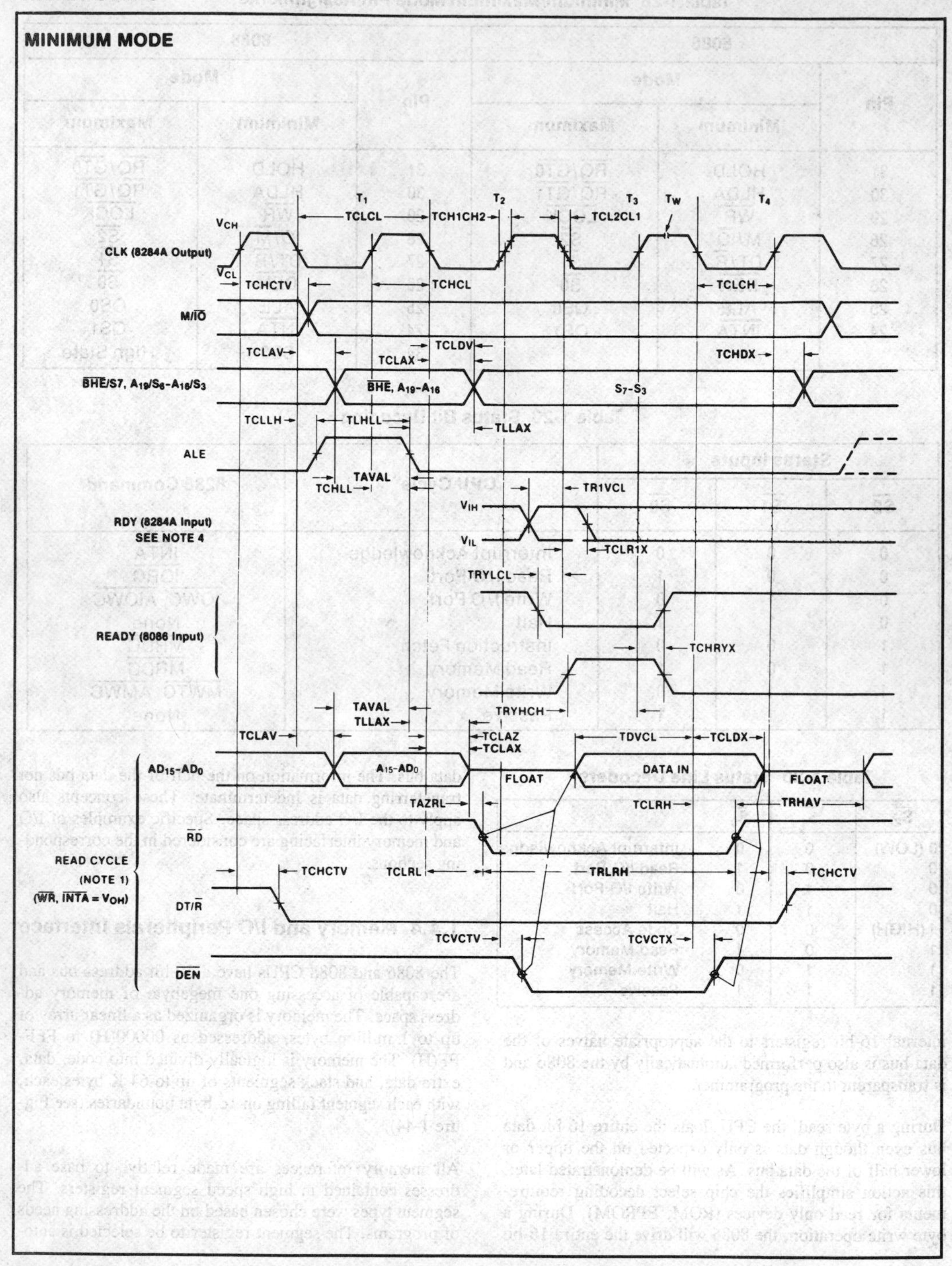

Figure 1-31 Minimum Mode Waveforms

WAVEFORMS (Continued)

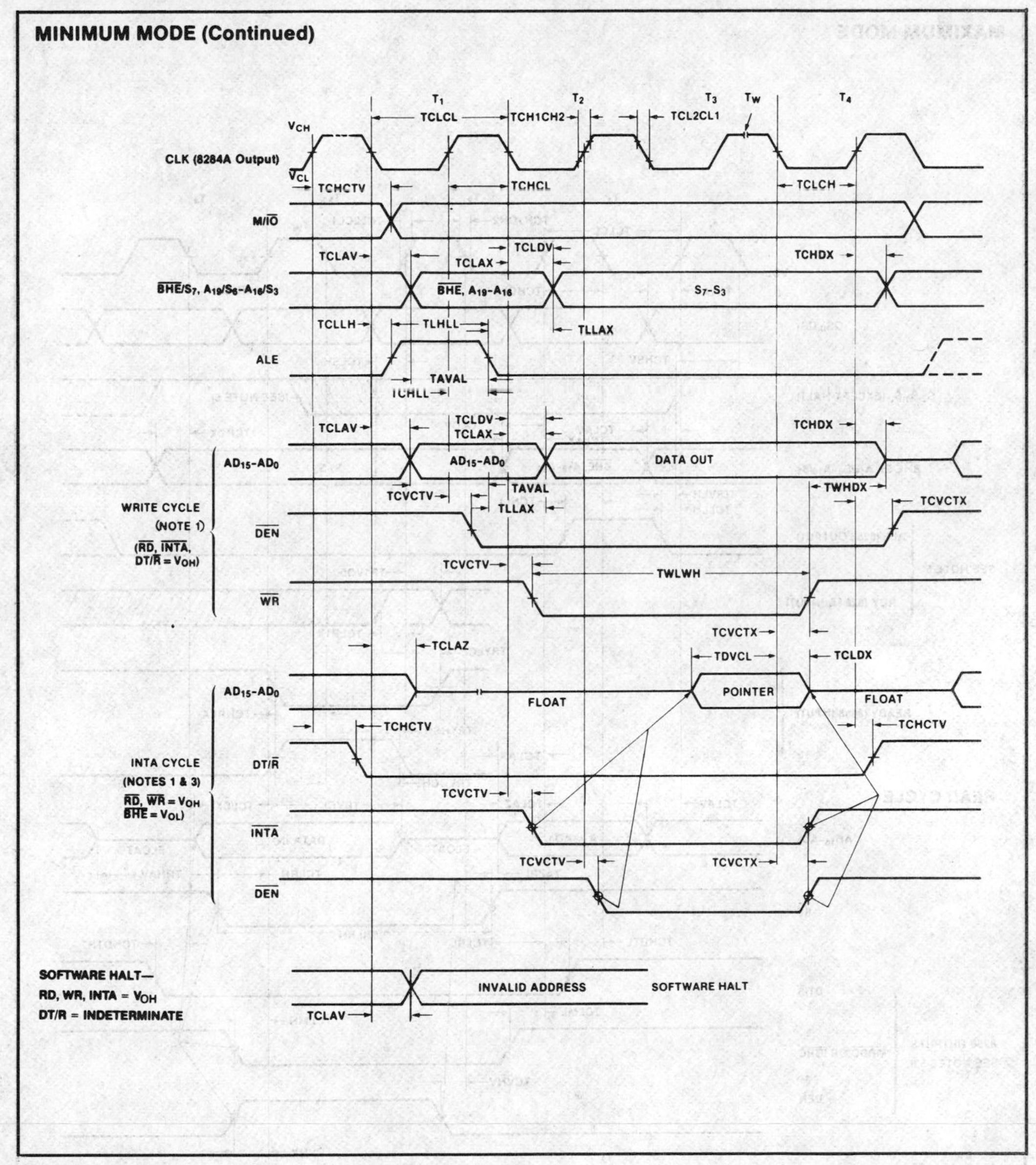

NOTES:
1. All signals switch between V_{OH} and V_{OL} unless otherwise specified.
2. RDY is sampled near the end of T_2, T_3, T_W to determine if T_W machines states are to be inserted.
3. Two INTA cycles run back-to-back. The 8086 LOCAL ADDR/DATA BUS is floating during both INTA cycles. Control signals shown for second INTA cycle.
4. Signals at 8284A are shown for reference only.
5. All timing measurements are made at 1.5V unless otherwise noted.

Figure 1-31 Minimum Mode Waveforms (continued)

WAVEFORMS

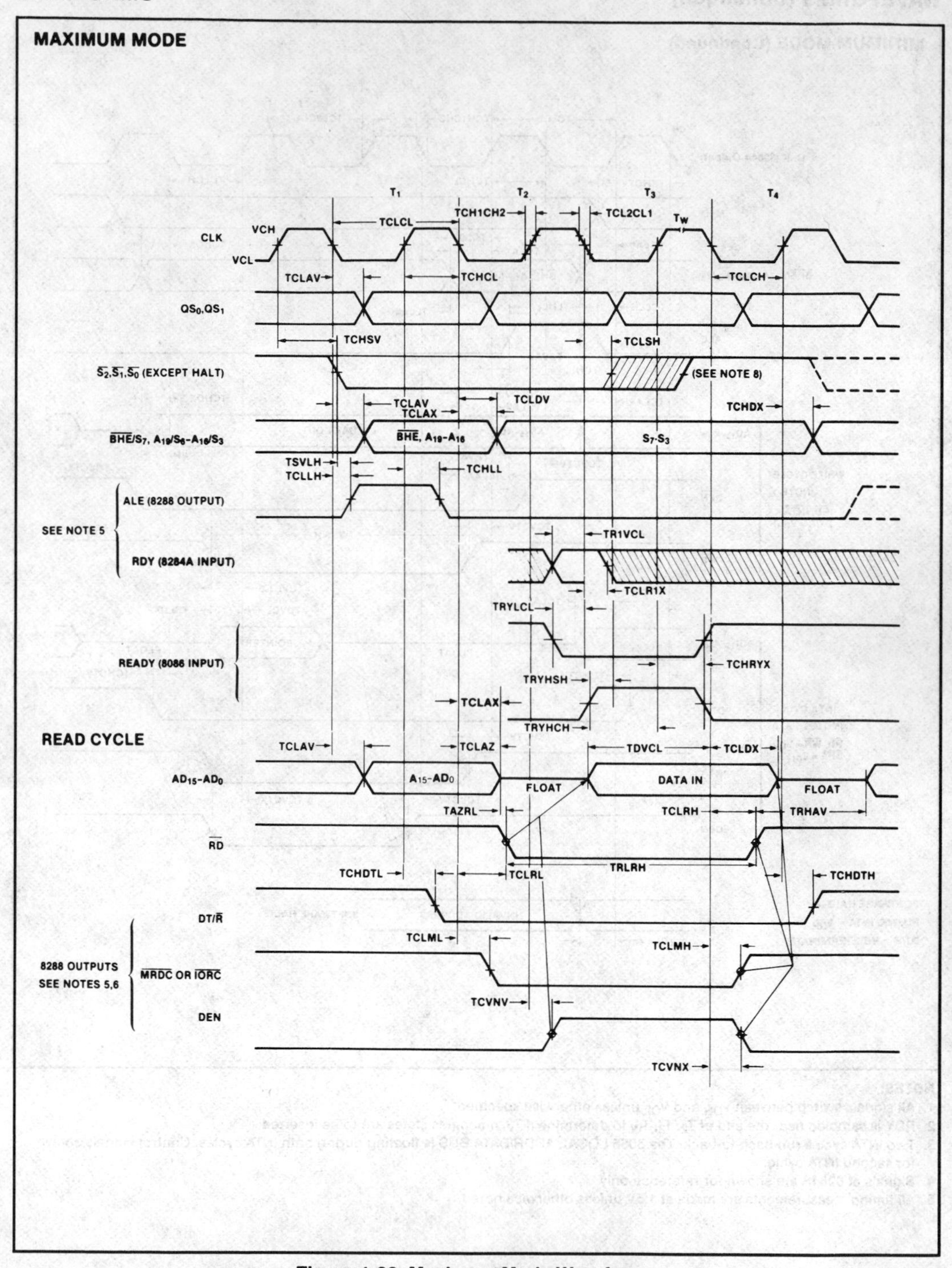

Figure 1-32 Maximum Mode Waveforms

WAVEFORMS (Continued)

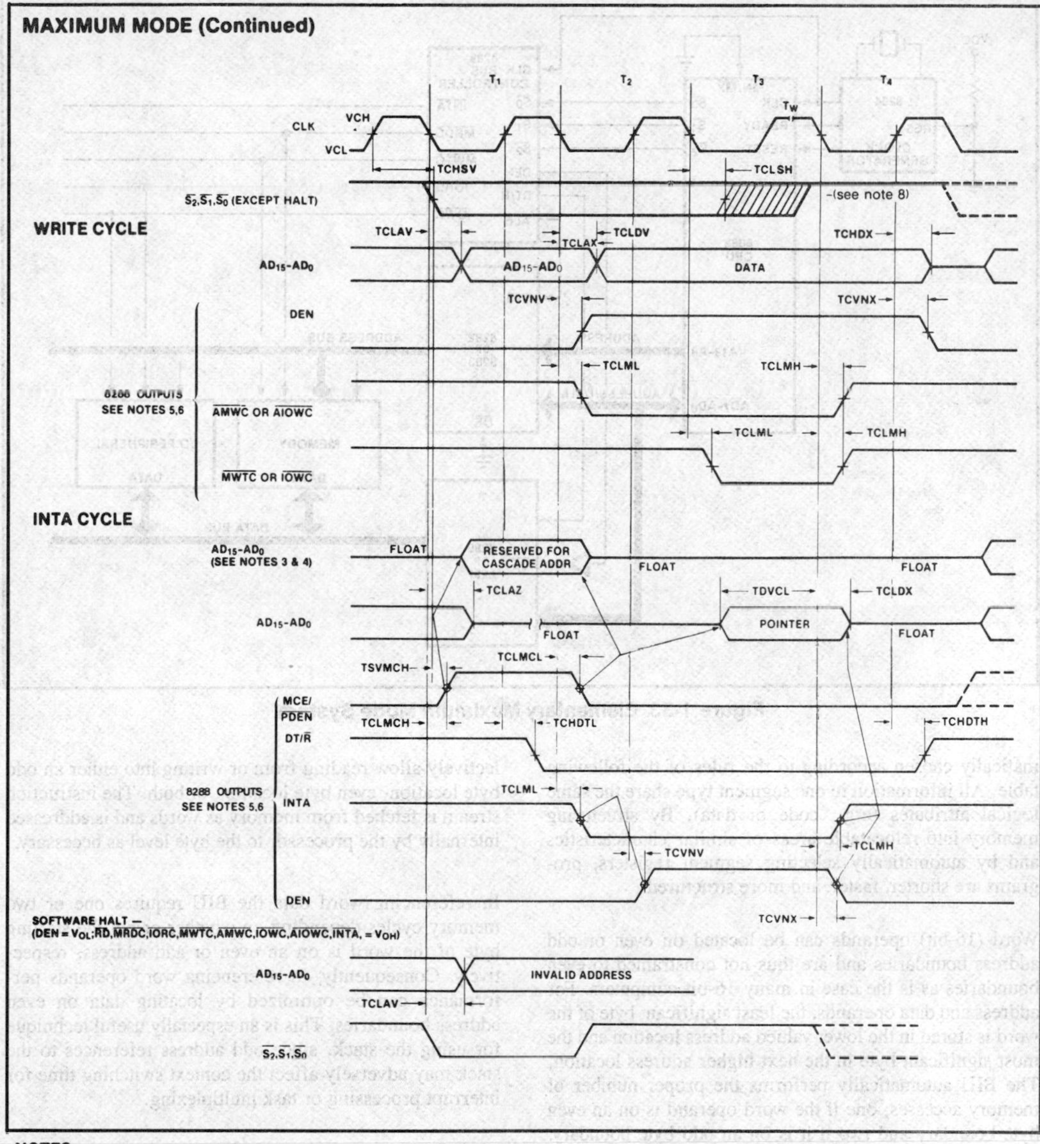

NOTES:

1. All signals switch between V_{OH} and V_{OL} unless otherwise specified.
2. RDY is sampled near the end of T_2, T_3, T_W to determine if T_W machines states are to be inserted.
3. Cascade address is valid between first and second INTA cycle.
4. Two INTA cycles run back-to-back. The 8086 LOCAL ADDR/DATA BUS is floating during both INTA cycles. Control for pointer address is shown for second INTA cycle.
5. Signals at 8284A or 8288 are shown for reference only.
6. The issuance of the 8288 command and control signals ($\overline{MRDC}$, $\overline{MWTC}$, $\overline{AMWC}$, $\overline{IORC}$, $\overline{IOWC}$, $\overline{AIOWC}$, $\overline{INTA}$ and DEN) lags the active high 8288 CEN.
7. All timing measurements are made at 1.5V unless otherwise noted.
8. Status inactive in state just prior to T_4.

Figure 1-32 Maximum Mode Waveforms

210912-001

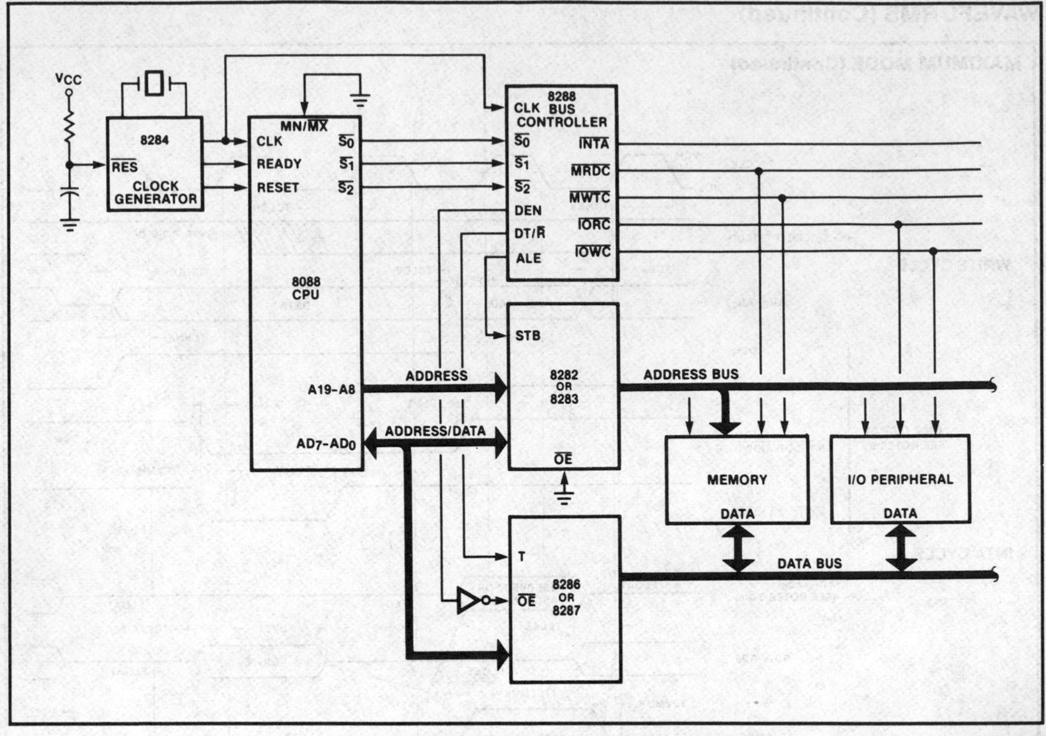

Figure 1-33 Elementary Maximum Mode System

matically chosen according to the rules of the following table. All information in one segment type share the same logical attributes (e.g., code or data). By structuring memory into relocatable areas of similar characteristics and by automatically selecting segment registers, programs are shorter, faster, and more structured.

Word (16-bit) operands can be located on even or odd address boundaries and are thus not constrained to even boundaries as is the case in many 16-bit computers. For address and data operands, the least significant byte of the word is stored in the lower valued address location and the most significant byte in the next higher address location. The BIU automatically performs the proper number of memory accesses, one if the word operand is on an even byte boundary and two if it is on an odd byte boundary. Except for the performance penalty, this double access is transparent to the software. This performance penalty does not occur for instruction fetches, only word operands.

Physically, the memory is organized as a high bank (D15-D8) and a low bank (D7-D0) of 512K 8-bit bytes addressed in parallel by the processor's address lines A19-A1. Byte data with even addresses is transferred on the D7-D0 bus lines while odd addressed byte data (A0 HIGH) is transferred on the D15-D8 bus lines. The processor provides two enable signals, BHE* and A0, to selectively allow reading from or writing into either an odd byte location, even byte location, or both. The instruction stream is fetched from memory as words and is addressed internally by the processor to the byte level as necessary.

In referencing word data the BIU requires one or two memory cycles depending on whether or not the starting byte of the word is on an even or add address, respectively. Consequently, in referencing word operands performance can be optimized by locating data on even address boundaries. This is an especially useful technique for using the stack, since odd address references to the stack may adversely affect the context switching time for interrupt processing or task multiplexing.

Certain locations in memory are reserved for specific CPU operations (see Figure 1-45). Locations from address FFFF0H through FFFFFH are reserved for operations including a jump to the initial program loading routine. Following RESET, the CPU will always begin execution at location FFFF0H where the jump must be. Locations 00000H through 003FFH are reserved for interrupt operations. Each of the 256 possible interrupt types has its service routine pointed to by a 4-byte pointer element consisting of a 16-bit segment address and a 16-bit offset address. The pointer elements are assumed to

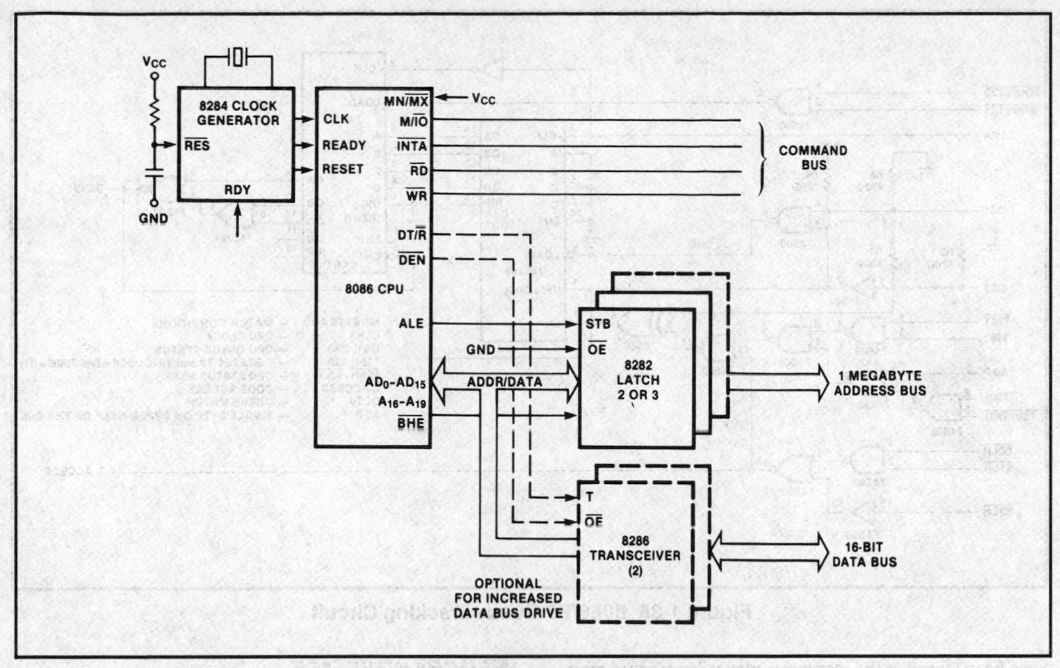

Figure 1-34 8086/88 Minimum Mode System

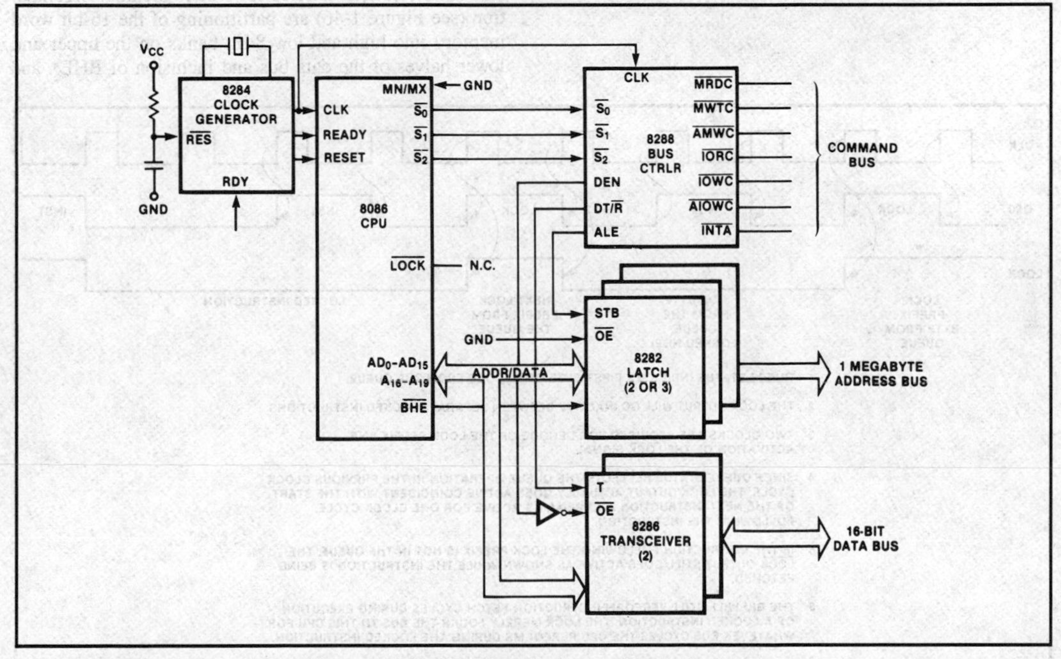

Figure 1-35 8086/88 Maximum Mode System

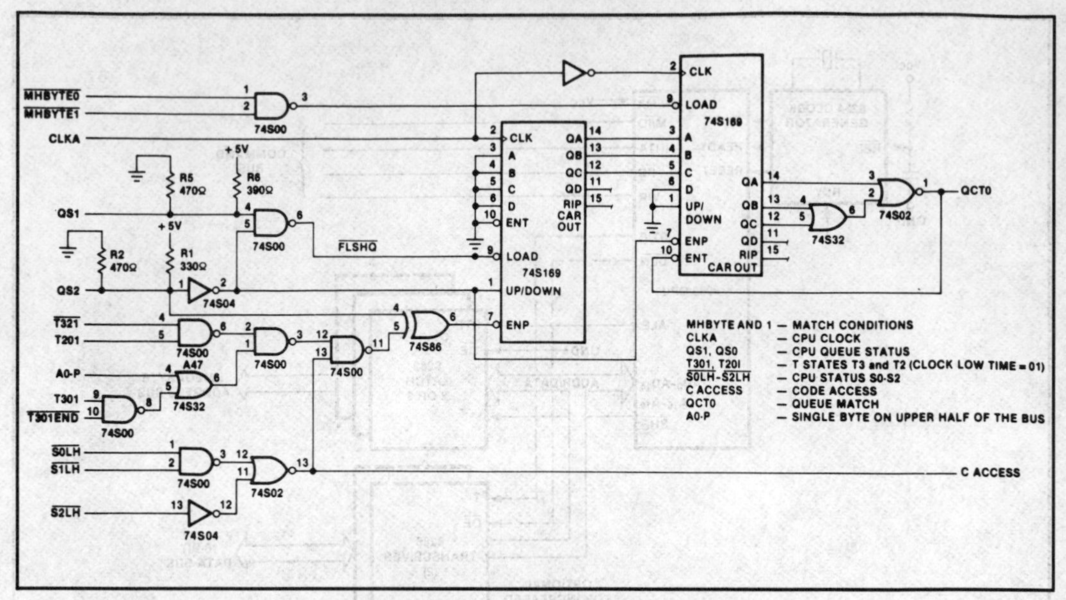

Figure 1-36 8086/88 Queue Tracking Circuit

have been stored at the respective places in reserved memory prior to occurrence of interrupts.

MEMORY INTERFACE

The basic characteristics of 8086/8088 memory organization (see Figure 1-46) are partitioning of the 16-bit word memory into high and low 8-bit banks on the upper and lower halves of the data bus and inclusion of BHE* and

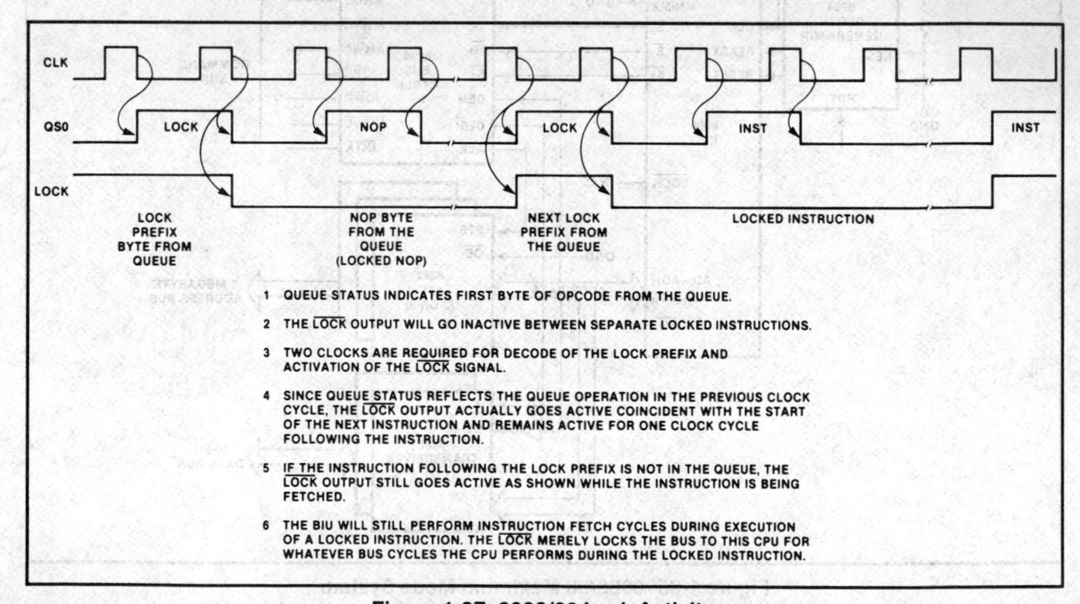

Figure 1-37 8086/88 Lock Activity

A0 in selection of the banks. Specific implementations depend on the type of memory and system configuration.

ROM and EPROM

ROM's and EPROM's are the easiest devices to interface to the 8086/8088 system (see Figure 1-47). The byte format of these devices provides a simple bus interface and, since they are read only devices, A0 and BHE* do not need to be included in their chip enable/select decoding. (Chip enable is similar to chip select and also determines if the device is in active or standby power mode.) The address lines connected to the devices start with A1 and continue up to the maximum number of address lines the device can accept. The remaining address lines are used for chip enable/ select decoding. To connect the devices directly to the multiplexed bus, they must have output enables. The output enable is also necessary to avoid bus contention in other configurations. No special decode techniques are required for generating chip enable/selects. Each valid decode selects one device on the upper and lower halves of bus to allow byte and word access. Byte access is achieved by reading the full word onto the bus with the 8086 only accepting the desired byte. If RD*, WR* and M/IO* are not decoded to form separate commands for memory and I/O in a minimum mode 8086, M/IO* (high active) must be a condition of chip enable/select decode. This is also true if the I/O space overlaps the memory space assigned to the EPROM/ROM. The output enable is controlled by the system memory read signal.

Four parameters must be evaluated when determining the compatibility of static ROM's and PROM's to an 8086/8088 system. The parameters, equations and evaluation techniques given in the I/O section are also applicable to these devices. The relationship of parameters is given in Table 1-32. TACC and TCE are related to the same equation and differ only by the delay associated with the chip enable/select decoder. The following example shows a 2716 EPROM memory residing on the multiplexed bus of a minimum mode 8086 configuration:

TACC = 3TCLCL − 140 − address buffer delay = 430 ns (8282 = 30 ns max delay)

TCE = TACC − decoder delay = 412 ns (8205 decoder delay = 18 ns)

TOE = 2TCLCL − 195 = 205 ns

TDF = = 155

The results of the calculations in the previous example represent the times a minimum mode configuration requires from the component for full speed compatibility with the system.

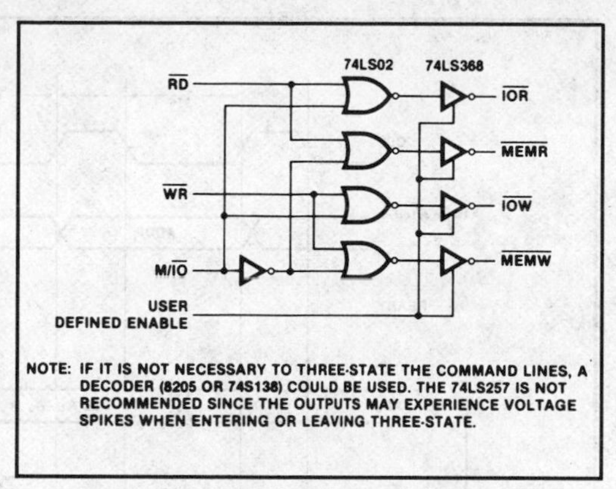

Figure 1-38 Decoding Memory and I/O RD* and WR* Commands

Static RAM

Several new memory design requirements are introduced when interfacing static RAM's to the system. To begin with, A0 and BHE* must be included in the chip select/chip enable decoding of the devices and write timing must be considered in the compatibility analysis.

Data bus connections must be restricted to either the upper half or the lower half of the data bus for each device. Also, devices must not straddle the upper and lower halves of the data bus. In order to select either the upper byte, lower byte or the full 16-bit word for a write operation, BHE* must be a condition of decode for selecting the upper byte and A0 must be a condition of decode for selecting the lower byte. Several selection techniques for

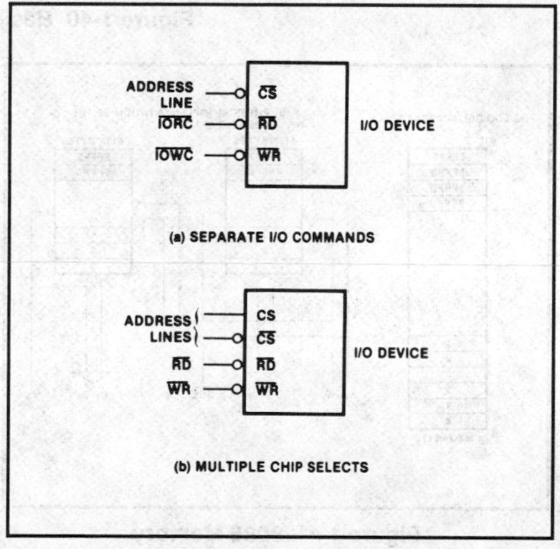

Figure 1-39 Linear Select for I/O

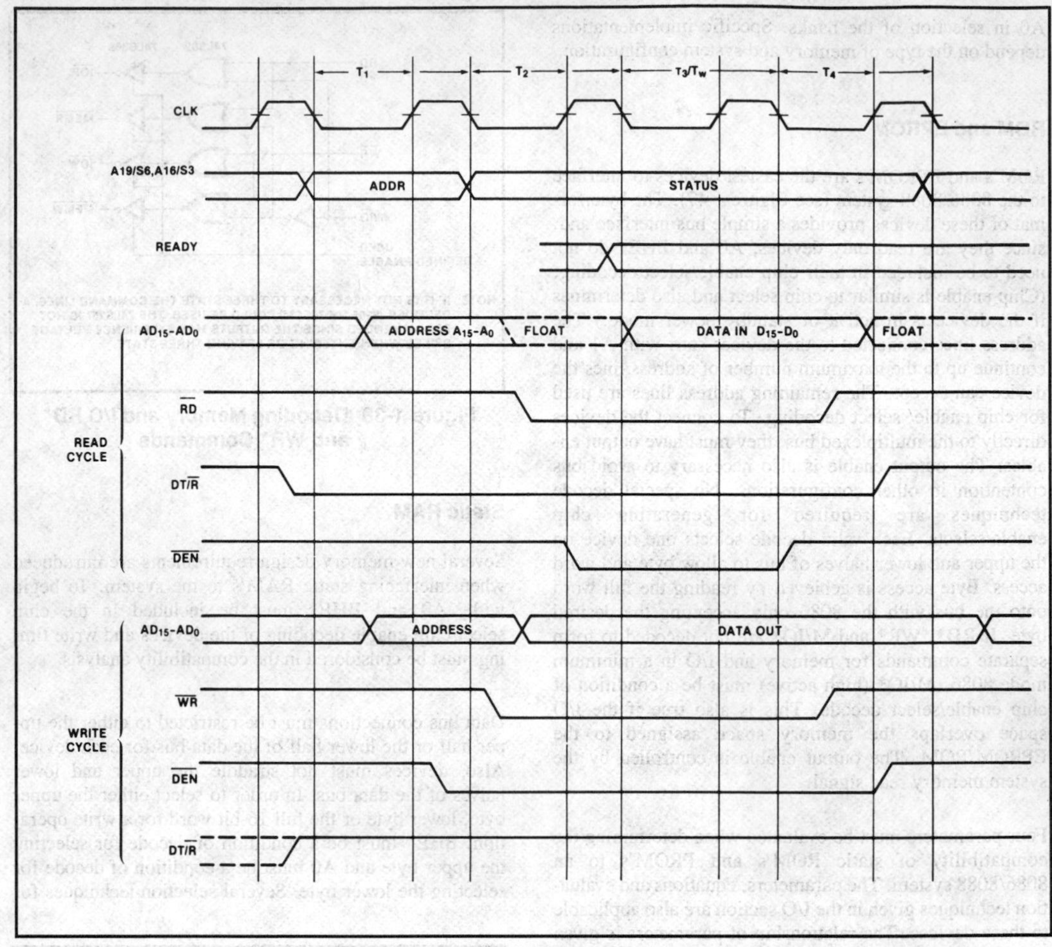

Figure 1-40 Basic 8086/88 Bus Cycles

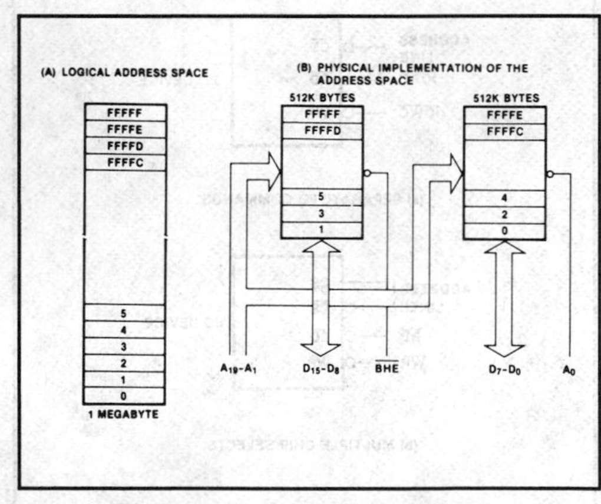

Figure 1-41 8086 Memory

devices with single chip selects and no output enables are illustrated in Figure 1-48 and Figure 1-49 illustrates selection techniques for devices with chip selects and output enables.

In the first examples (see Figure 1-48) A0 and BHE* must be included to decode or enable the chip selects. Since these memories do not have output enables, read and write are used as enables for chip select generation to prevent bus contention. If read and write are not used to enable the chip selects, devices with common input/output pins will be subjected to severe bus contention between chip select and write active. For devices with separate input/output lines, the outputs can be externally buffered with the buffer enable controlled by read. This solution will only allow bus contention between memory devices in the array during chip select transition periods.

For devices with output enables (see Figure 1-49), write may be gated with BHE* and A0 to provide upper and lower bank write strobes. This simplifies chip select decoding by eliminating BHE* and A0 as a condition of decode. Although both devices are selected during a byte write operation, only one will receive a write strobe. No bus contention will exist during the write since a read command must be issued to enable the memory output drivers.

If multiple chip selects are available at the device, BHE* and A0 may directly control device selection. This allows normal chip select decoding of the address space and direct connection of the read and write commands to the devices. Alternately, the multiple chip select inputs of the device could directly decode the address space (linear select) and be combined with the separate write strobe technique to minimize the control circuits needed to generate chip selects.

As with the EPROM's and ROM's, if separate commands are not provided for memory and I/O in the minimum mode 8086 and the address spaces overlap, M/IO* (high active) must be a condition of chip select decode. Also, the address lines connected to the memory devices must start with A1 rather than A0.

The write timing parameters listed in Table 1-33 may also need to be considered to analyze RAM compatibility (depending on the RAM device being considered). CPU clock relative timing is listed in Table 1-34. The equations specify the device requirements at the CPU and provide a base for determining device requirements in other configurations. For example, consider the write timing requirements of a 2148 in a maximum mode buffered 8086 system (see Figure 1-50). The write parameters of the 2148 that must be analyzed are TWP write pulse width, TWR write recovery time, TDW data valid at end of write, and TDH data hold from write time.

TWA = 2TCLCL − TCLMLmax + TCLMHmin
= 375 ns.
TWR = 2TCLCL − TCLMHmax + TCLLHmin
+ TSHOVmin = 170ns.
TDW = 2TCLCL − TCDLVmax + TCLMHmin
− TIVOVmax = 265ns.
TDH = TCLCH − TCLMHmax + TCHDXmin
+ TIVOVmin = 95ns.

A comparison of these results with the 2148 family indicates the standard 2148 write timing is fully compatible with this 8086 configuration. The read timing must also be analyzed to determine the complete compatibility of the devices.

Dynamic RAM

A dynamic RAM is one of the most complex devices to design into an 8086 system. In order to help the Design

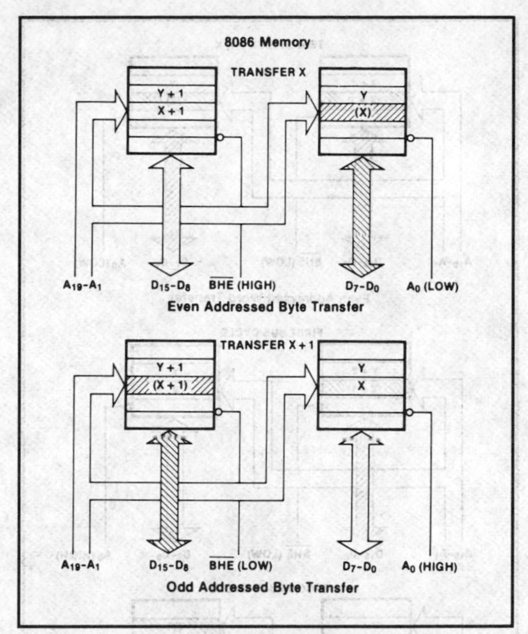

Figure 1-42 Memory Even and Odd Data Byte Transfers

Engineer and simplify the design task somewhat, Intel provides the 8202, 8203, 8207, and 8208 dynamic RAM controllers as part of the 8086 family of peripheral devices. The following paragraphs describe the use of the 8202 with the 8086 in designing a dynamic memory system for an 8086 system.

For example, a standard interconnection for an 8202 in an 8086 system (see Figure 1-51) accommodates 64K words (128 bytes) of dynamic RAM which is addressable as words or bytes. To access the RAM, the 8086 must initiate a bus cycle with an address that selects the 8202 (via PCS*) and the appropriate transfer command (MRDC* or MWTC*). If the 8202 is not performing a refresh cycle, the access starts immediately, otherwise, the 8086 must wait for completion of the refresh. XACK* from the 8202 is connected to the 8284 RDY input to force the CPU to wait until the RAM cycle is completed before the CPU can terminate the bus cycle. This effectively synchronizes the asynchronous events of refresh and CPU bus cycles. The normal write command (MWTC*) is used rather than the advanced command (AMWC*) to guarantee that data is valid at the dynamic RAMs before the write command is issued. Gating WE* with A0 and BHE* provides selective write strobes to the upper and lower banks of memory to allow byte and word write operations. The logic which generates the strobe for the data latches allows read data to propagate to the system as soon as the data is available and latches the data on the trailing edge of CAS*.

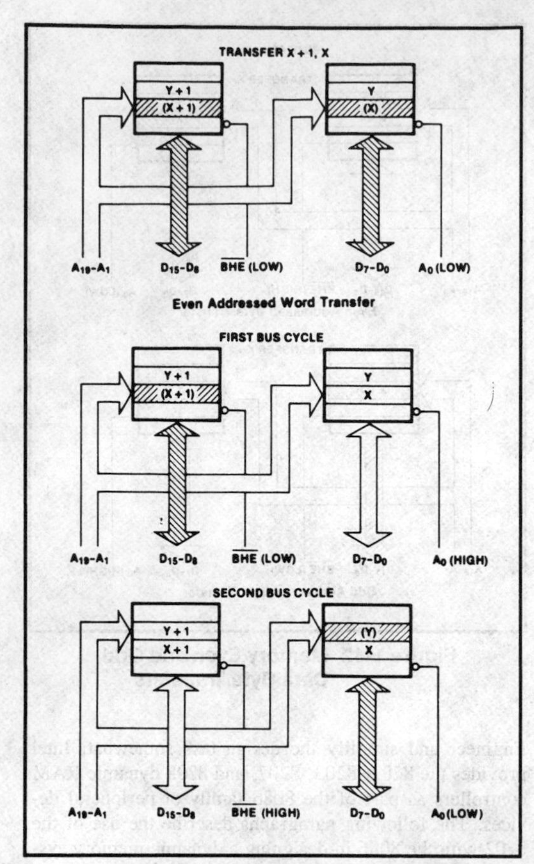

Figure 1-43 Memory Even and Odd Data Word Transfers

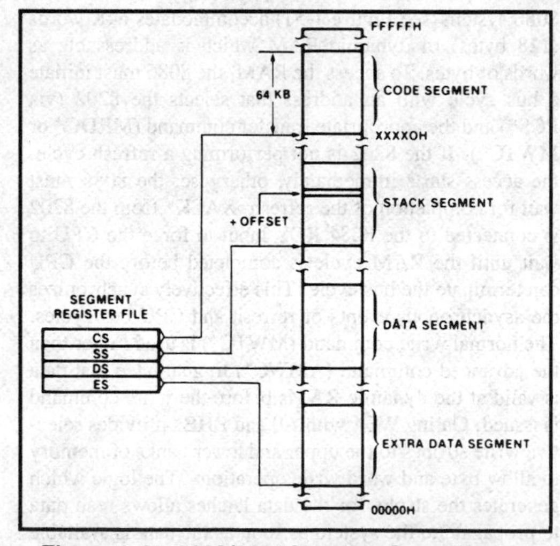

Figure 1-44 8086/8088 Memory Organization

Table 1-31 Status Information

S3	S4	
0	0	Alternate (relative to the ES segment)
1	0	Stack (relative to the SS segment)
0	1	Code/None (relative to the CS segment or a default of zero)
1	1	Data (relative to the DS segment)

S5 = IF (interrupt enable flag)
S6 = 0 (indicates the 8086 is on the bus)

Table 1-32 EPROM/ROM Parameters

TOE — Output Enable to Valid Data ≡ TRLDV
TACC — Address to Valid Data ≡ TAVDV
TCE — Chip Enable to Valid Data ≡ TSLDV
TDF — Output Enable High to Output Float ≡ TRHDZ

a. Read Cycle

For no wait state operation, the 8086 requires data to be valid from MRDC* in:

2TCLCL − TCLML − TDVCL − buffer delays = 291 ns.

Since the 8202 is CAS* access limited, only CAS* access time needs to be examined. The 8202/2118 guarantees data valid from 8202 RD* low to be:

(tph + 3tp + 100 ns) 8202 TCC delay + TCAC for the 2118

A 25 MHz 8202 and 2118-3 provide only 297 ns, which is insufficient for no wait state operation. If only 64K bytes are accessed, the 8202 requires only (tph + 3tp = 85 ns) giving 282 ns access and no wait states required (see Figures 1-52 and 1-53). Refer to the devices respective data sheets for additional information.

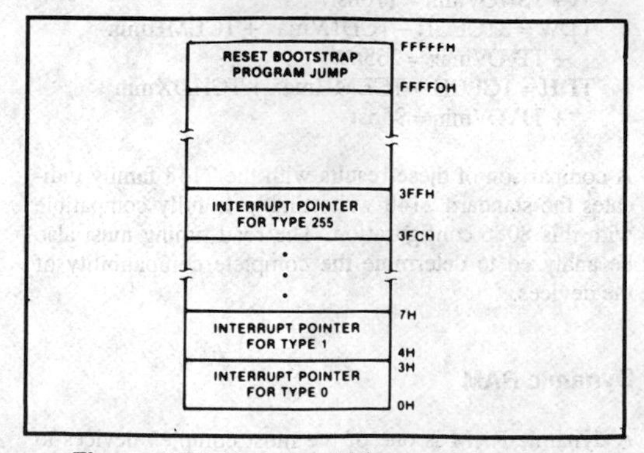

Figure 1-45 Reserved Memory Locations

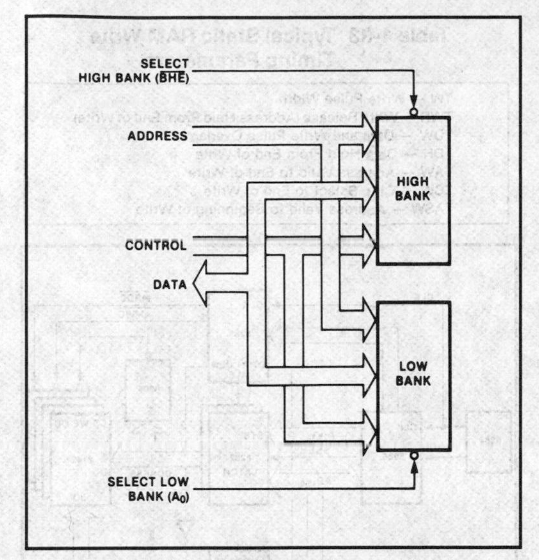

Figure 1-46 8086/8088 Memory Array

a. Write Cycle

An important consideration for dynamic RAM write cycles is to guarantee data to the RAM is valid when both CAS* and WE* are active. For the 2118, if WE* is valid prior to CAS*, the data setup is to CAS* and if CAS* is valid before WE* (as would occur during a read modify write cycle) the data setup time is to WE*.

For the 8202, the WR* to CAS* delay is analyzed to determine the data setup time to CAS* inherently provided by the 8202 command to RAS*/CAS* timing. The minimum delay from WR* to CAS* is:

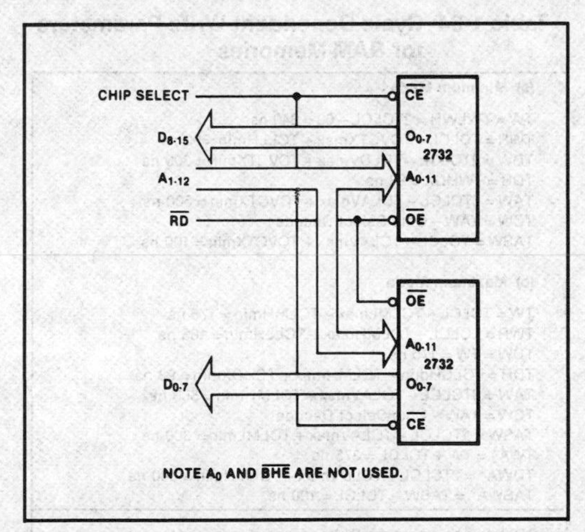

Figure 1-47 EPROM/ROM Bus Interface

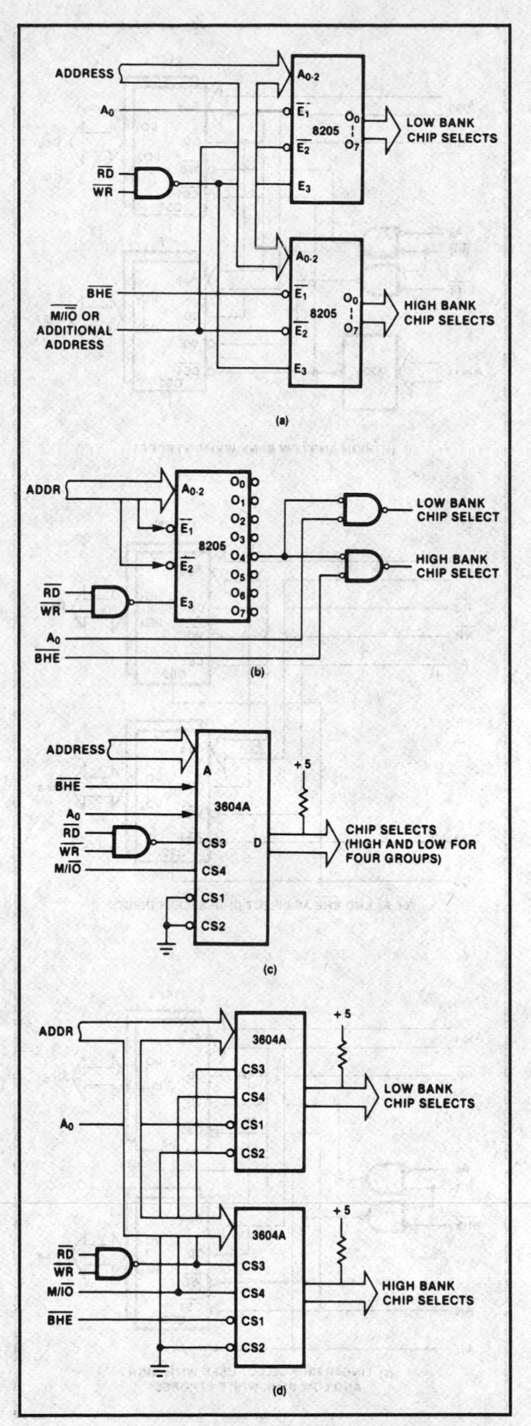

Figure 1-48 Chip Select Generation for Devices Without Output Enables

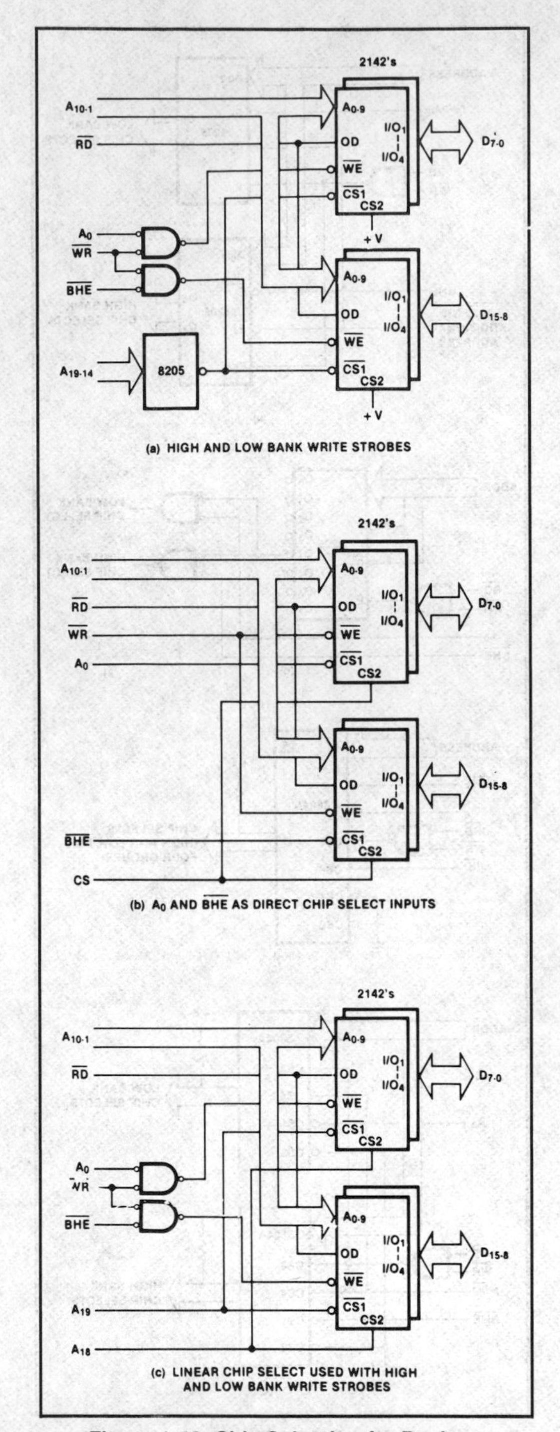

Figure 1-49 Chip Selection for Devices With Output Enables

Table 1-33 Typical Static RAM Write Timing Parameters

TW — Write Pulse Width
TWR — Write Release (Address Hold From End of Write)
TDW — Data and Write Pulse Overlap
TDH — Data Hold From End of Write
TAW — Address Valid to End of Write
TCW — Chip Select to End of Write
TASW — Address Valid to Beginning of Write

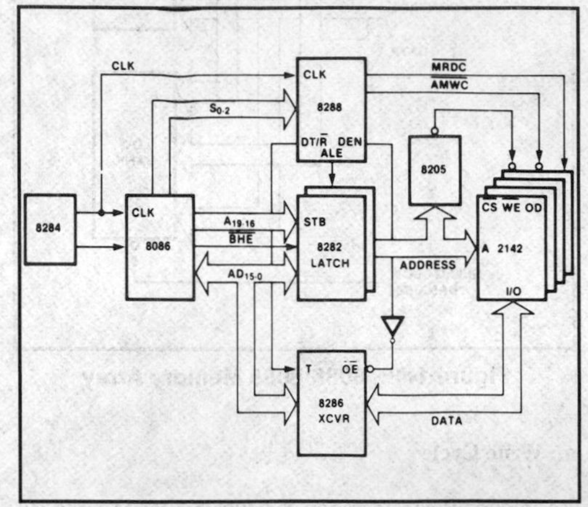

Figure 1-50 Sample Compatibility Analysis Configuration

TCCmin = tph + 2tp + 25 = 127 ns @ 25 MHz

Subtracting buffer delays and data setup at the 2118, we have 83 ns to generate valid data after the write command is issued by the CPU (in this case the 8288). Since the 8086 will not guarantee valid data until TCLAVmax − T-CLMLmin = 100 ns from the advanced write signal, the

Table 1-34 Cycle Dependent Write Parameters for RAM Memories

(a) Minimum Mode

TW = TWLWH = 2TCLCL − 60 = 340 ns
TWR = TCLCL − TCVCTXmax + TCLLHmin = 90 ns
TDW = 2TCLCL − TCLDVmax + TCVCTXmin = 300 ns
TDH = TWHDX = 88 ns
TAW = 3TCLCL − TCLAVmax + TCVCTXmin = 500 ns
TCW = TAW − Chip Select Decode
TASW = TCLCL − TCLAVmax + TCVCTXmin = 100 ns

(b) Maximum Mode

TW = TCLCL − TCLMLmax + TCLMHmin = 175 ns
TWR = TCLCL − TCLMHmax + TCLLHmin = 165 ns
TDW = TW = 175 ns
TDH = TCLCHmin − TCLMHmax + TCHDXmin = 93 ns
TAW = 3TCLCL − TCLAVmax + TCLMHmin = 500 ns
TCW = TAW − Chip Select Decode
TASW = 2TCLCL − TCLAVmax + TCLMLmin = 300 ns
TWA* = TW + TCLCL = 375 ns
TDWA* = 2TCLCL − TCLDVmax + TCLMHmin = 300 ns
TASWA* = TASW − TCLCL = 100 ns

*Relative to Advanced Write.

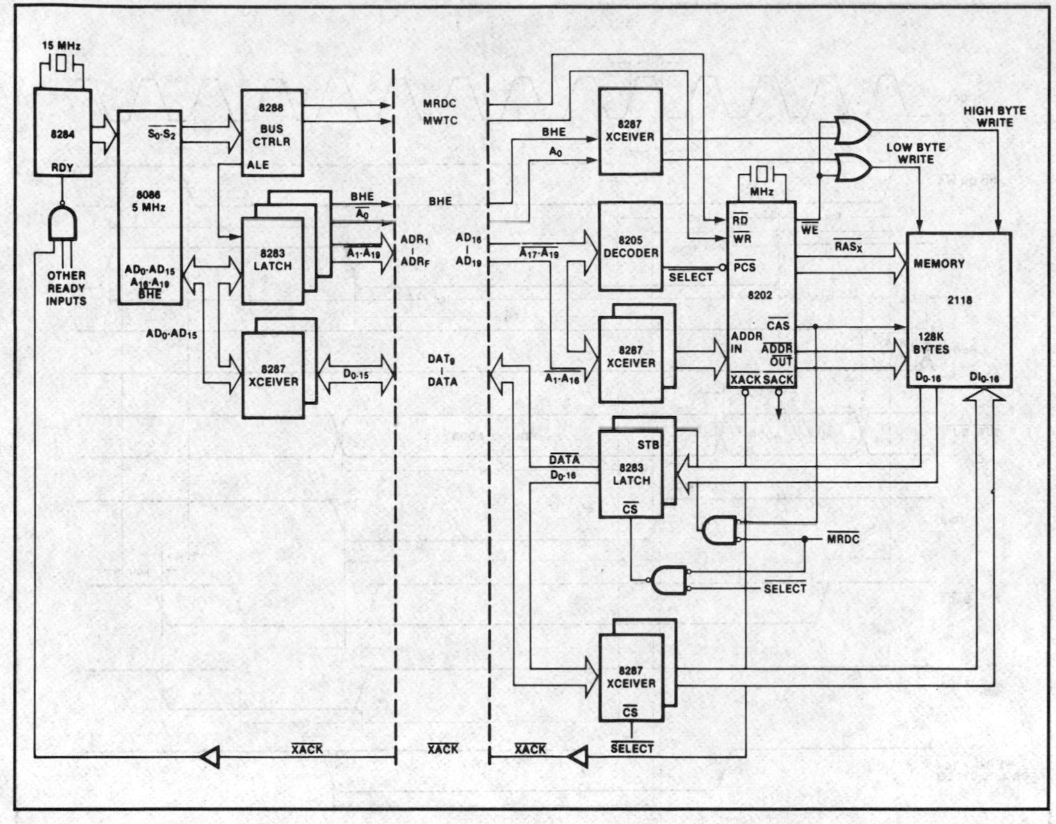

Figure 1-51 5 MHz 8086 System Using an 8202 Dynamic RAM Controller

normal write signal is used. The normal write MWTC* guarantees data is valid 100 ns before it is active. The worst case write pulse width is approximately 175 ns which is sufficient for all 2118's.

c. Synchronization

To force the 8086 to wait during refresh the XACK* or SACK* lines must be returned to the 8284A ready input. The maximum delay from RD* to SACK* (if the 8202 is not performing refresh) is TAC = tp + 40 = 80 ns. To prevent a wait state at the 8086, RDY must be valid at the 8284A TCLCHmin − TCLMLmax − TR1VCLmax = 48 ns after the command is active. This implies that under worst case conditions, one wait state will be inserted for every read cycle. Since MWTC* does not occur until one clock later, two wait states may be inserted for writes.

The XACK* from command delay will assert RDY TCC + TCX = (tph + 3tp + 100) + (5tp + 20) = 460 ns after the command. This will typically insert one or two wait states.

Unless 2118-3's are used in 64K byte or less memories, SACK* must not be used since it does not guarantee a wait state. From the previous access time analysis we saw that other configurations required a wait state.

I/O PERIPHERAL INTERFACE

The 8086 can interface with 8-and 16-bit I/O devices using either I/O instructions or memory mapped I/O. The I/O instructions allow the I/O devices to reside in a separate I/O address space while memory mapped I/O allows the full power of the instruction set to be used for I/O operations. Up to 64K bytes of I/O mapped I/O may be defined in an 8086 system. To the programmer, the separate I/O address space is only accessible with INPUT and OUTPUT commands which transfer data between I/O devices and the AX (for 16-bit data transfers) or AL (for 8-bit data transfers) register. The first 256 bytes of the I/O space (0 to 255) are directly addressable by the I/O instructions while the entire 64K is accessible via register indirect addressing through the DX register. The latter technique is particularly desirable for service procedures that handle more than one device by allowing the desired

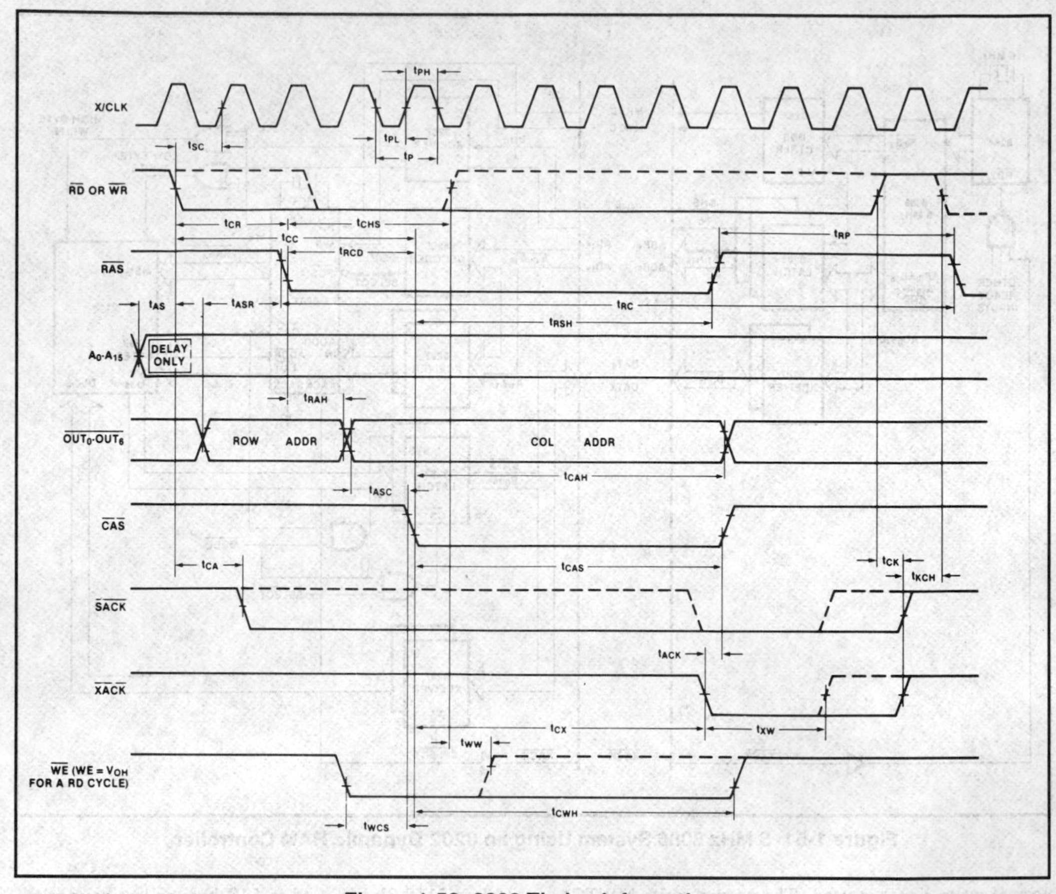

Figure 1-52 8202 Timing Information

device address to be passed to the procedure as a parameter. I/O devices may be connected to the local CPU bus or the buffered system bus.

Eight-Bit I/O

Eight-bit I/O devices may be connected to either the upper or lower half of the data bus. Assigning an equal number of devices to the upper and lower halves of the bus will distribute the bus loading. If a device is connected to the upper half of the data bus, all I/O addresses assigned to the device must be odd (A0 = 1). If the device is on the lower half of the bus, its addresses must be even (A0 = 0). The address assignment directs the 8-bit transfer to the upper (odd byte address) or lower (even byte address) half of the 16-bit data bus. Since A0 will always be a one or zero for a specific device, A0 cannot be used as an address input to select registers within a specific device. If a device on the upper half of the bus and one on the lower half are assigned addresses that differ only in A0 (adjacent odd and even addresses), A0 and BHE* must be conditions of chip select decode to prevent a write to one device from erroneously performing a write to the other.

One technique for generating I/O device chip selects uses separate 8205's to generate chip selects for odd and even addressed byte peripherals (see Figure 1-54). If a word transfer is performed to an even addressed device, the adjacent odd addressed I/O device is also selected. This allows accessing the devices individually with byte transfers or simultaneously as a 16-bit device with word transfers. Another technique restricts the chip selects to byte transfers, however a word transfer to an odd address will cause the 8086 to run two byte transfers that the decode technique will not detect. A third technique simply uses a single 8205 to generate odd and even device selects for byte transfers and will only select the even addressed 8-bit device on a word transfer to an even address.

One last technique for interfacing with 8-bit peripherals (see Figure 1-55) multiplexes the 16-bit data bus onto an

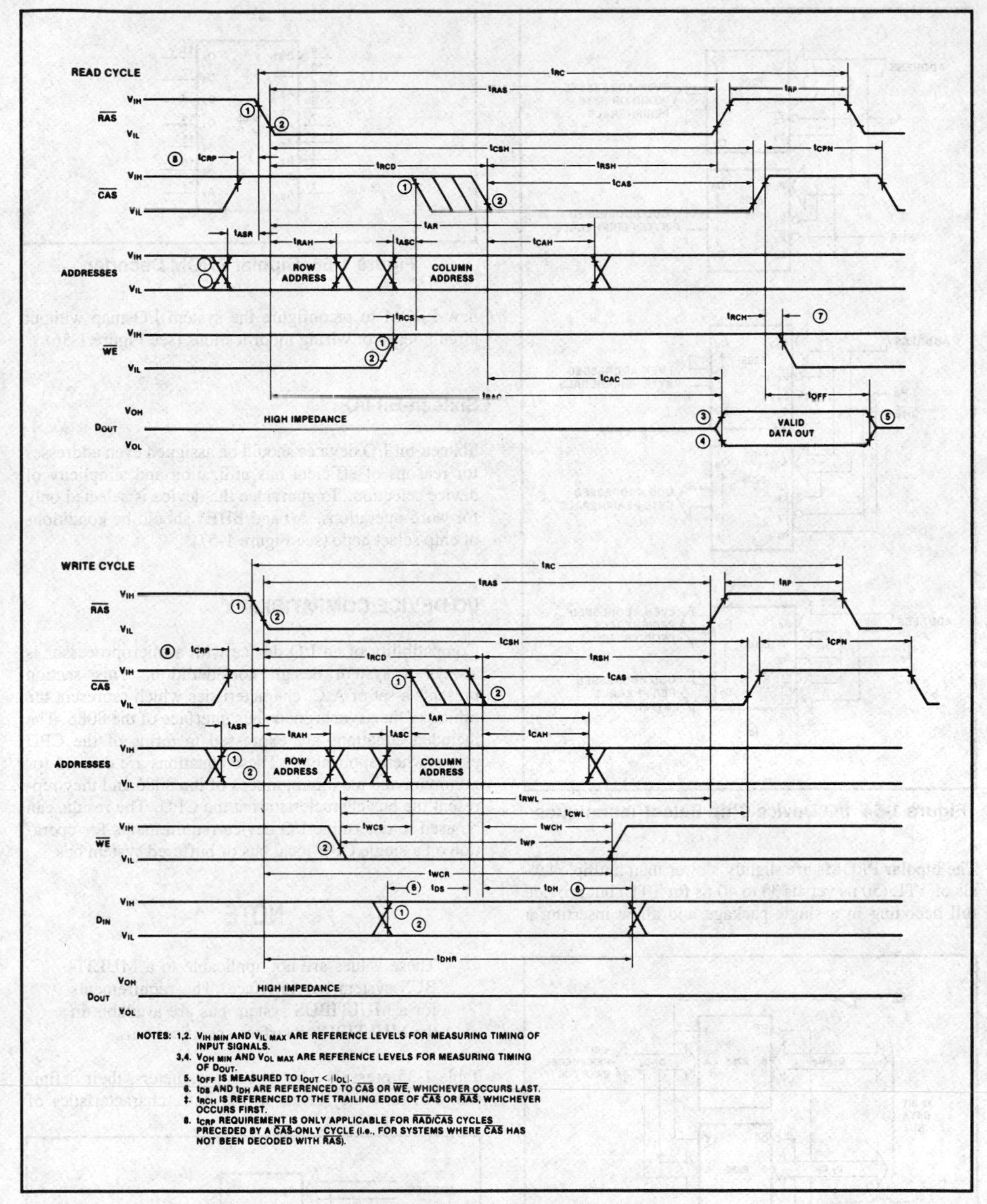

Figure 1-53 2118 Family Timing

8-bit bus to accommodate byte oriented DMA or block transfers to memory mapped 8-bit I/O. Devices connected to this interface may be assigned a sequence of odd and even addresses rather than all odd or even.

If greater than 256 bytes of the I/O space or memory mapped I/O is used, additional decoding beyond these sample techniques may be necessary. This decoding can be done with additional TTL, 8205's or bipolar PROMs.

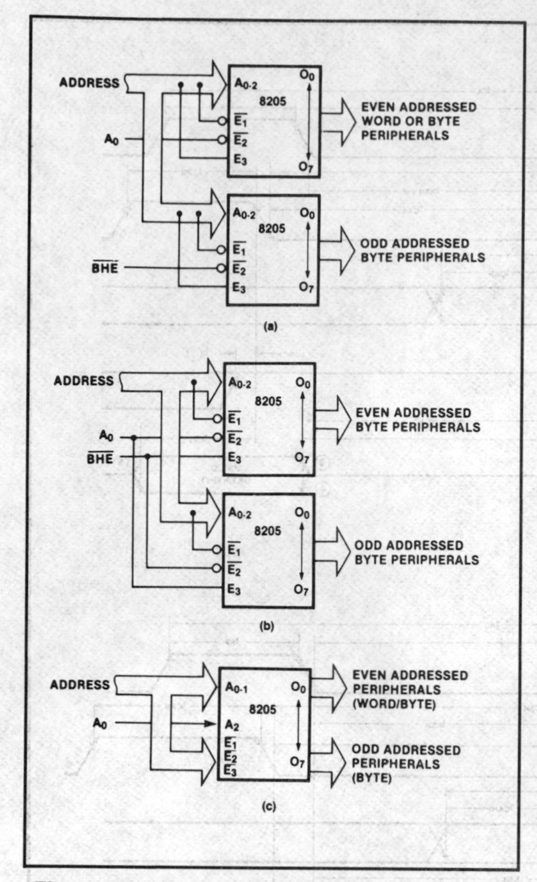

Figure 1-54 I/O Device Chip Select Techniques

The bipolar PROMs are slightly slower than multiple levels of TTL (50 ns versus 30 to 40 ns for TTL) but provide full decoding in a single package and allow inserting a

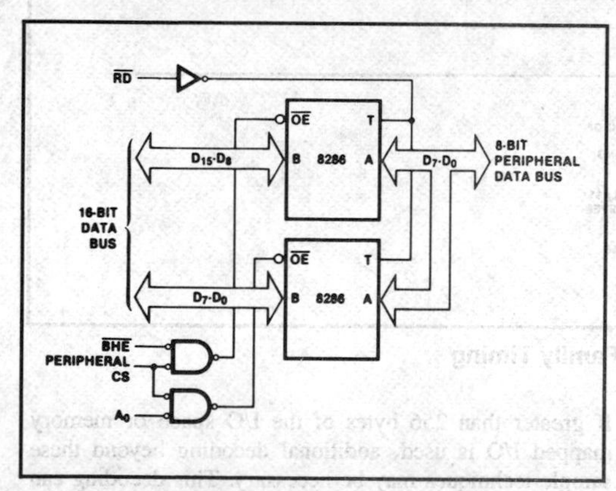

Figure 1-55 16-bit to 8-bit Bus Conversion

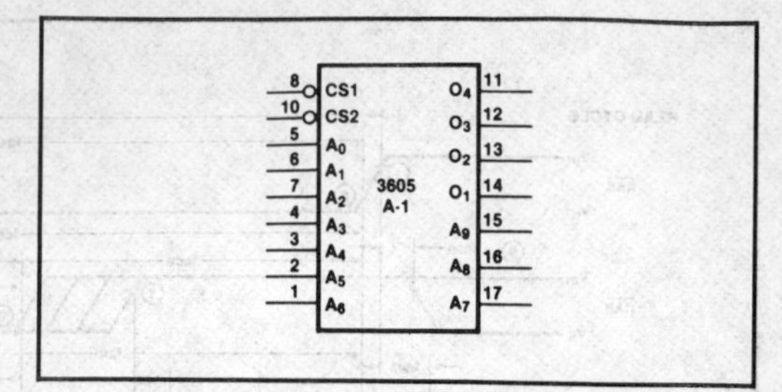

Figure 1-56 Bipolar PROM Decoder

new PROM to reconfigure the system I/O map without circuit board or wiring modifications (see Figure 1-56).

Sixteen-Bit I/O

Sixteen-bit I/O devices should be assigned even addresses for reasons of efficient bus utilization and simplicity of device selection. To guarantee the device is selected only for word operations, A0 and BHE* should be conditions of chip select code (see Figure 1-57).

I/O DEVICE COMPATIBILITY

Compatibility of an I/O device with a microprocessor is always a system design consideration. This section presents a set of A.C. characteristics which represent the timing of the asynchronous bus interface of the 8086. The included equations are expressed in terms of the CPU clock (when applicable). These equations are derived for minimum and maximum modes of the 8086 and they represent the bus characteristics at the CPU. The results can be used to determine I/O device requirements for operation on a single CPU local bus or buffered system bus.

NOTE

These values are not applicable to a MULTIBUS system bus interface. The requirements for a MULTIBUS system bus are available in the MULTIBUS interface specification.

Table 1-35 presents a list of bus parameters, their definition and how they relate to the A.C. characteristics of

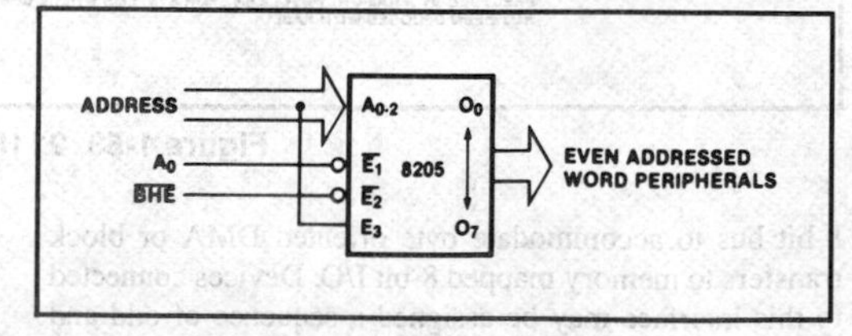

Figure 1-57 16-bit I/O Decode

Table 1-35 Peripheral Compatibility Parameters

Parameter	Equivalent
TAVRL — Address stable before RD leading edge	(TAR)
TRHAX — Address hold after RD trailing edge	(TRA)
TRLRH — Read pulse width	(TRR)
TRLDV — Read to data valid delay	(TRD)
TRHDZ — Read trailing edge to data floating	(TDF)
TAVDV — Address to valid data delay	(TAD)
TRLRL — Read cycle time	(TRCYC)
TAVWL — Address valid before write leading edge	(TAW)
TAVWLA — Address valid before advanced write	(TAW)
TWHAX — Address hold after write trailing edge	(TWA)
TWLWH — Write pulse width	(TWW)
TWLWHA — Advanced write pulse width	(TWW)
TDVWH — Data set up to write trailing edge	(TDW)
TWHDX — Data hold from write trailing edge	(TWD)
TWLCL — Write recovery time	(TRV)
TWLCLA — Advanced write recovery time	(TRV)
TSVRL — Chip select stable before RD leading edge	(TAR)
TRHSX — Chip select hold after RD trailing edge	(TRA)
TSLDV — Chip select to data valid delay	(TRD)
TSVWL — Chip select stable before WR leading edge	(TAW)
TWHSX — Chip select hold after WR trailing edge	(TWA)
TSVWLA — Chip select stable before advanced write	(TAW)

Symbols in parentheses are equivalent parameters specified for Intel peripherals.

Table 1-36 Peripherals Cycle Dependent Parameter Requirements

(a) Minimum Mode
TAVRL = TCLCL + TCLRLmin − TCLAVmax = TCLCL − 100
TRHAX = TCLCL − TCLRHmax + TCLLHmin = TCLCL − 150
TRLRH = 2TCLCL − 60 = 2TCLCL − 60
TRLDV = 2TCLCL − TCLRLmax − TDVCLmin = 2TCLCL − 195
TRHDZ = TRHAVmin = 155 ns
TAVDV = 3TCLCL − TDVCLmin − TCLAVmax = 3TCLCL − 140
TRLRL = 4TCLCL = 4TCLCL
TAVWL = TCLCL + TCVCTVmin − TCLAVmax = TCLCL − 100
TWHAX = TCLCL + TCLLHmin − TCVCTXmax = TCLCL − 110
TWLWH = 2TCLCL − 40 = 2TCLCL − 40
TDVWH = 2TCLCL + TCVCTXmin − TCLDVmax = 2TCLCL − 100
TWHDX = TWHDZmin = 89
TWLCL = 4TCLCL = 4TCLCL
TWHDXB = TCLCHmin + (− TCVCTXmax + TCVCTXmin) = TCLCHmin − 50
Note: Delays relative to chip select are a function of the chip select decode technique used and are equal to: equivalent delay from address − chip select decode delay.

(b) Maximum Mode
TAVRL = TCLCL + TCLMLmin − TCLAVmax = TCLCL − 100
TRHAX = TCLCL − TCLMHmax + TCLLHmin = TCLCL − 40
TRLRH = 2TCLCL − TCLMLmax + TCLMHmin = 2TCLCL − 25
TRLDV = 2TCLCL − TCLMLmax − TDVCLmin = 2TCLCL − 65
TRHDZ = TRHAVmin = 155
TAVDV = 3TCLCL − TDVCLmin − TCLAVmax = 3TCLCL − 140
TRLRL = 4TCLCL = 4TCLCL
TAVWLA = TAVRL = TCLCL − 100
TAVWL = TAVRL + TCLCL = 2TCLCL − 100
TWHAX = TRHAX = TCLCL − 40
TWLWHA = TRLRH = 2TCLCL − 25
TWLWH = TRLRH − TCLCL = TCLCL − 25
TDVWH = 2TCLCL + TCLMHmin − TCLDVmax = 2TCLCL − 100
TWHDX = TCLCHmin − TCLMHmax + TCHDZmin = TCLCHmin − 30
TWLCL = 3TCLCL = 3TCLCL
TWLCLA = 4TCLCL = 4TCLCL

Intel peripherals. Table 1-36 presents Cycle dependent values of the parameters. For each equation, if more than one signal path is involved, the equation reflects the worst case path. For example:

TAVRL (address valid before read active) =
(1) Address from CPU to RD* active
(2) ALE (to enable the address through the address latches) to RD* active

The worst case delay path is (1).

For maximum mode 8086 configurations, TAVWLA, TWLWHA and TWLCLA relate to the advanced write signal while TAVWL, TWLWH and TWLCL relate to the normal write signal.

In the given list of equations, TWHDXB represents the data hold time from the trailing edge of write for the minimum mode with a buffered data bus. For this equation, TCVCTX cannot be a minimum for data hold and a maximum for write inactive. The maximum difference is 50 ns giving the result TCLCH-50. If the reader wishes to verify the equations or derive others, refer to the index under "Bus Timing" for assistance with interpreting the 8086 bus timing diagrams.

Figure 1-58 shows four representative configurations and the compatible Intel peripherals (including wait states if required) for each configuration given in Table 1-37. Configuration 1 and 2 consist of minimum mode demultiplexed bus 8086 systems without (1) and with (2) data bus transceivers. Configurations 3 and 4 consist of maximum mode systems with one (3) and two (4) levels of address and data buffering. The last configuration is characteristic of a multi-board system with bus buffers on each board. The 5 MHz parameter values for these configurations (refer to Table 1-38) demonstrate the relaxed device requirements for even a large complex configuration. The analysis assumes all components are exhibiting the specified worst case parameter values under the corresponding temperature, voltage and capacitive load conditions. If the capacitive loading on the 8282/83 or 8286/87 is less than the maximum, refer to the graphs of delay versus capacitive loading in the respective data sheets to determine the appropriate delay values.

To determine peripheral compatibility, modify the equations given for the CPU to account for additional delays from address latches and data transceivers in the configuration. Once the system configuration is selected, determine the system requirements at the peripheral interface and use the results to evaluate compatibility of the peripheral to the system. During this process, consider: (1) can the device operate at maximum bus bandwidth and if not, how many wait states are required, and (2) are there any problems that cannot be resolved by wait states.

Examples of the first consideration include TRLRH (read pulse width) and TRLDV (read access or RD* active to output data valid). Consider address access time (valid address to valid data) for the maximum mode fully buffered configuration:

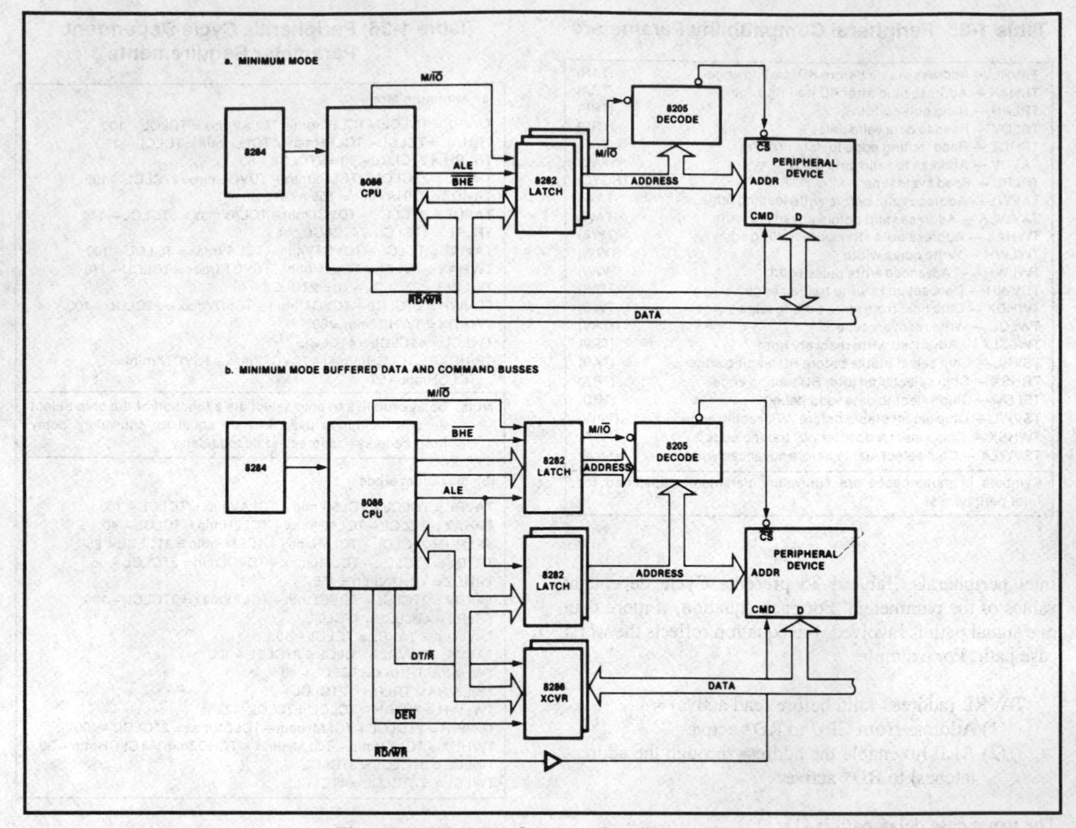

Figure 1-58 8086 System Configurations

TAVDV = 3TCYC − 140 ns − address latch delay − address buffer delay − chip select decode delay − 2 transceiver delays

Table 1-37 Compatible Peripherals for a 5 MHz 8086/88

	Configuration			
	Minimum Mode		Maximum Mode	
	Unbuffered	Buffered	Buffered	Fully Buffered
8251A	✓	1W	✓	✓
8253-5	✓	1W	✓	✓
8255A-5	✓	1W	✓	✓
8257-5	✓	1W	✓	✓
8259A	✓	✓	✓	✓
8271	✓	1W	✓	✓
8273	✓	1W	✓	✓
8275	✓	1W	✓	✓
8279-5	✓	1W	✓	✓
8041A*	✓	1W	✓	✓
8741A	✓	1W	✓	✓
8291	✓	✓	✓	✓

*Includes other Intel peripherals based on the 8041A (i.e., 8292, 8294, 8295).

✓ implies full operation with no wait states.
W implies the number of wait states required.

Assuming inverting latches, buffers and transceivers with 22 ns max delays (8283, 8287) and a bipolar PROM decode with 50 ns delay, the result is:

TAVDV = 322 ns @ 5 MHz

This result gives the address to data valid delay required at the peripheral (in this configuration) to satisfy zero wait state CPU access time. If the maximum delay specified for the peripheral is less than the result, this parameter is compatible with zero wait state CPU operation. If not, wait states must be inserted until TAVDV + n * TCYC (n is the number of wait states) is greater than the peripherals maximum delay. If several parameters require wait states, either the largest number required should always be used or different transfer cycles can insert the maximum number required for that cycle.

The second consideration includes TAVRL (address set up to read) and TWHDX (data hold after write). Incompatibilities in this area cannot be resolved by the insertion of wait states and may require either additional hardware, slowing down the CPU (if the parameter is related to the

Table 1-38 Peripheral Requirements for Full Speed Operation with a 5 MHz 8086/88

	Configuration			
	Minimum Mode		Maximum Mode	
	Unbuffered	Buffered	Buffered	Fully Buffered
TAVRL	70	72	70	58
TRHAX	57	27	169	141
TRLRH	340	320	375	347
TRLDV	205	150	305	261
TRHDZ	155	158	382	360
TAVDV	430	400	400	372
TRLRL	800	770	800	772
TAVWL	70	72	270	258
TAVWLA	—	—	70	58
TWHAX	97	67	169	141
TWLWH	360	340	175	147
TWLWHA	—	—	375	347
TDVWH	300	339	270	258
TWHDX	88	15	95	13
TWLCL	800	772	600	572
TWLCLA	—	—	800	772
TSVRL	52	54	52	40
TRHSX	50	50	171	143
TSLDV	412	382	382	354
TSVWL	52	54	252	240
TWHSX	90	90	171	143
TSVWLA	—	—	52	40

— Not applicable.

clock) or not using the device. As an example, consider address valid prior to advanced write lower (TAVWLA) for the maximum mode fully buffered:

TAVWLA = TCYC − 100 ns − address latch delay − address buffer delay − chip select decode delay + write buffer delay (minimum)

Assuming inverting latches and buffers with 22 ns delay (8283/8287) and an 8205 address decoder with 18 ns delay:

TAVWLA = 38 ns which is the time a 5 MHz 8086 system provides.

Multiple Communications Lines Example

Consider an interrupt drive procedure for handling multiple communications lines. On receiving an interrupt from one of the lines, the invoked procedure polls the lines (reading the status of each) to determine which line to service. The procedure does not enable lines but simply services input and output requests until the associated output buffer is empty (for output requests) or until an input line is terminated (for the example, only EOT is considered). On detection of the terminate condition, the routine will disable the line. It is assumed that other routines will fill a lines output buffer and enable the device to request output or empty the input buffer and enable the device to input additional characters.

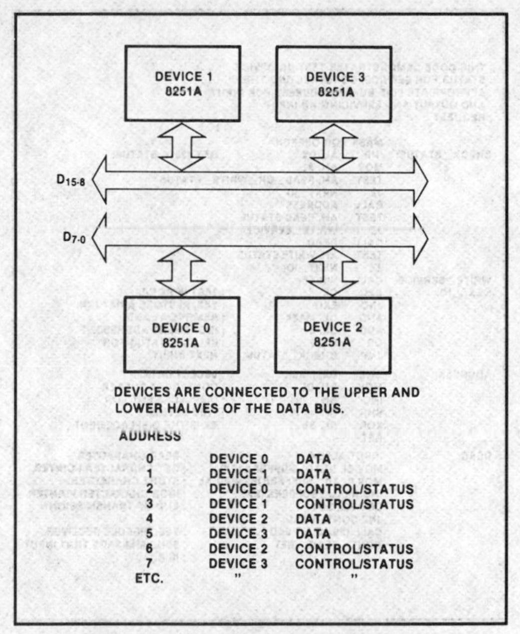

Figure 1-59 Device Assignment

The routine begins operation by loading CX with a count of the number of lines in the system and DX with the I/O address of the first line. The I/O addresses are designed with 8251's as the I/O devices (see Figure 1-59). The status of each line is read to determine if it needs service. If yes, the appropriate routine is called to input or output a character. After servicing the line or if no service is needed, CX is decremented and DX is incremented to test the next line. After all lines have been tested and serviced, the routine terminates. If all interrupts from the lines are OR'd together, only one interrupt is used for all lines. If the interrupt is input to the CPU through an 8259A interrupt controller, the 8259A should be programmed in the level triggered mode to guarantee all line interrupts are serviced.

To service either an input or an output request (see Figure 1-60), the called routine transfers DX to BX, and shifts BX to form the offset for this device into the table of input or output buffers. The first entry in the buffer is an index to the next character position in the buffer and is loaded into the SI register. By specifying the base address of the table of buffers as a displacement into the data segment, the base + index + displacement addressing mode allows direct access to the appropriate memory location.

Memory – I/O Block Transfers Example

The memory mapped I/O and the 8086 string primitive instructions may be used to perform block transfers between memory and I/O. By assigning a block of the

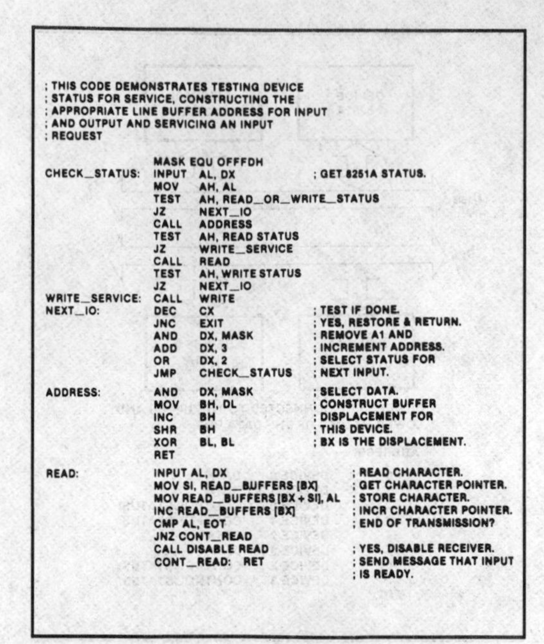

```
; THIS CODE DEMONSTRATES TESTING DEVICE
; STATUS FOR SERVICE, CONSTRUCTING THE
; APPROPRIATE LINE BUFFER ADDRESS FOR INPUT
; AND OUTPUT AND SERVICING AN INPUT
; REQUEST

                MASK EQU OFFFDH
CHECK_STATUS:   INPUT   AL, DX                  ; GET 8251A STATUS.
                MOV     AH, AL
                TEST    AH, READ_OR_WRITE_STATUS
                JZ      NEXT_IO
                CALL    ADDRESS
                TEST    AH, READ STATUS
                JZ      WRITE_SERVICE
                CALL    READ
                TEST    AH, WRITE STATUS
                JZ      NEXT_IO
WRITE_SERVICE:  CALL    WRITE
NEXT_IO:        DEC     CX                      ; TEST IF DONE.
                JNC     EXIT                    ; YES, RESTORE & RETURN.
                AND     DX, MASK                ; REMOVE A1 AND
                ADD     DX, 3                   ; INCREMENT ADDRESS.
                OR      DX, 2                   ; SELECT STATUS FOR
                JMP     CHECK_STATUS            ; NEXT INPUT.
ADDRESS:        AND     DX, MASK                ; SELECT DATA.
                MOV     BH, DL                  ; CONSTRUCT BUFFER
                INC     BH                      ; DISPLACEMENT FOR
                SHR     BH                      ; THIS DEVICE.
                XOR     BL, BL                  ; BX IS THE DISPLACEMENT.
                RET
READ:           INPUT AL, DX                    ; READ CHARACTER.
                MOV SI, READ_BUFFERS [BX]       ; GET CHARACTER POINTER.
                MOV READ_BUFFERS [BX + SI], AL  ; STORE CHARACTER.
                INC READ_BUFFERS [BX]           ; INCR CHARACTER POINTER.
                CMP AL, EOT                     ; END OF TRANSMISSION?
                JNZ CONT_READ
                CALL DISABLE READ               ; YES, DISABLE RECEIVER.
                CONT_READ:  RET                 ; SEND MESSAGE THAT INPUT
                                                ; IS READY.
```

Figure 1-60 I/O Input Request Code Example

memory address space (equivalent in size to the maximum block to be transferred to the I/O device) and decoding this address space to generate the I/O device's chip select, the block transfer capability is easily implemented. Figure 1-61 gives an interconnect for 16-bit I/O devices while Figure 1-62 incorporates the 16-bit bus to 8-bit bus multiplexing scheme to support 8-bit I/O devices. A code example to perform such a transfer is shown in Figure 1-63.

1.4.5 System Design Alternatives

Two implementation alternatives must be considered when referring to the system data bus: 1) the multiplexed address/data bus (see Figure 1-64); and 2) a data bus buffered from the multiplexed bus by transceivers (see Figure 1-65).

If memory or I/O devices are connected directly to the multiplexed bus, the designer must guarantee the devices do not corrupt the address on the bus during T1. To avoid this, device output drivers should not be enabled by the device chip select. They should have an output enable controlled by the system read signal (see Figure 1-66). The 8086 timing guarantees that read is not valid until the address is latched by ALE (see Figure 1-67). All Intel peripherals, EPROM products, and RAM's for microprocessors provide output enable or read inputs to allow connection to the multiplexed bus.

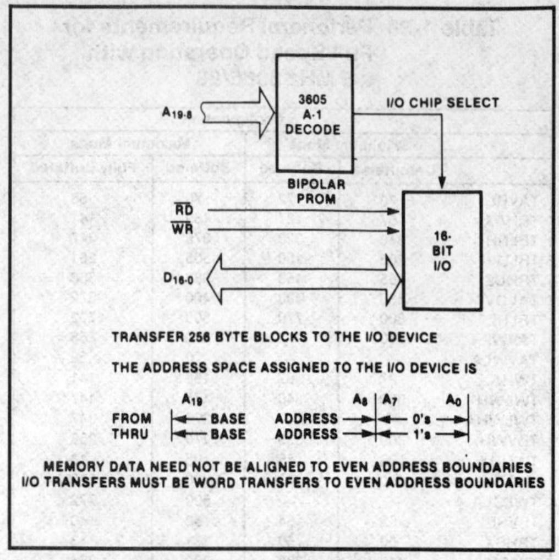

Figure 1-61 Block Transfer to 16-bit I/O Using 8086/88 String Primitives

There are several techniques available for interfacing devices without output enables to the multiplexed bus. Note that each of these techniques introduces other restrictions or limitations. Consider the case of chip select gated with read and write (see Figure 1-68). Two problems exist with this technique. First, the chip select access time is reduced to the read access time, and may require a faster

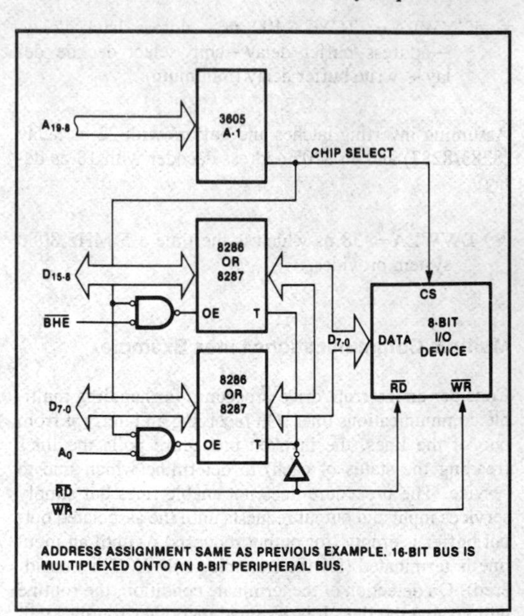

Figure 1-62 Block Transfer to 8-bit I/O Using 8086/88 String Primitives

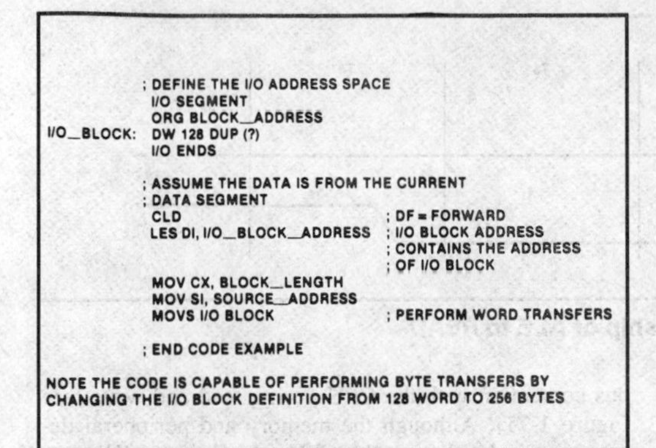

```
            ; DEFINE THE I/O ADDRESS SPACE
            I/O SEGMENT
            ORG BLOCK_ADDRESS
I/O_BLOCK:  DW 128 DUP (?)
            I/O ENDS

            ; ASSUME THE DATA IS FROM THE CURRENT
            ; DATA SEGMENT
            CLD                            ; DF = FORWARD
            LES DI, I/O_BLOCK_ADDRESS      ; I/O BLOCK ADDRESS
                                           ; CONTAINS THE ADDRESS
                                           ; OF I/O BLOCK
            MOV CX, BLOCK_LENGTH
            MOV SI, SOURCE_ADDRESS
            MOVS I/O BLOCK                 ; PERFORM WORD TRANSFERS

            ; END CODE EXAMPLE

NOTE THE CODE IS CAPABLE OF PERFORMING BYTE TRANSFERS BY
CHANGING THE I/O BLOCK DEFINITION FROM 128 WORD TO 256 BYTES
```

Figure 1-63 Code For Block Transfers

device if maximum system performance (i.e., no wait states) is to be achieved (see Figure 1-69). Second, the designer must verify that the chip select-to-write setup and hold times for the device are not violated (see Figure 1-70). Alternate techniques can be extracted from the bus interfacing techniques, also described in this chapter, but are subject to the associated restrictions. In general, for best results, use devices with output enables.

To guarantee the specified A.C. characteristics, the 8086's drive capability of 2.0 mA and capacitive loading of 100 pF subsequently limits the fan out of the multiplexed bus. Assuming capacitive loads of 20 pF per I/O device, 12 pF per address latch and 5-12 pF per memory device, a system mix of three peripherals and two to four memory devices (per bus line) approach the loading limit.

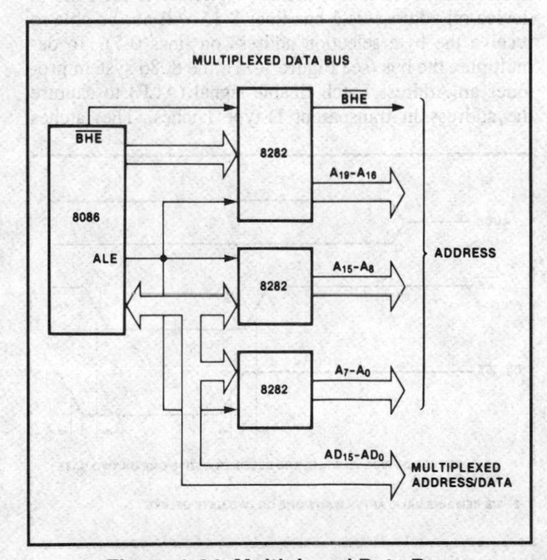

Figure 1-64 Multiplexed Data Bus

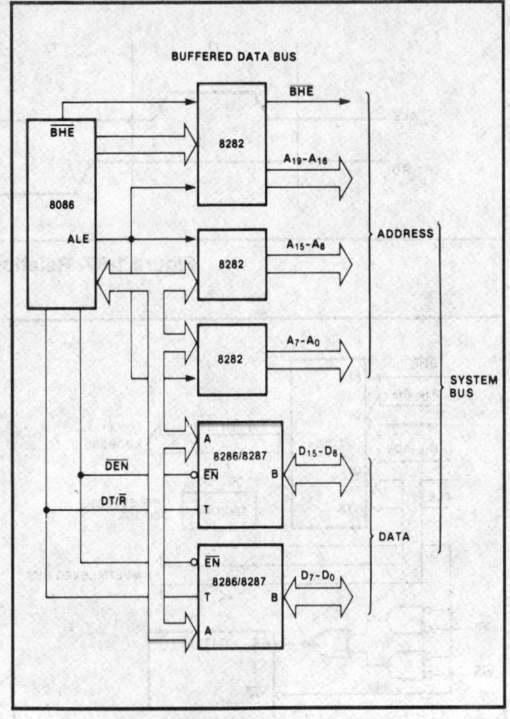

Figure 1-65 Buffered Data Bus

The data bus must be buffered using inverting or non-inverting octal buffers to satisfy the capacitive loading and drive requirements of larger systems. To enable and control the direction of the transceivers, the 8086 provides Data Enable (DEN) and Data Transmit/Receive (DT/R*) signals (see Figure 1-65). These signals provide the appropriate timing to guarantee isolation of the multiplexed bus from the system during T1 and elimination of

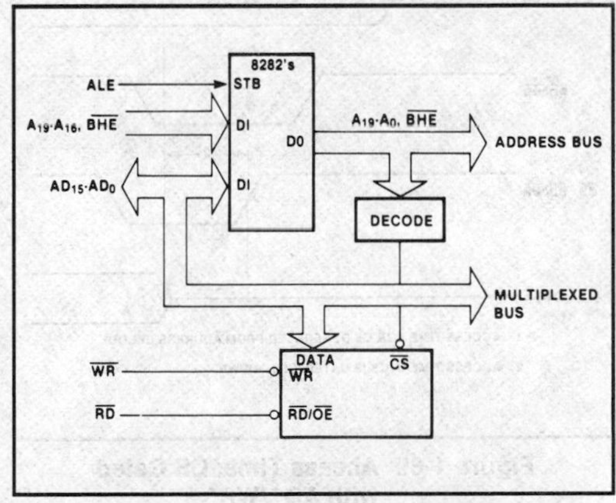

Figure 1-66 Devices With Output Enable on the Multiplexed Bus

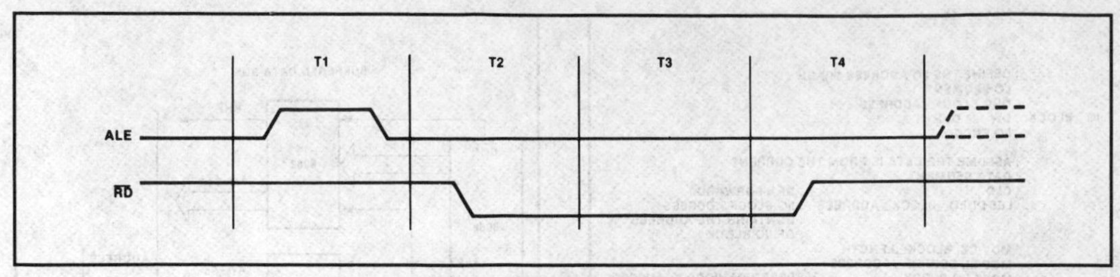

Figure 1-67 Relationship of ALE to READ

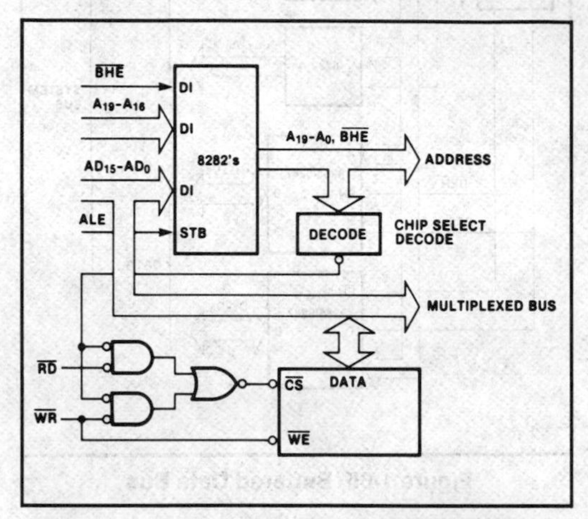

Figure 1-68 Devices Without Output Enable on the Multiplexed Bus

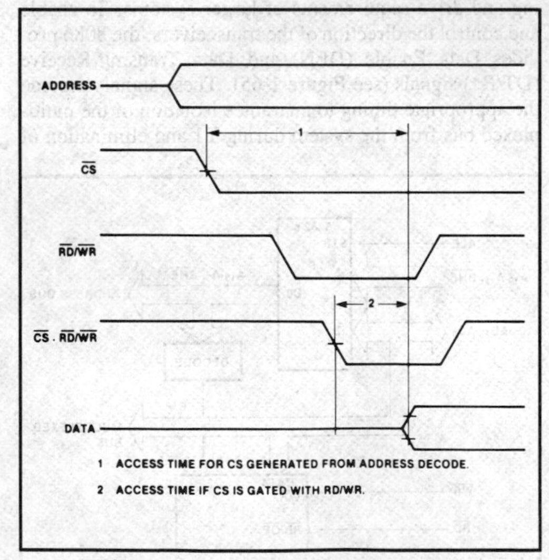

Figure 1-69 Access Time: CS Gated with AD*/WR*

bus contention with the CPU during read and write (see Figure 1-71). Although the memory and peripheral devices are isolated from the CPU (see Figure 1-72), bus contention may still exist in the system if the devices do not have an output enable control other than chip select. As an example, bus contention will exist during transition from one chip select to another (the newly selected device begins driving the bus before the previous device has disabled its drivers). Another, more severe case exists during a write cycle: from chip select to write active, a device whose outputs are controlled only by chip select, will drive the bus simultaneously with write data being driven through the transceivers by the CPU (see Figure 1-73). The same technique given for circumventing these problems on the multiplexed bus can be applied here with the same limitations.

Since the majority of system memories and peripherals require a stable address for the duration of the bus cycle, the address on the multiplexed address/data bus during T1 should be latched and the latched address used to select the desired peripheral or memory location. Since the 8086 has a 16-bit data bus, the multiplexed bus components of the 8085 family are not applicable to the 8086 (a device on address/data bus lines 8-15 will not be able to receive the byte selection address on lines 0-7). To demultiplex the bus (see Figure 1-74), the 8086 system provides an Address Latch Enable signal (ALE) to capture the address in transparent D-type latches. The latches

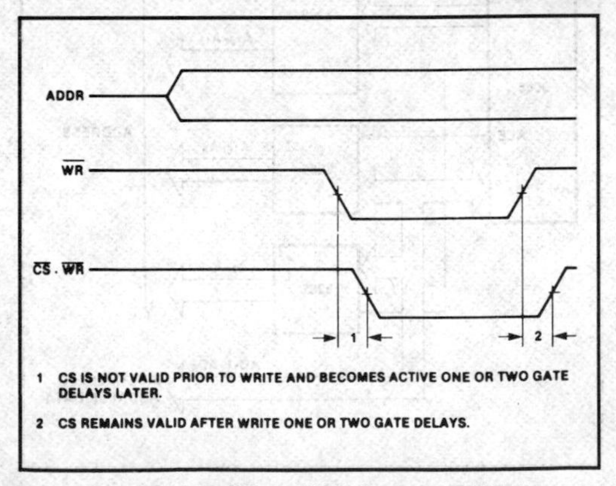

Figure 1-70 CE to WR* Setup and Hole

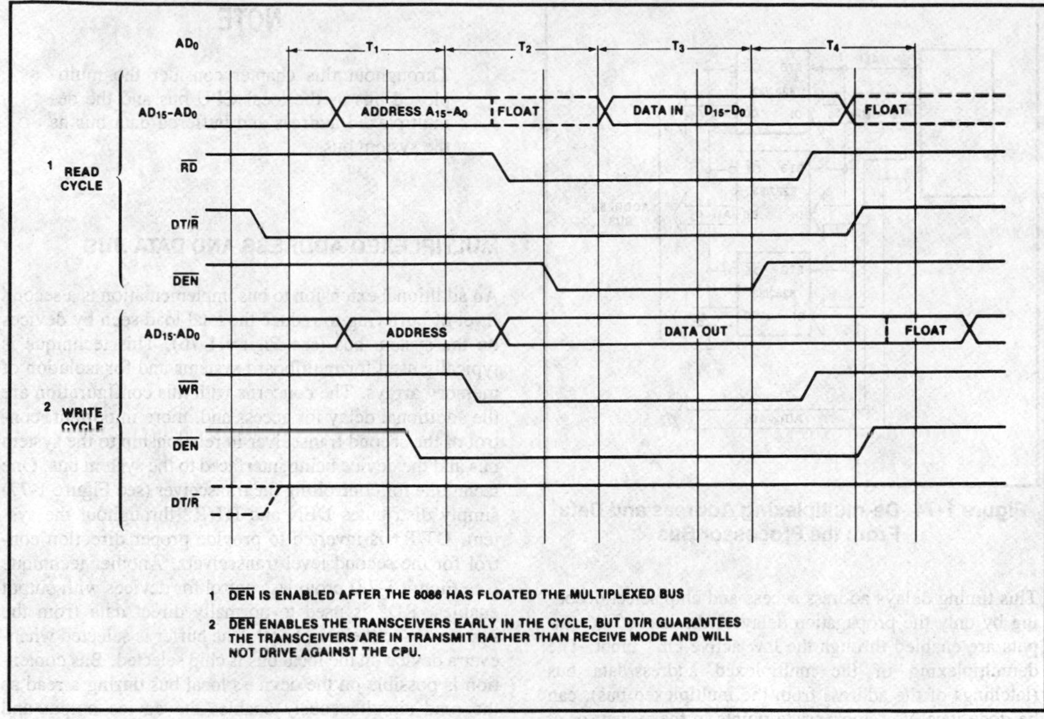

Figure 1-71 Bus Transceiver Control

may be either inverting or non-inverting. These devices propagate the address through to the outputs while ALE is high and latch the address on the falling edge of ALE.

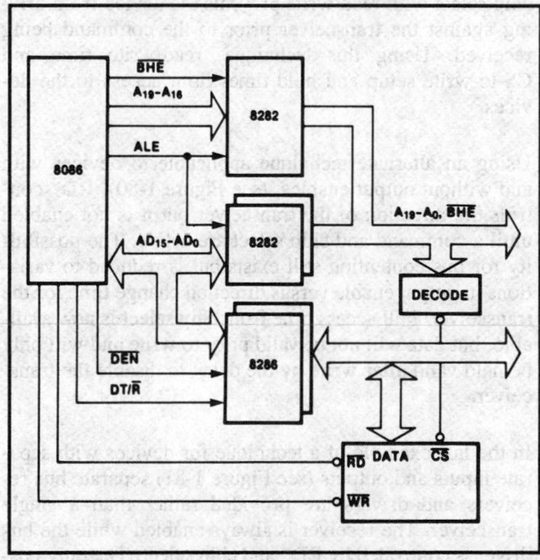

Figure 1-72 Devices With Output Enable on the System Bus

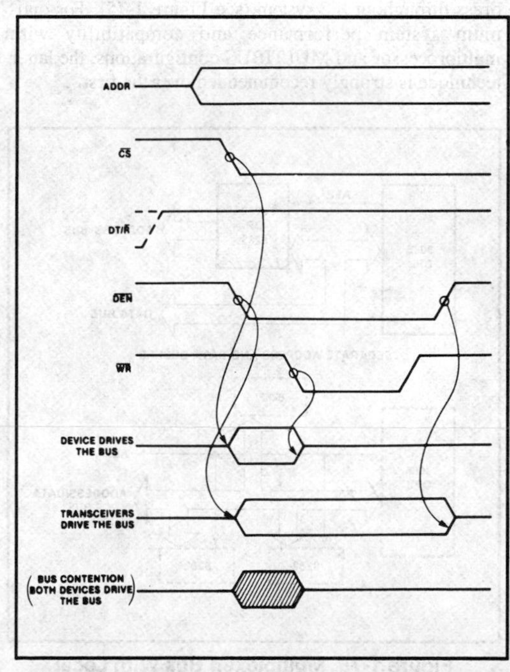

Figure 1-73 CS*/Bus Driving Device Timing

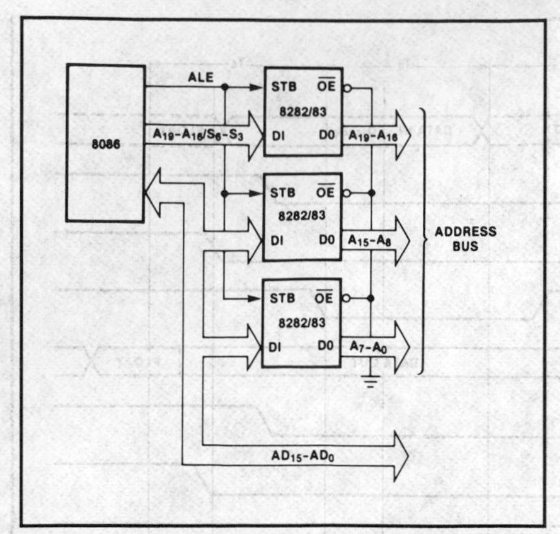

Figure 1-74 De-multiplexing Address and Data From the Processor Bus

This timing delays address access and chip select decoding by only the propagation delay of the latch. The outputs are enabled through the low active OE* input. The demultiplexing of the multiplexed address/data bus (latchings of the address from the multiplexed bus), can be done locally at appropriate points in the system or at the CPU with a separate address bus distributing the address throughout the system (see Figure 1-75). For optimum system performance and compatibility with multiprocessor and MULTIBUS configurations, the latter technique is strongly recommended over the first.

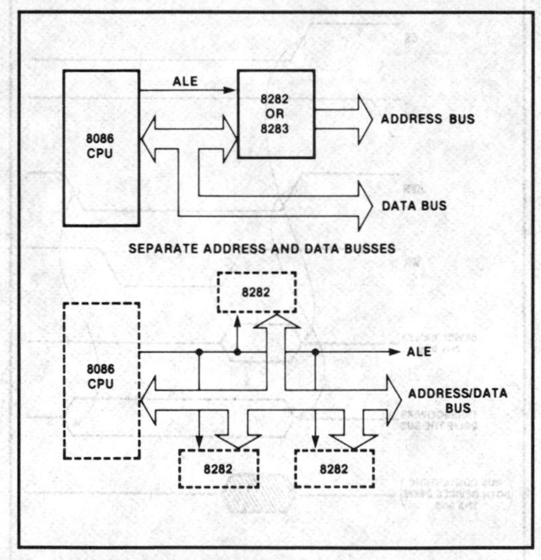

Figure 1-75 Multiplexed Bus With Local Address Demultiplexing

NOTE

Throughout this chapter consider the multiplexed bus as the local CPU bus and the demultiplexed address and buffered data bus as the system bus.

MULTIPLEXED ADDRESS AND DATA BUS

An additional extension to bus implementation is a second level of buffering to reduce the total load seen by devices on the system bus (see Figure 1-76). This technique is typically used for multiboard systems and for isolation of memory arrays. The concerns with this configuration are the additional delay for access and, more important, control of the second transceiver in relationship to the system bus and the device being interfaced to the system bus. One technique for controlling the transceiver (see Figure 1-77) simply distributes DEN and DT/R* throughout the system. DT/R* is inverted to provide proper direction control for the second level transceivers. Another technique (see Figure 1-78) provides control for devices with output enables. RD* is used to normally direct data from the system bus to the peripheral. The buffer is selected whenever a device on the local bus is chip selected. Bus contention is possible on the device's local bus during a read as the read simultaneously enables the device output and changes the transceiver direction. Contention may also occur as the read is terminated.

For devices without output enables, the same technique can be applied (see Figure 1-79) if the chip select to the device is conditioned by read or write. Controlling the chip select with read/write prevents the device from driving against the transceiver prior to the command being received. Using this technique, read/write time and CS-to-write setup and hold times limit access to the devices.

Using an alternate technique applicable to devices with and without output enables, (see Figure 1-80). RD* controls the direction of the transceiver but it is not enabled until a command and chip select are active. The possibility for bus contention still exists but is reduced to variations in output enable versus direction change time for the transceiver. Full access time from chip select is now available, but data will not be valid prior to write and will only be held valid after write by the delay to disable the transceiver.

In the last example of a technique for devices with separate inputs and outputs (see Figure 1-81) separate bus receivers and drivers are provided rather than a single transceiver. The receiver is always enabled while the bus driver is controlled by RD* and chip select. The only possibility for bus contention in this system occurs as multiple devices during chip selection changes.

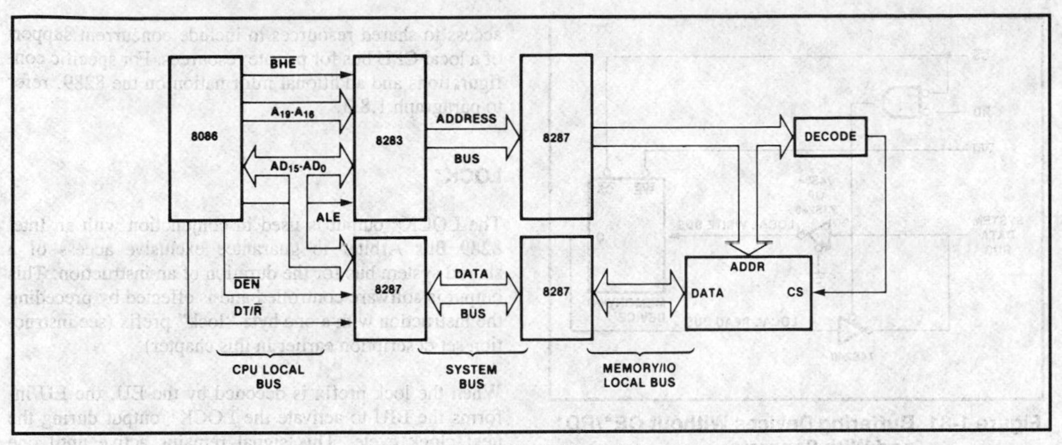

Figure 1-76 Fully Buffered System

1.4.6 Multiprocessor/Coprocessor Applications

The 8086 architecture supports multiprocessor systems based on the concept of a shared system bus (see Figure 1-82). All CPU's in the system communicate with each other and share resources using the system bus. The bus may be either the Intel MULTIBUS system bus or an extension of the system bus. Arbitration logic consists of the major addition required to the demultiplexed system bus

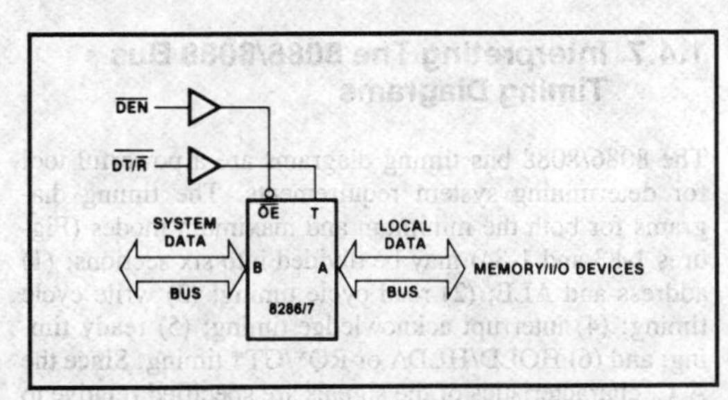

Figure 1-77 Controlling System Transceivers with DEN and DT/R*

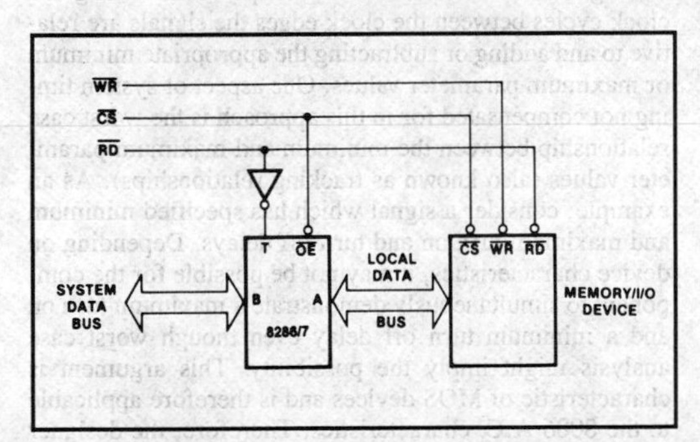

Figure 1-78 Buffering Devices with OE*/RD*

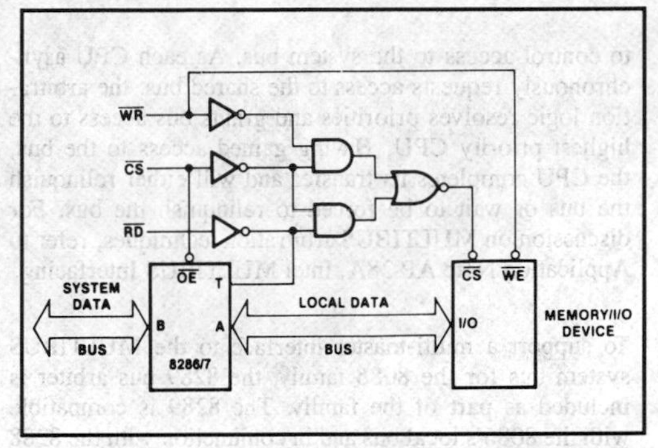

Figure 1-79 Buffering Devices Without OE*/RD* and With Common or Separate Input/Output

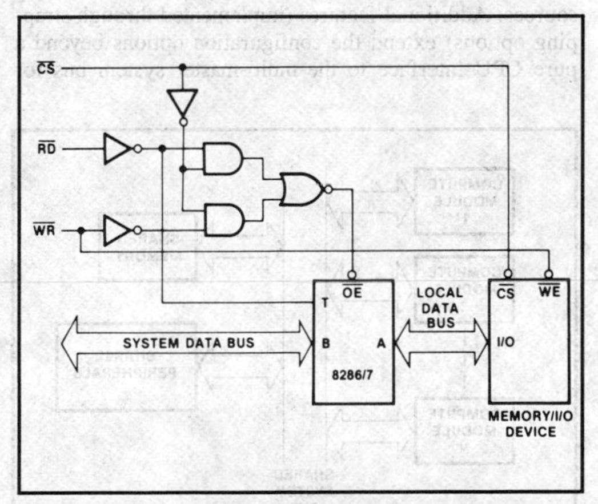

Figure 1-80 Buffering Devices Without OE*/RD* and With Common or Separate Input/Output

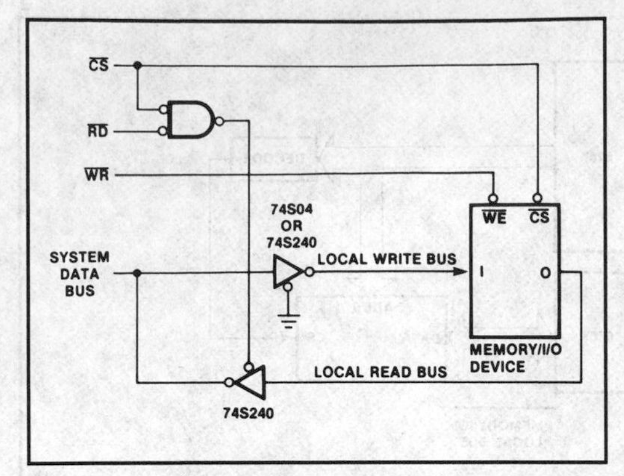

Figure 1-81 Buffering Devices Without OE*/RD* and With Separate Input/Output

to control access to the system bus. As each CPU asynchronously requests access to the shared bus, the arbitration logic resolves priorities and grants bus access to the highest priority CPU. Having gained access to the bus, the CPU completes its transfer and will either relinquish the bus or wait to be forced to relinquish the bus. For discussion on MULTIBUS arbitration techniques, refer to Application Note AP-28A, Intel MULTIBUS Interfacing.

To support a multi-master interface to the MULTIBUS system bus for the 8086 family, the 8289 bus arbiter is included as part of the family. The 8289 is compatible with the 8086's local bus and in conjunction with the 8288 bus controller, implements the MULTIBUS protocol for bus arbitration. The 8289 provides a variety of arbitration and prioritization techniques to allow optimization of bus availability, throughput, and utilization of shared resources. Additional features (implemented through strapping options) extend the configuration options beyond a pure CPU interface to the multi-master system bus for

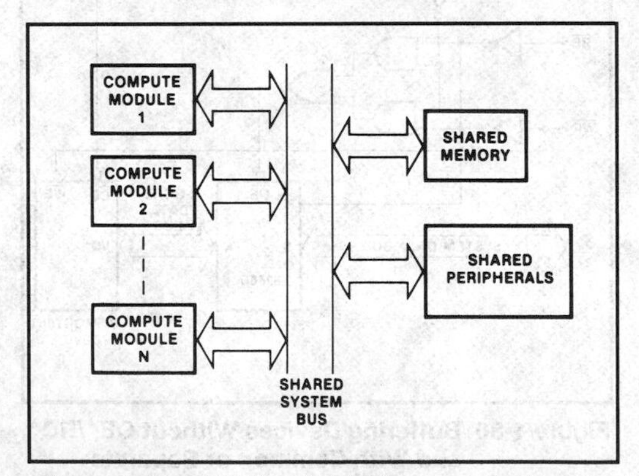

Figure 1-82 8086 Family Multiprocessor System

access to shared resources to include concurrent support of a local CPU bus for private resources. For specific configurations and additional information on the 8289, refer to paragraph 1.8.3.

LOCK*

The LOCK* output is used in conjunction with an Intel 8289 Bus Arbiter to guarantee exclusive access of a shared system bus for the duration of an instruction. This output is software controlled and is effected by preceding the instruction with a one byte "lock" prefix (see instruction set description earlier in this chapter).

When the lock prefix is decoded by the EU, the EU informs the BIU to activate the LOCK* output during the next clock cycle. This signal remains active until one clock cycle after the execution of the associated instruction is concluded.

QS0, QS1

The QS1 and QS0 (Queue Status) outputs permit external monitoring of the CPU's internal instruction queue to allow instruction set extension processing by a coprocessor. (The corresponding Intel ICE modules use these status bits during "trace" operations.) The encoding of the QS1 and QS0 bits is shown in Table 1-39.

1.4.7 Interpreting The 8086/8088 Bus Timing Diagrams

The 8086/8088 bus timing diagrams are a powerful tool for determining system requirements. The timing diagrams for both the minimum and maximum modes (Figures 1-83 and 1-84) may be divided into six sections: (1) address and ALE; (2) read cycle timing; (3) write cycle timing; (4) interrupt acknowledge timing; (5) ready timing; and (6) HOLD/HLDA or RQ*/GT* timing. Since the A.C. characteristics of the signals are specified relative to the CPU clock, the relationship between the majority of the signals can be reduced by simply determining the clock cycles between the clock edges the signals are relative to and adding or subtracting the appropriate minimum or maximum parameter values. One aspect of system timing not compensated for in this approach is the worst case relationship between the minimum and maximum parameter values (also known as tracking relationships). As an example, consider a signal which has specified minimum and maximum turn on and turn off delays. Depending on device characteristics, it may not be possible for the component to simultaneously demonstrate a maximum turn on and a minimum turn off delay even though worst case analysis might imply the possibility. This argument is characteristic of MOS devices and is therefore applicable to the 8086 A.C. characteristics. Therefore, the designer should assume that in worst case analysis mixing mini-

Table 1-39 Queue Status Bit Decoding

QS1	QS0	Queue Status
0 (low)	0	No Operation. During the last clock cycle, nothing was taken from the queue.
0	1	First Byte. The byte taken from the queue was the first byte of the instruction.
1 (high)	0	Queue Empty. The queue has been reinitialized as a result of the execution of a transfer instruction.
1	1	Subsequent Byte. The byte taken from the queue was a subsequent byte of the instruction.

The queue status is valid during the CLK cycle after which the queue operation is performed.

mum and maximum delay parameters will typically exceed the worst case obtainable and should therefore receive further subjective degradation to obtain worst-worst case values. This following paragraphs provide guidelines for specific areas of 8086 timing sensitive to tracking relationships.

MINIMUM MODE BUS TIMING

The minimum mode address and ALE timing relationship determines the ability to capture a valid address from the multiplexed bus. Since the D-type latches capture the address on the trailing edge of ALE, the critical timing involves the state of the address lines when ALE terminates. If the address valid delay is assumed to be maximum TCLAV and ALE terminates at TCHLLmin, its earliest point (assuming zero minimum delay), the address would be valid only if TCLCHmin-TCLAVmax = 8 ns prior to ALE termination. This result is unrealistic in the assumption of maximum TCLAV and minimum TCHLL. To provide an accurate measure of the true worst case, a separate parameter specifies the minimum time for address valid prior to the end of ALE (TAVAL). TAVAL = TCLCH-60 ns overrides the clock related timings and guarantees 58 ns of address setup to ALE termination for a 5 MHz 8086. The address is guaranteed to remain valid beyond the end of ALE by the TLLAX parameter. This specification overrides the relationship between TCHLL and TCLAX which might seem to imply the address may not be valid by the end of the latest possible ALE. TLLAX holds for the entire address bus. The TCLAXmin specification on the address indicates the earliest the bus will go invalid if not restrained by a slow ALE. TLLAX and TCLAX apply to the entire multiplexed bus for both read and write cycles. AD15-0 is tri-stated for read cycles and immediately switched to write data during write cycles. AD19-16 immediately switch from address to status for both read and write cycles. TLHLLmin, which takes precedence over the value obtained by relating TCLLHmax and TCHLLmin, guarantees the minimum ALE pulse width.

To determine the worst case delay-to-valid address on a demultiplexed address bus, two paths are considered: (1) delay of valid address and (2) delay to ALE. Since the D-type latches are flow through devices, a valid address is not transmitted to the address bus until ALE is active. A comparison of address valid delay TCLAVmax with ALE active, delay TCLLHmax indicates TCLAVmax is the worst case. Subtracting the latch propagation delay gives the worst case address bus valid delay from the start of the bus cycle.

Minimum Mode Read Cycle Timing

Read timing consists of conditioning the bus, activating the read command and establishing the data transceiver enable and direction controls. DT/R* is established early in the bus cycle and requires no further consideration. During read, the DEN* signal must allow the transceivers to propagate data to the CPU with the appropriate data setup time and continue to do so until the required data hold time. The DEN* turn on delay allows TCLCL + TCHCLmin − TCVCTV max − TDVCL = 127 ns transceiver enable time prior to valid data required by the CPU. Since the CPU data hold time TCLDXmin and minimum DEN* turnoff delay TCVCTXmin are both 10 ns relative to the same clock edge, the hold time is guaranteed. Additionally, DEN* must disable the transceivers prior to the CPU, redriving the bus with the address for the next bus cycle. The maximum DEN* turn off delay (TCVCTXmax), compared with the minimum delay for addresses out of the 8086 (TCLCL + TCLAVmin), indicates the transceivers are disabled at least 105 ns before the CPU drives the address onto the multiplexed bus.

If memory or I/O devices are connected directly to the multiplexed address and data bus, the TAZRL parameter guarantees the CPU will float the bus before activating read, allowing the selected device to drive the bus. At the end of the bus cycle, the TRHAV parameter specifies the bus float delay the device being deselected must satisfy to avoid contention with the CPU driving the address for the next bus cycle. The next bus cycle may start as soon as the cycle following T4 or any number of clock cycles later.

The minimum delay from read active to valid data at the CPU is 2TCLCL − TCLRLmax − TDVCL = 205 ns. The minimum pulse width is 2TCLCL − 75 ns = 325 ns. This specification (TRLRH) overrides the result which could

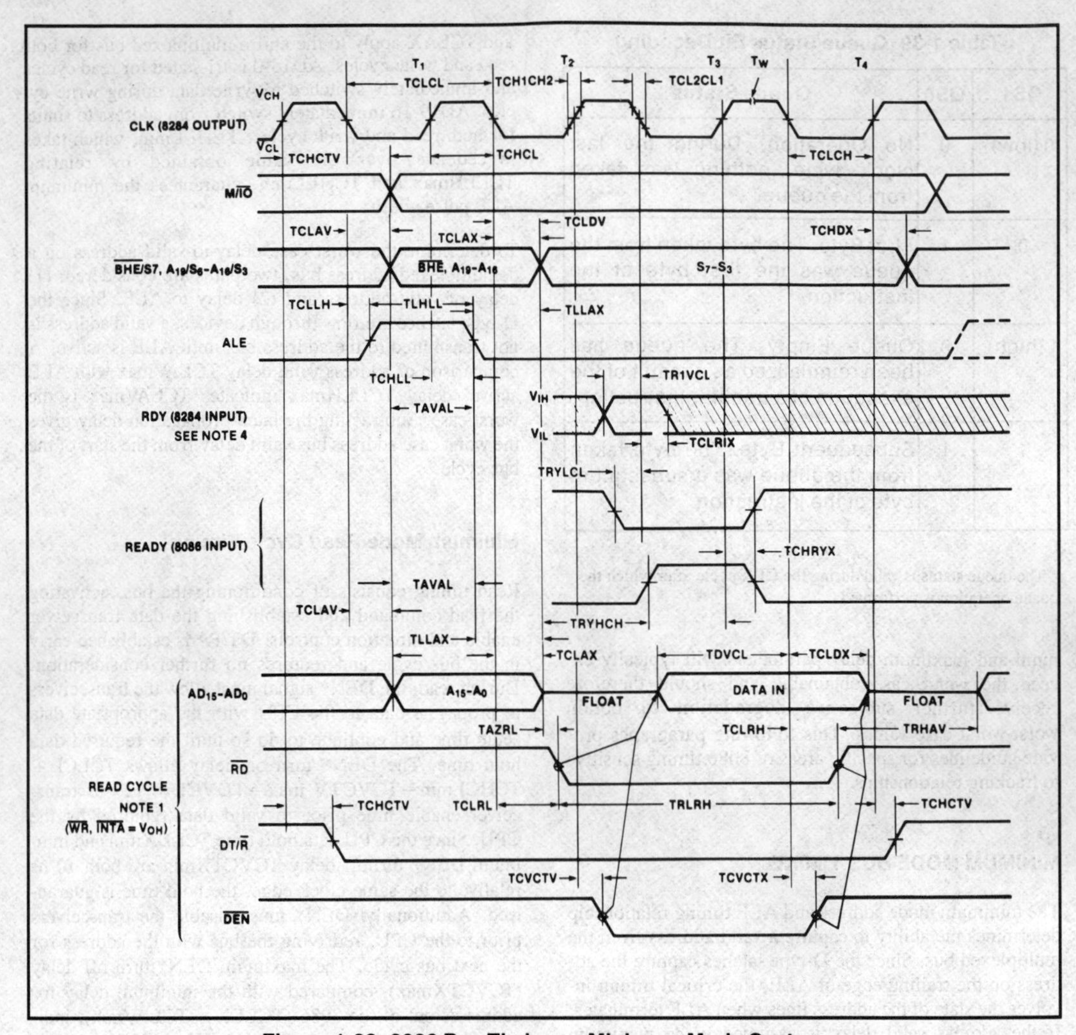

Figure 1-83 8086 Bus Timing — Minimum Mode System

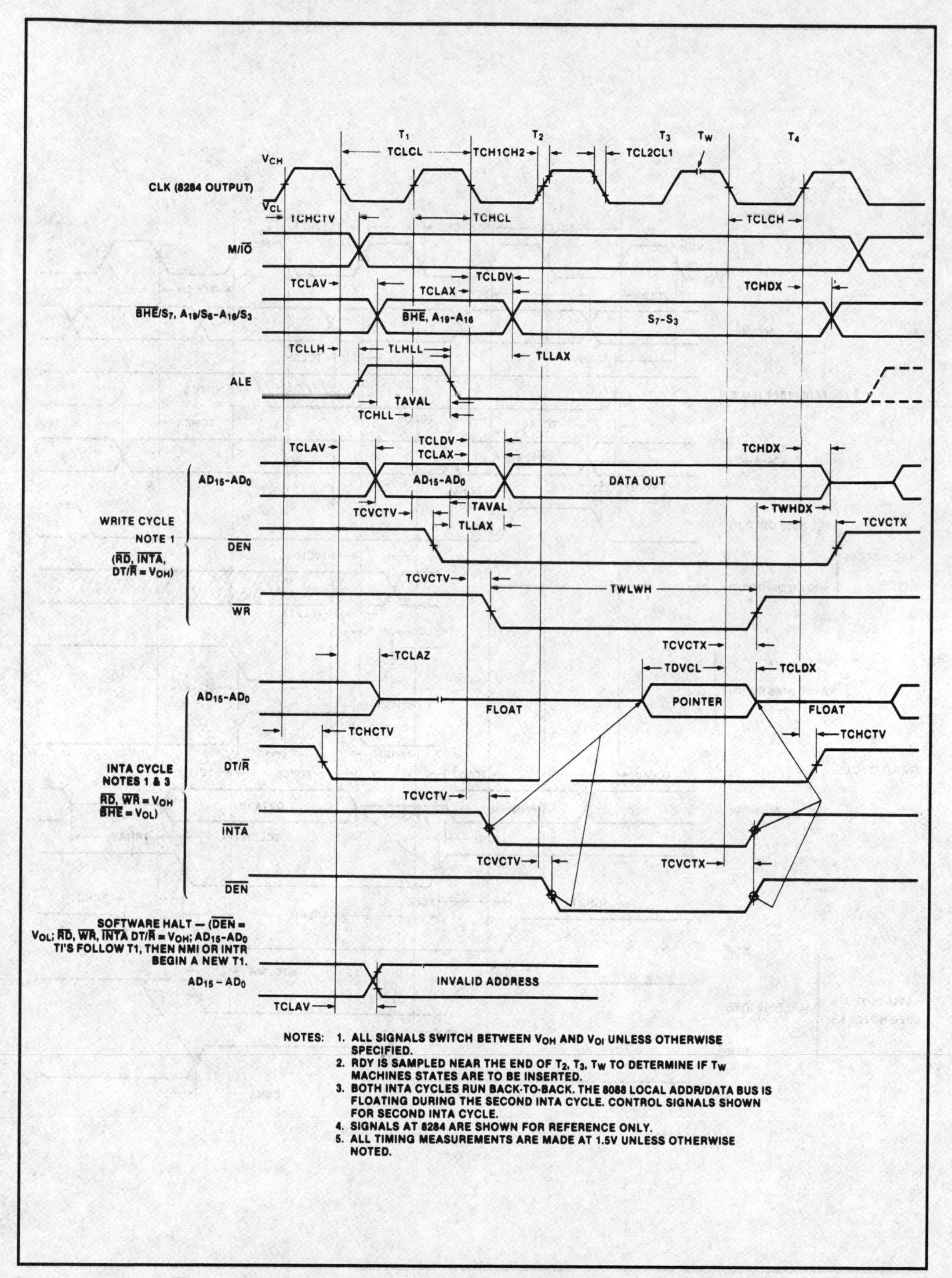

Figure 1-83 8086 Bus Timing — Minimum Mode System (continued)

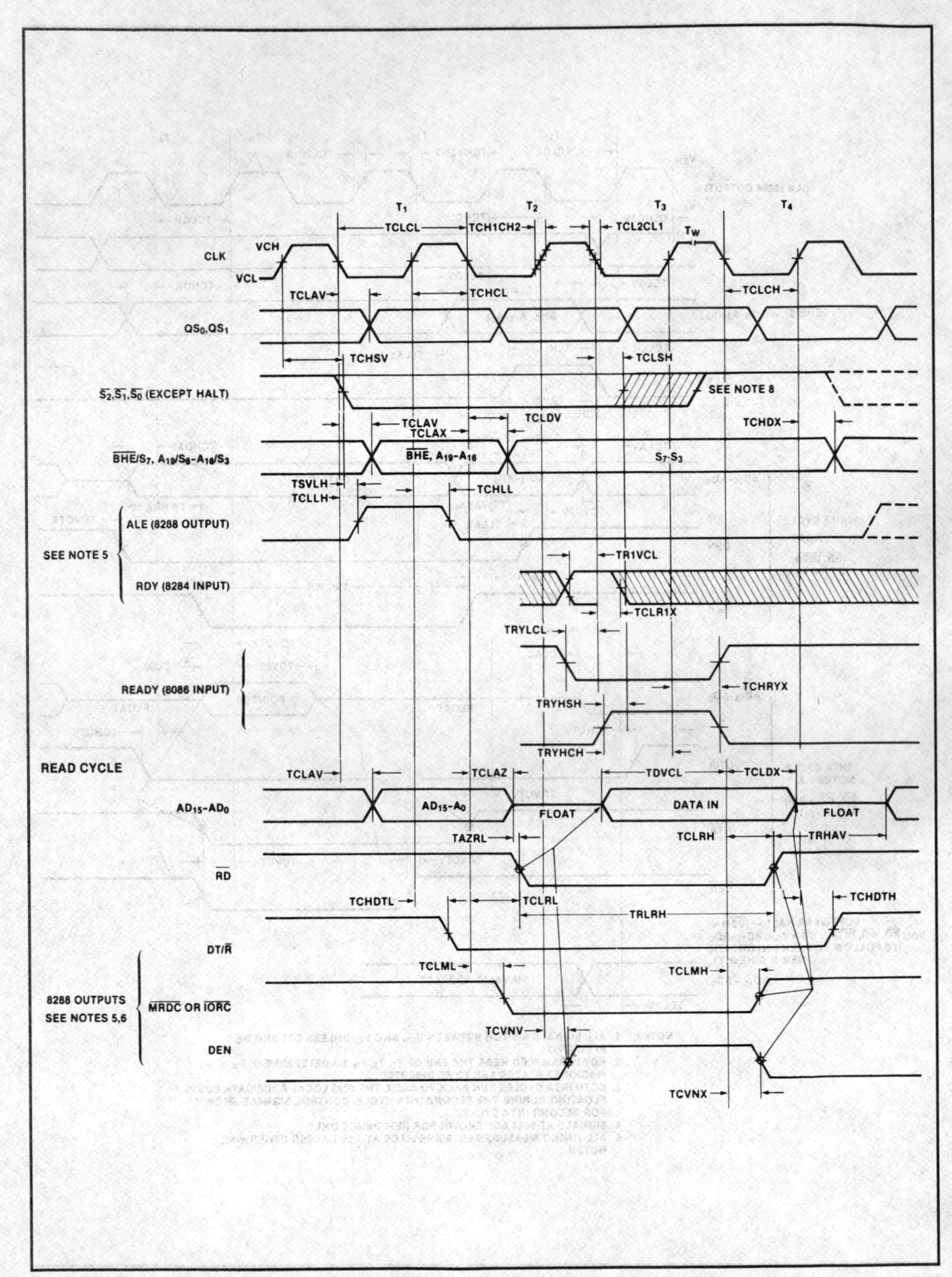

Figure 1-84 8086 Bus Timing — Maximum Mode System (Using 8288)

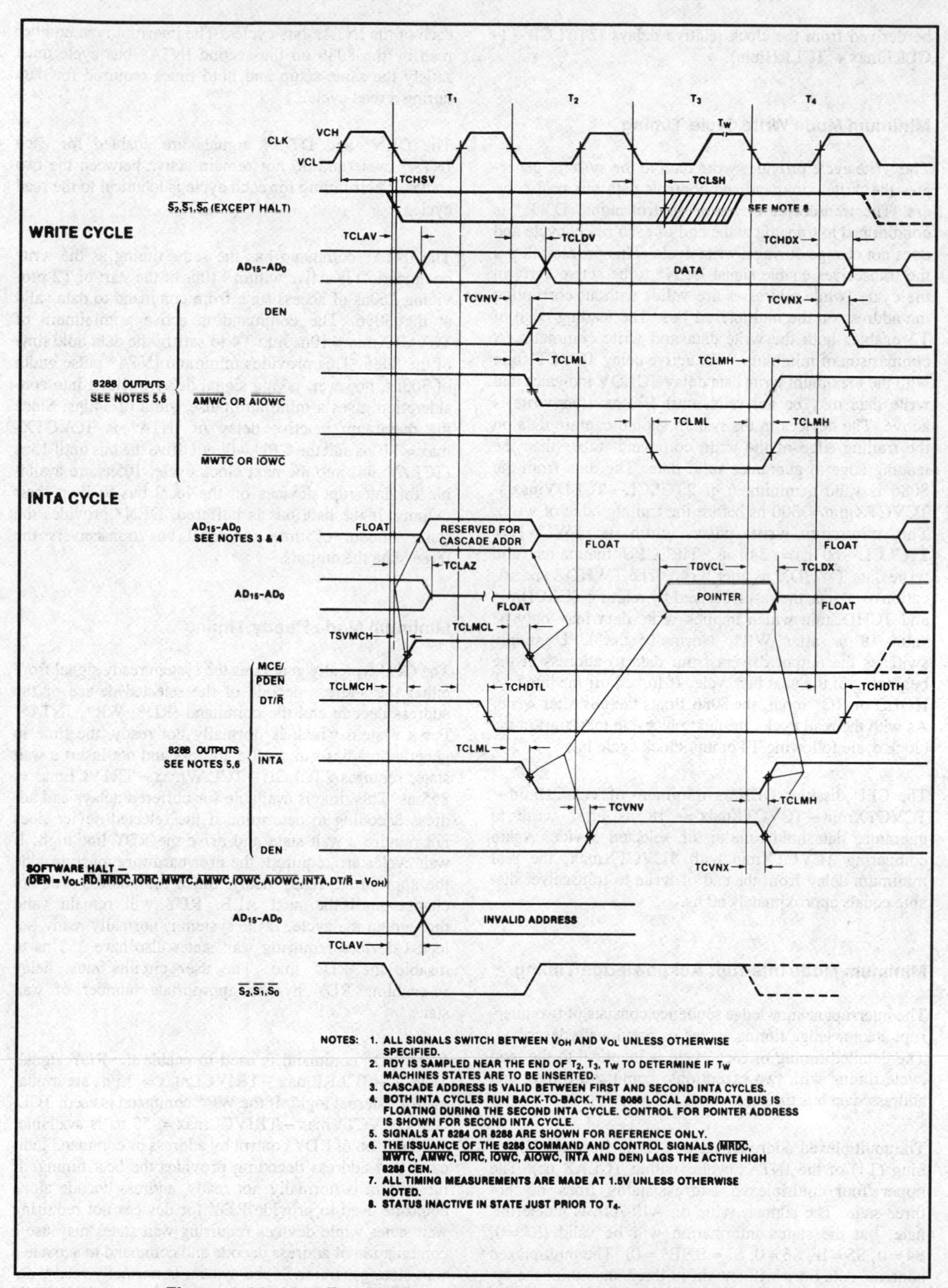

Figure 1-84 8086 Bus Timing — Maximum Mode System (continued)

be derived from the clock relative delays (2TCLCL – T-CLRLmax + TCLRHmin).

Minimum Mode Write Cycle Timing

The write cycle provides write data to the system, generates the write command and controls data bus transceivers. The transceiver direction control signal DT/R* is conditioned to transmit at the end of each ready cycle and does not change during a write cycle. This process allows the transceiver enable signal DEN* to be active early in the cycle (while addresses are valid) without corrupting the address on the multiplexed bus. The leading edge of T2 enables both the write data and write command. A comparison of minimum WR* active delay TCVCTVmin with the maximum write data delay TCLDV indicates that write data may be not valid until 100 ns after write is active. The devices in the system should capture data on the trailing edge of the write command rather than the leading edge to guarantee valid data. The data from the 8086 is valid a minimum of 2TCLCL – TCLDVmax + TCVCTXmin = 300 ns before the trailing edge of write. The minimum write pulse width is TWLWH = 2TCLCL – 60 ns = 340 ns. The CPU maintains valid write data TWHDX ns after write. The TWHDZ specification overrides the result derived by relating TCLCHmin and TCHDZmin which implies write data may only be valid 18 ns after WR*. Normally the CPU simply switches the output drivers from data to address at the beginning of the next bus cycle. If forced off the bus by a HOLD or RQ* input, the 8086 floats the bus after write. As with the read cycle, the next bus cycle may start in the clock cycle following T4 or any clock cycle later.

The CPU disables DEN* a minimum of TCLCHmin + TCVCTXmin – TCVCTXmax = 18 ns after write to guarantee data hold time to the selected device. Again comparing TCVCTXmin with TCVCTXmax, the real minimum delay from the end of write to transceiver disable equals approximately 60 ns.

Minimum Mode Interrupt Acknowledge Timing

The interrupt acknowledge sequence consists of two interrupt acknowledge timing cycles as previously described. The detailed timing of each cycle is identical to the read cycle timing with two exceptions: command timing and address/data bus timing.

The multiplexed address/data bus floats from the beginning (T1) of the INTA* cycle (within TCLAZ ns). The upper four multiplexed address/status lines do not three-state. The address value on A19-A16 is indeterminate, but the status information will be valid (S3 = 0, S4 = 0, S5 = IF, S6 = 0, S7 = BHE* = 0). The multiplexed address/ data lines will remain in three-state until the cycle after T4 of the INTA* cycle. This sequence occurs for each of the INTA* bus cycles. The interrupt type number read by the 8086 on the second INTA* bus cycle must satisfy the same setup and hold times required for data during a read cycle.

The DEN* and DT/R* signals are enabled for each INTA* cycle and do not remain active between the two cycles. Their timing for each cycle is identical to the read cycle.

The INTA* command has the same timing as the write command. It is active within 110ns of the start of T2 providing 260ns of access time from command to data valid at the 8086. The command is active a minimum of TCVCTXmin = 10ns into T4 to satisfy the data hold time of the 8086. This provides minimum INTA* pulse width of 300ns, however, taking signal delay tracking into consideration gives a minimum pulse width of 340ns. Since the maximum inactive delay of INTA* is TCVCTX-max = 110ns and the CPU will not drive the bus until 15ns (TCLAVmin) into the next clock cycle, 105ns are available for interrupt devices on the local bus to float their outputs. If the data bus is buffered, DEN* provides the same amount of time for local bus transceivers the three-state the outputs.

Minimum Mode Ready Timing

The CPU typically generates the system ready signal from either the address decode of the selected device or the address decode and the command (RD*, WR*, INTA*. For a system which is normally not ready, the time to generate ready from a valid address and not insert a wait state, requires 2TCLCL – TCLAVmax – TR1VCLmax = 255 ns. This time is available for buffered delays and address decoding to determine if the selected device does not require a wait state and drive the RDY line high. If wait cycles are required, the user hardware must provide the appropriate ready delay. Since the address will not change until the next ALE, RDY will remain valid throughout the cycle. If the system is normally ready, selected devices requiring wait states also have 255 ns to disable the RDY line. The user circuits must delay re-enabling RDY by the appropriate number of wait states.

If the RD* command is used to enable the RDY signal, TCLCL – TCLRLmax – TRIVCLmax = 15 ns are available for external logic. If the WR* command is used, TCL-CL – TCVCTVmax – TRIVCLmax = 55 ns is available. Comparison of RDY control by address or command indicates that address decoding provides the best timing. If the system is normally not ready, address decode alone could be used to provide RDY for devices not requiring wait states while devices requiring wait states may use a combination of address decode and command to activate a wait state generator. If the system is normally ready, devices not requiring wait states do nothing to RDY while devices needing wait states should disable RDY via the address decode and use a combination of address decode and command to activate a delay to re-enable RDY.

If the system requires no wait states for memory and a fixed number of wait states for RD* and WR* to all I/O devices, the M/IO* signal can be used as an early indication of the need for wait cycles. This techniques allows a common circuit to control ready timing for the entire system without feedback of address decodes.

Minimum Mode TEST* Timing

The TEST* input is sampled by the 8086 only during execution of the WAIT instruction. The TEST* signal should be active for a minimum of 6 clock cycles during the WAIT instruction to guarantee detection.

MAXIMUM MODE BUS TIMING

The maximum mode 8086 bus operations are logically equivalent to the minimum mode operation. Detailed timing analysis now involves signals generated by the CPU and the 8288 bus controller. The 8288 also provides additional control and command signals which expand the flexibility of the system.

Maximum Mode Address and ALE Timing

In the maximum mode, the address information continues to come from the CPU while the ALE strobe is generated by the 8288. To determine the worst case relationships between ALE and the address, we first must determine 8288 ALE activation relative to the S0*-S2* status from the CPU. The maximum mode timing diagram specifies two possible delay paths to generate ALE. The first is TCHSV + TSVLH measured from the rising edge of the clock cycle preceding T1. The second path is TCLLH measured from the start of T1. Since the 8288 initiates a bus cycle from the states lines leaving the passive states (S0* − S2* = 1), if the 8086 is late in issuing the status (TCHSVmax) while the clock high time is a minimum (TCHCLmin), the status will not have changed by the start of T1 and ALE is issued TSVLH ns after the status changes. If the status changes prior to the beginning of T1, the 8288 will not issue the ALE until TCLLH ns after the start of T1. The resulting worst case delay to enable ALE (relative to the start of T1) is TCHSVmax + TSVLHmax − TCHCLmin = 58 ns. Note, when calculating signal relationships, be sure to use the proper maximum mode values rather than equivalent minimum mode values.

The trailing edge of ALE is triggered in the 8288 by the positive clock edge in T1 regardless of the delay to enable ALE. The resulting minimum ALE pulse width is TCLCHmax − 58 ns = 75 ns assuming the TCHLL = 0. TCLCHmax must be used since TCHCLmin was assumed to derive the 58 ns ALE enable delay. The address is guaranteed to be valid TCLCHmin + TCHLLmin − TCLAVmax = 8 ns prior to the trailing edge of ALE to capture the address in the latches. Again we have assumed a very conservative TCHLL = 0. Note, since the address of ALE are driven by separate devices, no tracking of A.C. characteristics can be assumed.

The address hold time to the latches is guaranteed by the address remaining valid until the end of T1 while ALE is disabled a maximum of 15 ns from the positive clock transition in T1 (TCHCLmin − TCHLLmax = 52 ns address hold time). The multiplexed bus transitions from address to status and write data or tri-state (for read) are identical to the minimum mode timing. Also, since the address valid delay (TCLAV) remains the critical path in establishing a valid address, the address access times to valid data and ready are the same as the minimum mode system.

Maximum Mode Read Cycle Timing

The maximum mode system offers read signals generated by both the 8086 and the 8288. The 8086 RD* output signal timing is identical to the minimum mode system. Since the A.C. characteristics of the read commands generated by the 8288 are significantly better than the 8086 output, access to devices on the demultiplexed buffered system bus should use the 8288 commands. The 8086 RD* signal is available for devices which reside directly on the multiplexed bus. The following evaluations for read, write and interrupt acknowledge only consider the 8288 command timing.

The 8288 provides separate memory and I/O read signals which conform to the same A.C. characteristics. The commands are issued TCLML ns after the start of T2 and terminate TCLMH ns after the start of T4. The minimum command length is 2TCLCL − TCLMLmax + TCLMLmin = 375 ns. The access time to valid data at the CPU is 2TCLCL − TCLMLmax − TDVCLmax = 335 ns. Since the 8288 was designed for systems with buffered data busses, the commands are enabled before the CPU has tri-stated the multiplexed bus and should not be used with devices which reside directly on the multiplexed bus (to do so could result in bus contention during 8086 bus float and device turn-on).

The direction control for data bus transceivers is established in T1 while the transceivers are not enabled by DEN until the positive clock transition of T2. This provides TCLCH + TCVNVmin = 123 ns for 8086 bus float delay and TCHCLmin + TCLCL − TCVNVmax − TDVCLmax = 187 ns of transceiver active to data valid at the CPU. since both DEN and command are valid a minimum of 10 ns into T4, the CPU data hold time TCLDX is guaranteed. A maximum DEN disable of 45 ns (TCVNXmax) guarantees the transceivers are disabled by the start of the next 8086 bus cycle (215 ns minimum from the same clock edge). On the positive clock transition of T4, DT/R* is returned to transmit in preparation for a possible write operation on the next bus cycle. Since the system memory and I/O devices reside on a buffered system bus, they must tri-state their outputs before the device for the next bus cycle is selected (approximately 2TCLCL) or the transceivers drive write data onto the bus (approximately 2TCLCL).

Maximum Mode Write Cycle Timing

In the maximum mode, the 8288 provides normal and advanced write commands for memory and I/O. The advanced write commands are active a full clock cycle ahead of the normal write commands and have timing identical to the read commands. The advanced write pulse width is 2TCLCL − TCLMLmax + TCLMHmin = 375 ns while the normal write pulse width is TCLCL − TCLMLmax + TCLMHmin = 175 ns. Write data setup time to the selected device is a function of either the data valid delay from the 8086 (TCLDV) or the transceiver enable delay TCVNV. The worst case delay to valid write data is TCLDV = 110 ns minus transceiver propagation delays. This implies the data may not be valid until 100 ns after the advanced write command but will be valid approximately TCLCL − TCLDVmax + TCLMLmin 100 ns prior to the leading edge of the normal write command. Data will be valid 2TCLCL − TCLDVmax + TCLMHmin = 300 ns before the trailing edge of either write command. The data and command overlap for the advanced command is 300 ns while the overlap with the normal write command is 175 ns. The transceivers are disabled a minimum of TCLCHmin − TCLMHmax + TCVNXmin = 85 ns after the write command while the CPU provides valid data a minimum of TCLCHmin − TCLMHmax + TCHDZmin = 85 ns. This guarantees write data hold of 85 ns after the write command. The transceivers are disabled TCLCL − TCVNXmax + TCHDTLmin = 155 ns (assuming TCHDTL = 0) prior to transceiver direction change for a subsequent read cycle.

Maximum Mode Interrupt Acknowledge Timing

The maximum mode INTA* sequence is logically identical to the minimum mode sequence. The transceiver control (DEN and DT/R*) and INTA* command timing of each interrupt acknowledge cycle is identical to the read cycle. As in the minimum mode system, the multiplexed address/data bus will float from the leading edge of T1 for each INTA* bus cycle and not be drive by the CPU until after T4 of each INTA* cycle. The setup and hold times on the vector number for the second cycle are the same as data setup and hold for the read. If the device providing the interrupt vector number is connected to the local bus, TCLCL − TCLAZmax + TCLMLmin = 130 ns are available from 8086 bus float to INTA* command active. The selected device on the local bus must disable the system data bus transceivers since DEN is still generated by the 8288.

If the 8288 is not in the IOB (I/O Bus) mode, the 8288 MCE/PDEN* output becomes the MCE output. This output is active during each INTA* cycle and overlaps the ALE signal during T1. The MCE is available for gating cascade addresses from a master 8259A onto three of the upper AD15-AD8 lines and allowing ALE to latch the cascade address into the address latches. The address lines may then be used to provide CAS and address selection to slave 8259A's located on the system bus (see Figure 1-85). MCE is active within 15 ns of status or the start of T1 for each INTA* cycle. MCE should not enable the CAS lines onto the multiplexed bus during the first cycle since the CPU does not guarantee to float the bus until 80 ns into the first INTA* cycle. The first MCE can be inhibited by gating MCE with LOCK*. The 8086 LOCK* output is activated during T2 of the first cycle and disabled during T2 of the first cycle and disabled during T2 of the second cycle. The overlap of LOCK* with MCE allows the first MCE to be masked and the second MCE to gate the cascade address onto the local bus. Since the 8259A will not provide a cascade address until the second cycle, no information is lost. As with ALE, MCE is guaranteed valid within 58 ns of the start of T1 to allow 75 ns CAS address setup to the trailing edge of ALE. MCE remains active TCHCLmin − TCHLLmax + TCLMCLmin = 52 ns after ALE to provide data hold time to the latches.

If the 8288 is strapped in the IOB mode, the MCE output becomes PDEN* and all I/O references are assumed to be devices on the local bus rather than the demultiplexed system bus. Since INTA* cycles are considered I/O cycles, all interrupts are assumed to come from the local system and cascade addresses are not gated onto the system address bus. Additionally, the DEN signal is not enabled since no I/O transfers occur on the system bus. If the local I/O bus is also buffered by transceivers, the PDEN* signal is used to enable those transceivers. PDEN* A.C. characteristics are identical to DEN with PDEN* enabled for I/O references and DEN enabled for instruction or memory data references.

Maximum Mode Ready Timing

Ready timing based on address valid timing is the same for maximum and minimum mode systems. The delay from 8288 command valid to RDY valid at the 8284 is TCLCL − TCLMLmax − TRIVCLmin = 130 ns. This time is available for external circuits to determine the need to insert wait states and disable RDY or enable RDY to avoid wait states. INTA*, all read commands and advanced write commands provide this timing. The normal write command is not valid until after the RDY signal must be valid. Since both normal and advanced write

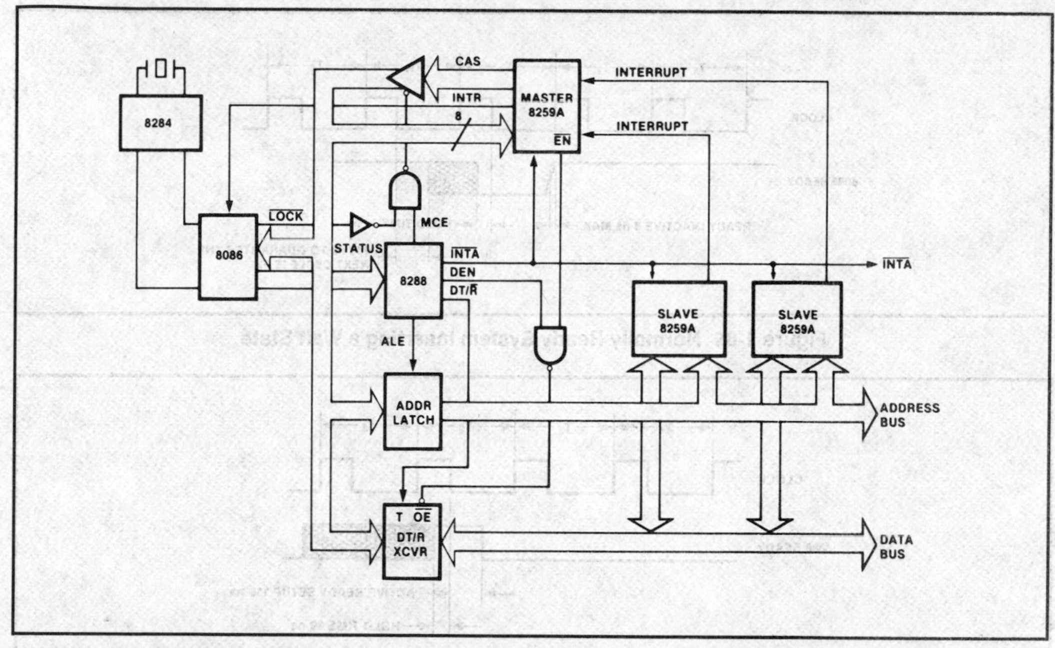

Figure 1-85 Max Mode 8086 with Master 8259A on the Local Bus and Slave 8259A's on the System Bus

commands are generated by the 8288 for all write cycles, the advanced write may be used to generate a RDY indication even though the selected device uses the normal write command.

Since separate commands are provided for memory and I/O, no M/IO* signal is specifically available as in the minimum mode to allow an early 'wait state required' indication for I/O devices. The S2* status line, however is logically equivalent to the M/IO* signal and can be used for this purpose.

Other Maximum Mode Considerations

The RQ*/GT* timing is covered in the Bus Exchange Mechanisms section paragraph 1.6.2 Maximum Mode (RQ*/GT*) later in this chapter and will not be duplicated here. The only additional signals to be considered in the maximum mode of operation are the queue status line QS0 and QS1. These signals are changed on the leading edge of each clock cycle (high to low transition) including idle and wait cycles (the queue status independent of bus activity). External logic may sample the lines on the low to high transition of each clock cycle. When sampled, the signals indicate the queue activity in the previous clock cycle and therefore lag the CPU's activity by one cycle. The TEST* input requirements are identical to those stated for the minimum mode.

To inform the 8288 of HALT status when a HALT instruction is executed, the 8086 will initiate a status transition from passive to HALT status. The status change will cause the 8288 to emit an ALE pulse with an indeterminate address. Since no bus cycle is initiated (no command is issued), the results of the address will not affect the CPU operation (i.e., no response such as READY is expected from the system). This external hardware to latch and decode all transitions in system status.

1.4.8 Wait State Insertion

The ready signal is used in the system to accommodate memory and I/O devices that cannot transfer information at the maximum CPU bus bandwidth. Ready is also used in multiprocessor systems to force the CPU to wait for access to the system bus or MULTIBUS system bus. To insert a wait state in the bus cycle, the READY signal to the CPU must be inactivate (low) by the end of T2. To avoid insertion of a wait state, READY must be active (high) within a specified setup time prior to the positive transition during T3. Depending on the size and characteristics of the system, ready implementation may take one of two approaches.

The classical ready implementation is to have the system 'normally not ready'. When the selected device receives the command (RD*/WR*/INTA*) and has had sufficient time to complete the command, it activates READY to the CPU, allowing the CPU to terminate the bus cycle. This implementation is characteristic of large multiprocessor, MULTIBUS systems or systems where propagation de-

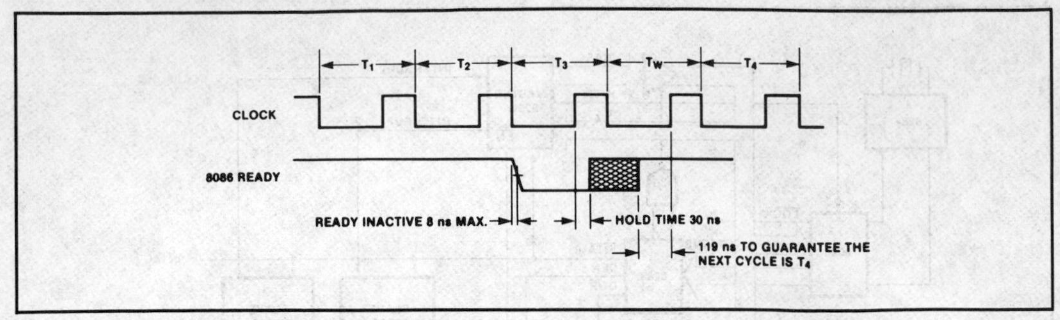

Figure 1-86 Normally Ready System Inserting a Wait State

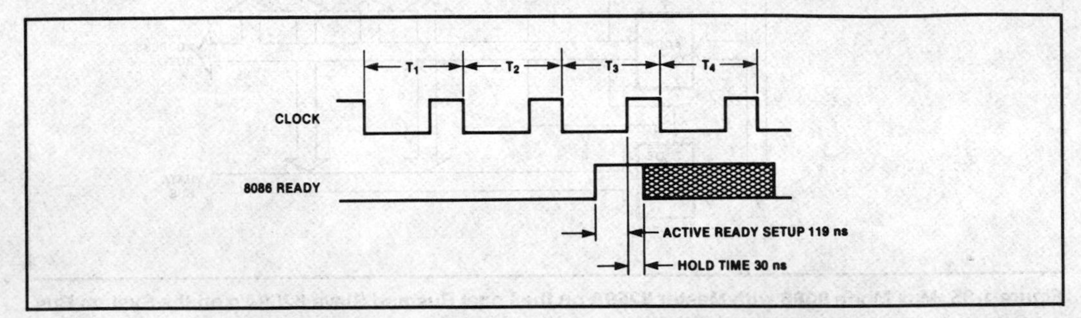

Figure 1-87 Normally Not Ready System Avoiding a Wait State

lays, bus access delays and device characteristics inherently slow down the system. for maximum system performance, devices that can run with no wait states must return 'READY' within the previously described limit. Failure to respond in time will only result in the insertion of one or more wait cycles.

An alternate technique is to have the system 'normally ready'. All devices are assumed to operate at the maximum CPU bus bandwidth. Devices that do not meet the requirement must disable READY by the end of T2 to guarantee the insertion of wait cycles. This implementation is typically applied to small single CPU systems and reduces the logic required to control the ready signal. Since the failure of a device requiring wait states to disable READY by the end of T2 will result in premature termination of the bus cycle, the system timing must be carefully analyzed when using this approach.

The 8086 has two different timing requirements on READY depending on the system implementation. for a 'normally ready' system to insert a wait state, the READY must be disabled within 8 ns (TRYLCL) after the end of T2 (start of T3) (see Figure 1-86). To guarantee proper operation of the 8086, the READY input must not change from ready to not ready during the clock low time of T3. For a 'normally not ready' system to avoid wait states, READY must be active within 119 ns (TRYHCH) of the positive clock transition during T3 (see Figure 1-87). For both cases, READY must satisfy a hold time of 30 ns (TCHRYX) from the T3 or TW positive clock transition.

To generate a stable READY signal which satisfies the previous setup and hold times, the 8284 provides two separate system ready inputs (RDY1, RDY2) and a single synchronized ready output (READY) for the CPU. The RDY inputs are qualified with separate access enables (AEN1*, AEN2*, low active) to allow selecting one of the two ready signals (see Figure 1-88). The gated signals are logically OR'ed and sampled at the beginning of each CLK cycle to generate READY to the CPU (see Figure

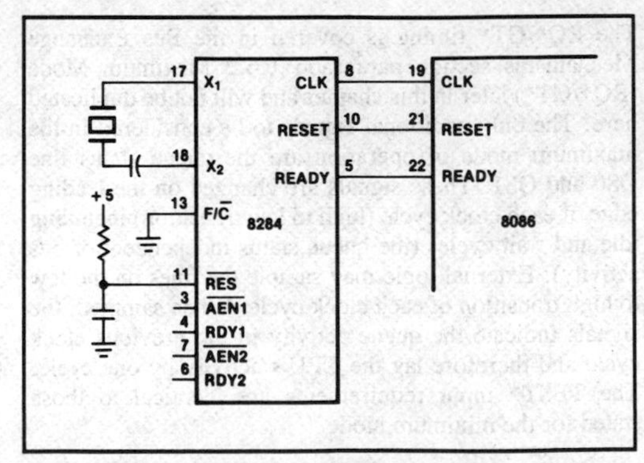

Figure 1-88 Ready Inputs to the 8284 and Output to the 8086/88

1-89). The sampled READY signal is valid within 8 ns (TRYLCL) after CLK to satisfy the CPU timing requirements on 'not ready' and ready. Since READY cannot change until the next CLK, the hold time requirements are also satisfied. The system ready inputs to the 8284 (RDY1, RDY2) must be valid 35 ns (TRIVCL) before T3 and AEN* must be valid 60 ns before T3. For a system using only one RDY input, the associated AEN* is tied to ground while the other AEN* is connected to 5 volts through approximately 1K ohms (see Figure 1-90). If the system generates a low active ready signal, it can be connected to the 8284 AEN* input if the additional setup time required by the 8284 AEN* input is satisfied. In this case, the associated RDY input would be tied high (see Figure 1-91).

1.4.9 8086/8088 Instruction Sequence

Figure 1-92 illustrates the internal operation and bus activity that occur as an 8086 CPU executes a sequence of instructions. This figure presents the signals and timing relationships that help illustrate 8086 operation. The following discussion interprets the figure.

Figure 1-92 shows the repeated execution of an instruction loop. This loop is defined in both machine code and assembly language by Figure 1-93. The loop demonstrates both the effects of a program jump on the queue and makes the instruction sequence easy to follow. The program sequence consists of seven instructions and 16 bytes, and is typical of the tight loops found in many application programs. This particular sequence contains several sort, fast-executing instructions that demonstrate both the effect of the queue on CPU performance and the interaction between the execution unit (EU) fetching code from the queue and the bus interface unit (BIU) filling the queue and performing the requested bus cycles. For the purpose of this discussion, code, stack, and memory data references are aligned on even word boundaries. The entire sequence of instructions has taken 55 clock cycles. Eighteen opcode bytes were fetched, one word memory read occurred, and one word stack write was performed.

Consider that the loop starts in clock cycle 1 with the queue reinitialization that occurs as part of the JMP instruction. The EU completes JMP instruction execution. While the BIU performs an opcode fetch to begin refilling the queue.

In clock cycle 8, the queue status lines indicate that the first byte of the MOV immediate instruction has been removed from the queue (one clock cycle after it was placed there by the BIU fetch) and that execution of this instruction has begun. The second byte of this instruction is taken from the queue in clock cycle 10 and then, during clock cycle 12, the EU pauses to wait one clock cycle for the second BIU opcode fetch to complete and for the third byte of the MOV immediate instruction to be come available for execution (recall that the queue status lines indicate queue activity that has occurred in the previous clock).

Clock cycle 13 begins the execution of the PUSH AX instruction, and during clock cycle 15, the BIU begins the fourth opcode fetch. The BIU finishes the fourth fetch in clock cycle 18 and prepares for another fetch when it receives a request from the EU for a memory write (the stack push). Instead of completing the opcode fetch and forcing the EU to wait for additional clock cycles, the BIU immediately aborts the fetch cycle (resulting in two idle clock cycles, TI, in clock cycles 19 and 20) and performs the required memory write. This interaction between the EU and BIU results in a single clock extension to the execution time of the PUSH AX instruction, the maximum delay that can occur in response to an EU bus cycle request.

Execution continues during clock cycle 24 with the execution of sequential register-to-register MOV instructions. The first of these instructions takes full advantage of the prefetched opcode to complete this operation in two clock cycles. The second MOV instruction, however, depletes the queue and requires two additional clock cycles (28 and 29).

During clock cycle 30, the ADD memory indirect to AX instruction begins. In the time required to execute this instruction, the BIU completes two opcode fetch cycles and a memory read, then begins a fourth opcode fetch cycle. Note that in the case of the memory read, the EU's request for a bus cycle occurs at a point in the BIU fetch cycle where it can be incorporated directly (idle states are not required and no EU delay is imposed).

During clock cycle 44, the EU begins the ADD immediate instruction, taking four bytes from the queue and completing instruction execution in four clock cycles. Also during this time, the BIU senses a full queue during clock cycle 45 and enters a series of bus idle states (five or six bytes constitute a full queue in the 8086; the BIU waits until it can fetch a full word or opcode before accessing the bus).

At clock cycle 47, the BIU again begins a bus cycle sequence, one that becomes an "overfetch" since the EU is executing a JMP instruction. As part of the JMP instruction, the queue reinitialization (which began the instruction sequence) occurs.

The example can be easily extended to incorporate wait states in the bus access cycles. In the case of a single wait state, each bus cycle would be lengthened to five clock cycles with a wait state (TW) inserted between every T3 and T4 state of the bus cycle. As a first approximation, the instruction sequence execution time would appear to be lengthened by 10 clock cycles, one cycle for each useful read or write bus cycle that occurs. Actually, this ap-

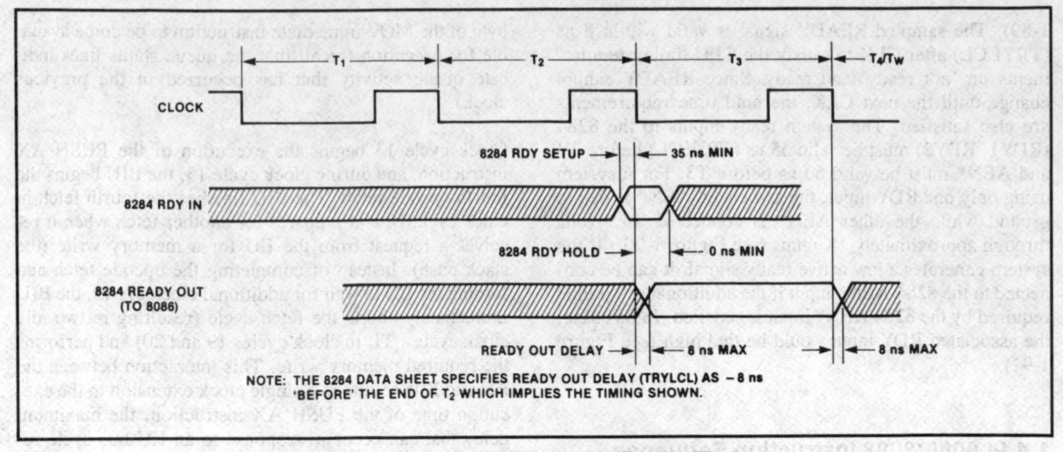

Figure 1-89 8284 With 8086/88 Ready Timing

proximation for the number of wait states inserted is incorrect since the queue can compensate for wait states by making use of previously idle bus time. For the example code sequence, this compensation reduced the actual execution time by one wait state, and the sequence was completed in 64 clock cycles, one less than the approximated 65 clock cycles.

This example is, deliberately, partially bus limited and indicates the types of EU and BIU interaction that can occur in this type of situation. Most application code sequences, however, use a high proportion of more complex, longer-executing instructions and addressing modes, and therefore tend to be execution limited. In this case, less BIU-EU interaction is required, the queue more often is full, and more idle states occur on the bus.

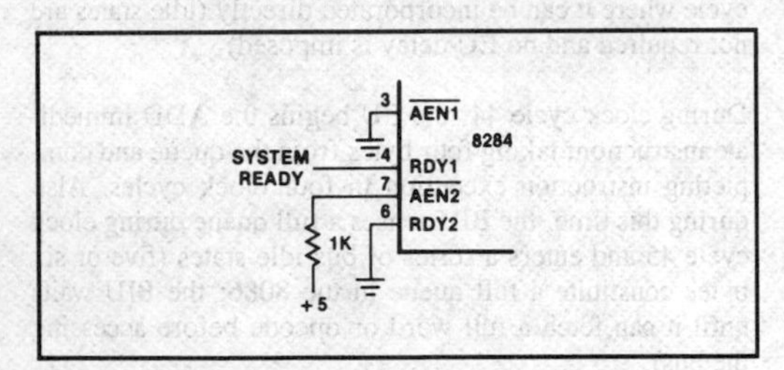

Figure 1-90 Using RDY1/RDY2 to Generate Ready

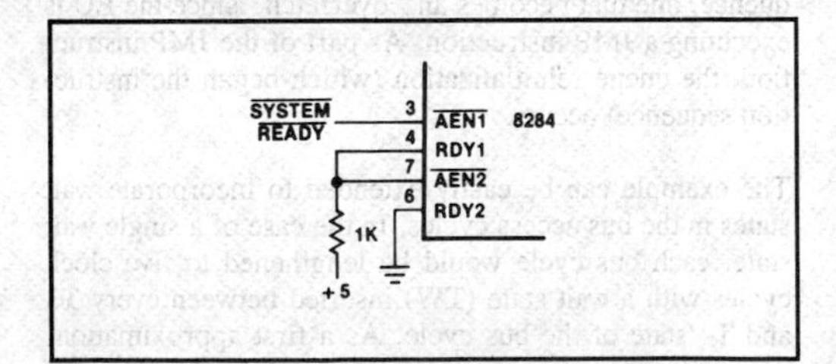

Figure 1-91 Using AEN1*/AEN2* to Generate Ready

1.5 BUS EXCHANGE MECHANISMS

The 8086 supports protocols for transferring control of the local bus between itself and other devices capable of acting as bus masters. The minimum mode configuration offers a signal level handshake similar to the 8080 and 8085 systems. The maximum mode provides an enhanced pulse sequence protocol designed to optimize utilization of CPU pins while extending the system configurations to two prioritized levels of alternate bus masters. These protocols are simply techniques for arbitration of control of the CPU's local bus and should not be confused with the need for arbitration of the system bus.

1.5.1 Minimum Mode (HOLD/HLDA)

The minimum mode 8086 system uses a hold request input (HOLD) to the CPU and a hold acknowledge (HLDA) output from the CPU. To gain control of the bus, a device must assert HOLD to the CPU and wait for the HLDA before driving the bus. When the 8086 can relinquish the bus, it floats the RD*, WR*, INTA* and M/IO* command lines, the DEN* and DT/R* bus control lines and the multiplexed address/data/status lines. The ALE signal is not tri-stated. The CPU acknowledges the request with HLDA to allow the requestor to take control of the bus. The requestor must maintain the HOLD request active until it no longer requires the bus. The HOLD request to the 8086 directly affects the execution unit. The CPU will continue to execute from its internal queue until either more instructions are needed or an operand transfer is required. This allows a high degree of overlap between CPU and auxiliary bus master operation. When the re-

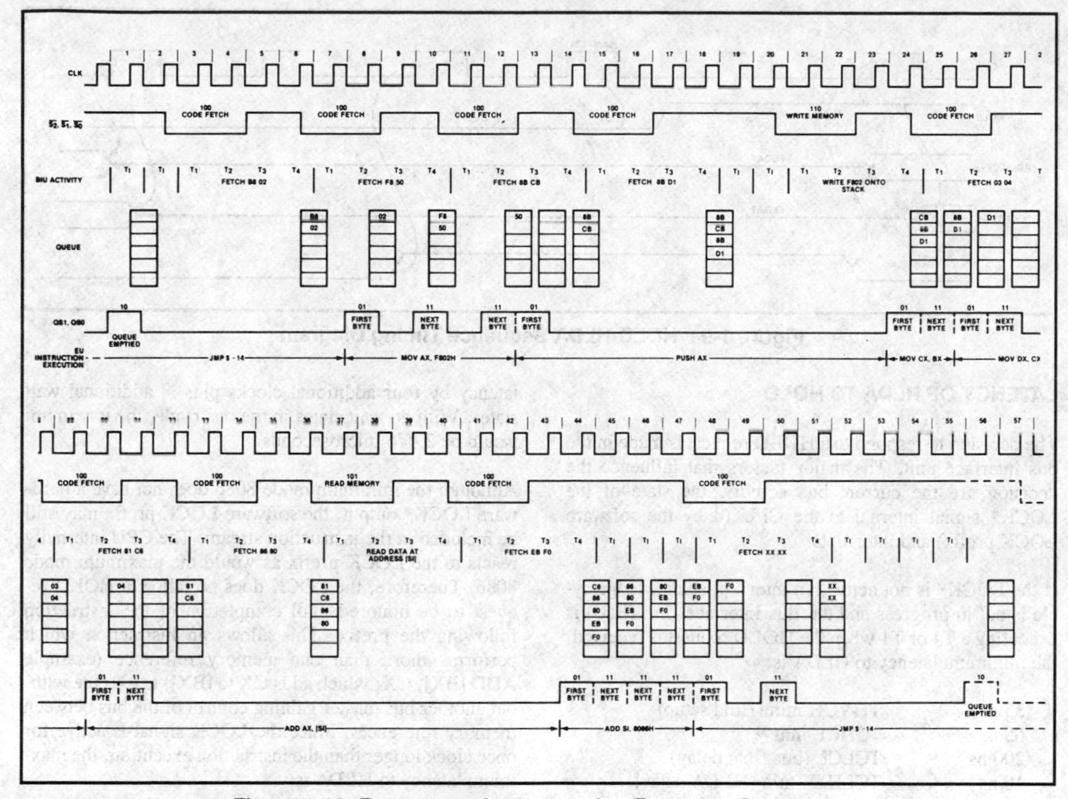

Figure 1-92 Representative Instruction Execution Sequence

questor drops the HOLD signal, the 8086 will respond by dropping HLDA. The CPU will not re-drive the bus, command and control signals from tri-state until it needs to perform a bus transfer. Since the 8086 may still be executing from its internal queue when HOLD device is driving the bus. To prevent the command lines from drifting below the minimum VIH level during the transition of bus control, 22K ohm pull up resistors should be connected to the bus command lines. The timing diagram in Figure 1-94 shows the handshake sequence and 8086 timing to sample HOLD, float the bus, and enable/disable HLDA relative to the CPU clock.

To guarantee valid system operation, the designer must assure that the requesting device does not assert control of the bus prior to the 8086 relinquishing control and that the device relinquishes control of the bus prior to the 8086 driving the bus. The HOLD request into the 8086 must be stable THVCH ns prior to the CPU's low to high clock transition. Since this input is not synchronized by the CPU, signals driving the HOLD input should be synchronized with the CPU clock to guarantee the setup time is not violated. Either clock edge may be used. The maximum delay between HLDA and the 8086 floating the bus is TCLAZmax − TCLHAVmin − 70 ns. If the system cannot tolerate the 70 ns overlap, HLDA active from the 8086 should be delayed to the device. The minimum delay for the CPU to drive the control bus from HOLD inactive is THVCHmin + 3TCLCL = 635 ns and THVCHmin + 3TCLCL + TCHCL = 701 ns to drive the multiplexed bus. If the device does not satisfy these requirements, HOLD inactive to the 8086 should be delayed. The delay from HLDA inactive to driving the busses is TCLCL + TCLCHmin − TCHAVmax = 158 ns for the control bus and 2TCLCL − TCLHAVmax = 240 ns for the data bus.

ASSEMBLY LANGUAGE	MACHINE CODE
MOV AX, 0F802H	B802F8
PUSH AX	50
MOV CX, BX	8BCB
MOV DX, CX	8BD1
ADD AX, [SI]	0304
ADD SI, 8086H	81C68680
JMP $ −14	EBF0

Figure 1-93 Instruction Loop Sequence

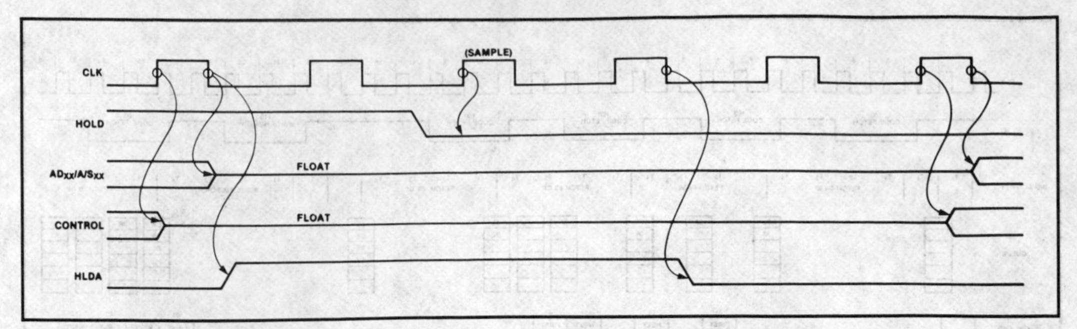

Figure 1-94 HOLD/HLDA Sequence Timing Diagram

LATENCY OF HLDA TO HOLD

The decision to respond to a HOLD request is made in the bus interface unit. The major factors that influence the decision are the current bus activity, the state of the LOCK* signal internal to the CPU (d by the software LOCK prefix) and interrupts.

If the LOCK* is not active, an interrupt acknowledge cycle is not in progress and the Bus Interface Unit (BIU) is executing a T4 or T1 when the HOLD request is received, the minimum latency to HLDA is:

35 ns	THVCH min (Hold setup)
65 ns	TCHCL min
200 ns	TCLCL (bus float delay)
10 ns	TCLHAV min (HLDA delay)
310 ns	@ 5 MHz

The maximum delay under these conditions is:

34 ns	(just missed setup time)
200 ns	delay to next sample
82 ns	TCHCL max
200 ns	TCLCL (bus float delay)
160 ns	TCLHAV max (HLDA delay)
677 ns	@ 5 MHz

If the BIU just initiated a bus cycle when the HOLD request was received, the worst case response time is:

34 ns	THVCH (just missed)
82 ns	TCHCL max
7*200	bus cycle execution
N*200	N wait states/bus cycle
160 ns	TCLHAV max (HLDA delay)

1.676 microseconds @ 5 MHz, no wait states

Note, the 200 ns delay for just missing is included in the delay for bus cycle execution. If the operand transfer is a word transfer to an odd byte boundary, two bus cycles are executed to perform the transfer. The BIU will not acknowledge a HOLD request between the two bus cycles. This type of transfer would extend the above maximum latency by four additional clocks plus N additional wait states. With no wait states in the bus cycle, the maximum would be 2.476 microseconds.

Although the minimum mode 8086 does not have a hardware LOCK* output, the software LOCK prefix may still be included in the instruction stream. The CPU internally reacts to the LOCK prefix as would the maximum mode 8086. Therefore, the LOCK does not allow a HOLD request to be honored until completion of the instruction following the prefix. This allows an instruction which performs more than one memory reference (example ADD [BX], CX; which adds CX to [BX]) to execute without another bus master gaining control of the bus between memory references. Since the LOCK signal is active for once clock longer than the instruction execution, the maximum latency to HLDA is:

34 ns	THVC (just missed)
200 ns	delay to next sample
82 ns	TCHCL max
(M + 1)*200	ns LOCK instruction execution
200 ns	set up HLDA (internal)
160 ns	TCLHAV max (HLDA delay)

(M*200 ns) + 876 ns @ 5MHz

If the HOLD request is made at the beginning of an interrupt acknowledge sequence, the maximum latency to HLDA is:

34 ns	THVCH (just missed)
82 ns	TCHCL max
2600 ns	13 clock cycles for INTA
160 ns	TCLHAV max

2.876 microseconds @ 5 MHz

MINIMUM MODE DMA CONFIGURATION

A typical use of the HOLD/HLDA signals in the minimum mode 8086 system is bus control exchange with DMA devices like the Intel 8257-5 or 8237 DMA controllers. Figure 1-95 illustrates a general interconnect for this type of configuration using the 8237-2. The DMA controller resides on the upper half of the 8086's local bus and shares the A8-A15 demultiplexing address latch of the 8086. All registers in the 8237-2 must be assigned odd addresses to allow initialization and interrogation by the CPU over the upper half of the data bus. The 8086 RD*/WR* commands must be demultiplexed to provide separate I/O and memory commands which are compatible with the 8237-2 commands. The AEN control from the 8237-2 must disable the 8086 commands from the command bus, disable the address latches from the lower (A0-A7) and upper (A19-A16) address bus and select the 8237-2 address strobe (ADSTB) to the A8-A15 address latch. If the data bus is buffered, a pull-up resistor on the DEN line will keep the buffers disabled. The DMA controller will only transfer bytes between memory and I/O and requires the I/O devices to reside on an 8-bit bus derived from the 16-bit to 8-bit bus multiplex circuit given in Section 4. Address lines A7-A0 are drive directly by the 8237 and BHE* is generated by inverting A0. If A19-A16 are used, they must be provided by an additional port with either a fixed value or initialized by software and enabled onto the address bus by AEN.

Figure 1-96 gives an interconnection for placing the 8257 on the system bus. By using a separate latch to hold the upper address from the 8257-5 and connecting the outputs to the address bus as shown, 16-bit DMA transfers are provided. In this configuration, AEN simultaneously enables A0 and BHE* to allow word transfers. AEN still disables the CPU interface to the command and address busses.

RQ*/GT* TO HOLD/HLDA CONVERSION

Consider a circuit for translating a HOLD/HLDA handshake sequence into a RQ*/GT* pulse sequence (see Figures 1-97 and 1-98). After receiving the grant pulse, the HLDA is enabled TCHCLmin ns before the CPU has tri-stated the bus. If the requesting circuit drives the bus within 20 ns of HLDA, it may be desirable to delay the acknowledge one clock period. The HLDA is dropped not later than one clock period after HOLD is disabled. The HLDA also drops at the beginning of the release pulse to provide 2TCLCL + TCLCH for the requestor to relinquish control of the status lines and 3TCLCL to float the remaining signals.

1.5.2 Maximum Mode (RQ*/GT*)

The maximum mode 8086 configuration supports a significantly different protocol for transferring bus control. When viewed with respect to the HOLD/HLDA sequence of the minimum mode, the protocol appears difficult to implement externally. However, it is necessary to understand the intent of the protocol and its purpose within the system architecture.

The maximum mode RQ*/GT* sequence is intended to transfer control of the CPU local bus between the CPU and alternate bus masters which reside totally on the local bus and share the complete CPU interface to the system bus. The complete interface includes the address latches, data transceivers, 8288 bus controller and 8289 multi-master bus arbiter. If the alternate bus masters in the system do not reside directly on the 8086 local bus, system bus arbitration is required rather than local CPU bus arbitration. To satisfy the need for multi-master system bus arbitration at each CPU's system interface, the 8289 bus arbiter should be used rather than the CPU RQ*/GT* logic.

RQ*/GT* USAGE

The RQ*/GT* protocol was developed to allow up to two instruction set extension processor (co-processors) or other special function processors (like the 8089 I/O processor in local mode) to reside directly on the 8086 local bus. Each RQ*/GT* pin of the 8086 supports the full protocol for exchange of bus control. The sequence consists of a request from the alternate bus master to gain control of the system bus, a grant from the CPU to indicate the bus has been relinquished and a release pulse from the alternate master when done. The two RQ*/GT* pins (RQ*/GT0* and RQ*/GT1*) are prioritized with RQ*/GT0* having the highest priority. The prioritization only occurs if requests have been received on both pins before a response has been given to either. For example, if a request is received on RQ*/GT1* followed by a request on RQ*/GT0* prior to a grant on RQ*/GT1*, RQ*/GT0* will gain priority over RQ*/GT1*. However, if RQ*/GT1* had already received a grant, a request on RQ*/GT0* must wait until a release pulse is received on RQ*/GT1*.

The request/grant sequence interaction with the bus interface unit is similar to HOLD/HLDA. The CPU continues to execute until a bus transfer for additional instructions or data is required. If the release pulse is received before the CPU needs the bus, it will not drive the bus until a transfer is required.

Upon receipt of a request pulse, the 8086 floats the multiplexed address, data and status bus, the S0*, S1*, and S2* status lines, the LOCK* pin and RD*. This action does not disable the 8288 command outputs from driving the command bus and does not disable the address latches from driving the address bus. The 8288 contains internal pull-up resistors on the S0*, S1*, and S2* status lines to maintain the passive state while the 8086 outputs are tri-state. The passive state prevents the 8288 from initiating any commands or activating DEN to enable the transceivers buffering the data bus. If the device issuing the RQ* does not use the 8288, it must disable the 8288 command outputs by disabling the 8288 AEN* input. Also, address latches not used by the requesting device must be disabled.

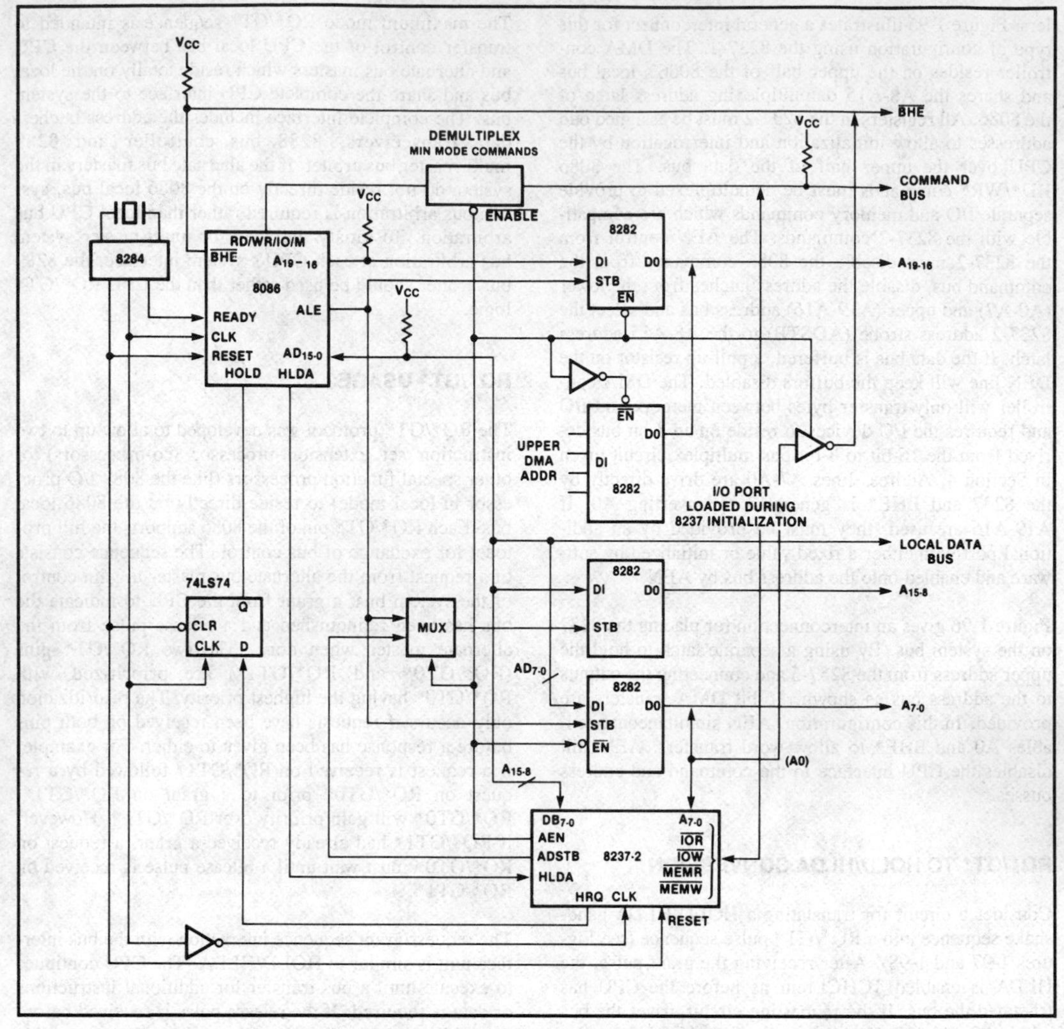

Figure 1-95 DMA Using the 8237-2

RQ*/GT* OPERATION

To request a transfer of bus control via the RQ*/GT* lines (see Figure 1-99), the device must drive the line low for no more than one CPU clock interval to generate a request pulse. The pulse must be synchronized with the CPU clock to guarantee the appropriate setup and hold times to the clock edge which samples the RQ*/GT* lines in the CPU. After issuing a request pulse, the device must begin sampling for a grant pulse with the next low to high clock edge. Since the 8086 can respond with a grant pulse in the clock cycle immediately following the request, the RQ*/GT* line may not return to the positive level between the request and grant pulses. Therefore edge triggered logic is not valid for capturing a grant pulse. It also implies the circuits which generates the request pulse must guarantee the request is removed in time to detect a grant from the CPU. After receiving the grant pulse, the requesting device may drive the local bus. Since the 8086 does not float the address and data bus, LOCK* or RD* until the high to low clock transition following the low to high clock transition the requestor uses to sample for the grant, the requestor should wait the float delay of the 8086 (TCLAZ) before driving the local bus. This precaution prevents bus contention during the access of bus control by the requestor.

To return control of the bus to the 8086, the alternate bus master relinquishes bus control and issues a release pulse on the same RQ*/GT* line. The 8086 may drive the

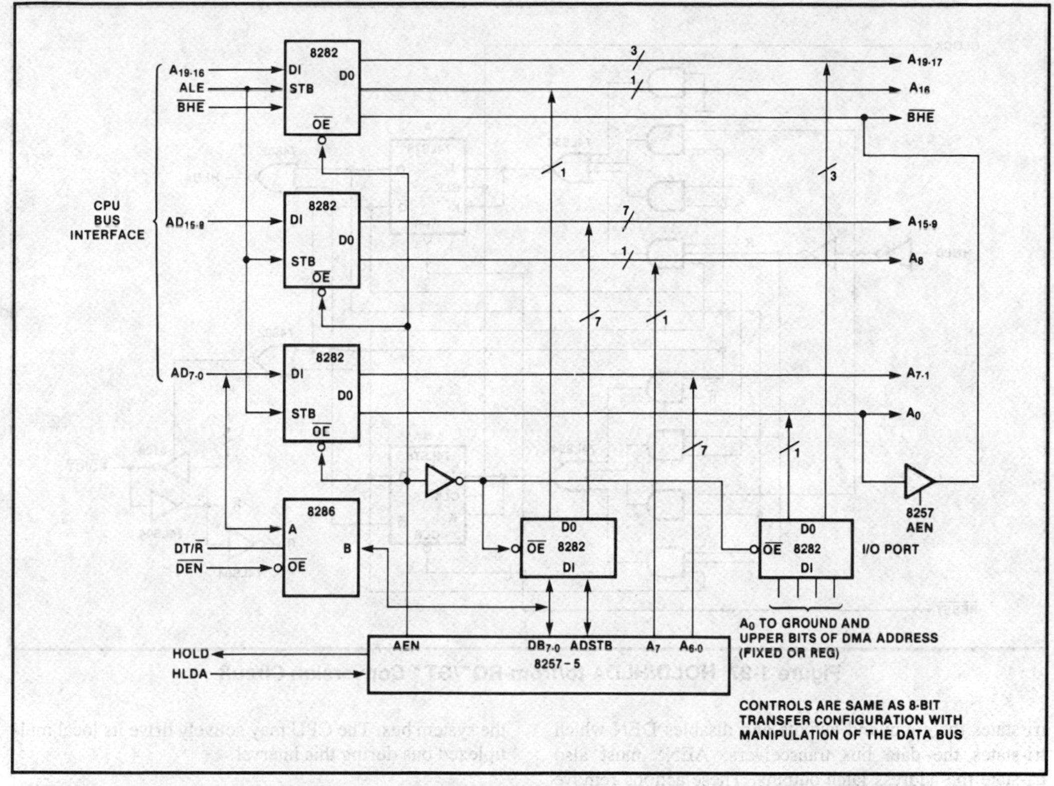

Figure 1-96 8086/88 Minimum System, 8257 on System Bus 16-bit Transfers

S0*-S2* status lines, RD* and LOCK*, three clock cycles after detecting the release pulse and the address/data bus TCHCLmin ns (clock high time) after the status lines. The alternate bus master should be tri-stated off the local bus and have other 8086 interface circuits (8288 and address latches) re-enabled within the 8086 delay to regain control of the bus.

RQ*/GT* LATENCY

The RQ* to GT* latency for a single RQ*/GT* line is similar to the HOLD to HLDA latency. The cases given for the minimum mode 8086 also apply to the maximum mode. For each case the delay from RQ* detection by the CPU to GT* detection by the requestor is: (HOLD to HLDA delay) – (THVCH + TCHCL + TCLHAV)

This gives a clock cycle maximum delay for an idle bus interface. All other cases are the minimum mode result minus 476 ns. If the 8086 has previously issued a grant on one of the RQ*/GT* lines, a request on the other RQ*/GT* line will not receive a grant until the first device releases the interface with a release pulse on its RQ*/GT* line. The delay from release on one RQ*/GT* line to a grant on the other is typically one clock period (see Figure 1-100). Occasionally the delay from a release on RQ*/GT* to a grant on RQ*/GT* will take two clock cycles and is a function of a pending request for transfer of control from the execution unit. The latency from request to grant when the interface is under control of a bus master on the other RQ*/GT* line is a function of the other bus master. The protocol embodies no mechanism for the CPU to force an alternate bus master off the bus. A watchdog timer should be used to prevent an errant alternate bus master from 'hanging' the system.

HOLD/HLDA INTERFACE TO MAXIMUM MODE SYSTEMS

To allow a device with a simple HOLD/HLDA protocol to gain control of a single CPU system bus, the circuit in Figure 1-101 could be used. The design is effectively a simple bus arbiter which isolates the CPU from the system bus when an alternate bus master issues a HOLD request. The output of the circuit, Address ENable (AEN*), disables the 8288 and 8284 when the 8086 indicates idle status (S0*, S1*, S2* = 1), LOCK* is not active and a HOLD request is active. With AEN* inactive, the 8288

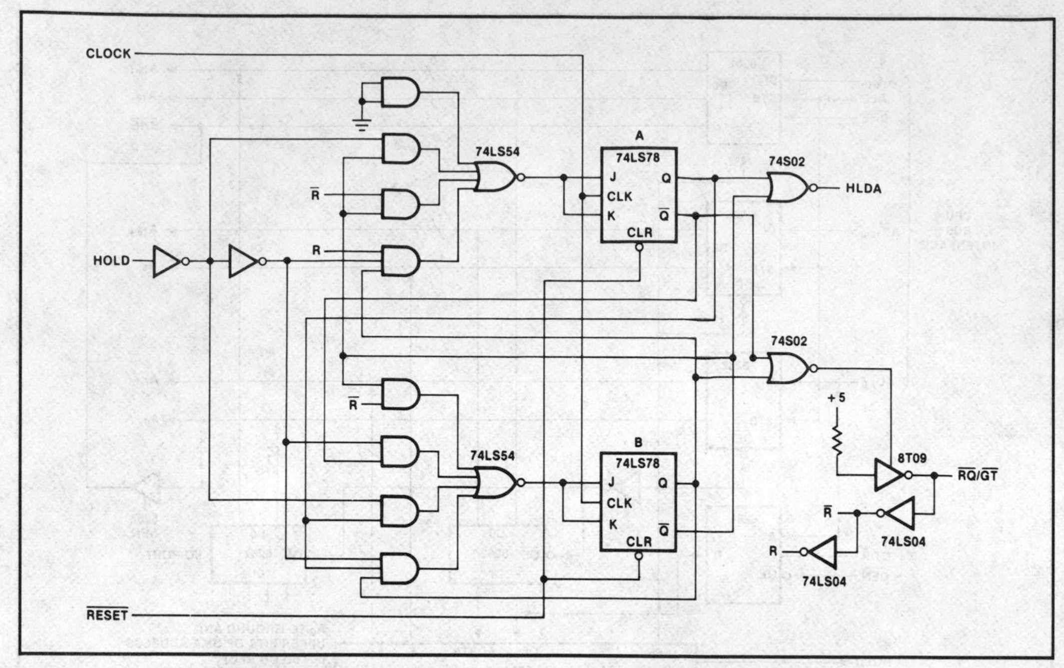

Figure 1-97 HOLD/HLDA-to/from-RQ*/GT* Conversion Circuit

tri-states the command outputs and disables DEN which tri-states the data bus transceivers. AEN* must also tri-state the address latch outputs. These actions remove the 8086 from the system bus and allow the requesting device to drive the system bus. The AEN* signal to the 8284 disables the ready input and forces a bus cycle initiated by the 8086 to wait until the 8086 regains control of the system bus. The CPU may actively drive its local multiplexed bus during this interval.

The requesting device will not gain control of the bus during an 8086 initiated bus cycle, a locked instruction or an interrupt acknowledge cycle. The LOCK* signal from the 8086 is active between INTA* cycles to guarantee the

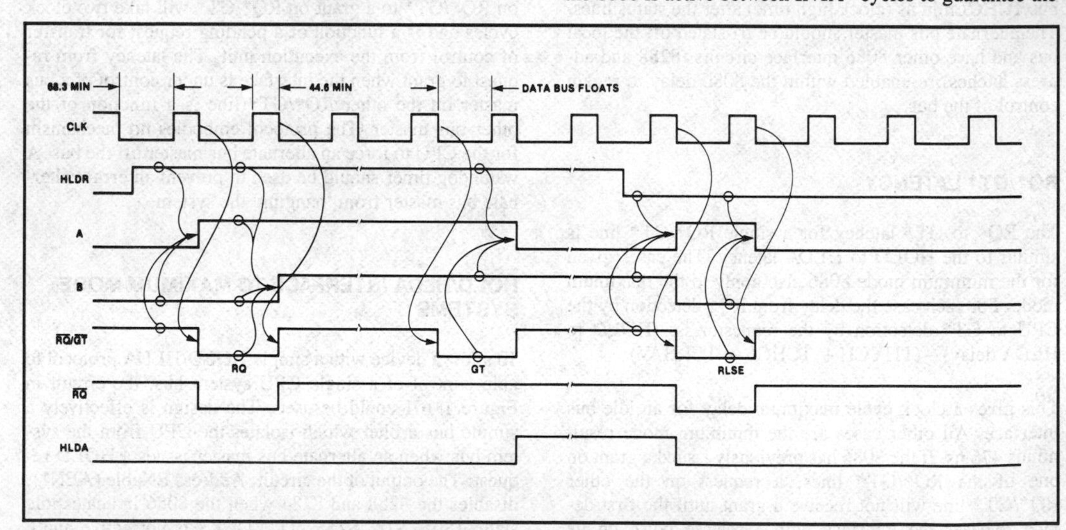

Figure 1-98 HOLD/HLDA-to/from-RQ*/GT* Conversion Timing

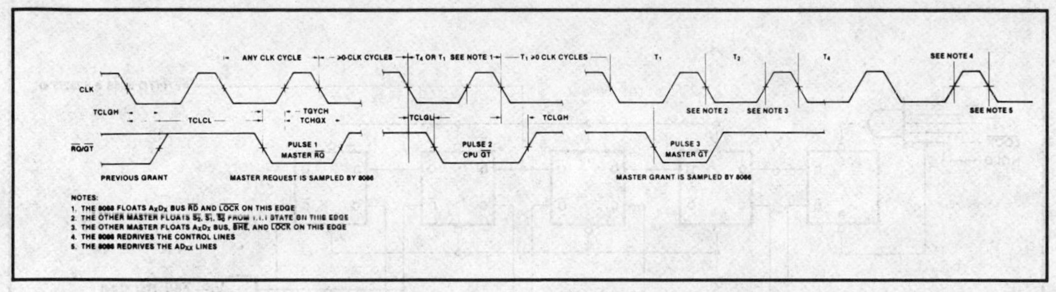

Figure 1-99 Request/Grant Sequence Timing

CPU maintains control of the bus. Unlike the minimum mode 8086 HOLD response, this arbitration circuit allows the requestor to gain control of the bus between consecutive bus cycles which transfer a word operand on an odd address boundary and are not locked. Depending on the characteristics of the requesting device, any of the 74LS74 outputs can be used to generate a HLDA to the device.

Upon completion of its bus operations, the alternate bus master must relinquish control of the system bus and drop the HOLD request. After AEN* goes inactive, the address latches and data transceivers are enabled but, if a CPU initiated bus cycle is pending, the 8288 will not drive the command bus until a minimum of 105 ns or maximum of 275 ns later. If the system is normally not ready, the 8284 AEN* input may immediately be enabled with ready returning to the CPU when the selected device completes the transfer. If the system is normally ready,

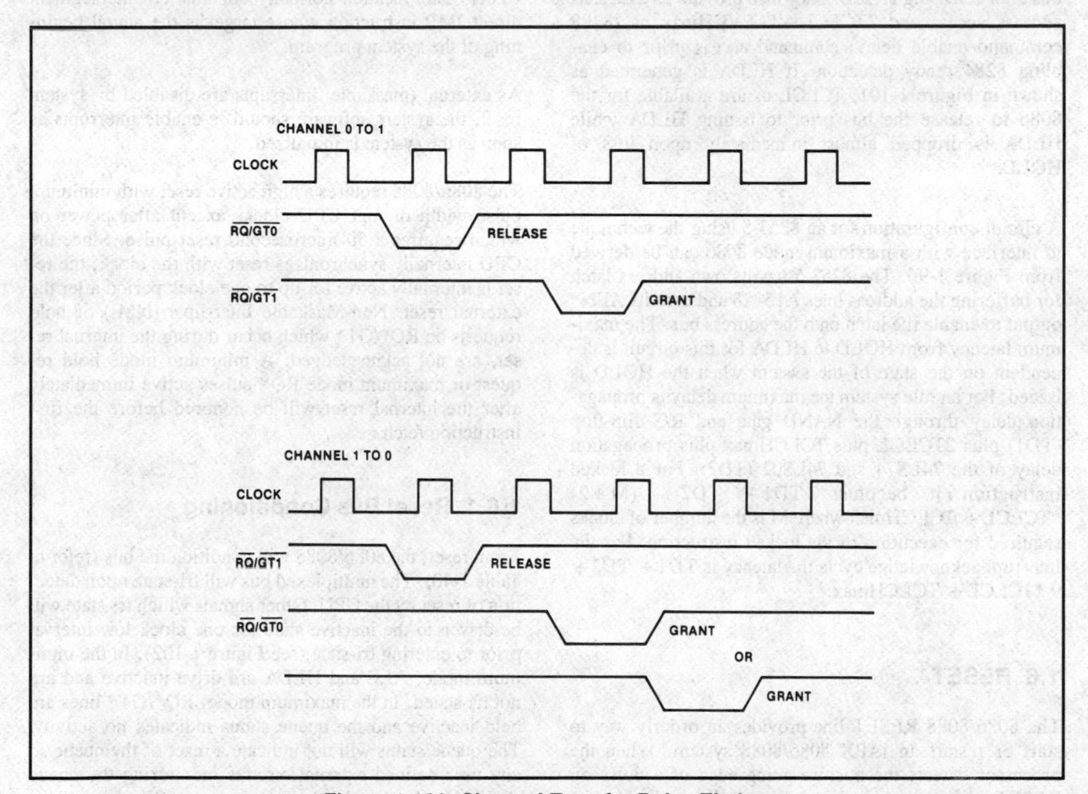

Figure 1-100 Channel Transfer Delay Timing

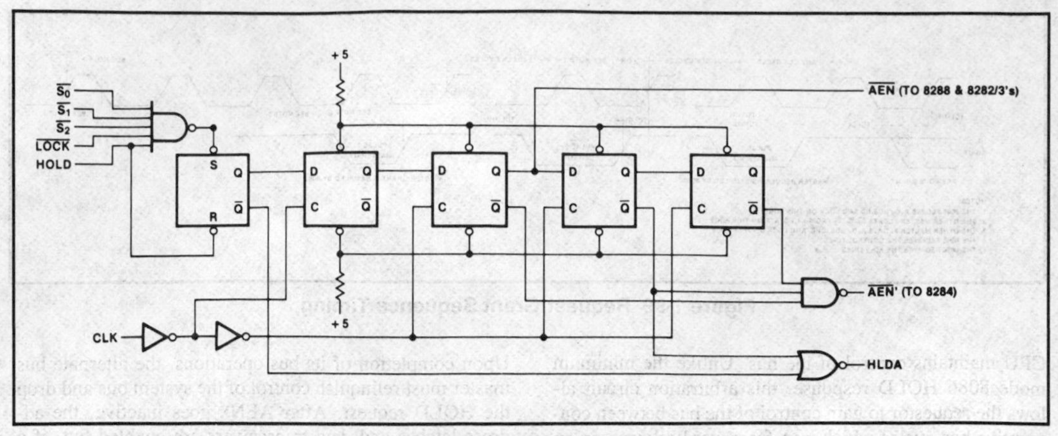

Figure 1-101 Circuit to Translate HOLD into AEN Disable for Maximum Mode 8086/88

the 8284 AEN* input must be delayed long enough to provide access time equivalent to a normal bus cycle. The 74LS74 latches in the design provide a minimum of TCLCHmin for the alternate device to float the system bus after releasing HOLD. They also provide 2TCLCL ns address access and 2TCLCL − TAEVCHmax ns (8288 command enable delay) command access prior to enabling 8284 ready detection. If HLDA is generated as shown in Figure 1-101, TCLCL ns are available for the 8086 to release the bus prior to issuing HLDA while HLDA is dropped almost immediately upon loss of HOLD.

A circuit configuration for an 8257-5 using the technique to interface with a maximum mode 8086 can be derived from Figure 1-96. The 8257-5 has its own address latch for buffering the address lines A15-A8 and uses its AEN* output to enable the latch onto the address bus. The maximum latency from HOLD to HLDA for this circuit is dependent on the state of the system when the HOLD is issued. For an idle system the maximum delay is propagation delay through the NAND gate and R/S flip-flop (TD1) plus 2TCLCL plus TCLCHmax plus propagation delay of the 74LS74 and 74LS02 (TD2). For a locked instruction it becomes: TD1 + TD2 + (M + 2) *TCLCL + TCLCHmax where M is the number of clocks required for execution of the locked instruction. For the interrupt acknowledge cycle the latency is TD1 + TD2 + 9 *TCLCL + TCLCHmax.

1.6 RESET

The 8086/8088 RESET line provides an orderly way to start or restart an iAPX 8086/8088 system. When the processor detects the positive-going edge of a pulse on RESET, it terminates all activities until he signal goes LOW, at which time the internal CPU registers are initialized to the reset condition (see Figure 1-102).

Upon RESET, the code segment register and the instruction pointer are initialized to FFFFH and 0 respectively. Therefore, the 8086 executes its first instruction following system reset from absolute memory location FFFF0H. This location normally contains an intersegment direct JMP instruction whose target is the actual beginning of the system program.

As external (maskable) interrupts are disabled by system reset, the system software should re-enable interrupts as soon as the system is initialized.

The 8086/8088 requires a high active reset with minimum pulse width of four CPU clocks except after power on which requires a 50 microsecond reset pulse. Since the CPU internally synchronizes reset with the clock, the reset is internally active for up to one clock period after the external reset. Non-Maskable Interrupts (NMI) or hold requests on RQ*/GT* which occur during the internal reset, are not acknowledged. A minimum mode hold request or maximum mode RQ* pulses active immediately after the internal reset will be honored before the first instruction fetch.

1.6.1 Reset Bus Conditioning

From reset, the 8086/8088 will condition the bus (refer to Table 1-40). The multiplexed bus will tri-state upon detection of reset by the CPU. Other signals which tri-state will be driven to the inactive state for one clock low interval prior to entering tri-state (see Figure 1-102). In the minimum mode, ALE and HLDA are drive inactive and are not tri-stated. In the maximum mode, RQ*/GT* lines are held inactive and the queue status indicates no activity. The queue status will not indicate a reset of the queue so any user defined external circuits monitoring the queue should also be reset by the system reset. 22K ohm pull-up resistors should be connected to the CPU command and bus control lines to guarantee the inactive state of these

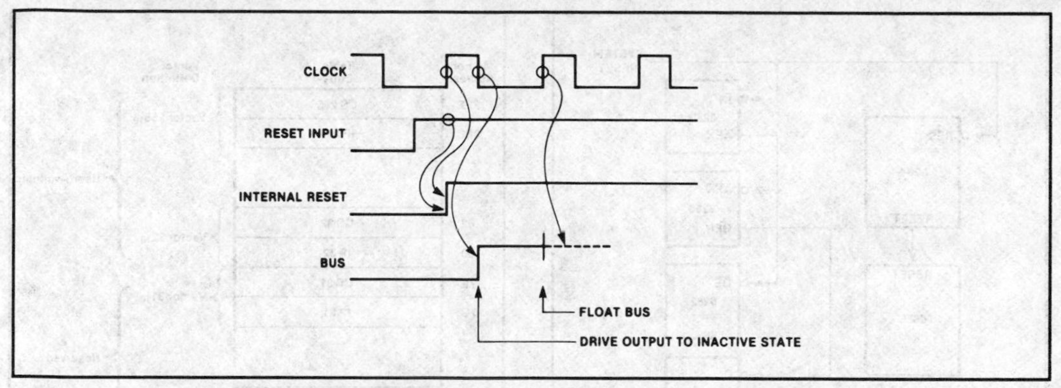

Figure 1-102 8086/88 Bus Conditioning on Reset Timing Diagram

Table 1-40 Condition of 8086/88 Bus and Output Signal Pins during Reset

Signals	Condition
$AD_{15\text{-}0}$	Three-State
$A_{19\text{-}16}/S_{6\text{-}3}$	Three-State
BHE/S_7	Three-State
$\overline{S2}/(M/\overline{IO})$	Driven to "1" then three-state
$\overline{S1}/(DT/\overline{R})$	Driven to "1" then three-state
$\overline{S0}/\overline{DEN}$	Driven to "1" then three-state
$LOCK/\overline{WR}$	Driven to "1" then three-state
$\overline{RD}$	Driven to "1" then three-state
$\overline{INTA}$	Driven to "1" then three-state
ALE	0
HLDA	0
$\overline{RQ}/\overline{GT0}$	1
$\overline{RQ}/\overline{GT1}$	1
QS0	0
QS1	0

Table 1-41 8288 Outputs During Passive Modes

ALE	0
DEN	0
$DT/\overline{R}$	1
$MCE/\overline{PDEN}$	0/1
COMMANDS	1

lines in systems where leakage currents or bus capacitance may cause the voltage levels to settle below the minimum high voltage of devices in the system. In maximum mode systems, the 8288 contains internal pull-ups on the S0*-S2* inputs to maintain the inactive state for these lines when the CPU floats the bus. The high state of the status lines during reset causes the 8288 to treat the reset sequence as a passive state (refer to Table 1-41). If the reset occurs during a bus cycle, the return of the status lines to the passive state will terminate the bus cycle and return the command lines to the inactive state.

NOTE

The 8288 does not tri-state the command outputs based on the passive state of the status lines.

If the CPU needs to be tri-stated off the bus during reset in a single CPU system, connect the reset signal to the 8288's AEN* input and output enable of the address latches (see Figure 1-103). This connection forces the command and address bus interface to tri-state while the inactive state of DEN from the 8288 tri-states the transceivers on the data bus.

1.6.2 Multiple Processor Considerations

For multiple processor systems using arbitration of a multi-master bus, the system reset should be connected to the INIT* input of the 8289 bus arbiter in addition to the 8284 reset input (see Figure 1-104). The low active INIT* input forces all 8289 outputs to their inactive state. The inactive state of the 8289 AEN* output will force the 8288 to tri-state the command outputs and the address latches to tri-state the address bus interface. DEN inactive from the

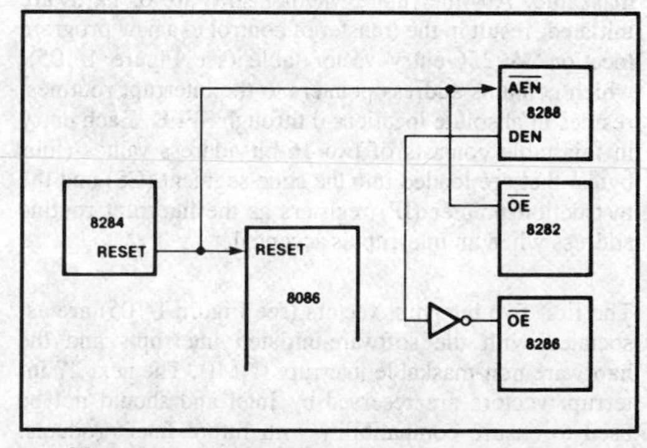

Figure 1-103 Reset Disable for Max Mode 8086/8088 Bus Interface

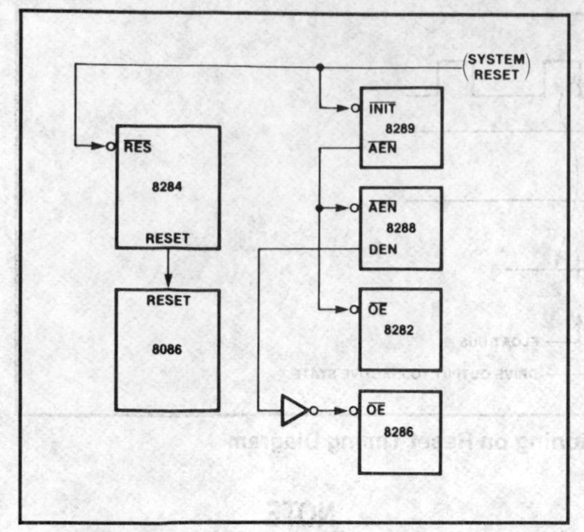

Figure 1-104 Reset Disable for Max Mode 8086/88 Bus Interface in Multi CPU System

8288 will tri-state the data bus interface. For the multi-master CPU configuration, the reset should be common to all CPU's (8289's and 8284's) and satisfy the maximum of either the CPU reset requirements or 3 TBLBL (3 8289 bus clock times) + 3 TCLCL (3 8086 clock cycle times) to satisfy 8289 reset requirements. If the 8288 command outputs are tri-stated during reset, the command lines should be pulled up to V_{cc} through 2.2K ohm resistors.

1.7 INTERRUPTS

CPU interrupts can be software or hardware initiated. Software interrupts originate directly from program execution (i.e., execution of a breakpointed instruction) or indirectly through program logic (i.e., attempting to divide by zero). Hardware interrupts originate from external logic and are classified as either non-maskable or maskable. All interrupts, whether software or hardware initiated, result in the transfer of control to a new program location. A 256-entry vector table (see Figure 1-105), which contains address pointers to the interrupt routines, resides in absolute locations 0 through 3FFH. Each entry in this table consists of two 16-bit address values (four bytes) that are loaded into the code segment (CS) and the instruction pointer (IP) registers as the interrupt routine address when an interrupt is accepted.

The first five interrupt vectors (see Figure 1-105) are associated with the software-initiated interrupts and the hardware non-maskable interrupt (NMI). The next 27 interrupt vectors are reserved by Intel and should not be used to ensure compatibility with future Intel products. The remaining interrupt vectors (vectors 32 through 255) are available for user interrupt routines.

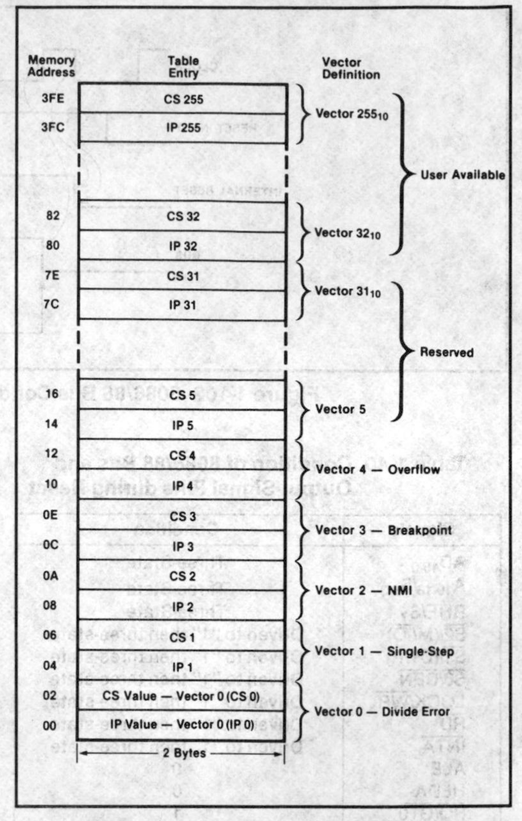

Figure 1-105 Interrupt Vector Table

1.7.1 Classes of Interrupts

The four classes of interrupts are prioritized with software-initiated interrupts having the highest priority and with maskable and single step interrupts sharing the lower priority (refer to iAPX 86/88,186/188 User's Manual Programmer's Reference). Since the CPU disables maskable and single step interrupts when acknowledging any interrupt, if recognition of maskable interrupts or single step operation is required as part of the interrupt routine, the routine first must set the mask bits.

Refer to Table 1-42 for the processing times for the various classes of interrupts.

To determine interrupt latency (the time interval between the posting of the interrupt request and the execution of "useful" instructions within the interrupt routine), additional time must be included for the completion on an instruction being executed when the interrupt is posted (interrupts are generally processed only at instruction boundaries), for saving the contents of any additional reg-

Table 1-42 Interrupt Processing Timing

Interrupt Class	Processing Time
External Maskable Interrupt (INTR)	61 clocks
Non-Maskable Interrupt (NMI)	50 clocks
INT (with vector)	51 clocks
INT Type 3	52 clocks
INTO	53 clocks
Single Step	50 clocks

isters prior to interrupt processing (interrupts automatically save only CS, IP and Flags) and for any wait states that may be incurred during interrupt processing.

The predefined interrupt types in the 8086 are listed below and a brief description of how each is involved is included in this section. When invoked, the CPU will transfer control to the memory location specified by the vector associated with the specific type. The user must provide the interrupt service routine and initialize the interrupt vector table with the appropriate service routine address. The user may additionally invoke these interrupts through hardware or software. If the preassigned function is not used in the system, the user may assign some other function to the associated type. However, for compatibility with future Intel hardware and software products for the 8086 family, interrupt types 0-31 should not be assigned as user defined interrupts. Interrupt classes include the following:

Type 0 — Divide Error
Type 1 — Single Step
Type 2 — Non-Maskable Interrupt
Type 3 — One Byte Interrupt
Type 4 — Interrupt On Overflow
User Defined Software Interrupt
User Defined Hardware Interrupt

1.7.2 Divide Error — Type 0

Type 0 interrupts are invoked whenever a division operation is attempted during which the quotient exceeds the maximum value (e.g., division by zero). The interrupt is non-maskable and is entered as part of the execution of the divide instruction. If interrupts are not re-enabled by the divide error interrupt service routine, the service routine execution time should be included in the worst case divide instruction execution time (primarily when considering the longest instruction execution time and its effect on latency to servicing hardware interrupts).

1.7.3 Single Step — Type 1

This interrupt type occurs one instruction after the TF (Trap Flag) is set in the flag register. It is used to allow software single stepping through a sequence of code. Single stepping is initiated by copying the flags onto the stack, setting the TF bit on the stack and popping the flags. The interrupt routine should be the single step routine itself. The interrupt sequence saves the flag and pro gram counter, then resets the TF flag to allow the single step routine to execute normally. To return to the routine under test, an interrupt return restores the IP, CS and flags with TF set. This allows the execution of the next instruction in the program under test before trapping back to the single step routine. Single Step is not masked by the IF (Interrupt Flag) bit in the flag register.

1.7.4 Non-Maskable Interrupt — Type 2

Interrupt Type 2 is the highest priority hardware interrupt and is non-maskable. The input is edge triggered but is synchronized with the CPU clock and must be active for two clock cycles to guarantee recognition. The interrupt signal may be removed prior to entry to the service routine. Since thc input must make a low to high transition to generate an interrupt, spurious transitions on the input should be suppressed. If the input is normally high, the NMI must be two CPU clock times to guarantee triggering. This input is typically reserved for catastrophic failures like power failure or timeout of a system watchdog timer.

1.7.5 One Byte Interrupt — Type 3

A special form of the software interrupt instruction which requires a single byte of code space involves Type 3 interrupts. It is primarily used as a breakpoint interrupt for software debug. With full representation within a single byte, the instruction can map into the smallest instruction for absolute resolution in setting breakpoints. This interrupt is not maskable.

1.7.6 Interrupt on Overflow — Type 4

This non-maskable interrupt occurs if the overflow flag (OF) is set in the flag register and the INTO instruction is executed. The instruction allows trapping to an overflow error service routine.

Interrupt types 0 and 2 can occur without specific action by the programmer (except for performing a divide for Type 0) while types 1, 3, and 4 require a conscious act by the programmer to generate these interrupt types. All but type 2 are invoked through software activity and are directly associated with a specific instruction.

1.7.7 User-Defined Software Interrupts

The user can generate an interrupt through the software with a two byte interrupt instruction INT nn. The first byte is the INT opcode while the second byte (nn) contains the top number of the interrupt to be performed. The INT instruction is not maskable by the interrupt enable flag. This instruction can be used to transfer control to routines that are dynamically relocatable and whose location in memory is not known by the calling program. This technique also saves the flags of the calling program on the stack prior to transferring control. The called procedure must return control with an interrupt return (IRET) instruction to remove the flags from the stack and fully restore the state of the calling program.

All interrupts invoked through software (all interrupts discussed thus far with the exception of NMI) are not maskable with the IF flag and initiate the transfer of control at the end of the instruction in which they occur. They do not initiate interrupt acknowledge bus cycles and will disable subsequent maskable interrupts by resetting the IF and TF flags. The interrupt vector for these interrupt types is either implied or specified in the instruction. Since the NMI is an asynchronous event to the CPU, the point of recognition and initiation of the transfer of control is similar to the maskable hardware interrupts.

1.7.8 User-Defined Hardware Interrupts

The maskable interrupts initiated by the system hardware are activated through the INTA pin of the 8086 and are masked by the IF bit of the status register (interrupt flag). During the last clock cycle of each instruction, the state of the INTA pin is sampled. The 8086 deviates from this rule when the instruction is MOV or POP to a segment register. For this case, the interrupts are not sampled until completion of the following instruction. This delay allows a 32-bit pointer to be loaded to the stack pointer registers SS and SP without the danger of an interrupt occurring between the two loads. An uninterruptable instruction sequence follows:

```
MOV SS, NEW$STACK$SEGMENT
MOV SP, NEW$STACK$POINTER
```

Another exception includes the WAIT instruction which waits for a low active input on the TEST* pin. This instruction also continuously samples the interrupt request during its execution and allows servicing interrupts during the wait. When an interrupt is detected, the WAIT instruction is again fetched prior to servicing the interrupt to guarantee the interrupt routine will return to the WAIT instruction.

Also, since prefixes are considered part of the instruction they precede, the 8086 will not sample the interrupt line until completion of the instruction the prefix(es) precede(s). Other than HALT or WAIT, the string primitives preceded by the repeat (REP) prefix deviate from this rule. The repeated string operations will sample the interrupt line at the completion of each repetition. This includes repeat string operations which include the lock prefix. If multiple prefixes precede a repeated string operation, and the instruction is interrupted, only the prefix immediately preceding the string primitive is restored. To allow correct resumption of the operation, use the following or a similar programming technique:

```
LOCKED$BLOCK$MOVE:
  LOCK REP MOVS DEST, CS:SOURCE
          AND CX,     CX
          JNZ LOCKED$BLOCK$MOVE
```

The code bytes generated by the 8086 assembler for the MOVS instruction are (in descending order): LOCK prefix, REP prefix, Segment Override prefix and MOVS. Upon return from the interrupt, the segment override prefix is restored to guarantee that one additional transfer is performed between the correct memory locations. The instructions following the Move operation test the repetition count value to determine if the move was completed and return if not.

If the INTR pin is high when sampled and the IF bit is set to enable interrupts, the 8086 executes an interrupt acknowledge sequence. To guarantee the interrupt will be acknowledged, the INTR input must be held active until the interrupt acknowledge is issued by the CPU. If the BIU is running a bus cycle when the interrupt condition is detected (as would occur if the BIU is fetching an instruction when the current instruction completes), the interrupt must be valid at the 8086 two clock cycles prior to T4 of the bus cycle if the next cycle is to be an interrupt acknowledge cycle. If the two clock setup is not satisfied, another pending bus cycle will be executed before the interrupt acknowledge is issued. If a hold request is also pending (this might occur if an interrupt and hold request are made during execution of locked instruction), the interrupt is serviced after the hold request is serviced.

1.7.9 Interrupt Acknowledge

The interrupt acknowledge sequence (see Figure 1-106) is only generated in response to an interrupt request (INTR) on the 8086 INTR input. The CPU provides a single INTR that can be software masked by clearing the interrupt enable bit in the flags register through the execution of a CLI instruction. The INTR input is level triggered and synchronized internally to the positive transition of the CLK signal. In order to be accepted before the next instruction, INTR must be active during the clock period preceding the end of the current instruction (and the interrupt enable bit must be set). When a maskable interrupt is

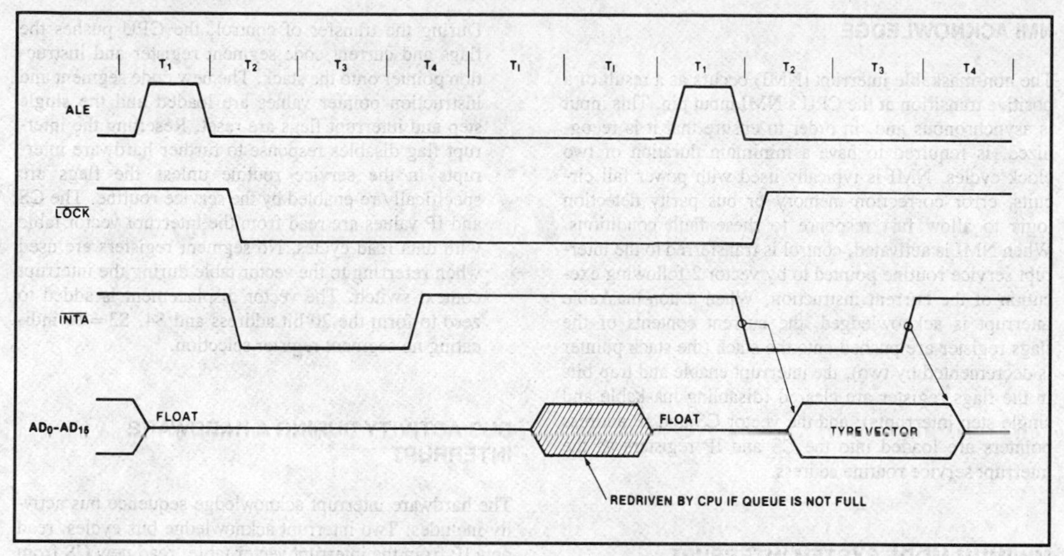

Figure 1-106 Interrupt Acknowledge Timing

acknowledged, the CPU executes two interrupt acknowledge (INTA*) bus cycles. The two INTA* bus cycles are typically separated by two idle clock cycles.

During the bus cycles the INTA* command is issued rather than read. No address is provided by the 8086 during either bus cycle (BHE* and status are valid). However, ALE is still generated and will load the address latches with indeterminate information. This condition requires that devices in the system do not drive their outputs without being qualified by the Read Command. The ALE is useful in maximum mode systems with multiple 8259A priority interrupt controllers. During the INTA* bus cycle, DT/R* and DEN are conditioned to allow the 8086 to receive a one byte interrupt type number from the interrupt system.

The first INTA* bus cycle signals an interrupt acknowledge cycle is in progress and allows the system to prepare to present the interrupt type number on the next INTA* bus cycle. The CPU does not capture information on the bus during the first cycle. During the first bus cycle, the CPU floats the address/data bus and activates the INTA* (Interrupt Acknowledge) command output during states T2 and T4.

During the second bus cycle, the CPU again activates its INTA* command output. In response to the second INTA*, the external interrupt system (e.g., an Intel 8259A Programmable Interrupt Controller) places a byte on the data bus that identifies the source of the interrupt (the vector number or vector "type"). This byte is read by the CPU and then multiplied by four and the resultant value used as a pointer into the interrupt vector table. Before calling the corresponding interrupt routine, the CPU saves the machine status by pushing the current contents of the flags register onto the stack. The CU then clears the interrupt enable and trap bits in the flags register to prevent subsequent maskable and single step interrupts, and establishes the interrupt routine return linkage by pushing the current CS and IP register contents onto the stack before loading the new CS and IP register values from the vector table.

In the minimum mode, the CPU will not recognize a hold request from another bus master until the full interrupt acknowledge sequence is completed. In the maximum mode, the CPU activates the LOCK* output from state T2 of the first bus cycle until state T2 of the second bus cycle to signal all 8289 Bus Arbiters in the system that the bus should not be accessed by any other processor.

The type number must be transferred to the 8086 on the lower half of the 16-bit data bus during the second cycle. This implies that devices which present interrupt type numbers to the 8086 must be located on the lower half of the 16-bit data bus. The timing of the INTA* bus cycles (with exception of address timing) is similar to read cycle timing.

NOTE

For readers familiar with the 8080 and the 8085, the 8086 interrupt acknowledge sequence deviates from the form used on 8080 and 8085 in that no instruction is issued as part of the sequence. The 8080 and 8085 required either a restart or call instruction be issued to affect the transfer of control.

NMI ACKNOWLEDGE

The non-maskable interrupt (NMI) occurs as a result of a positive transition at the CPU's NMI input pin. This input is asynchronous and, in order to ensure that it is recognized, is required to have a minimum duration of two clock cycles. NMI is typically used with power fail circuits, error correction memory or bus parity detection logic to allow fast response to these fault conditions. When NMI is activated, control is transferred to the interrupt service routine pointed to by vector 2 following execution of the current instruction. When a non-maskable interrupt is acknowledged, the current contents of the flags register are pushed onto the stack (the stack pointer is decremented by two), the interrupt enable and trap bits in the flags register are cleared (disabling maskable and single step interrupts), and the vector CS and IP address pointers are loaded into the CS and IP registers as the interrupt service routine address.

MINIMUM MODE SYSTEM INTERRUPT

In the minimum mode system, the M/IO* signal will be low indicating I/O during the INTA* bus cycles. The 8086 internal LOCK* signal will be active from T2 of the first bus cycle until T2 of the second to prevent the BIU from honoring a hold request between the two INTA* cycles.

MAXIMUM MODE SYSTEM INTERRUPT

In the maximum mode, the status lines S0*-S2* will request the 8288 to activate the INTA* output for each cycle. The LOCK* output of the 8086 will be active from T2 of the first cycle until T2 of the second to prevent the 8086 from honoring a hold request on either RQ*/GT* input and to prevent bus arbitration logic from relinquishing the bus between INTA*'s in multi-master systems. The consequences of READY are identical to those for READ and WRITE cycles.

INTERRUPT TYPE PROCESSING

Once the 8086 has the interrupt type number (from the bus for hardware interrupts, from the instruction stream for software interrupts or from the predefined condition), the type number is multiplied by four to form the displacement to the corresponding interrupt vector in the interrupt vector table. The four bytes of the interrupt vector include:

1. Least significant byte of the instruction pointer
2. Most significant byte of the instruction pointer.
3. Least significant byte of the code segment register.
4. Most significant byte of the code segment register.

During the transfer of control, the CPU pushes the flags and current code segment register and instruction pointer onto the stack. The new code segment and instruction pointer values are loaded and the single step and interrupt flags are reset. Resetting the interrupt flag disables response to further hardware interrupts in the service routine unless the flags are specifically re-enabled by the service routine. The CS and IP values are read from the interrupt vector table with data read cycles. No segment registers are used when referring to the vector table during the interrupt context switch. The vector displacement is added to zero to form the 20-bit address and S4, S3 = 10 indicating no segment register selection.

BUS ACTIVITY DURING A HARDWARE INTERRUPT

The hardware interrupt acknowledge sequence bus activity includes: Two interrupt acknowledge bus cycles, read new IP from the interrupt vector table, read new CS from the interrupt vector table, Push flags, Push old CS, Opcode fetch of the first instruction of the interrupt service routine, and Push old IP. After saving the old IP, the BIU will resume normal operation of prefetching instructions into the queue and servicing EU requests for operands. S5 (interrupt enable flag status) will go inactive in the second clock cycle following reading the new CS.

The elapsed time from the end of the instruction during which the interrupt occurred to the start of interrupt routine execution consists of 61 clock cycles. For software generated interrupts, the sequence of bus cycles is the same except no interrupt acknowledge bus cycles are executed. This reduces the delay to service routine execution to 51 clocks for INT nn and single step, to 52 clocks for INT3 and to 53 clocks for INTO. The same interrupt setup requirements with respect to the BIU that were stated for the hardware interrupts also apply to the software interrupts. If wait states are inserted by either the memories or the device supplying the interrupt type number, the given clock times will increase accordingly.

INTERRUPT PRECEDENCE

When considering the precedence of interrupts for multiple simultaneous interrupts, the apply following guidelines:

1. INTR is the only maskable interrupt and if detected simulta neously with other interrupts, resetting of IF by the other interrupts will mask INTR. This causes INTR to be the lowest priority interrupt serviced after all other interrupts unless the other interrupt service routines re-enable interrupts.
2. Of the non-maskable interrupts (NMI, single step and

software generated), in general, single step has the highest priority (will be serviced first) followed by NMI, followed by the software interrupts.

This priority implies that a simultaneous NMI and single step trap will cause the NMI service routine to follow single step; a simultaneous software trap and single step trap will cause the software interrupt service routine to follow single step and simultaneous NMI and software trap will cause the NMI service routine to be executed followed by the software interrupt service routine. An exception to this priority structure occurs if all three interrupts are pending. For this case, transfer of control to the software interrupt service routine followed by the NMI trap will cause both the NMI and software interrupt service routines to be executed without single stepping. Single stepping resumes upon execution of the instruction following the instruction causing the software interrupt (the next instruction in the routine being single stepped).

If the user does not wish to single step before INTR service routines, the single step routine need only disable interrupts during execution of the program being single stepped and re-enable interrupts on entry to the single step routine. Disabling the interrupts during the program under test prevents entry into the interrupt service routine while single step (TF = 1) is active. To prevent single stepping before NMI service routines, the single step routine must check the return address on the stack for the NMI service routines address and return control to that routine without single step enabled. As examples, consider Figures 1-107 and 1-108. In Figure 1-107 single step and NMI occur simultaneously while in Figure 1-108, NMI, INTR and a divide error all occur during a divide instruction being single stepped.

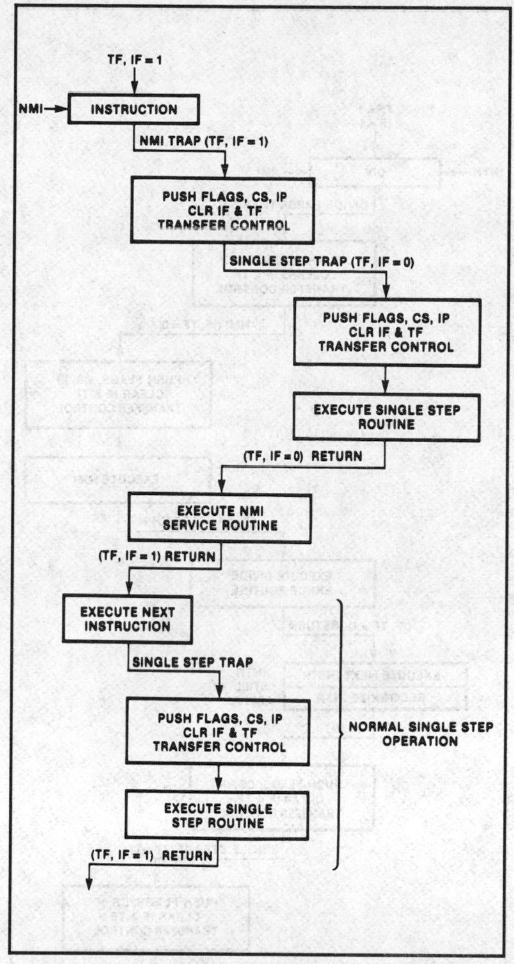

Figure 1-107 NMI During Single Stepping and Normal Single Step Operation

1.8 SUPPORT COMPONENTS

The following paragraphs provide descriptions of the various unique support components used in systems to support the 8086/88 CPU's. These components include the 8284A Clock Generator/Driver, the 8288 Bus Controller, the 8289 Bus Arbiter, the 8259A Programmable Interrupt Controller and the 8237A Programmable DMA Controller. These components may be used when designing both minimum and maximum mode applications for the 8086/8088 Microprocessors. The following paragraphs present detailed design information on the various support circuits and describe the benefits of each. The circuit designer should also refer to the Intel Microsystems Components Handbook (No. 230843-002) for detailed data sheets on each of the devices.

1.8.1 8284A Clock Generator and Driver

The 8284A Clock Generator/Driver is an integral part of the 8086 family that Intel offers to satisfy the 8086 requirement for an external clock signal. In addition to providing the primary (system) clock signal, this device provides both the hardware reset interface and the mechanism for the insertion of wait states in the bus cycle. An optimum 33% duty cycle clock with the required voltage levels and transition times can be obtained with the 8284A clock generator (see Figure 1-109). Either an external frequency source or a series resonant crystal may drive the 8284A.

CLOCK GENERATION

The 8086 requires a clock signal with fast rise and fall times (10 ns max) between low and high voltages of −0.5 to +0.6 low and 3.9 to VCC + 1.0 high (see Figure 1-110). The maximum clock frequency of the 8086 is 5 MHz, 8 MHz for the 8086-2 and 10 MHz for the 8086-1.

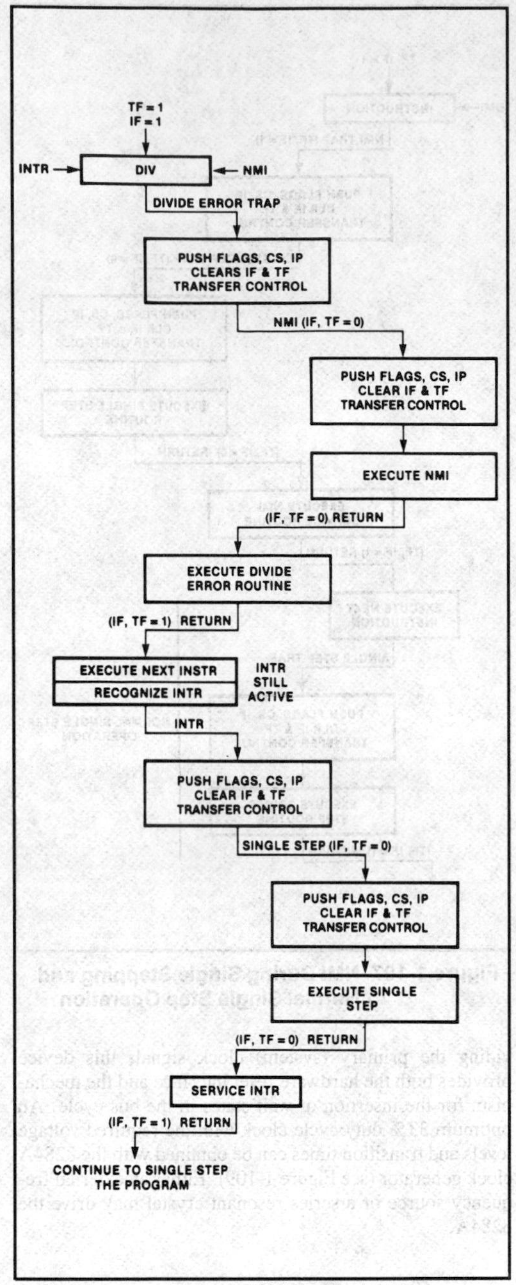

Figure 1-108 NMI, INTR, Single Step and Divide Error Simultaneous Interrupts

Since the design of the 8086 incorporates dynamic cells, a minimum frequency of 2 MHz is required to retain the state of the machine. Due to the minimum frequency requirement, single stepping or cycling of the CPU may not be accomplished by disabling the clock. In general, for frequencies below the maximum, the CPU clock need not satisfy the frequency dependent pulse width limitations stated in the 8086 data sheet. The values specified only reflect the minimum values which must be satisfied and are stated in terms of the maximum clock frequency. As the clock frequency approaches the maximum frequency of the CPU, the clock must conform to a 33% duty cycle to satisfy the CPU minimum clock low and high time specifications.

CRYSTAL CLOCK REFERENCE

The selected clock crystal must oscillate at 3X the desired CPU frequency. To select the crystal inputs of the 8284A as the frequency source for clock generation, the F/C* input to the 8284A must be strapped to ground. The strapping option allows selecting either the crystal or the external frequency input as the source for clock generation. Fundamental mode crystals are recommended for a more accurate and stable frequency generation. When selecting a crystal for use with the 8284A, the series resistance should be as low as possible. Since the other circuit components will tend to shift the operating frequency from resonance, the operating impedance will typically be higher than the specified series resistance. If the attenuation of the oscillator's feedback circuit reduces the loop gain to less than one, the oscillator will fail. A recommended crystal configuration is shown in Figure 1-111.

EXTERNAL FREQUENCY CLOCK REFERENCE

If a high accuracy frequency source, externally variable frequency source or a common source for driving multiple 8284A's is desired, the External Frequency Input (EFI) of the 8284A can be selected by strapping the F/C* input to 5 volts through approximately 1K ohms (see Figure 1-112). The external frequency source should be TTL compatible, have a 50% duty cycle and oscillate at three times the desired CPU operating frequency. The maximum EFI frequency the 8284A can accept is slightly above 24 MHz with minimum clock low and high times of 13 ns. Although no minimum EFI frequency is specified, it should not violate the CPU minimum clock rate. If a common frequency source is used to drive multiple 8284A's distributed throughout the system, each 8284A should be drive by its own line from the source. To minimize noise in the system, each line should be a twisted pair driven by a buffer like the 74LS04 with the ground of the twisted pair connecting the ground of the source and receiver. To minimize clock skew, the lines to all 8284A's should be of equal length. A simple technique for generating a master frequency source for additional 8284A's is shown in Figure 1-113 where an 8284A with a crystal is used to generate the desired frequency. The oscillator output of the 8284A (OSC) equals the crystal frequency and is used to drive the external frequency to all other 8284A's in the system.

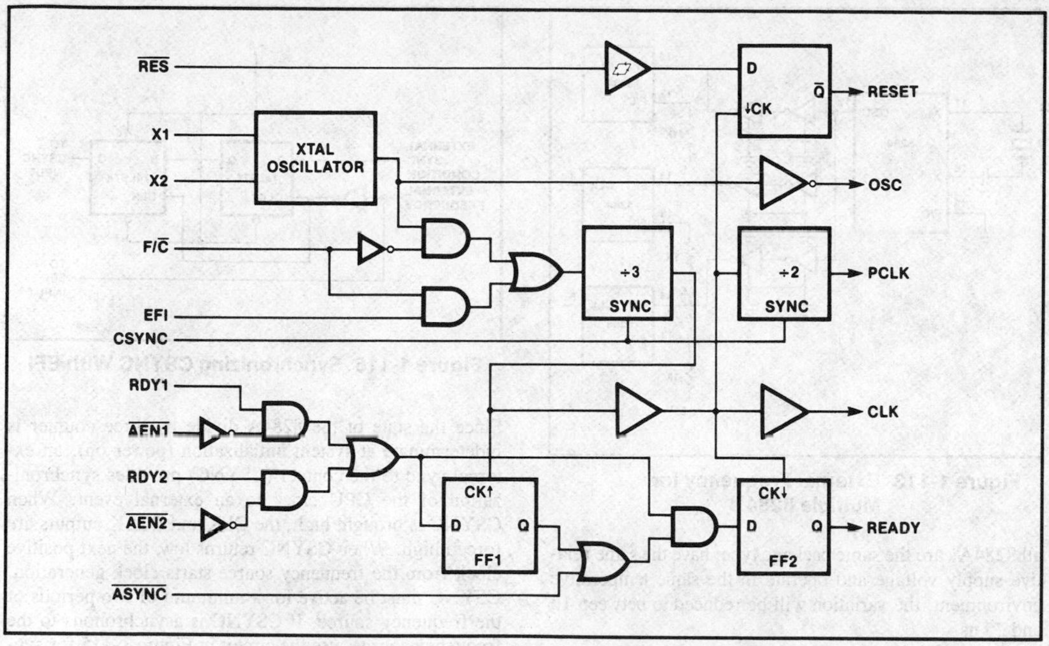

Figure 1-109 8284A Clock Generator/Driver Block Diagram

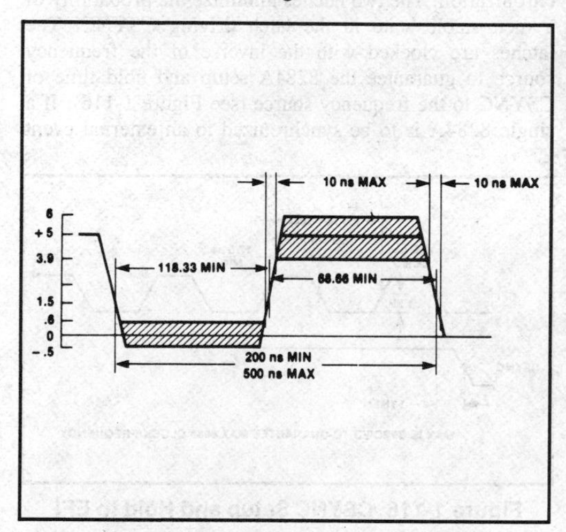

Figure 1-110 8086/88 Clock Waveform

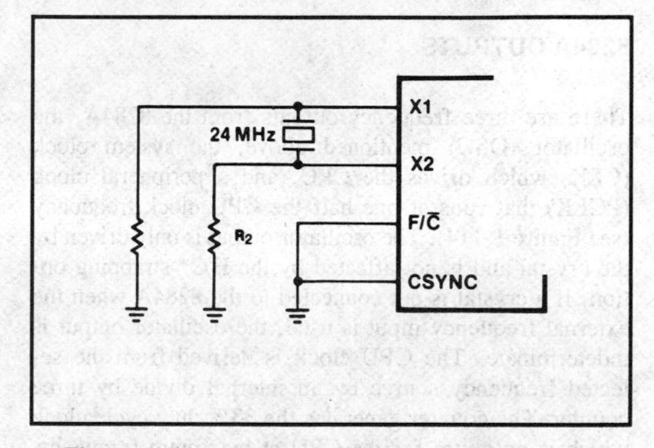

Figure 1-111 Recommended Crystal Clock Configuration

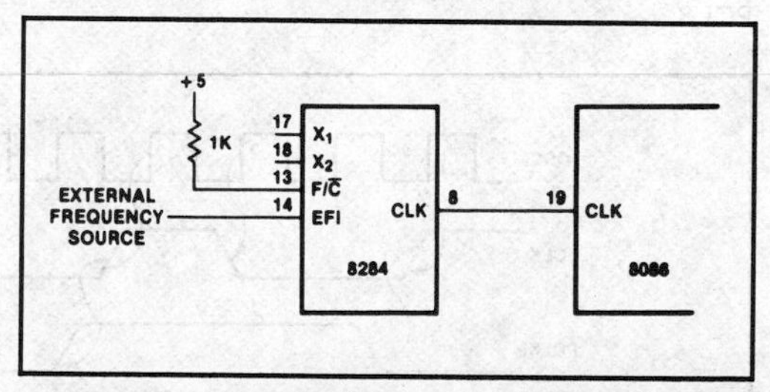

Figure 1-112 8284A Interfaced to an 8086/88

The oscillator output is inverted from the oscillator signal used to drive the CPU clock generator circuit. Because of this inversion, the oscillator output of one 8284A should not drive the EFI input of a second 8284A if both are driving clock inputs of separate CPU's that are to be synchronized. The variation on EFI to CLK delay over a range of 8284A's may approach 35 to 45 ns. If, however,

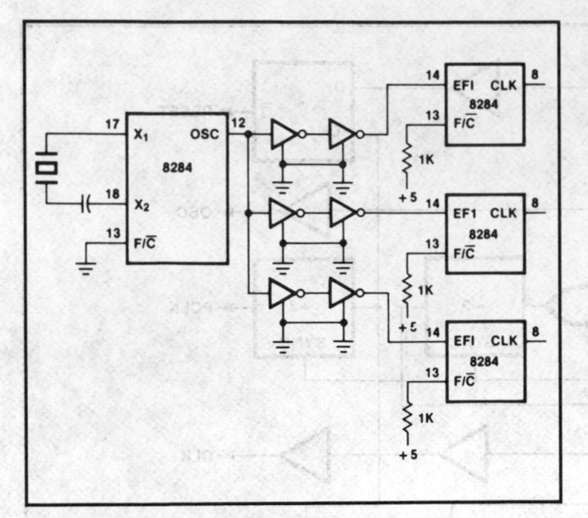

Figure 1-113 External Frequency for Multiple 8284's

all 8284A's are the same package type, have the same relative supply voltage and operate in the same temperative environment, the variation will be reduced to between 15 and 25 ns.

8284A OUTPUTS

There are three frequency outputs from the 8284A, the oscillator (OSC) mentioned above, the system clock (CLK) which drives the CPU, and a peripheral clock (PCLK) that runs at one half the CPU clock frequency (see Figure 1-114). The oscillator output is only driven by the crystal and is not affected by the F/C* strapping option. If a crystal is not connected to the 8284A when the external frequency input is used, the oscillator output is indeterminate. The CPU clock is derived from the selected frequency source by an internal divide by three counter. The counter generates the 33% duty cycle clock which is optimum for the CPU at maximum frequency. The peripheral clock has a 50% duty cycle and is derived from the CPU clock. The maximum skew is 20 ns between OSC and CLK, and 22 ns between CLK and PCLK.

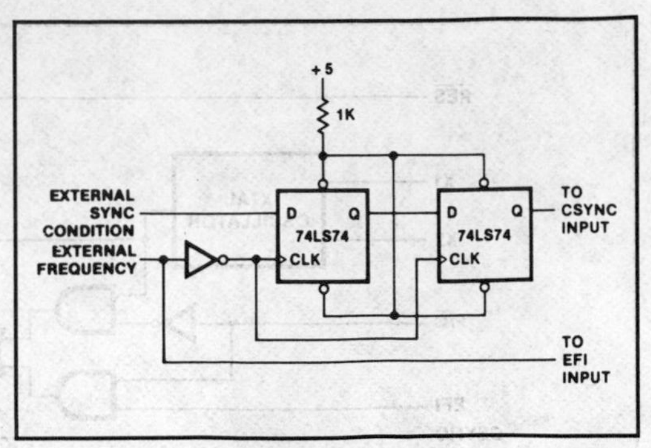

Figure 1-115 Synchronizing CSYNC With EFI

Since the state of the 8284A divide by three counter is indeterminate at system initialization (power on), an external sync to the counter (CSYNC) provides synchronization of the CPU clock to an external event. When CSYNC is brought high, the CLK and PCLK outputs are forced high. When CSYNC returns low, the next positive clock from the frequency source starts clock generation. CSYNC must be active for a minimum of two periods of the frequency source. If CSYNC is asynchronous to the frequency source, use the circuit in Figure 1-115 for synchronization. The two latches minimize the probability of a meta-stable state in the latch driving CSYNC. The latches are clocked with the inverse of the frequency source to guarantee the 8284A setup and hold time of CSYNC to the frequency source (see Figure 1-116). If a single 8284A is to be synchronized to an external event

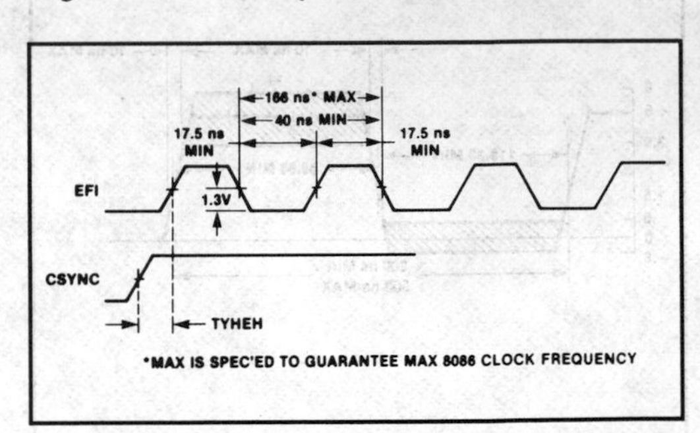

Figure 1-116 CSYNC Setup and Hold to EFI

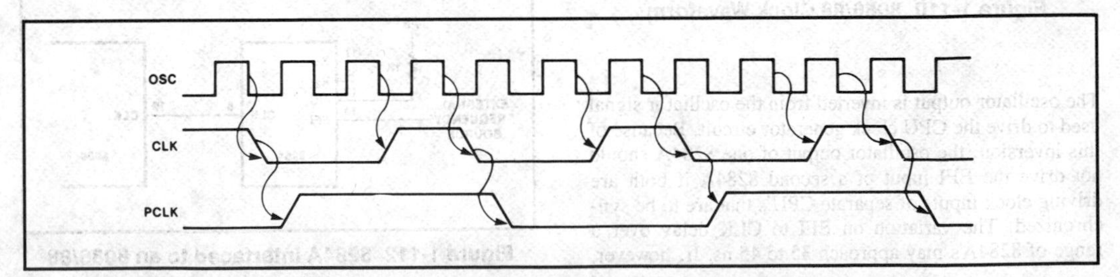

Figure 1-114 Oscillator to CLK and CLK to PCLK Timing Relationships

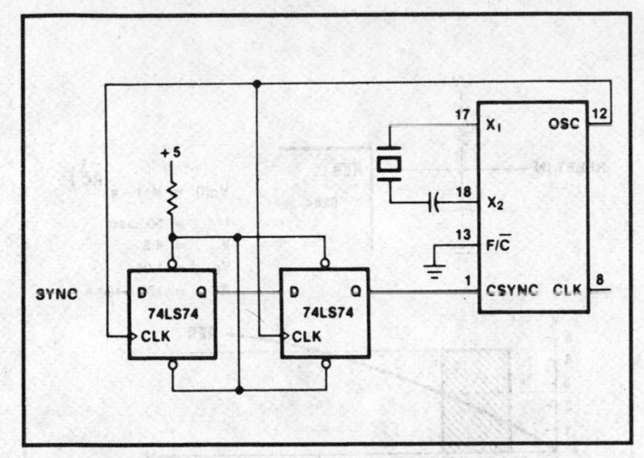

Figure 1-117 EFI From 8284A Oscillator

and an external frequency source is not used, the oscillator output of the 8284A may be used to synchronize CSYNC (see Figure 1-117). Since the oscillator output is inverted from the internal oscillator signal, the inverter in the previous example is not required. If multiple 8284A's are to be synchronized, an external frequency source must drive all 8284A's and a single CSYNC synchronization circuit must drive the CSYNC input of all 8284A's (see Figure 1-118). Since activation of CSYNC may cause violation of CPU minimum clock low time, it should only be enabled during reset or CPU clock high. CSYNC must also be disabled a minimum of four CPU clocks before the end of reset to guarantee proper CPU reset.

Due to the fast transitions and high drive (5 mA) of the 8284A CLK output, it may be necessary to put a 10 to 100 ohm resistor in series with the clock line to eliminate ringing (resistor value depending on the amount of drive required). If multiple sources of CLK are needed with minimum skew, CLK can be buffered by a high drive device (74S241) with outputs tied to 5 volts through 100 ohms to guarantee VOH = 3.9 min (8086 minimum clock

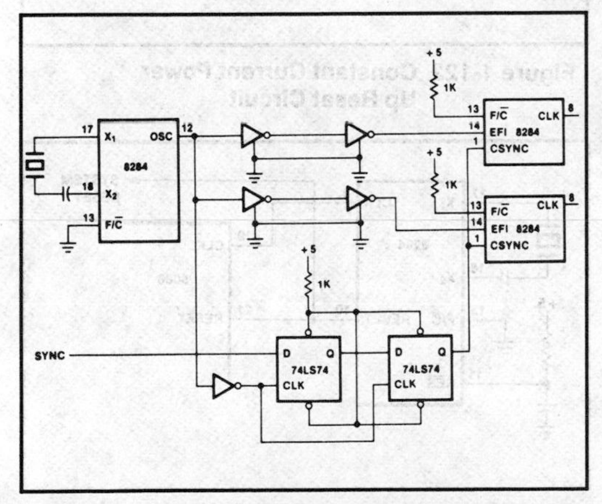

Figure 1-118 Synchronizing Multiple 8284As

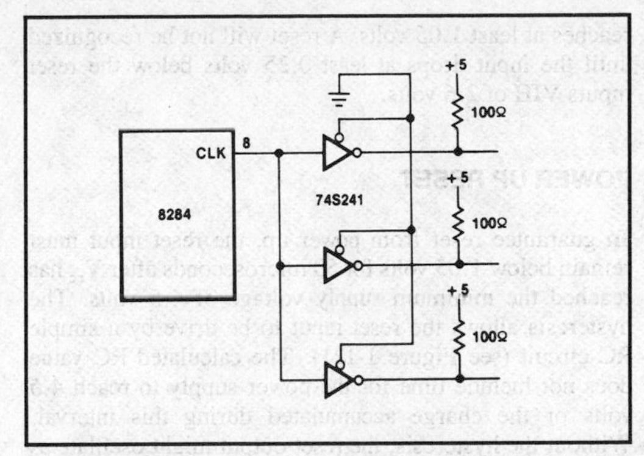

Figure 1-119 Buffering the 8284 CLK Output

input high voltage) (see Figure 1-119). A single 8284A should not be used to generate the CLK for multiple CPU's that do not share a common local (multiplexed) bus since the 8284A synchronizes ready to the CPU and can only accommodate ready for single CPU. If multiple CPU's share a local bus, they should be driven with the same clock to optimize transfer of bus control. Under these circumstances, only one CPU will be using the bus for a particular bus cycle which allows sharing a common READY signal (see Figure 1-120).

THE 8284A RESET FUNCTION

The reset signal to the 8086 can be generated by the 8284A; the 8284A has a Schmitt trigger input (RES*) for generating reset from a low active external reset. The hysteresis specified in the 8284A data sheet implies that at least 0.25 volts will separate the 0 and 1 switching point of the 8284A reset input. Inputs without hysteresis will switch from low to high and high to low at approximately the same voltage threshold. The inputs are guaranteed to switch at specified low and high voltages (VIL and VIH) but the actual switching point is anywhere in-between. Since VIL min is specified at 0.8 volts, the hysteresis guarantees that the reset will be active until the input

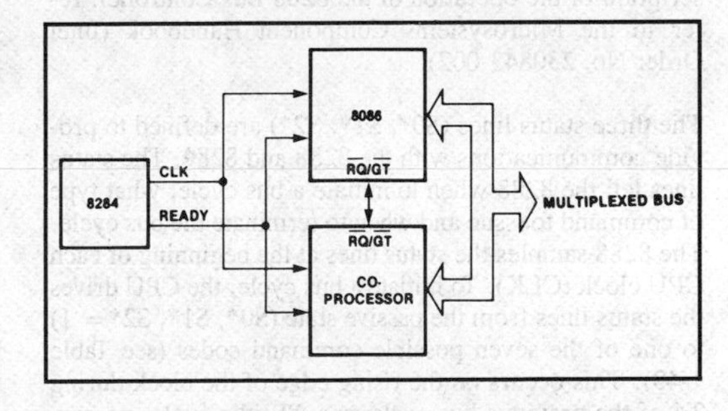

Figure 1-120 8086 and Coprocessor on the Local Bus Share a Common 8284

reaches at least 1.05 volts. A reset will not be recognized until the input drops at least 0.25 volts below the reset inputs VIH of 2.6 volts.

POWER UP RESET

To guarantee reset from power up, the reset input must remain below 1.05 volts for 50 microseconds after V_{cc} has reached the minimum supply voltage of 4.5 volts. The hysteresis allows the reset input to be drive by a simple RC circuit (see Figure 1-121). The calculated RC value does not include time for the power supply to reach 4.5 volts or the charge accumulated during this interval. Without the hysteresis, the reset output might oscillate as the input voltage passes through the switching voltage of the input. The calculated RC value provides the minimum required reset period of 50 microseconds for 8284A's that switch at the 1.05 volt level and a reset period of approximately 162 microseconds for 8284A's that switch at the 2.6 volt level. If tighter tolerance between the minimum and maximum reset times is necessary, the reset circuit shown in Figure 1-122 might be used rather than the simple RC circuit. This circuit provides a constant current source and a linear charge rate on the capacitor rather than the inverse exponential charge rate of the RC circuit. This implementation generates a maximum reset period of 124 microseconds.

The 8284A synchronizes the reset input with the CPU clock to generate the RESET signal to the CPU (see Figure 1-123). The output is also available as a general reset to the entire system. The reset has no effect on any clock circuits in the 8284A.

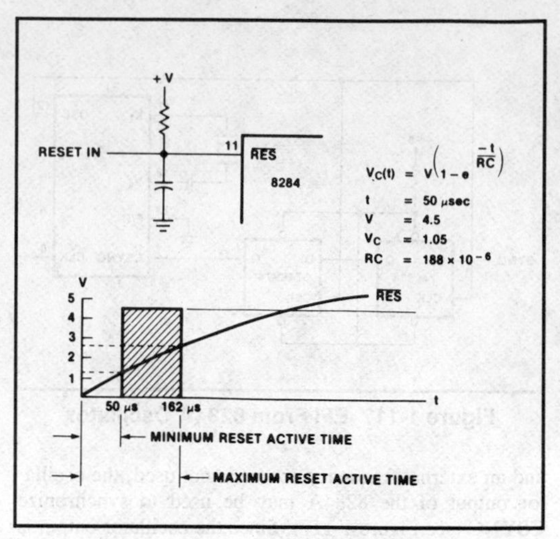

Figure 1-121 8284A Reset Circuit

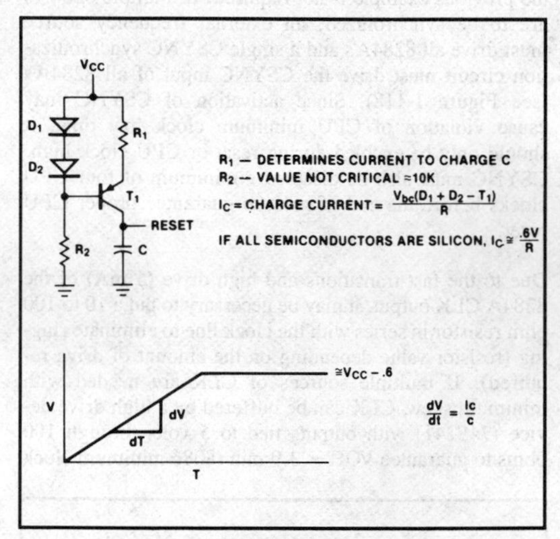

Figure 1-122 Constant Current Power Up Reset Circuit

1.8.2 8288 Bus Controller

The 8288 Bus Controller (Figure 1-124) uses the S2*, S1* and S0* status bit outputs from the CPU (and the 8089 IOP) to generate all bus control and command output signals required for a bus cycle. The status bit outputs are decoded as outlined in Table 1-43. For a detailed description of the operation of the 8288 Bus Controller, refer to the Microsystems Component Handbook (Intel Order No. 230843-002).

The three status lines (S0*, S1*, S2*) are defined to provide communications with the 8288 and 8289. The status lines tell the 8288 when to initiate a bus cycle, what type of command to issue and when to terminate the bus cycle. The 8288 samples the status lines at the beginning of each CPU clock (CLK). To initiate a bus cycle, the CPU drives the status lines from the passive state (S0*, S1*, S2* = 1) to one of the seven possible command codes (see Table 1-43). This occurs on the rising edge of the clock during T4 of the previous bus cycle or a TI (idle cycle, no current bus activity). The 8288 detects the status change by sampling the status lines on the high to low transition of each clock cycle. The 8288 starts a bus cycle by generat-

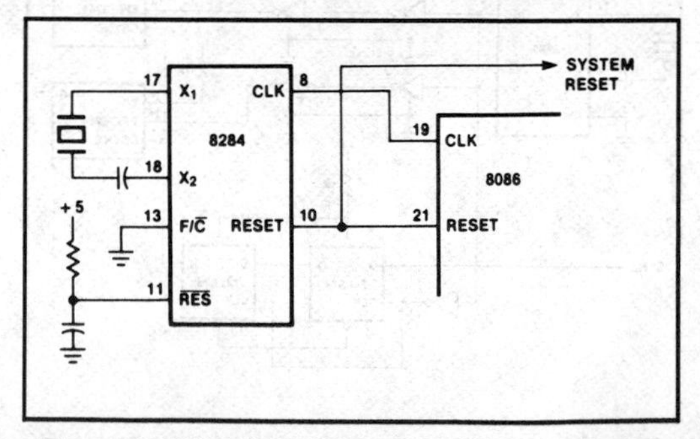

Figure 1-123 8086/88 Reset and System Reset

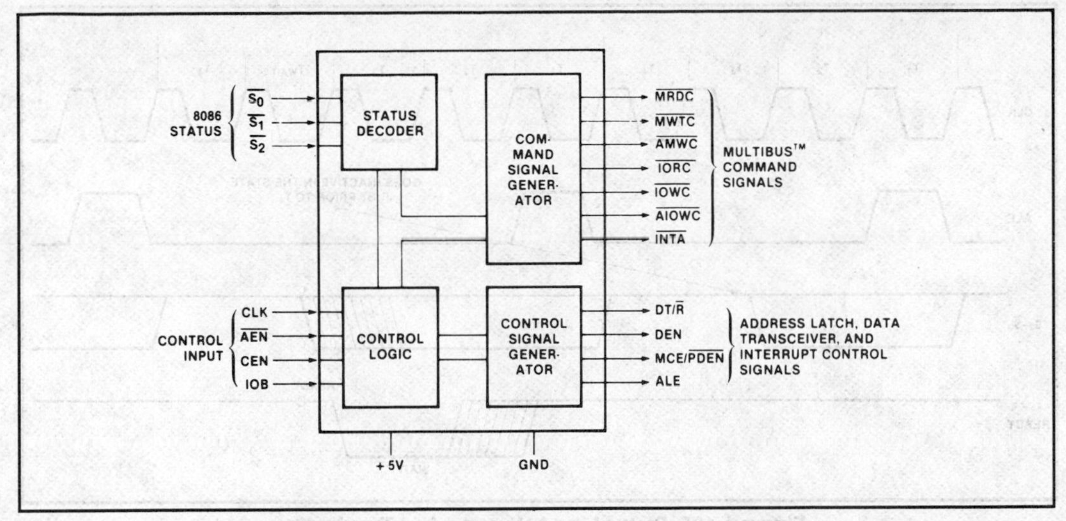

Figure 1-124 8288 Bus Controller Block Diagram

ing ALE and appropriate buffer direction control of the clock cycle immediately following detection of the status change (T1). The bus transceivers and the selected command are enabled in the next clock cycle (T2) (or T3 for normal write commands). When the status returns to the passive state, the 8288 will terminate the command (see Figure 1-125). Since the CPU will not return the status to the passive state until the 'ready' indication is received, the 8288 maintains active command and bus control for any number of wait cycles. The status lines may also be used by other processors on the 8086's local bus to monitor bus activity and control the 8288 if they gain control of the local bus.

The 8288 provides the bus control (DEN, DT/R*, ALE) and commands (INTA*, MRDC*, IORC*, MWTC*, AMWC*, IOWC*, AIOWC*) removed from the CPU. The command structure has separate read and write commands for memory and I/O to provide compatibility with the MULTIBUS command structure.

The advanced write commands are enabled one clock period earlier than the normal write to accommodate the wider write pulse widths often required by peripherals

Table 1-43 Status Line Decode Chart

$\overline{S_2}$	$\overline{S_1}$	$\overline{S_0}$	Processor State	8288 Command
0	0	0	Interrupt Acknowledge	$\overline{INTA}$
0	0	1	Read I/O Port	$\overline{IORC}$
0	1	0	Write I/O Port	$\overline{IOWC}$, $\overline{AIOWC}$
0	1	1	Halt	None
1	0	0	Code Access	$\overline{MRDC}$
1	0	1	Read Memory	$\overline{MRDC}$
1	1	0	Write Memory	$\overline{MWTC}$, $\overline{AMWC}$
1	1	1	Passive	None

and static RAMs. The normal write provides data setup prior to write to accommodate dynamic RAM memories and I/O devices which strobe data on the leading edge of write. The advanced write commands do not guarantee that data is valid prior to the leading edge of the command. The DEN signal in the maximum mode is inverted from the minimum mode to extend transceiver control by allowing logical conjunction of DEN with other signals. While not appearing to be a significant benefit of interrupt control and various system configurations will demonstrate the usefulness of qualifying DEN. Figure 1-126 compares the timing of the minimum and maximum mode bus transfer commands. Although the maximum mode configuration is designed for multiprocessor environments, large single CPU designs (either MULTIBUS systems or greater than two PC boards) should also use the maximum mode. Since the 8288 is a bipolar dedicated controller device, its output drive for the commands (32 mA) and tolerances on A.C. characteristics (timing parameters and worse case delays) provide better large system performance than the minimum mode 8086.

In addition to assuming the functions removed from the CPU, the 8288 provides additional strapping options and controls to support multiprocessor configurations and peripheral devices on the CPU local bus. These capabilities allow assigning resources (memory or I/O) as shared (available on the MULTIBUS system bus) or private (accessible only by this CPU) to reduce contention for access to the MULTIBUS system bus and improve multi-CPU system performance. The following paragraphs describe these strapping options.

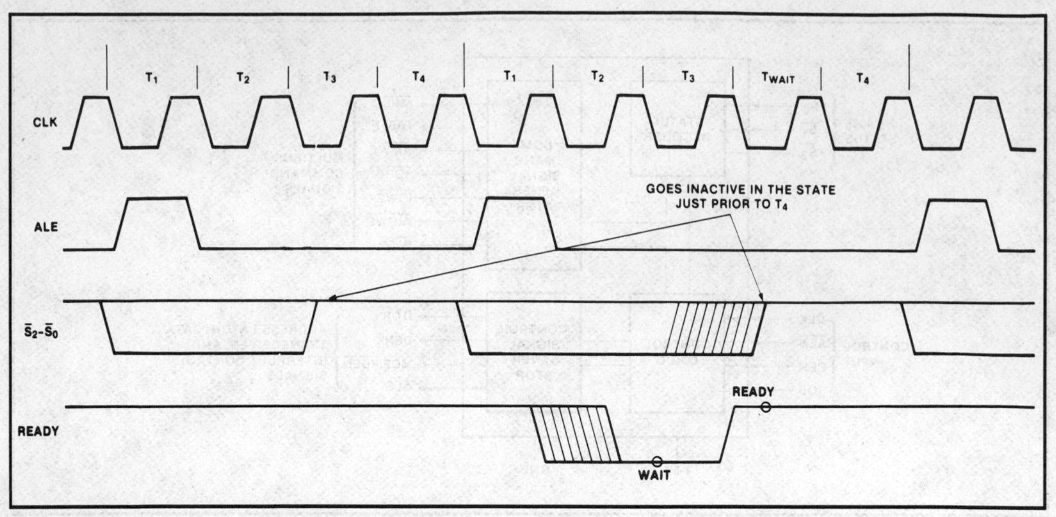

Figure 1-125 Status Line Activation And Termination

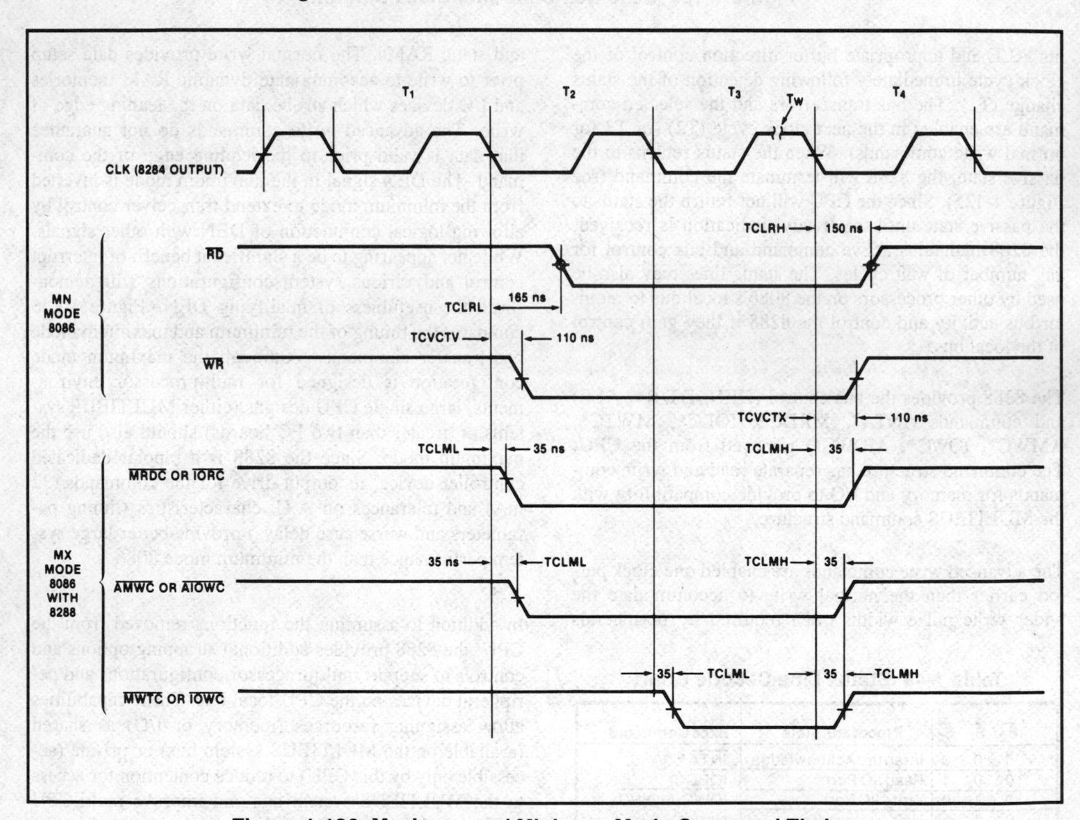

Figure 1-126 Maximum and Minimum Mode Command Timing

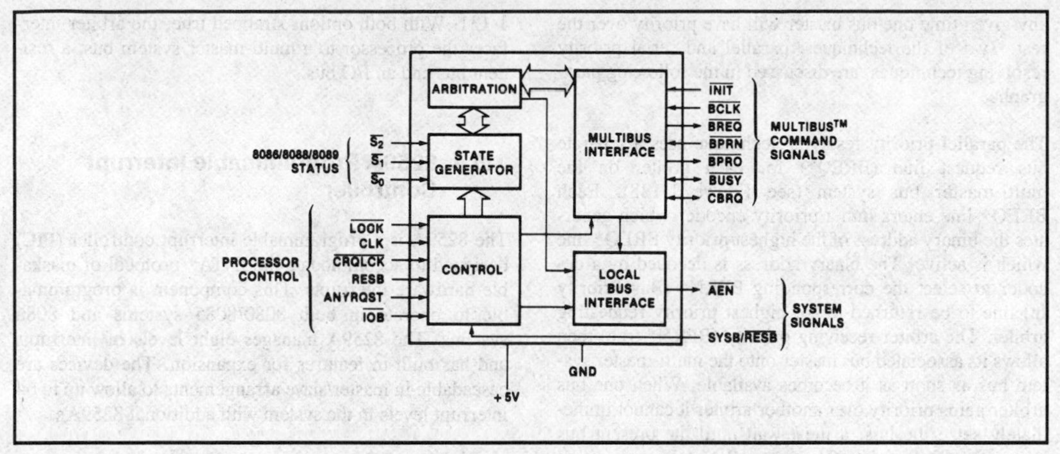

Figure 1-127 8289 Bus Arbiter Block Diagram

I/O BUS MODE

Strapping the IOB pin HIGH puts the 8288 in the I/O Bus mode of operation. In the I/O Bus mode all command lines (IORC*, IOWC*, AIOWC*, INTA*) are always enabled and not dependent on AEN*. When an I/O command is issued by the processor, the 8288 immediately activates the command lines using PDEN* and DT/R* to control the I/O bus transceiver. In this configuration the I/O command lines should not be used to control the system bus because there is no arbitration present. In this mode one 8288 can handle two external busses. No waiting is involved when the CPU wants to gain access to the I/O bus. Normal memory access requires a "Bus Ready" signal (AEN* LOW) before it will proceed. The IOB mode of operation is especially advantageous in a multi-processor system where there are I/O or peripherals are dedicated to only one processor.

SYSTEM BUS MODE

When the IOB pin is strapped LOW the 8288 is in the System Bus Mode of operation. No commands are issued in this mode until 115ns after the AEN* line is activated (LOW). The System Bus Mode assumes arbitration logic will inform the bus controller (on the AEN* line) when the bus is free for use. Both memory and I/O commands wait for arbitration. This mode is used when only one bus exists. In this case, both I/O and memory are shared by more than one processor.

1.8.3 8289 Bus Arbiter

The 8289 Bus Arbiter (see Figure 1-127) operates in conjunction with the 8288 Bus Controller to interface an 8086, 8088, or 8089 processor to a multi-master system bus (the 8289 is used as a general bus arbitration unit). The processor is unaware of the arbiter's existence and issues commands as though it has exclusive use of the system bus. If the processor does not have the use of the multi-master system bus, the bus arbiter prevents the bus controller, the data transceivers and the address latches from accessing the system bus (i.e., all bus driver outputs are forced into the high impedance state). Since the command was not issued, a transfer acknowledge (XACK) will not be returned and the processor will enter into wait states. Transfer acknowledges are signals returned from the addressed resource to indicate to the processor that the transfer is complete. This signal is typically used to control the ready inputs of the clock generator. The processor will remain in a wait state until the bus arbiter acquires the use of the multi-master system bus. At that time the bus arbiter will allow the bus controller, the data transceivers and the address latches to access the system bus. The 8089 uses the LOCK* output to guarantee exclusive access of a shared system bus for the duration of an instruction. LOCK* is software controlled and must be preceded by the instruction requiring exclusive access with a one byte "lock" prefix. When the lock prefix is decoded by the EU, the EU informs the BIU to activate the LOCK* output during the next clock signal. This signal remains active until one clock cycle after the execution of the associated data transfer is concluded. Once the command has been issued and a data transfer has taken place, a transfer acknowledge (XACK) is returned to the processor. The processor then completes its transfer cycle. In this way, the arbiter serves to multiplex a processor (or bus master) onto a multi-master system bus and avoid contention problems between bus masters.

Since there can be many bus masters on a multi-master system bus, some means of resolving priority between bus masters simutaneously requesting the bus must be provided. The 8289 provides several resolving techniques. These techniques are based on a priority concept that at any given time one bus master will have priority over the rest. Two of the techniques, parallel and serial priority resolving techniques, are discussed in the following paragraphs.

The parallel priority resolving technique uses a separate bus request line (BREQ*) for each arbiter on the multi-master bus system (see Figure 1-128). Each BREQ* line enters into a priority encoder which generates the binary address of the highest priority BREQ* line which is active. The binary address is decoded by a decoder to select the corresponding BPRN* (Bus Priority In) line to be returned to the highest priority requesting arbiter. The arbiter receiving priority (BPRN* true) then allows its associated bus master onto the multi-master system bus as soon as it becomes available. When one bus arbiter gains priority over another arbiter it cannot immediately seize the bus, it must wait until the present bus transaction is complete. Upon completing its transaction the present bus occupant recognizes that it no longer has priority and surrenders the bus by releasing BUSY*. BUSY* is an active low "OR" tied signal line which goes to every bus arbiter on the system bus. When BUSY* goes inactive (high), the arbiter which presently has bus priority (BPRN* true) then seizes the bus and pulls BUSY* low to keep other arbiters off the bus. Refer to Figure 1-129. Multi-master system bus transactions are synchronized to the bus clock (BCLK). This allows the parallel priority resolving circuits or any other priority resolving scheme to settle.

The serial priority resolving technique eliminates the need for the priority encoder-decoder arrangement by daisy-chaining the bus arbiters together, connecting the higher priority bus arbiter's BPRO* (Bus Priority Out) output to the BPRN* of the next lower priority. (See Figure 1-130).

There are two types of processors in the 8086 family -- an I/O processor (the 8089 IOP) and a non-I/O processor (the 8086 and 8088 CPU's). Consequently, there are two basic operating modes in the 8289 Bus Arbiter. One, the I/O Peripheral Bus (IOB) mode, permits the processor access to both an I/O peripheral bus and a multi-master system bus. The second, the Resident Bus (RESB) mode, permits the processor to communicate over both a resident bus and a multi-master system bus. Even though it is intended for the arbiter to be configured in the IOB mode when interfacing to an I/O processor and for it to be in the RESB mode when interfacing to a non-I/O processor, it is quite possible for the reverse to be true. That is, it is possible for a non-I/O processor to have access to an I/O peripheral bus or for an I/O processor to have access to a resident bus as well as access to a multi-master system bus. The IOB strapping option configures the 8289 Bus Arbiter into the IOB mode and RESB strapping optires it into the resident bus mode. If both strapping options are strapped false, a third mode of operation is created, the single bus mode, in which the arbiter interfaces the processor to a multi-master system bus only. See Figure 1-131. With both options strapped true, the arbiter interfaces the processor to a multi-master system bus, a resident bus and an I/O bus.

1.8.4 8259A Programmable Interrupt Controller

The 8259A is a programmable interrupt controller (PIC) designed to accommodate the INTA* protocol of maskable hardware interrupts. This component is programmable to operate in both 8080/8085 systems and 8086 systems. The 8259A manages eight levels of interrupts and has built-in features for expansion. The devices are cascadable in master/slave arrangements to allow up to 64 interrupt levels in the system with additional 8259A's.

Figures 1-132 and 1-133 are examples of 8259A's in minimum and maximum mode 8086 systems. The minimum mode configuration (a) shows an 8259A connected to the CPU's multiplexed bus. Configuration (b) illustrates an 8259A connected to a demultiplexed bus system. These interconnects are also applicable to maximum mode systems. The configuration given for a maximum mode system shows a master 8259A on the CPU's multiplexed bus witave 8259A's out on the buffered system bus. This configuration demonstrates several unique features of the maximum mode system interface. If the master 8259A receives interrupts from a mix of slave 8259A's and regular idevices, the slaves must provide the type number for devices connected to them while the master provides the type number for devices directly attached to its interrupt inputs. The master 8259A is programmable to determine if an interrupt is from a direct input or a slave 8259A and will use this information to enable or disable the data bus transceivers (via the NAND function of DEN and EN*). If the master must provide the type number, it will disable the data bus transceivers. If the slave provides the type number, the master will enable the data bus transceivers. The EN* output is normally high to allow the 8086/8288 to control the bus transceivers. To select the proper slave when servicing a slave interrupt, the master must provide a cascade address to the slave. If the 8288 is not strapped in the I/O bus mode (the 8288 IOB input connected to ground), the MCE/PDEN* output becomes a MCE or Master Cascade Enable output. This signal is only active during INTA* cycles (see Figure 1-134) and enables the master 8259A's cascade address onto the 8086's local bus during ALE. This allows the address latches to capture the cascade address with ALE and allows use of the dress bus for selecting the proper slave 8259A. The MCE is gated with LOCK* to minimize local bus contention between the 8086 tri-stating its bus outputs and the cascade address being enabled onto the bus. The first INTA* bus cycle allows the master to resolve internal priorities and output a cascade address to be transmitted to the slaves on the subsequent INTA* bus cycle.

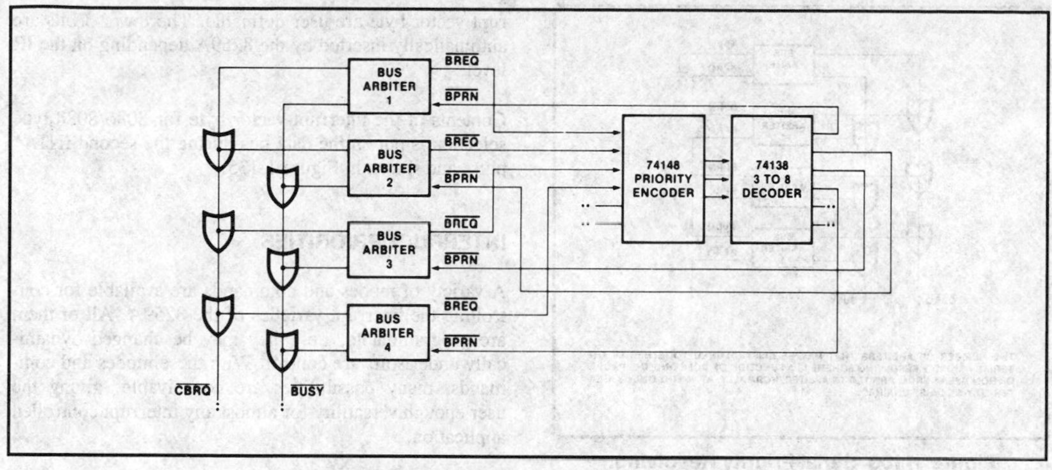

Figure 1-128 Resolving Technique

The following paragraphs provide a more detailed description of interrupt vectoring, the interrupt priority scheme, the edge and level triggering modes and interrupt cascading. For additional information on the 8259A, refer to Intel Application Note AP-59.

INTERRUPT VECTORING

Each IR input of the 8259A has an individual interrupt vector address in memory associated with it. Designation of each address depends upon the initial programming of the 8259A. The 8259A must be programmed in the MCS-86/88 mode of operation to insure correct interrupt vectoring when used in an 8086/8088 system.

When programmed in the MCS-86/88 mode, the 8259A should only be used with an MCS-86 or MCS-88 system. In this mode, the 8086/8088 will handle interrupts in the format described in the 8259A — 8086/8088 Overview.

Upon interrupt in the MCS-86/88 mode, the 8259A will output a single interrupt-vector byte to the data bus. This is in response to only two INTA* pulses issued by the 8086/8088 after the 8259A has raised INT high.

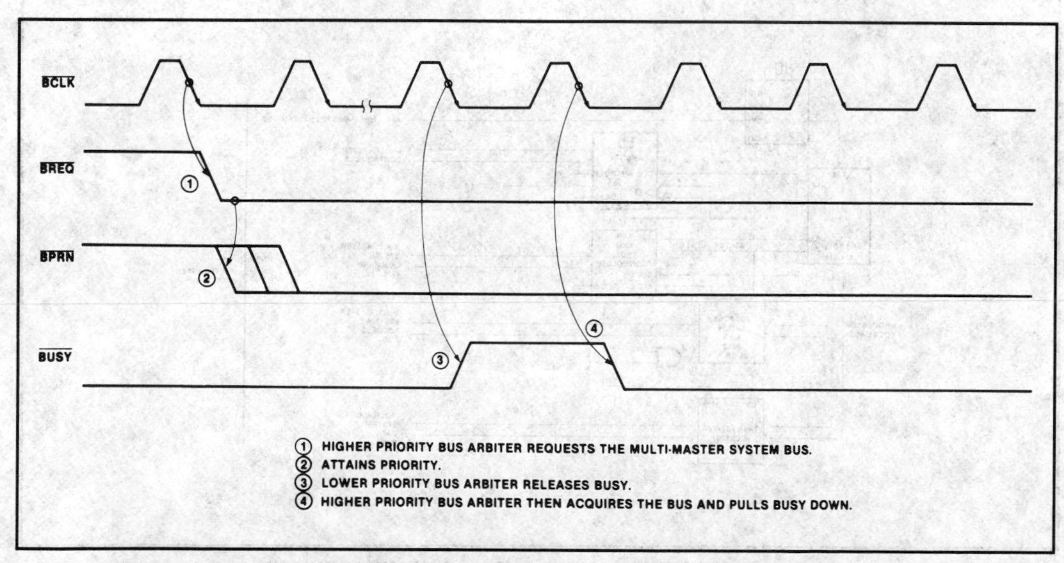

Figure 1-129 Higher Priority Arbiter Obtaining the Bus from a Lower Priority Arbiter

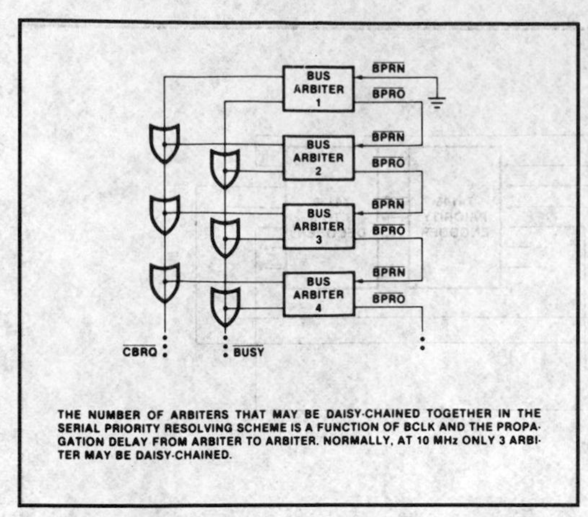

Figure 1-130 Serial Priority Resolving.

The first INTA* pulse is used only for set-up purposes internal to the 8259A. As in the MCS-80/85 mode, this setup includes priority resolution and cascade mode operations which will be covered later. Unlike the MCS-80/85 mode, no CALL opcode is placed on the data bus.

The second INTA* pulse is used to enable the single interrupt-vector byte to select one of 256 interrupt "types" in the 8086/8088 memory. Interrupt type selection for all eight IR levels is made when initially programming the 8259A. However, reference to only one interrupt is needed for programming. The upper 5 bits of the interrupt vector byte are user definable. The lower 3 bits are automatically inserted by the 8259A depending on the IR level.

Contents of the interrupt-vector byte for 8086/8088 type selection is put on the data bus during the second INTA* pulse and shown in Figure 1-135.

INTERRUPT PRIORITIES

A variety of modes and commands are available for controlling the interrupt varieties of the 8259A. All of them are programmable, i.e., they may be changed dynamically under software control. With these modes and commands, many possibilities are conceivable, giving the user enough versatility for almost any interrupt controlled application.

Fully Nested Mode

The fully nested mode is a general purpose priority mode. This mode supports a multilevel-interrupt structure in which priority order of all eight IR inputs are arranged from highest to lowest.

Unless otherwise programmed, the fully nested mode is entered by default upon initialization. At this time, IR0 is assigned the highest priority through IR7 the lowest. The fully nested mode, however, is not confined to this IR structure alone. Once past initialization, other IR inputs can be assigned highest priority also, keeping the

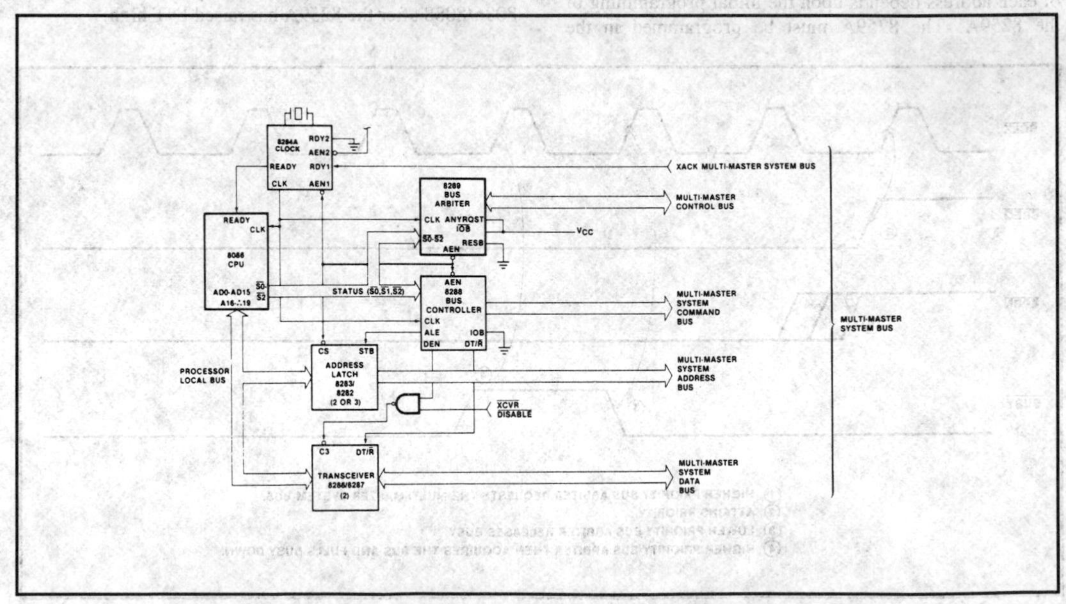

Figure 1-131 Typical Medium Complexity CPU Circuit

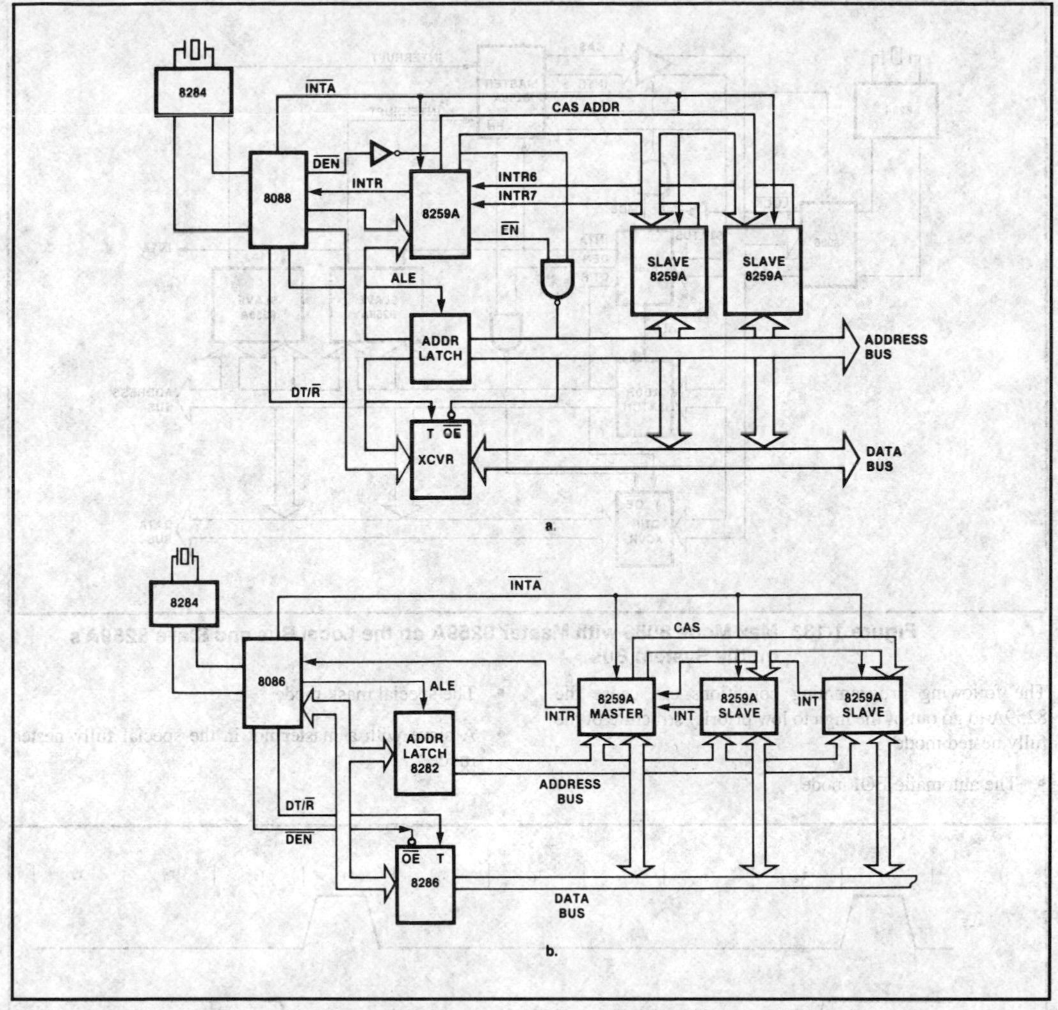

Figure 1-132 Min Mode 8086 with Master 8259A on the Local Bus and Slave 8259A's on the System Bus

multilevel-interrupt structure of the fully nested mode. Figure 1-136 shows some variations of the priority structures in the fully nested mode.

In general, when an interrupt is acknowledged, the highest priority request is determined from the IRR (Interrupt Request Register). The interrupt vector is then placed on the data bus. In addition, the corresponding bit in the ISR (In-Service Register) is set to designate the routine in service. This ISR bit remains set until an EOI (End-Of-Interrupt) command is issued to the 8259A. EOI's will be explained in greater detail shortly.

In the fully nested mode, while an ISR bit is set, all further requests of the same or lower priority are inhibited from generating an interrupt to the microprocessor. A higher priority request, though, can generate an interrupt, thus vectoring program execution to its service routine. Interrupts are only acknowledged, however, if the microprocessor has previously executed an"Enable Interrupts" instruction. This is because the interrupt request pin on the microprocessor gets disabled automatically after acknowledgement of any interrupt. The assembly language instruction used to enable interrupts is "STI". Interrupts can be disable by using the instruction "CLI". When a routine is completed a "return" instruction "IRET" is executed.

A single 8259A is essentially always in the fully nested mode unless certain programming conditions disturb it.

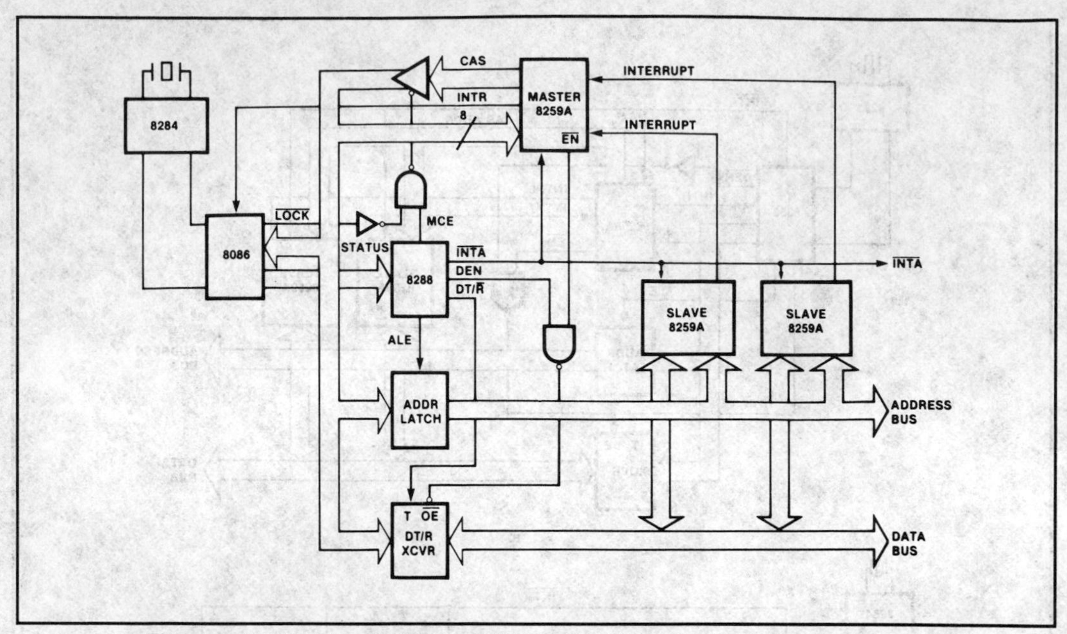

Figure 1-133 Max Mode 8086 with Master 8259A on the Local Bus and Slave 8259A's on the System Bus

The following programming conditions can cause the 8259A to go out of the high to low priority structure of the fully nested mode.

- The automatic EOI mode
- The special mask mode
- A slave with a master not in the special fully nested mode

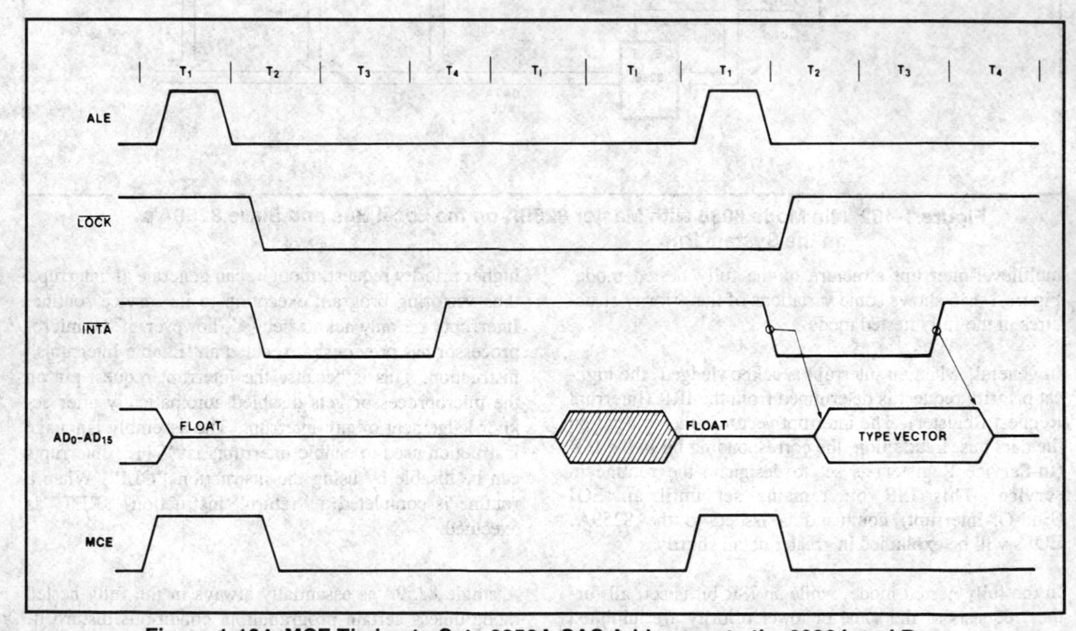

Figure 1-134 MCE Timing to Gate 8259A CAS Address onto the 8086 Local Bus

IR	D7	D6	D5	D4	D3	D2	D1	D0
7	T7	T6	T5	T4	T3	1	1	1
6	T7	T6	T5	T4	T3	1	1	0
5	T7	T6	T5	T4	T3	1	0	1
4	T7	T6	T5	T4	T3	1	0	0
3	T7	T6	T5	T4	T3	0	1	1
2	T7	T6	T5	T4	T3	0	1	0
1	T7	T6	T5	T4	T3	0	0	1
0	T7	T6	T5	T4	T3	0	0	0

Figure 1-135 Interrupt Vector Byte

Additional details on these interrupt modes can be found in Intel Application Note AP-59. These modes are mentioned here so that the designer will be aware of them. As long as these program conditions are not enacted, the fully nested mode remains undisturbed.

End of Interrupt (EOI)

Upon completion of an interrupt service the 8259A must be informed so that its ISR can be updated. This is done to keep track of which interrupt levels are in the process of being serviced and their relative priorities. Three different End-Of-Interrupt (EOI) formats are available to the designer. These are: 1) non-specific EOI command; 2) specific EOI command; and, 3) automatic EOI command. Selection of which EOI to use is dependent on the interrupt operation the designer wishes to perform.

a. Non-Specific EOI Command

The microprocessor sends a non-specific EOI command to let the 8259A know when a service routine has been completed. This command does not specify the the exact interrupt level. The 8259A automatically determines the interrupt level and resets the correct bit in the ISR.

To use the non-specific EOI command the 8259A must be in a mode of operation where it can predetermine in-service routine levels. For this reason the non-specific EOI command should only be used when the most recent level acknowledged and serviced is always the highest priority level. When the 8259A receives a non-specific EOI

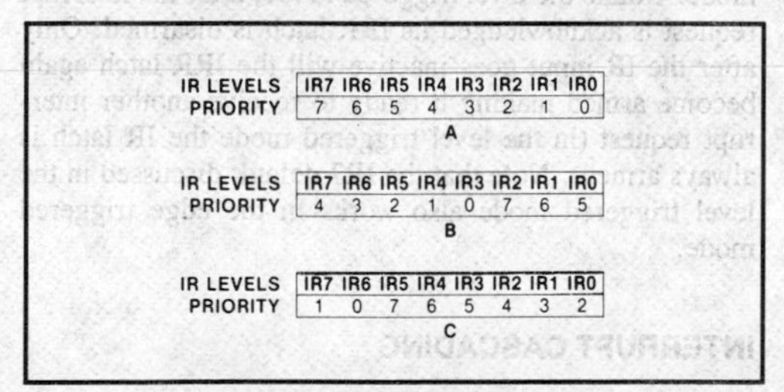

Figure 1-136 Priority Structure Variations — Fully Nested Mode

command, it resets the highest priority ISR bit. This confirms to the 8259A that the highest priority routine of the routines in service is finished.

b. Specific EOI Command

A specific EOI command is sent from the microprocessor to let the 8259A know when a service routine of a particular interrupt level is completed. Unlike the non-specific EOI command which automatically resets the highest priority ISR bit, a specific EOI command specifies an exact ISR bit to be reset. One of the eight IR levels of the 8259A can be specified in this command. The purpose of the specific EOI command is to reset the ISR bit of a completed service routine whenever the 8259A cannot automatically determine the completion.

c. Automatic EOI Mode

When programmed in the automatic EOI mode the microprocessor does not need to issue a command to notify the 8259A of a completed interrupt routine. The 8259A accomplishes this by performing a non-specific EOI automatically at the trailing edge of the last INTA* pulse (second pulse). The advantage of automatic EOI over the other EOI commands is that no command has to be issued. This simplifies programming and lowers code requirements within interrupt routines. However, special consideration must be taken when deciding to use the automatic EOI mode because it disturbs the fully nested mode.

Automatic Rotation — Equal Priority

Automatic rotation of priorities is used in applications where interrupting devices are of equal priority, such as communications channels. The concept is that once a peripheral is serviced, all other equal priority peripherals should be given a chance to be serviced before the original peripheral is serviced again. This is accomplished by automatically assigning a peripheral the lowest priority after it has been serviced. Therefore, worst case, the device would have to wait until all other devices have been serviced before being serviced again.

There are two methods of accomplishing automatic rotation. One is the "rotate on non-specific EOI command" which is used with the non-specific EOI command. The other is the "rotate in automatic EOI mode" which is used with the automatic EOI mode.

a. Rotate On Non-Specific EOI Command

When the rotate on non-specific EOI command is issued, the highest ISR bit is reset as in a normal non-specific EOI command. However, after the ISR bit is reset the corresponding IR level is assigned the lowest priority. Other IR priorities rotate to conform to the fully nested mode based on the newly assigned low priority.

b. Rotate On Automatic EOI Mode

The rotate in automatic EOI mode operates similar to the non-specific EOI command. The main difference is that priority is done automatically after the last INTA* pulse of an interrupt request. To enter or exit this mode a rotate-in-automatic-EOI set command and a rotate-in-automatic-EOI clear command is provided. After these two commands, no other commands are needed, as in the automatic EOI mode. However, when using any form of the automatic EOI mode, special consideration since the guideline for the automatic EOI mode also stands for the rotate in automatic EOI mode.

Specific Rotation — Specific Priority

The specific rotation mode provides the designer with versatile capabilities in interrupt controlled operations. This priority mode is very useful in applications where a specific device's interrupt priority must be altered. Unlike automatic rotation, which automatically sets priorities, specific rotation is completely user controlled. The user selects which interrupt level is to receive lowest or highest priority. This can be done during the main program or within interrupt routines. Two specific rotation commands are available to the user, the "set priority command" and the "rotate on specific EOI command".

a. Set Priority Command

The set priority command allows the programmer to assign an IR level to the lowest priority. All other interrupt levels will conform to the fully nested mode based on the newly assigned low priority.

b. Rotate On Specific EOI Command

The rotate on specific EOI command is a combination of the set priority and the specific EOI command. As in the set priority command, a specified IR level is assigned lowest priority. As in the specific EOI command, a specified level will be reset in the ISR. Therefore, the rotate on specific EOI command accomplishes both tasks in only one command.

INTERRUPT TRIGGERING

There are two basic ways of sensing an active interrupt request. One is a level sensitive input and the other is an edge sensitive input. The 8259A provides the edge triggered mode and the level triggered mode to allow the user the capability of either method. Selection of one of these methods is done during the programmed initialization of the 8259A.

Level Triggered Mode

When the 8259A is in the level triggered mode it will recognize any active (high) level on the IR input as an interrupt request. If the IR input remains active after an EOI command has been issued, resetting its ISR bit, another interrupt will be generated. This assumes the processor INT pin is enabled. Unless repetitious interrupt generation is desired, The IR input must be brought to an inactive state before an EOI command is issued in its service routine. However, necessary timing requirements must be obeyed (see Figure 1-137). Note that the request on the IR line must remain until after the falling edge of the first INTA* pulse. On any IR input, if the request goes inactive before the first INTA* pulse, the 8259A will respond as if IR7 was active. In any design where there is a possibility of this happening, the IR7 default feature can be used as a safeguard. This can be accomplished by using the IR7 routine as a "cleanup routine" which might check the 8259A status or merely return program executi to its pre-interrupt location.

Edge Triggered Mode

In the edge triggered mode the 8259A will only recognize interrupts if generated by an inactive (low) to active (high) transition on the IR input. The edge triggered mode incorporates an edge lockout method of operation. This means that after the rising edge of an interrupt request and the acknowledge of the request, the positive level of the IR input will not generate further interrupts on this level. The user does not neeto worry about quickly removing the request to avoid generating further interrupts. Before another interrupt can be generated the IR input must return to the inactive state.

Timing requirements for the edge triggered mode are shown Figure 1-137. As in the level triggered mode, the request on the IR input must remain active until after the falling edge of the first INTA* pulse in the edge triggered mode. Unlike the level triggered mode, after the interrupt request is acknowledged its IRR latch is disarmed. Only after the IR input goes inactive will the IRR latch again become armed making it ready to receive another interrupt request (in the level triggered mode the IR latch is always armed). Note that the IR7 default discussed in the level triggered mode also works in the edge triggered mode.

INTERRUPT CASCADING

More than one 8259A can be used to expand the priority interrupt scheme to up to 64 levels without additional

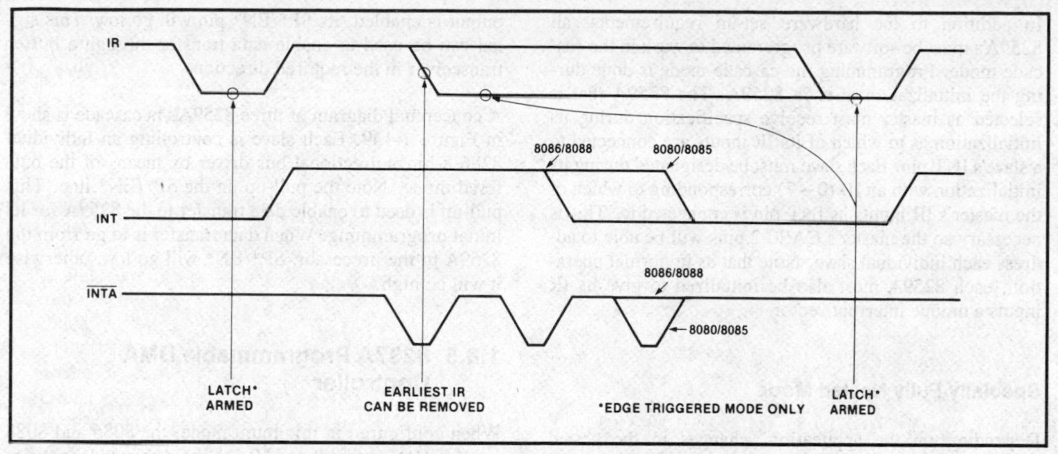

Figure 1-137 IR Triggering Timing Requirements

hardware. This method for expanded interrupt capability is called cascading. The 8259A supports cascading operations with the cascade mode. Additionally, the specially fully nested mode and the buffered mode are available for increased flexibility when cascading 8259A's under certain applications.

Cascade Mode

In the cascade mode, basic operation consists of one 8259A acting as a master to the others which are acting as slaves. A specific hardware set-up is required to establish operation in the cascade mode (see Figure 1-138). Figure 1-138 shows a typical system containing a master and two slaves, providing 22 interrupt levels. Note that the master is designated by a high on the SP*/EN* pin, while the SP*/EN* pins on the slaves are grounded (this can also be done by software, see the buffered mode). Also the INT output pin of each slave is connected to the an IR input pin on the master. The CAS0-2 pins on all 8259A's are paralleled. These pins, which act as outputs when the 8259A is a master and inputs for the slaves, serve as a private 8259A bus. They control which slave has control of the system bus for interrupt vectoring operation with the processor. All other pins are connected as in normal operation (each receives an INTA pulse).

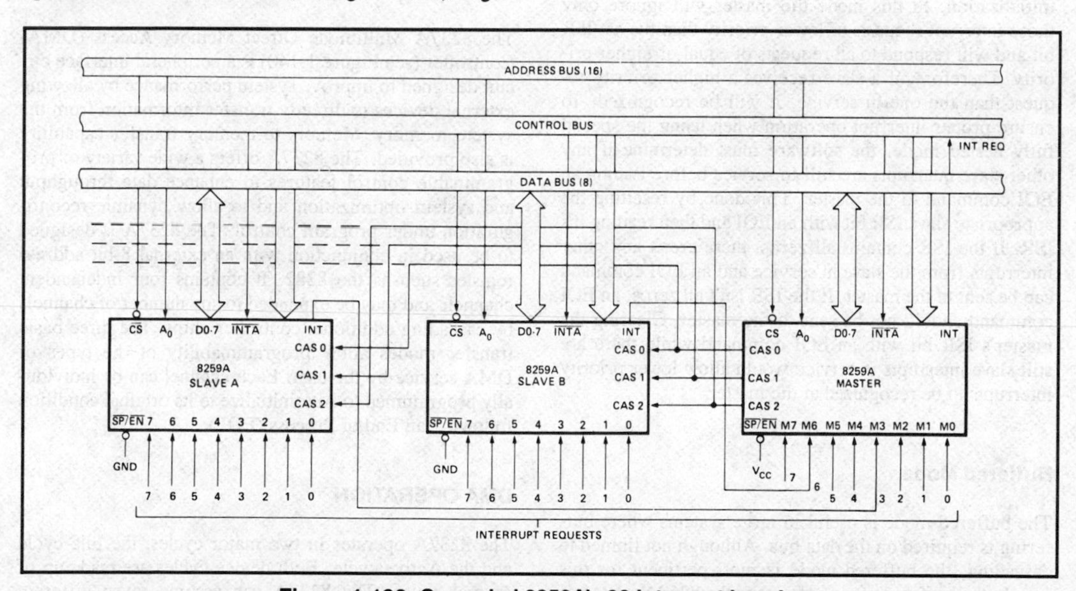

Figure 1-138 Cascaded 8259A's 22 Interrupt Levels

In addition to the hardware set-up requirements, all 8259A's must be software programmed to work in the cascade mode. Programming the cascade mode is done during the initialization of each 8259A. The 8259A that is selected as master must receive specification during its initialization as to which of its IR inputs are connected to a slave's INT pin. Each slave must be designated during its initialization with an ID (0 – 7) corresponding to which of the master's IR inputs its INT pin is connected to. This is necessary so the master's CAS0-2 pins will be able to address each individual slave. Note that as in normal operation, each 8259A must also be initialized to give its IR inputs a unique interrupt vector.

Specially Fully Nested Mode

Depending on the application, changes in the nested structure of the cascade mode may be desired. This is because the nested structure of a slave 8259A differs from that of the normal fully nested mode. In the cascade mode, if a slave receives a higher priority interrupt request than the one in service (through the same slave), it will not be recognized by the master. This is because the master's ISR bit is set, ignoring all requests of equal or lower priority. In this case, the higher priority slave interrupt will not be serviced until after the master's ISR bit is reset by an EOI command. This will normally be after completion of the lower priority routine.

If the user wishes to have a truly fully nested structure within a slave 8259A, the specially fully nested mode should be used. The specially fully nested mode is programmed in the master only. This is done the master's initialization. In this mode the master will ignore only those interrupt requests of lower priority than the set ISR bit and will respond to all requests of equal or higher priority. Therefore, if a slave receives a higher priority request than the one in service, it will be recognized. To ensure proper interrupt operation when using the special fully nested mode, the software must determine if any other slave interrupts are still in service before issuing an EOI command to the master. This done by resetting the appropriate slave ISR bit with an EOI and then reading it's ISR. If the ISR contains all zeros, there aren't any other interrupts from the slave in service and an EOI command can be sent to the master. If the ISR isn't all zeros, an EOI command should not be sent to the master. Clearing the master's ISR bit with an EOI command while there are still slave interrupts in service would allow lower priority interrupts to be recognized at the master.

Buffered Mode

The buffered mode is useful in large systems where buffering is required on the data bus. Although not limited to cascading, the buffered mode is most pertinent for this use. In the buffered mode, whenever the 8259A's data bus output is enabled, its SP*/EN* pin will go low. This signal can be used to enable data transfer through a buffer transceiver in the required direction.

A conceptual diagram of three 8259A's in cascade is show in Figure 1-139. Each slave is controlling an individual 8286 8-bit bidirectional bus driver by means of the buffered mode. Note the pull-up on the SP*/EN* line. This pull-up is used to enable data transfer to the 8259A for its initial programming. When data transfer is to go from the 8259A to the processor, SP*/EN* will go low, otherwise it will be high.

1.8.5 8237A Programmable DMA Controller

When configured in minimum mode, the 8086 and 8088 provide HOLD (hold) and HLDA (hold acknowledge) signals that are compatible with the 8237A DMA controller. The 8237A can request use of the bus for direct transfer of data between an I/O device and memory by activating HOLD. The CPU will complete the current bus cycle, if one is in progress, and the issue HLDA, granting the bus to the DMA controller. The CPU will not attempt to use the bus until HOLD goes inactive.

The 8086 addresses memory that is physically organized in two separate banks, one containing even-addressed bytes and one containing odd-addressed bytes. An 8-bit DMA controller must alternately select these banks to access logically adjacent bytes in memory. Used as a maximum mode DMA controller, the 8089 provides a simple way to interface a high-speed 8-bit device to an 8086-based system (refer to Chapter 4).

The 8237A Multimode Direct Memory Access (DMA) Controller (see Figure 1-140) is a peripheral interface circuit designed to improve system performance by allowing external devices to directly transfer information from the system memory. Memory-to-memory transfer capability is also provided. The 8237A offers a wide variety of programmable control features to enhance data throughput and system optimization and to allow dynamic reconfiguration under program control. The 8237A is designed to be used in conjunction with an external 8-bit address register such as the 8282. It contains four independent channels and may be expanded to any number of channels by cascading additional controller chips. The three basic transfer modes allow programmability of the types of DMA service by the user. Each channel can be individually programmed to Autoinitialize to its original condition following an End of Process (EOP).

DMA OPERATION

The 8237A operates in two major cycles, the Idle cycle and the Active cycle. Both device cycles are made up of several states. The 8237A can assume seven different

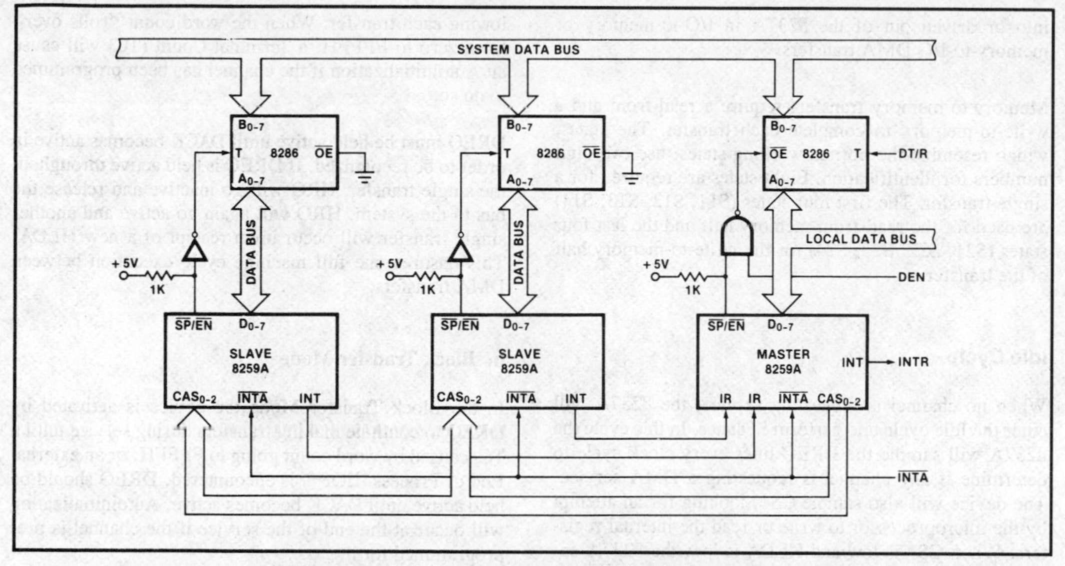

Figure 1-139 Cascade-Buffered Mode Example

states, each composed of one or more complete clock cycles. State I (SI) is the inactive state. This state is entered when the 8237A has no valid DMA requests pending. In the SI state, the DMA controller is inactive, but may be in the Program Condition, being programmed by the processor. State S0 (S0) is the first state of a DMA service. At this point the 8237A has requested a hold, but the processor has not yet returned an acknowledge. The 8237 may still be programmed until it receives HLDA from the CPU. An acknowledge from the CPU signals that DMA transfers can begin. S1, S2, S3 and S4 are working the states of the DMA service. If more time is needed to complete a transfer than is available with normal timing, wait states (SW) can be inserted between S2 or S3 and S4 by use of the Ready line on the 8237A. Note that the data transferred directly from the I/O device-to-memory (or visa versa) with IOR* and MEMW* (or MEMR* and IOW*) being active at the same time. The data is not read

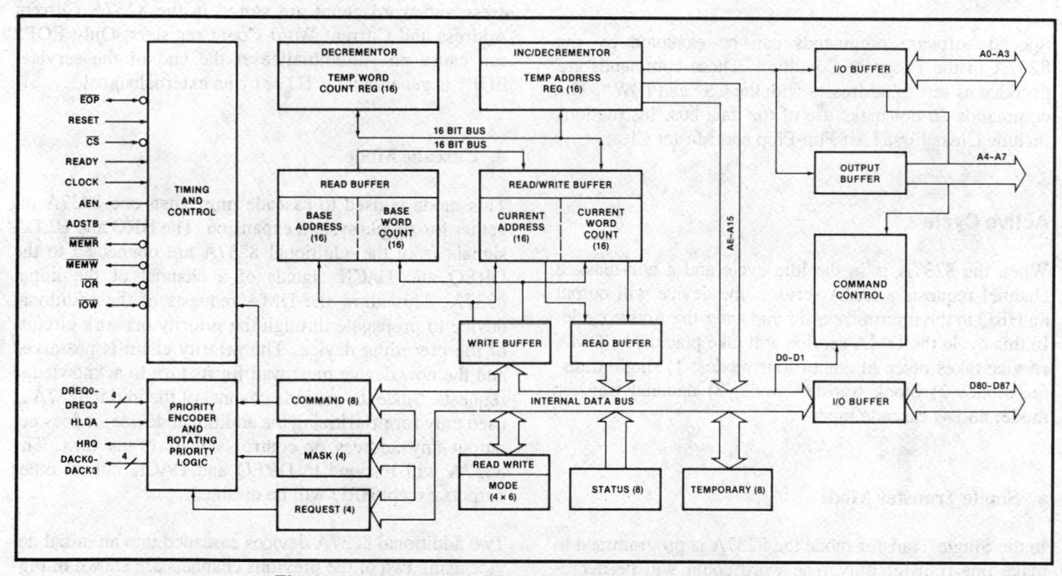

Figure 1-140 8237A DMA Controller Block Diagram

into or driven out of the 8237A in I/O-to-memory or memory-to-I/O DMA transfers.

Memory-to-memory transfers require a read-from and a write-to-memory to complete each transfer. The states, which resemble the normal working states, use two digit numbers for identification. Eight states are required for a single transfer. The first four states (S11, S12, S13, S14) are used for the read-from-memory half and the last four states (S21, S22, S23, S24) for the write-to-memory half of the transfer.

Idle Cycle

When no channel is requesting service, the 8237A will enter the Idle cycle and perform SI states. In this cycle the 8237A will sample the DREQ lines every clock cycle to determine if any channel is requesting a DMA service. The device will also sample CS*, looking for an attempt by the microprocessor to write or read the internal registers. When CS* is low and HLDA is low, the 8237A enters the Program condition. The CPU can now establish, change or inspect the internal definition of the part by reading from or writing to the internal registers. Address lines A0-A3 are inputs to the device and select which registers will be read or written. The IOR* and IOW* lines are used to select and time reads or writes. An internal flip-flop is used to generate an additional bit of address due to the number and size of the internal registers. This bit is used to determine the upper or lower byte of the 16-bit Address and Word Count registers. The flip-flop is reset by Master Clear or Reset. A separate software command can also reset this flip-flop.

Special software commands can be executed by the 8237A in the Program Condition. These commands are decoded as sets of addresses with the CS* and IOW*. The commands do not make use of the data bus. Instructions include Clear First/Last Flip-Flop and Master Clear.

Active Cycle

When the 8237A is in the Idle cycle and a non-masked channel requests a DMA service, the device will output an HRQ to the microprocessor and enter the Active cycle. In this cycle the DMA service will take place. The DMA service takes place in one of four modes: 1) single transfer mode; 2) block transfer mode; 3) demand transfer mode; and 4) cascade mode.

a. Single Transfer Mode

In the Single Transfer mode the 8237A is programmed to make one transfer only. The word count will be decremented and the address decremented of incremented following each transfer. When the word count "rolls over" from zero to FFFFH, a Terminal Count (TC) will cause an Autoinitialization if the channel has been programmed to do so.

DREQ must be held active until DACK becomes active in order to be recognized. If DREQ is held active throughout the single transfer, HRQ will go inactive and release the bus to the system. HRQ will again go active and another single transfer will occur upon receipt of a new HLDA. This ensures one full machine cycle execution between DMA transfers.

b. Block Transfer Mode

In the Block Transfer Mode the device is activated by DREQ to continue making transfers during service until a TC, caused by word count going to FFFFH, or an external End of Process (EOP*) is encountered. DREQ should be held active until DACK becomes active. Autoinitialization will occur at the end of the service if the channel is preprogrammed for it.

c. Demand Transfer Mode

In this mode the device is programmed to continue making transfers until a TC of external EOP* is encountered, or until DREQ goes inactive. Therefore, transfers may continue until the I/O device has exhausted its data capacity. After the I/O device has had a chance to catch up, the DMA service is re-established by means of a DREQ. During the time between services when the microprocessor is allowed to operate, the intermediate values of address and word count are stored in the 8237A Current Address and Current Word Count registers. Only EOP* can cause an Autoinitialize at the end of the service. EOP* is generated by TC or by an external signal.

d. Cascade Mode

This mode is used to cascade more than one 8237A together for simple system expansion. The HRQ and HLDA signals from the additional 8237A are connected to the DREQ and DACK signals of a channel of the initial 8237A. This allow the DMA requests of the additional device to propagate through the priority network circuits of the preceding device. The priority chain is preserved and the new device must wait for its turn to acknowledge requests. Since the cascade channel of the initial 8237A is used only for prioritizing the additional device, it does not output any address or control signals of its own. The 8237A will respond to DREQ and DACK but all other outputs except HRQ will be disabled.

Two additional 8237A devices cascaded into an initial device using two of the previous channels are shown in Figure 1-141. This forms a two level DMA system. More

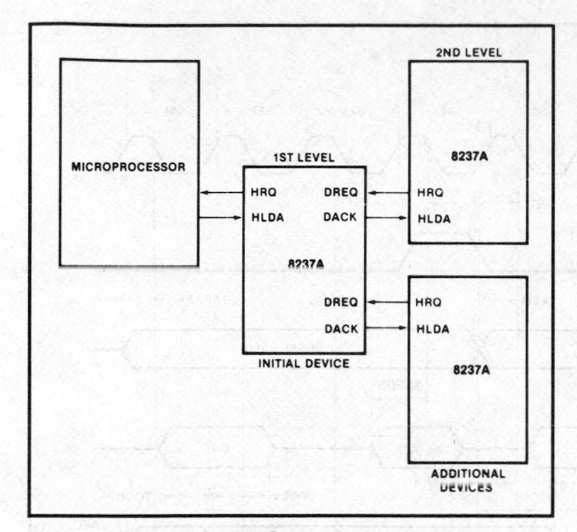

Figure 1-141 Cascaded 8237As

8237As could be added at the second level by using the remaining channels of the first level. Additional devices can also be added by cascading into the channels of the second level devices, forming a third level.

TRANSFER TYPES

Each of the three active transfer modes can perform three different types of transfers. These are Read, Write, and Verify. Write transfers move data from an I/O device to the memory by activating MEMW* and IOR*. Read transfers move data from memory to an I/O device by activating MEMR* and IOW*. Verify transfers are pseudo transfers. The 8237A operates as in Read or Write transfers generating addresses, and responding to EOP, however, the memory and I/O control lines all remain inactive. Verify mode is not permitted during memory to memory operation.

Memory-to-Memory Transfers

The 8237A includes a memory-to-memory transfer feature to perform block moves of data from one memory address space to another with a minimum of program space and effort. (See Figure 1-142 for timing.) Channels 0 and 1 are selected to operate in the memory-to-memory mode by programming a bit in the Command register. A transfer is initiated by setting the software DREQ for channel 0. The 8237A requests a DMA service in the normal manner. After HLDA is true, the device reads data from the memory using eight-state transfers in the Block Transfer mode. The channel 0 Current Address register is the source for the address used and is decremented or incremented in the normal manner. The data byte read from the memory is stored in the 8237A internal Temporary register. Channel 1 then writes the data from the Temporary register to memory using the address in its Current Address register and incrementing or decrementing it in the normal manner. The channel 1 Current Count is decremented. When the word count of the channel goes to FFFFH, a TC is generated causing an EOP* output terminating the service. To allow a single word to be written to a block of memory Channel 0 may be programmed to retain the same address for all transfers.

The 8237A will respond to external EOP* signals during memory-to-memory transfers. Data comparators in block schemes may use this input to terminate the service when a match is found. Memory-to-memory operations can be detected as an active AEN with no DACK outputs.

DMA REGISTERS

The 8237A contains 344 bits of internal memory in the form of registers. Table 1-44 lists the registers by name and shows the size of each. The following paragraphs provide a detailed description of each register and their functions.

Current Address Register

Each channel has a 16-bit Current Address register. This register holds the value of the address used during DMA transfers. The address is automatically incremented or decremented after each transfer and the intermediate values of the address are stored in the Current Address register during the transfer. This register is written or read by the microprocessor in successive 8-bit bytes. The register may also be reinitialized back to its original value by an Autoinitialize. Autoinitialize takes place after EOP*.

Current Word Register

Each channel has a 16-bit Current Word Register. This register determines the number of transfers to be performed. The actual number of transfers will be one more than the number programmed in the Current Word register (programming a count of 100 will result in 101 transfers, etc.). The word count is decremented after each transfer. The immediate value of the word count is stored in the register during the transfer. When the value in the register goes from zero to FFFFH, a TC will be generated. This register is loaded or read in successive 8-bit bytes by the microprocessor in the Program Condition. Following the end of a DMA service it may also be reinitialized by an Autoinitialization back to its original value. Autoinitialize can occur only when EOP* occurs. If it is not Autoinitialized, this register will have a count of FFFFH after TC.

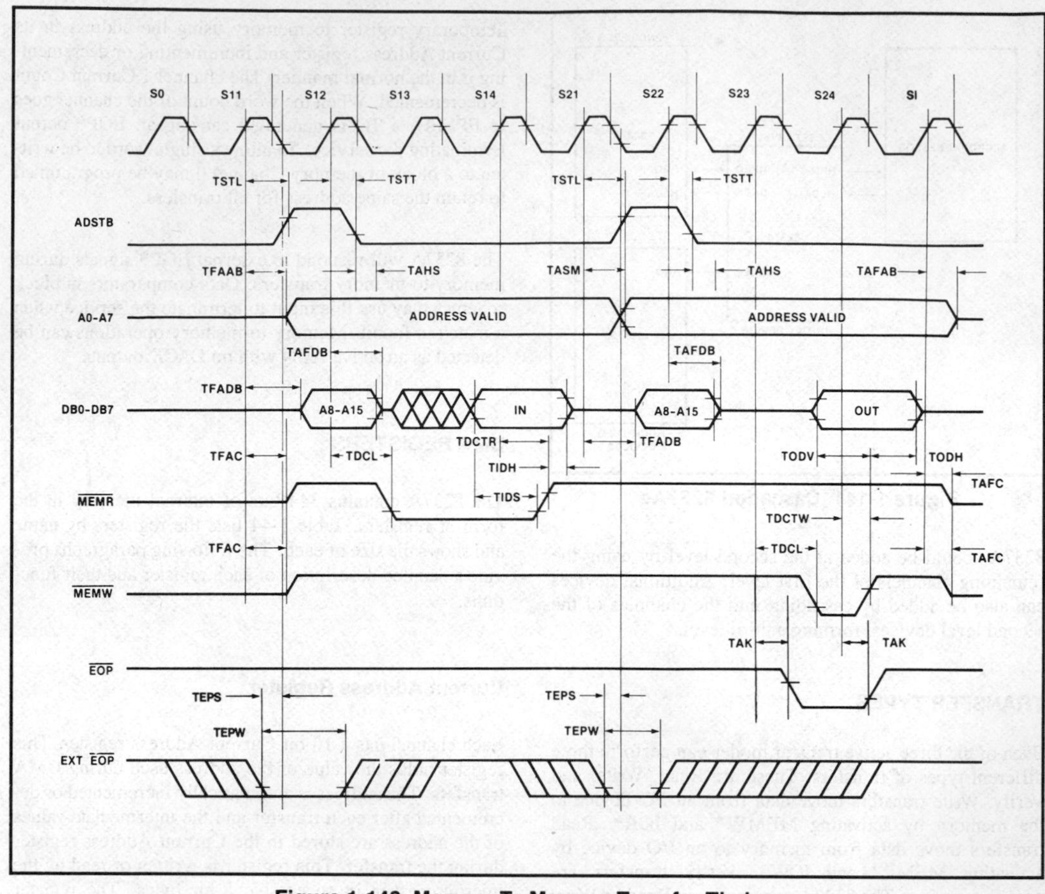

Figure 1-142 Memory-To-Memory Transfer Timing

Base Address and Base Word Count Registers

Each channel has a pair of Base Address and Base Word Count Registers. These 16-bit registers store the original value of their associated current registers. During Autoinitialize these values are used to restore the current registers to their original values. The base registers are written simultaneously with their corresponding current register in 8-bit bytes in the Program Condition by the microprocessor. These registers cannot be read by the microprocessor.

Table 1-44 8237A Internal Registers

Name	Size	Number
Base Address Registers	16 bits	4
Base Word Count Registers	16 bits	4
Current Address Registers	16 bits	4
Current Word Count Registers	16 bits	4
Temporary Address Register	16 bits	1
Temporary Word Count Register	16 bits	1
Status Register	8 bits	1
Command Register	8 bits	1
Temporary Register	8 bits	1
Mode Registers	6 bits	4
Mask Register	4 bits	1
Request Register	4 bits	1

Command Register

The 8-bit Command register controls the operation of the 8237A (see Figure 1-143). This register is programmed by the microprocessor in the Program Condition and is cleared by Reset or a Master Clear instruction. Figure 1-143 lists the function of each of the command bits. Figure 1-144 shows the address coding.

Mode Register

Each channel has a 6-bit Mode register associated with it (see Figure 1-145). When the register is being written to

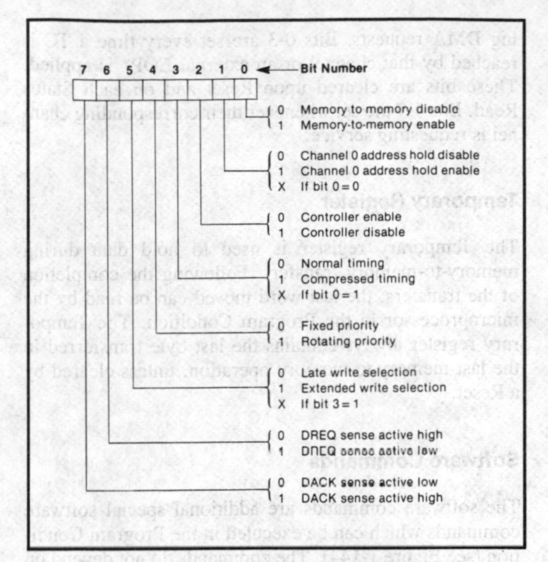

Figure 1-143 Command Register

by the microprocessor in the Program condition, bits 0 and 1 determine which channel Mode register is to be written.

Request Register

The 8237A can respond to requests for DMA service which are initiated by software as well as by a DREQ. Each channel has a request bit associated with it in the 4-bit Request register (see Figure 1-146). These are non-maskable and subject to prioritization by the Priority Encoder network. Each register bit is set or reset separately under software control or is cleared upon generation of a TC or external EOP*. The entire register is cleared by a Reset. To set or reset a bit, the software loads

Signals						Operation
A3	A2	A1	A0	$\overline{IOR}$	$\overline{IOW}$	
1	0	0	0	0	1	Read Status Register
1	0	0	0	1	0	Write Command Register
1	0	0	1	0	1	Illegal
1	0	0	1	1	0	Write Request Register
1	0	1	0	0	1	Illegal
1	0	1	0	1	0	Write Single Mask Register Bit
1	0	1	1	0	1	Illegal
1	0	1	1	1	0	Write Mode Register
1	1	0	0	0	1	Illegal
1	1	0	0	1	0	Clear Byte Pointer Flip/Flop
1	1	0	1	0	1	Read Temporary Register
1	1	0	1	1	0	Master Clear
1	1	1	0	0	1	Illegal
1	1	1	0	1	0	Clear Mask Register
1	1	1	1	0	1	Illegal
1	1	1	1	1	0	Write All Mask Register Bits

Figure 1-144 Software Command Codes

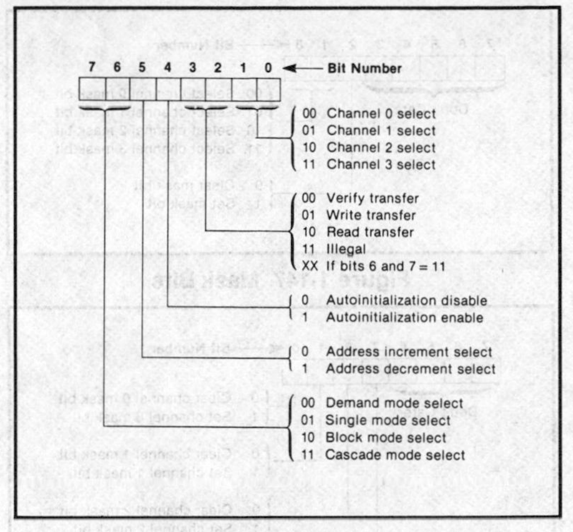

Figure 1-145 Mode Register

the proper form of the word. See Table 1-45 for register address coding. In order to make a software request, the channel must be in Block Mode.

Mask Register

Each channel has a mask bit (see Figure 1-147) which can be set to disable the incoming DREQ. Each mask bit is set when its associated channel produces an EOP* if the channel is not programmed for Autoinitialize. Each bit of the 4-bit Mask register (see Figure 1-148) may also be set or cleared separately under software control. The entire register is also set by a Reset. This disables all DMA requests until a clear Mask register instruction allows

Table 1-45 Definition of Register Codes

Register	Operation	Signals						
		$\overline{CS}$	$\overline{IOR}$	$\overline{IOW}$	A3	A2	A1	A0
Command	Write	0	1	0	1	0	0	0
Mode	Write	0	1	0	1	0	1	1
Request	Write	0	1	0	1	0	0	1
Mask	Set/Reset	0	1	0	1	0	1	0
Mask	Write	0	1	0	1	1	1	1
Temporary	Read	0	0	1	1	1	0	1
Status	Read	0	0	1	1	0	0	0

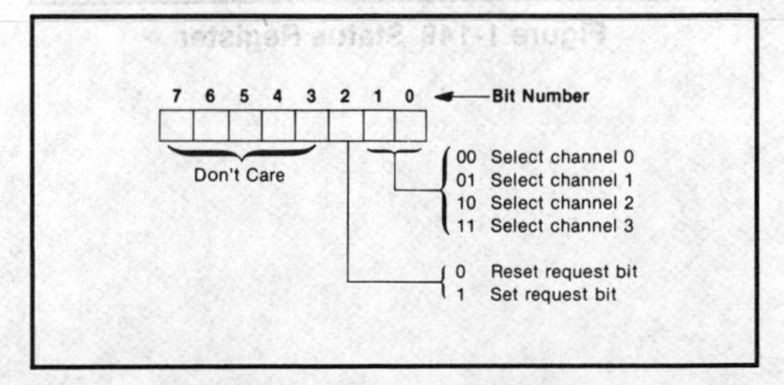

Figure 1-146 Request Register

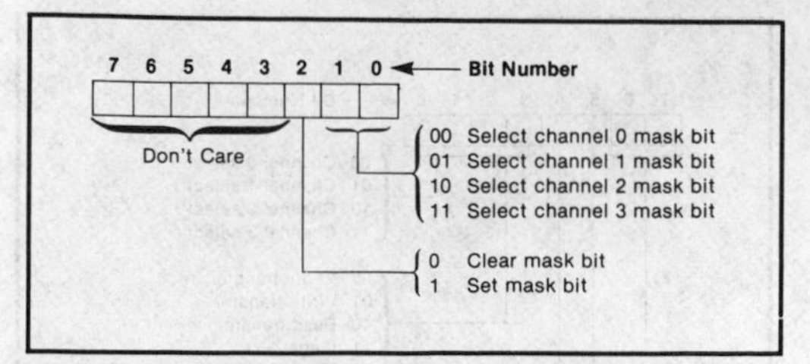

Figure 1-147 Mask Bits

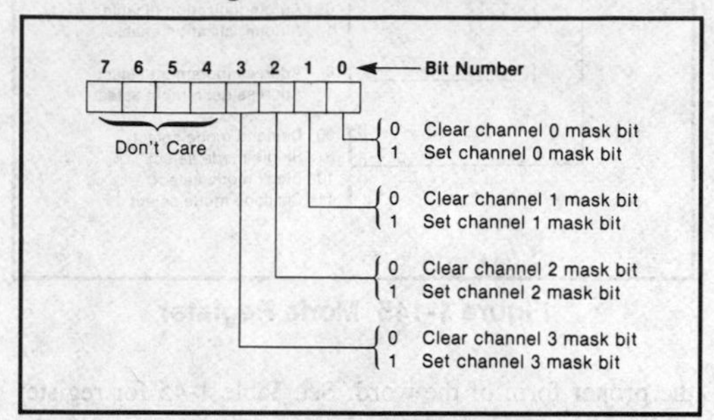

Figure 1-148 Mask Register

them to occur. The instruction to separately set or clear the mask bits is similar in form to that used with the Request register. See Table 1-45 for instruction addressing.

Status Register

The Status register (see Figure 1-149) is available to be read out of the 8237A by the microprocessor. This register contains information about the status of the devices at this point. This information includes which channels have reached a terminal count and which channels have pending DMA requests. Bits 0-3 are set every time a TC is reached by that channel or an external EOP* is applied. These bits are cleared upon Reset and on each Status Read. Bits 4-7 are set whenever their corresponding channel is requesting service.

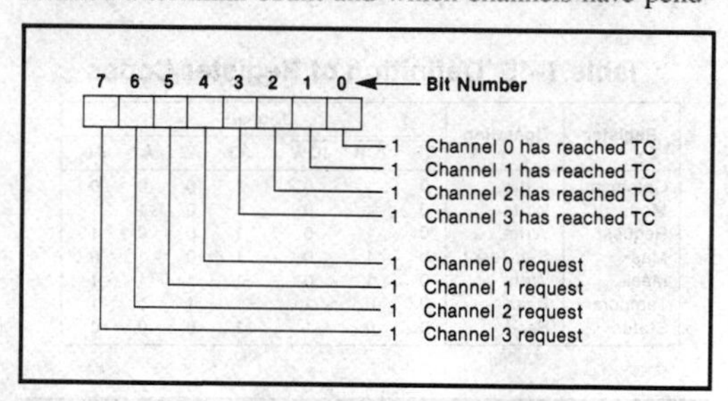

Figure 1-149 Status Register

Temporary Register

The Temporary register is used to hold data during memory-to-memory transfers. Following the completion of the transfers, the last word moved can be read by the microprocessor in the Program Condition. The Temporary register always contains the last byte transferred in the last memory-to-memory operation, unless cleared by a Reset.

Software Commands

The software commands are additional special software commands which can be executed in the Program Condition (see Figure 1-144). The commands do not depend on any specific bit pattern on the data bus. The software command are Clear First/Last Flip-Flop, Master Clear and Clear Mask Register. Figure 1-144 lists the address codes for the software commands.

a. Clear First/Last Flip/Flop

This command is executed prior to writing or reading new address or word count information to the 8237A. This initializes the flip-flop to a known state so that subsequent accesses to register contents by the microprocessor will address upper and lower bytes in the correct sequence.

b. Master Clear

This software instruction has the same effect as the hardware Reset. The Command, Status, Request, Temporary, and Internal First/Last Flip-Flop registers are cleared and the Mask register is set. The 8237A will enter the Idle cycle.

c. Clear Mask Register

This command clears the mask bits of all four channels, enabling them to accept DMA requests.

80186/80188 CPU

2

CHAPTER 2
80186/80188 CPU

2.1 INTRODUCTION—THE HIGH INTEGRATION CONCEPT

This chapter presents hardware design data for the 80186/80188 CPU's and describes the features that distinguish them from the 8086/8088. The 80186/80188 are upward compatible from the 8086/8088. In compatible modes of operation the 80186/188 operate virtually the same as the 8086/88. This chapter also describes the use of the 80186/188 with various input/output peripheral and memory devices. As the reader will discover, the integrated devices of the iAPX186 (a DMA unit, timer, interrupt controller, bus controller, chip select logic, and ready generation logic all integrated onto the chip) greatly simplify system configuration.

The iAPX86/88 family consists of two devices: the 80186 processor with a 16-bit external bus and the 80188 processor with an 8-bit external bus. Internally, both devices use the same processor with the same integrated components. Except where noted, all references to the 80186 in this chapter apply equally to the 80188. Also, all parametric values in this chapter are from the iAPX186 Advance Information Data Sheet and pertain to 8 MHz devices.

2.2 COMPONENT OVERVIEW

The 80186 and 80188 microprocessors each contain a number of the most common iAPX system components integrated onto a single chip (see Figure 2-1). These on-board devices include:

- Clock generator
- Two, independent, high speed DMA channels
- Programmable Interrupt Controller
- Three programmable 16-bit timers
- Programmable memory and peripheral chip select logic
- Programmable wait state generator
- Local bus controller.

This high scale integration doubles the throughput of the standard 5 MHz 8086. The 80186/88 instruction set is completely upward compatible with iAPX86 object code and contains only ten new instructions in addition to the complete 8086 instruction set. Device compatibility extends to 8086 bus support components that include:

- 8282 and 8283 Octal Latches
- 8286 and 8287 Bus Transceivers
- 8288 Bus Controller for the iAPX86/88
- 8289 Bus Arbiter

In addition, the 80186 may be interfaced to the 8087 Numeric Data Co-Processor to make use of the "number crunching" capabilities of that device.

2.2.1 Architectural Overview

The 80186/188 device architecture consists of the same Bus Interface Unit (BIU) and Execution Unit (EU) as the 8086/88 (see Figure 2-1). The 80186 and 80188 CPUs have the same basic register set, memory organization, and addressing modes as the 8086 and 8088. The differences between the 80186 and 80188 are the same as the differences between the 8086 and 8088: the 80186 has a 16-bit architecture and a 16-bit bus interface; the 80188 has a 16-bit internal architecture, but an 8-bit data bus interface; the 80186 has a 6-byte prefetch queue and the 80188 has a 4-byte prefetch queue. The execution times of the two processors differ accordingly. For each non-immediate 16-bit read/write instruction, 4 additional clock cycles are required by the 80188. In addition, the 80186/188 contain a programmable interrupt controller, three 16-bit programmable timers, a chip select unit, and a two channel programmable direct memory access (DMA) unit.

EXECUTION UNIT AND BUS INTERFACE UNIT

As in the 8086/88, the EU is responsible for the execution of all instructions, for providing data and addresses to the BIU, and for manipulating the general registers and the flag register. Except for a few control pins, the EU is completely isolated from the "outside" world. The BIU executes all external bus cycles and consists of the segment and communications registers, the instruction pointer and the instruction object code queue. The BIU combines segment and offset values in its dedicated hardware adder to derive 20-bit addresses, transfers data to and from the EU on the Arithmetic Logic Unit (ALU) data bus and loads "pre-fetched" instructions into the queue from which they are fetched by the EU.

When the EU is ready to execute an instruction, it fetches the instruction object code byte from the BIU's instruction queue and then executes the instruction. If the queue is empty when the EU is ready to fetch an instruction byte, the EU waits for the instruction byte to be fetched. If a memory location or I/O port must be accessed during instruction execution, the EU requests the BIU to perform the required bus cycle.

The two processing sections of the CPU operate independently. In the 80186 CPU, when two or more bytes of the 6-byte instruction queue are empty and the EU does not

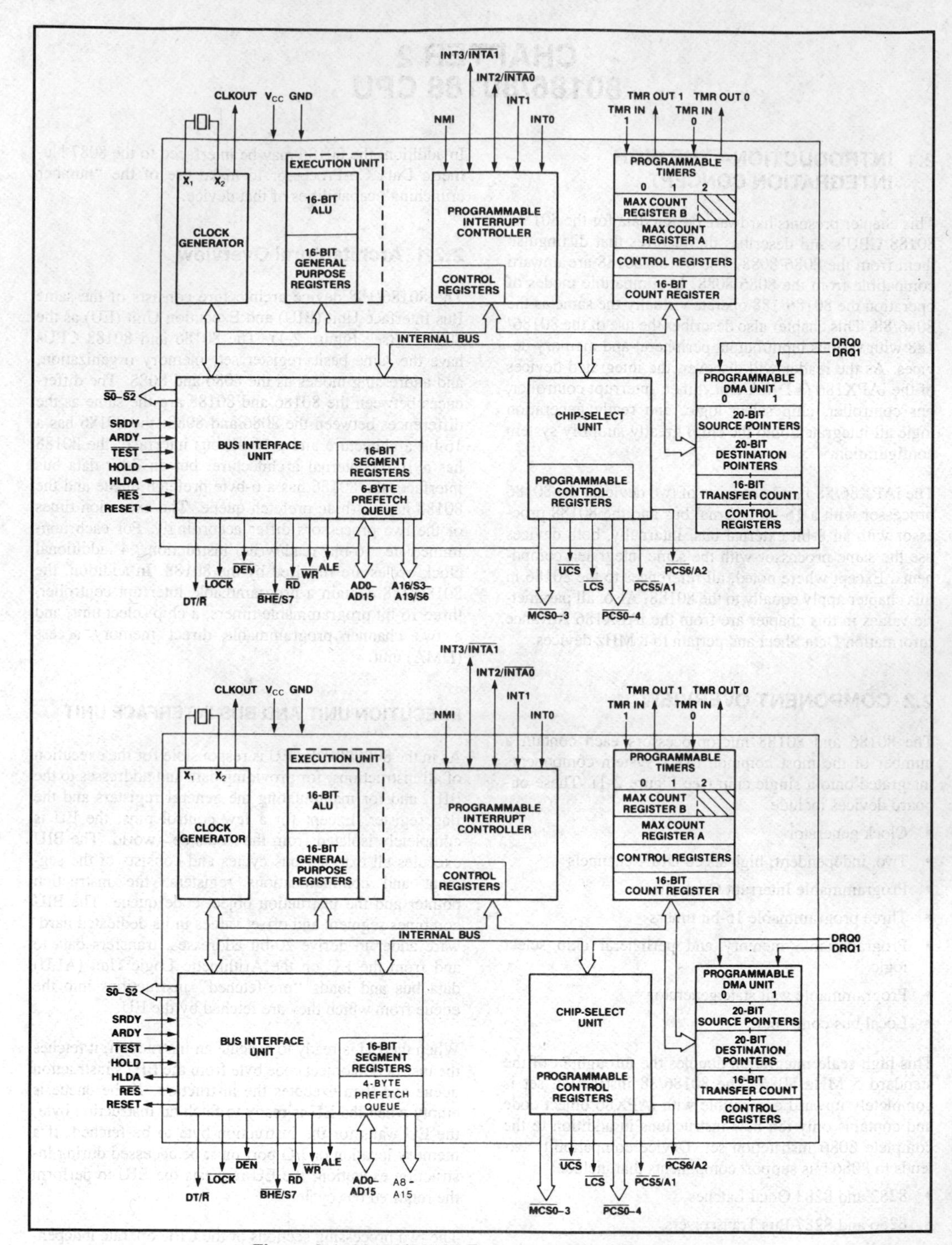

Figure 2-1 80186/80188 Functional Block Diagrams

require the BIU to perform a bus cycle, the BIU executes instruction fetch cycles to refill the queue. In the 80188 CPU, when one byte of the 4-byte instruction queue is empty, the BIU executes an instruction fetch cycle. Note that since the 80186 CPU has a 16-bit data bus, it can access *two* instruction object code bytes in a single bus cycle. The 80188 CPU, since it has an 8-bit data bus, can access only *one* instruction object code byte per bus cycle. If the EU issues a request for bus access while the BIU is in the process of an instruction fetch bus cycle, the BIU completes the cycle before honoring the EU's request.

CLOCK GENERATOR

The 80186/188 integrated circuits include a clock generator and crystal oscillator. The crystal oscillator can be used with a parallel resonant, fundamental mode crystal at 2X the desired CPU clock speed (i.e., 16 MHz for an 8 MHz 80186), or with an external oscillator also at 2X the CPU clock. The output of the oscillator is internally divided by two to provide the 50% duty cycle CPU clock that initiates all 80186 system timing. The CPU clock is externally available, and all timing parameters are referenced to this externally available signal. The clock generator also provides ready synchronization for the processor.

PROGRAMMABLE INTERRUPT CONTROLLER

The integrated 80186 interrupt controller arbitrates interrupt requests between all internal and external sources. The integrated interrupt controller has two major modes of operation, non-iRMX™ 86 mode (called master mode) and iRMX 86 mode. In the master mode, the integrated controller acts as the master interrupt controller for the system. It can be directly cascaded as the master system interrupt controller for up to two slave external 8259A interrupt controllers to allow up to 128 interrupts. In the iRMX 86 mode the integrated interrupt controller can be configured as a slave controller to an external master system interrupt controller. This provides complete compatibility with an 80130, 80150, and the iRMX 86 operating system. Some of the interrupt controller registers and interrupt controller pins change definition between the two modes, but the basic function of the integrated interrupt controller remains basically the same.

PROGRAMMABLE TIMERS

The integrated timer unit contains three independent programmable 16-bit timer/counters. Two of these timers can be used to count external events, to provide waveforms derived from either the CPU clock or an external clock of any duty cycle, or to interrupt the CPU after a specified number of timer "events". The third timer counts only CPU clocks and can be used to interrupt the CPU after a programmable number of CPU clocks, to give a count pulse to either or both of the other two timers after a programmable number of CPU clocks, or to give a DMA request pulse to the integrated DMA unit after a programmable number of CPU clocks.

CHIP SELECT AND READY GENERATION UNIT

The 80186 integrated chip select logic is used to enable memory or peripheral devices. Memory addressing uses six output lines and peripheral addressing uses seven output lines. The memory chip select lines are split into 3 groups in order to separately address the three major memory areas in a typical 80186 system. These major memory areas are upper memory for reset ROM, lower memory for interrupt vectors and mid-range memory for programs. The size of each of these areas is user programmable. The starting location of lower memory is 00000H and the ending location for upper memory is FFFFFH. Starting and ending locations for mid-range memory is user programmable.

The seven peripheral select lines each address one of seven contiguous 128 byte blocks above a user programmable base address. The base address for each of these blocks can be located in either memory or I/O space so that the peripheral devices may be either memory or I/O mapped.

Each of the programmed chip select areas has a set of programmable ready bits. These ready bits control an integrated wait state generator. This allows a programmable number of wait states (from 0 to 3) to be inserted whenever an access is made to the area of memory associated with the chip select area. Each set of ready bits also contains a bit which determines whether the external ready signals (ARDY and SRDY) will be used or ignored (i.e., a bus cycle will terminate even though a ready has not been returned on the external pins). A total of 5 sets of ready bits allow independent ready generation for each of upper memory, lower memory, mid-range memory, peripheral devices 0-3 and peripheral devices 4-6.

PROGRAMMABLE DIRECT MEMORY ACCESS UNIT

The 80186/188 contain an integrated programmable Direct Memory Access (DMA) Unit which contains two high speed DMA channels. This DMA unit performs transfers to or from any combination of I/O space and memory space in either byte or word units. Each DMA cycle requires from two to four bus cycles: one or two cycles to fetch the data to an internal register; and one or two cycles to deposit the data. This operation allows word data to be located on odd boundaries, or byte data to be moved from odd locations to even locations. (Locating word data on odd boundaries and moving bytes from odd to even locations is normally difficult, since odd bytes are transferred on the upper 8 data bits of the 16-bit data bus, while even data bytes are transferred on the lower 8 data bits of the data bus.)

Each DMA channel maintains a set of independent 20-bit source and destination pointers which are used to access the source and destination of the data transferred. Each of these pointers may independently address either I/O or memory space. After each DMA cycle, the pointers may be independently incremented, decremented, or maintained constant. Each DMA channel also keeps a transfer count which may be used to terminate a series of DMA transfers after a pre-programmed number of transfers.

INTERNAL PERIPHERAL INTERFACE

The 80186 CPU uses 16-bit registers, contained within an internal 256-byte control block, to control all integrated peripherals. This control block may be mapped into either memory or I/O space. Internal logic recognizes the address and responds to the bus cycle. During bus cycles to the internal registers, the bus controller signals the operation externally (i.e., the RD*, WR* status, address, data, etc., lines will be driven as in a normal bus cycle), and ignores D15-0, SRDY and ARDY. The base address of the control block must be on an even 256-byte boundary (i.e., the lower 8 bits of the base address are all zeros). The 80186 CPU may read from or write to all of the defined registers within this control block at any time. The current base address of the control block determines the location of any register contained within the 256-byte control block. Refer to Volume I of this manual for a description of control block programming.

The integrated iAPX 80186 peripherals operate semi-autonomously from the CPU. Access to them is, for the most part, through software read/write of the control and data locations in the control block. Most of these registers can be both read from and written to. A few dedicated lines, such as interrupts and DMA requests, provide real-time communication between the CPU and peripherals similar to the more conventional system that uses discrete peripheral blocks. The overall interaction and function of the peripheral blocks has not substantially changed.

CPU ENHANCEMENTS

The 80186 and 80188 are highly integrated microprocessors. They effectively combine 15 to 20 of the most common iAPX86 system components on a single chip (see Figure 2-1). The 80186 and 80188 provide higher performance and more highly integrated solutions to the total system problem of the microprocessor user. The higher performance results from the enhancements made to both the general and specific areas of CPU operation. These include faster effective address calculation, improvements in the execution speed of many instructions, and the addition of new instructions designed to improve the existing code, or to produce optimum 80186/188 code. Increased integration simplifies system construction, which results in lower part count, therefore, a substantial reduction in system cost for the user.

The 80186/188 have the same basic instruction set, memory organization, and addressing modes as the 8086/88. The differences between the 80186 and 80188 are the same as the differences between the 8086 and 8088: the 80186 has a 16-bit architecture and a 16-bit bus interface; the 80188 has a 16-bit internal architecture, but an 8-bit data bus interface. The instruction execution times of the two processors differ accordingly. For each non-immediate 16-bit data read/write instruction four additional clock cycles are required for the 80188.

CPU Execution Speed

Because of 80186/188 hardware enhancements in both the bus interface unit and the execution unit, most instructions require fewer clock cycles to execute than on the 8086/88. Execution speed is gained by performing the effective address calculations (base + displacement + index) with a dedicated hardware adder, which takes only 4 clock cycles in the 80186/188 bus interface unit, rather than with a microcode routine (used by the 8086/88). This results in an execution speed which is three to six times faster than the 8 MHz 8086/88.

In addition, the execution speed of specific instructions has been enhanced. All multiple-bit shift and rotate instructions execute 1.5 to 2.5 times faster than the 8 MHz 8086/88. Multiply and divide instructions execute three times faster. String move instructions run at bus bandwidth (i.e., data is transferred onto the bus in each consecutive CPU clock cycle), allowing transfers at 2 Megabytes per second (80186),and 1 Megabyte per second (80188), which is about twice the speed of the 8 MHz 8086 or 8088, respectively. Overall, the 80186/188 CPU's are 30-percent faster than the 8 MHz 8086/88 CPU's, and 50-percent faster than the 5 MHz 8086/88 CPU's.

2.2.2 Software Overview

The following paragraphs describe the functions of the new instructions and interrupts provided by the 80186/80188 CPU's. A description of the overall instruction set by category is also provided. In addition, a complete instruction set summary is provided in tabular form which recaps each device instruction by category, and provides timing cycles for each instruction.

NEW 80186/80188 INSTRUCTIONS

The 80186/188 CPU's add ten new instructions to those in the basic 8086/88 instruction set. These instructions are designed to simplify assembly language programming, enhance the performance of high-level language implementations, and reduce the size of object code for the 80186/188. The new instructions appear shaded in the instructions set summary at the back of the 80186 data sheet. The following paragraphs explain the operation of these new instructions. In order to use these new instructions with the 8086/80186 assembler, the "$mod186" switch must be given to the assembler. This can be done by placing the line: "$mod186" at the beginning of the assembly language file.

Push Immediate (PUSHI) Instruction

The PUSHI instruction allows immediate data to be pushed onto the processor stack. This data can be either an immediate byte (sign extended 8-bit value) or an immediate word (16-bit value). If the data is a byte, it will be sign extended to a word before it is pushed onto the stack (since all track operations are word operations).

Push All/Pop All (PUSHA, POPA) Instructions

These two instructions allow all of the eight of the 80186 general purpose registers to be saved onto the stack, or restored from the stack. The registers saved by this instruction (in the order they are pushed onto the stack) are AX, CX, DX, BX, SP, BP, SI and DI. The SP value pushed onto the stack is the value of the register before the first PUSH (AX) is performed; the value popped for the SP register is ignored.

PUSHA and POPA do not save any of the segment registers (CS, DS, SS, ES), the instruction pointer (IP), the flag register, or any of the integrated peripheral registers.

Integer Immediate Multiply (IMUL)

The IMUL instruction allows a value to be multiplied by an immediate value. The result of this operation is 16 bits long. One operand for this instruction is obtained using one of the 80186 addressing modes (meaning it can be in a register or in memory). The immediate value can be either a byte or a word, but will be sign extended if it is a byte. The 16-bit result of the multiplication can be placed in any of the 80186 general purpose or pointer registers.

IMUL requires three operands: the register in which the result is to be placed, the immediate, and the second operand. The second operand can be any of the 80186 general purpose register or a specified memory location.

Shifts/Rotates By An Immediate Value

The 80186 can perform multiple bit shifts or rotates where the number of bits to be shifted is specified by an immediate value. This is different from the 8086, where only a single bit shift can be performed, or a multiple shift can be performed where the number of bits to be shifted is specified in the CL register.

All of the shift/rotate instructions of the 80186 allow the number of bits shifted to be specified by an immediate value. Like all multiple bit shift operations performed by the 80186, the number of bits shifted is the number of bits specified modulus 32 (i.e., the maximum number of bits shifted by the 80186 multiple bit shifts is 31).

These instructions require two operands: the operand to be shifted (which may be a register or a memory location specified by any of the 80186 addressing modes) and the number of bits to be shifted.

Block Input/Output (INS/OUTS) Instructions

The two new 80186 input/output instructions (INS and OUTS) perform block input or output operations similar to the string move instructions of the processor.

The INS instruction performs block input from an I/O port to memory. The I/O address is specified by the DX register and the memory location is pointed to by the DI register. After the operation is performed, the DI register is adjusted by 1 (if a byte input is specified) or by 2 (if a word input is specified). The adjustment is either an increment or a decrement, as determined by the Direction bit in the flag register of the processor. The ES segment register is used for memory addressing, and cannot be overridden. When preceeded by a Repeat (REP) prefix, this instruction allows blocks of data to be moved from an I/O address to a block of memory. The I/O address in the DX register is not modified by this operation.

The OUTS instruction performs block output from memory to an I/O port. The I/O address is specified by the DX register and the memory location is pointed to by the SI register. After the operation is performed, the SI register is adjusted by 1 (if a byte output is specified) or by 2 (if a word output is specified). The adjustment is either an increment or a decrement, as determined by the Direction bit in the flag register of the processor. The DS segment register is used for memory addressing, but can be overridden by using the segment override prefix. When preceeded by a Repeat (REP) prefix, this instruction allows blocks of data to be moved from a block of memory to an I/O address. The I/O address in the DX register is not modified by this operation.

Like the string move instructions, these two instructions require two operands to specify whether word or byte operations are to take place. Additionally, this determination can be supplied by the mnemonic itself by adding a "B" or "W" to the basic mnemonic. For example:

```
INSB        ;perform byte input
REPOUTSW    ;perform word block output
```

Array Bounds (BOUND) Instruction

The 80186 supplies the BOUND instruction to facilitate bound checking of arrays. In this instruction, the calculated index into the arrays is placed in one of the general purpose registers of the 80186. Located in two adjacent word memory locations are the lower and upper bounds for the array index. The BOUND instruction compares the register contents to the memory locations, and if the value in the register is not between the values in the memory locations, an interrupt type 5 is generated. The comparisons performed are SIGNED comparisons. A register value equal to the upper bound or the lower bound will not cause an interrupt. This instruction requires two arguments: the register in which the calculated array index is placed, and the word memory location which contains the lower bound of the array which can be specified by any of the 80186 memory addressing modes). The location containing the upper bound of the array must follow immediately the memory location containing the lower bound of the array.

ENTER And LEAVE Instructions

The 80186 contains two instructions which are used to build and tear down stack frames of the higher level, block structured languages. The instruction used to build these stack frames is the ENTER instruction. The algorithm for this instruction is:

```
PUSH BP                    /*save the previous frame
                           pointer*/
if level=0 then
    BP:=SP;
else      templ:=SP;       /*save current frame pointer*/
    temp2:=level-1;
    do while temp2>0       /*copy down previous level
                           frame*/
        BP:=BP-2;          /*pointers*/
        PUSH [BP];
    BP:=templ;
    PUSH BP;               /*put current level frame pointer*/
/*in the save area*/
SP:=SP-disp;               /*create space on the stack for*/
/*local variables*/
```

Figure 2-2 shows the layout of the stack before and after this operation.

This instruction requires two operands. The first value (disp) specifies the number of bytes the local variables of this routine require. This is an unsigned value and can be as large as 65536. The second value (level) is an unsigned value which specifies the level of the procedure and can be as great as 255.

The 80186 includes the LEAVE instructions to tear down stack frames built by the ENTER instruction. As can be seen from the layout of the stack left by the ENTER instruction, this involves only moving the contents of the BP register to the SP register, and popping the old BP value from the stack.

Neither the ENTER nor the LEAVE instructions save any of the 80186 general purpose registers. If they must be saved, this must be done in addition to the ENTER and the LEAVE. In addition, the LEAVE instruction does not perform a return from a subroutine. If this is desired, the LEAVE instruction must be explicitly followed by the RET instruction.

ADDITIONAL INTERRUPTS

The 80186/80188 include two additional interrupts to detect program execution errors and escape opcodes. These two new interrupts are the Unused Opcode and Escape Opcode. The following paragraphs describe these new interrupts.

Unused Opcode

When opcodes 0FH, 63H -67H, F1H and FFFFH are executed an interrupt type 6 is generated. This interrupt is useful in detecting programs errors (e.g., the execution of data), and provides a set of opcodes which the user may define for specific purposes, emulating the action of the instruction in software.

Escape Opcode

The 80186/188 CPU's may be programmed to cause an interrupt type 7 when an escape opcode (D8H-DFH) is encountered. This provides a straightfoward method of giving instructions to coprocessors, e.g., the 8087. The programming is done by a bit in the relocation register. It is programmed not to cause a interrupt on reset.

80186/80188 INSTRUCTION SET

The 80186 and 80188 execute exactly the same instructions. This instruction set includes equivalents to the instructions typically found in previous microprocessors, such as the 8080/8085. Significant new operations include:

- Multiplication and division of signed and unsigned binary numbers as well as unpacked decimal numbers,
- move, scan and compare operations for strings up to 64k bytes in length,
- non-destructive bit testing,
- byte translation from one code to another,
- software generated interrupts,
- a group of instructions that can help coordinate the activities of multiprocessing systems.

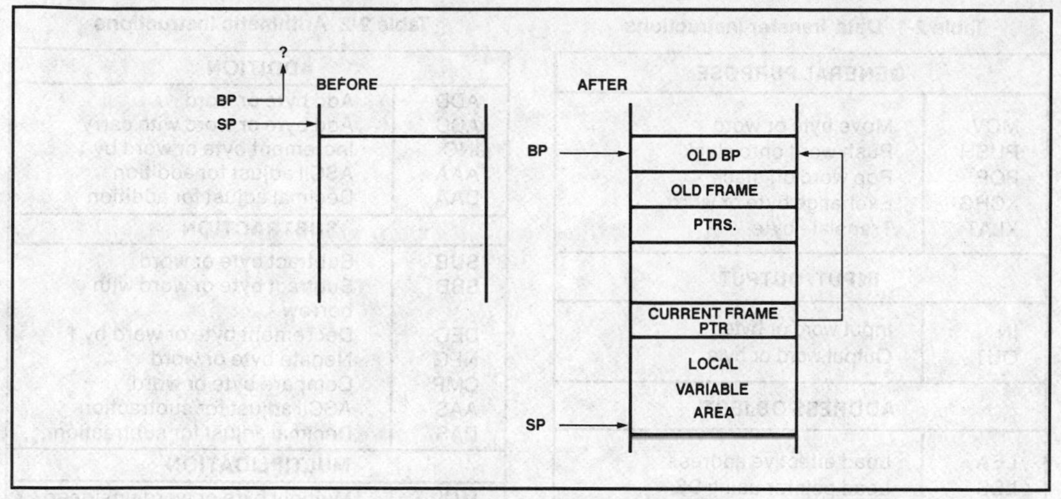

Figure 2-2 ENTER Instruction Stack Frame

In addition to these improvements, the 80186/80188 CPU's provide ten new instructions that are used to streamline existing code and produce optimum new iAPX 186 code (refer to the paragraphs on "NEW 80186/80188 INSTRUCTIONS" in paragraph 2.2.2).

The 80186/80188 instructions treat different types of operands uniformly. Nearly every instruction can operate on either byte or word data. Register, memory, and immediate operands may be specified interchangeably in most instructions. The exception is that immediate values serve as source and not destination operands. In particular, memory variables may be added to, subtracted from, shifted, compared, and so on, in place, without moving them in and out of registers. This saves instructions, registers, and execution time in assembly language programs. In high-level languages, where most variables are memory based, compilers can produce faster and shorter object programs.

The 80186/80188 instruction set basically exists on two levels. One is the assembly level and the other is the machine level. To the assembly language programmer, the 80186 appears to have a repertoire of about 100 instructions. One MOV (move) instruction, for example, transfers a byte or a word from a register or a memory location or an immediate value to either a register or a memory location. The CPU's, however, recognize 28 different MOV machine instructions ("move byte register to memory", "move word immediate to register", etc.).

The two levels of instruction set address two different requirements: efficiency and simplicity. The approximately 300 forms of machine-level instructions make very efficient use of storage. For example, the machine instructions that increments a memory operand is three or four bytes long because the address of the operand must be encoded in the instruction. To increment a register, however, does not require as much information, so the instruction can be shorter. The 80186/188 have eight different machine-level instructions that increment a different 16-bit register. Each of these instructions are only one byte long.

The 80186/188 instruction set is divided into seven functional groups. These are data transfer, arithmetic, bit manipulation, string manipulation, control transfer, high level and processor control instructions. The following paragraphs provide a functional description of the assembly-level instructions.

Data Transfer Instructions

Data transfer instructions move single bytes and words between memory and registers. These instructions also move single bytes and words between the AL or AX registers and I/O ports. Table 2-1 lists the four types of data transfer instructions and their functions. The data transfer instructions are categorized in four types: general purpose; input/output; address object; and flag transfer. The stack manipulation instructions, the instructions for transferring flag contents and the instructions for loading segment registers are included in this group. Figure 2-3 shows the flag storage formats primarily used by the LAHF instruction when converting 8080/8085 assembly language programs to run on the 80186 or 80188. The address object instructions manipulate the addresses of variables instead of the contents of values of the variables. This is useful for list processing, based variable and string operations.

Table 2-1 Data Transfer Instructions

GENERAL PURPOSE	
MOV	Move byte or word
PUSH	Push word onto stack
POP	Pop word off stack
XCHG	Exchange byte or word
XLAT	Translate byte
INPUT/OUTPUT	
IN	Input word or byte
OUT	Output word or byte
ADDRESS OBJECT	
LEA	Load effective address
LDS	Load pointer using DS
LES	Load pointer using ES
FLAG TRANSFER	
LAHF	Load AH register from flags
SAHF	Store AH register in flags
PUSHF	Push flags onto stack
POPF	Pop flags off stack

Table 2-2 Arithmetic Instructions

ADDITION	
ADD	Add byte or word
ADC	Add byte or word with carry
INC	Increment byte or word by 1
AAA	ASCII adjust for addition
DAA	Decimal adjust for addition
SUBTRACTION	
SUB	Subtract byte or word
SBB	Subtract byte or word with borrow
DEC	Decrement byte or word by 1
NEG	Negate byte or word
CMP	Compare byte or word
AAS	ASCII adjust for subtraction
DAS	Decimal adjust for subtraction
MULTIPLICATION	
MUL	Multiply byte or word unsigned
IMUL	Integer multiply byte or word
AAM	ASCII adjust for multiply
DIVISION	
DIV	Divide byte or word unsigned
IDIV	Integer divide byte or word
AAD	ASCII adjust for division
CBW	Convert byte to word
CWD	Convert word to doubleword

Arithmetic Instructions

Arithmetic operations (see Table 2-2) may be performed on four types of numbers: unsigned binary, signed binary (integers), unsigned packed decimal and unsigned unpacked decimal (see Table 2-3). Binary numbers may be 8 or 16 bits long. Decimal numbers are stored in bytes, two digits per byte for packed decimal and one digit per byte for unpacked decimal. The processor always assumes that the operands specified in arithmetic instructions contain data that represents valid numbers for the type of instruction being performed. Invalid data may produce unpredictable results.

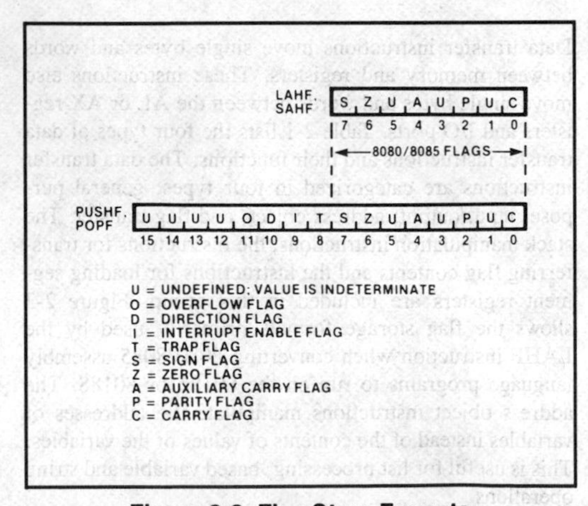

Figure 2-3 Flag Store Formats

Bit Manipulation Instructions

The 80186 and 80188 CPU's provide three groups of instructions for manipulating bits within both bytes and words. These three groups are logicals, shifts and rotates. Table 2-4 lists the three groups of bit manipulation instructions with their functions.

a. Logical

The logical instructions include the boolean operators "not", "and", "inclusive or", and "exclusive or". A TEST instruction that sets the flags, but does not alter either of its operands is also included.

b. Shifts

The bits in bytes and words may be shifted arithmetically or logically. Up to 255 shifts may be performed, according to the value of the count operand coded in the instruction. The count may be specified as a constant 1, or

Table 2-3 Arithmetic Interpretation of 8-Bit Numbers

HEX	BIT PATTERN	UNSIGNED BINARY	SIGNED BINARY	UNPACKED DECIMAL	PACKED DECIMAL
07	0 0 0 0 0 1 1 1	7	+7	7	7
89	1 0 0 0 1 0 0 1	137	−119	invalid	89
C5	1 1 0 0 0 1 0 1	197	−59	invalid	invalid

register CL, allowing the shift count to be a variable supplied at execution time. Also, the number of shifts may be specified as an immediate value in the instruction. This eliminates the need for a MOV immediate to the CL register if the number of shifts is known at assembly time. Before the 80186/80188 perform a shift or rotate, they AND the value to be shifted with 1FH. This limits the number of shifts occurring to 32 bits. Arithmetic shifts may be used to multiply and divide binary numbers by powers of two. Logical shifts can be used to isolate bits in bytes or words.

c. Rotates

Bits in bytes and words can also be rotated. Bits rotated out of an operand are not lost as in a shift, but are "circled" back into the other "end" of the operand. As in the shift instructions, the number of bits to be rotated is taken from the count operand, which may specify either a constant of 1, or the CL register. The carry flag may act as an extension of the operand in two of the rotate instructions, allowing a bit to be isolated in CF and then tested by a JC (jump if carry) or JNC (jump if not carry) instruction.

Table 2-4 Bit Manipulation Instructions

LOGICALS	
NOT	"Not" byte or word
AND	"And" byte or word
OR	"Inclusive or" byte or word
XOR	"Exclusive or" byte or word
TEST	"Test" byte or word
SHIFTS	
SHL/SAL	Shift logical/arithmetic left byte or word
SHR	Shift logical right byte or word
SAR	Shift arithmetic right byte or word
ROTATES	
ROL	Rotate left byte or word
ROR	Rotate right byte or word
RCL	Rotate through carry left byte or word
RCR	Rotate through carry right byte or word

String Instructions

The string instructions, also called primitives, allow strings of bytes or words to be operated on, one element (byte or word) at a time. Strings of up to 128k bytes may be manipulated with these instructions. Instructions are available to move, compare and scan for a value, as well as moving string elements to and from the accumulator and I/O ports. Table 2-5 lists the string instructions. These basic operations may be preceded by a special one-byte prefix that causes the instruction to be repeated by the hardware, allowing long strings to be processed much faster than would be possible with a software loop. The repetitions can be terminated by a variety of conditions, and a repeated operation may be interrupted and resumed.

Program Transfer Instructions

The instruction execution sequence for the 80816/80188 is determined by the content of the code segment register (CS) and the instruction pointer (IP). The CS register contains the base address of the current code segment (i.e., the 64k memory area where instructions are currently being fetched). The IP points to the memory address where the next instruction to be fetched is located. In most operating conditions, the next instruction to be executed will have already been fetched and will be waiting in the CPU instruction queue. The program transfer instructions operate on the instruction pointer and on the CS register. Changing the content of these causes normal sequential operation to be altered. When a program transfer occurs, the queue no longer contains the correct instruction. When the BIU obtains the next instruction from memory using the new IP and CS values, it passes the instruction directly to the EU and then begins refilling the queue from the new location.

Four groups of program transfers are available with the 80186/188 CPU's (see Table 2-6). These are unconditional transfers, conditional transfers, iteration control instructions, and interrupt-related instructions.

Table 2-5 String Instructions

REP	Repeat
REPE/REPZ	Repeat while equal/zero
REPNE/REPNZ	Repeat while not equal/not zero
MOVS	Move byte or word string
MOVSB/MOVSW	Move byte or word string
CMPS	Compare byte or word string
SCAS	Scan byte or word string
LODS	Load byte or word string
STOS	Store byte or word string

a. Unconditional Transfers

The unconditional transfer instructions may transfer control to a target instruction within the current code segment (intrasegment transfer) or to a different code segment (intersegment transfer). The ASM-86 Assembler terms an intrasegment transfer NEAR and an intersegment transfer FAR. The transfer is made unconditionally any time the instruction is executed.

b. Conditional Transfers

The conditional transfer instructions are jumps that may or may not transfer control depending on the state of the CPU flags at the time the instruction is executed. These 18 instructions (see Table 2-7) each test a different combination of flags for a condition. If the condition is "true" then control is transferred to the target specified in the instruction. If the condition is "false" then control passes to the instruction that follows the conditional jump. All conditional jumps are SHORT, that is, the target must be in the current code segment and within −128 to +127 bytes of the first byte of the next instruction (JMP 00H jumps to the first byte of the next instruction). Since jumps are made by adding the relative displacement of the target to the instruction pointer, all conditional jumps are self-relative and are appropriate for position-independent routines.

c. Iteration Control

The iteration control instructions can be used to regulate the repetition of software loops. These instructions use the CX register as a counter. Like the conditional transfers,

Table 2-6 Program Transfer Instructions

UNCONDITIONAL TRANSFERS	
CALL	Call procedure
RET	Return from procedure
JMP	Jump
CONDITIONAL TRANSFERS	
JA/JNBE	Jump if above/not below nor equal
JAE/JNB	Jump if above or equal/not below
JB/JNAE	Jump if below/not above nor equal
JBE/JNA	Jump if below or equal/not above
JC	Jump if carry
JE/JZ	Jump if equal/zero
JG/JNLE	Jump if greater/not less nor equal
JGE/JNL	Jump if greater or equal/not less
JL/JNGE	Jump if less/not greater nor equal
JLE/JNG	Jump if less or equal/not greater
JNC	Jump if not carry
JNE/JNZ	Jump if not equal/not zero
JNO	Jump if not overflow
JNP/JPO	Jump if not parity/parity odd
JNS	Jump if not sign
JO	Jump if overflow
JP/JPE	Jump if parity/parity even
JS	Jump if sign
ITERATION CONTROLS	
LOOP	Loop
LOOPE/LOOPZ	Loop if equal/zero
LOOPNE/LOOPNZ	Loop if not equal/not zero
JCXZ	Jump if register CX = 0
INTERRUPTS	
INT	Interrupt
INTO	Interrupt if overflow
IRET	Interrupt return

Table 2-7 Interpretation of Conditional Transfers

MNEMONIC	CONDITION TESTED	"JUMP IF ..."
JA/JNBE	(CF OR ZF)=0	above/not below nor equal
JAE/JNB	CF=0	above or equal/not below
JB/JNAE	CF=1	below/not above nor equal
JBE/JNA	(CF OR ZF)=1	below or equal/not above
JC	CF=1	carry
JE/JZ	ZF=1	equal/zero
JG/JNLE	((SF XOR OF) OR ZF)=0	greater/not less nor equal
JGE/JNL	(SF XOR OF)=0	greater or equal/not less
JL/JNGE	(SF XOR OF)=1	less/not greater nor equal
JLE/JNG	((SF XOR OF) OR ZF)=1	less or equal/not greater
JNC	CF=0	not carry
JNE/JNZ	ZF=0	not equal/not zero
JNO	OF=0	not overflow
JNP/JPO	PF=0	not parity/parity odd
JNS	SF=0	not sign
JO	OF=1	overflow
JP/JPE	PF=1	parity/parity equal
JS	SF=1	sign

Note: "above" and "below" refer to the relationship of two unsigned values; "greater" and "less" refer to the relationship of two signed values.

the iteration control instructions are self-relative and may only transfer to targets that are within −128 to +127 bytes of themselves, i.e., they are SHORT transfers.

d. Interrupt Instructions

Interrupt instructions allow interrupt service routines to be activated by programs as well as by external hardware devices. The effect of software interrupts is similar to hardware-initiated interrupts. However, the processor does not execute an interrupt acknowledge bus cycle if the interrupt originates in software or with an NMI.

High-Level Instructions

The 80186/188 CPU's have two instructions used with high-level languages. These are ENTER and LEAVE. Detailed descriptions of the operation of these two instructions are contained in the paragraphs on "NEW 80186/80188 INSTRUCTIONS" in paragraph 2.2.2.

Processor Control Instructions

The processor control instructions allow programs to control various CPU functions. Table 2-8 lists the groups of processor control instructions and their functions. One group of instructions updates flags, and another group is used primarily for synchronizing the processor with external events. A final instruction causes the CPU to do nothing. Except for the flag operations, none of the processor control instructions affect the flags.

Table 2-8 Processor Control Instructions

FLAG OPERATIONS	
STC	Set carry flag
CLC	Clear carry flag
CMC	Complement carry flag
STD	Set direction flag
CLD	Clear direction flag
STI	Set interrupt enable flag
CLI	Clear interrupt enable flag
EXTERNAL SYNCHRONIZATION	
HLT	Halt until interrupt or reset
WAIT	Wait for $\overline{TEST}$ pin active
ESC	Escape to external processor
LOCK	Lock bus during next instruction
NO OPERATION	
NOP	No operation

INSTRUCTION SET SUMMARY

Table 2-9 presents a reference data table of the complete 80186/80188 instruction set with timing cycles for each instruction. The instruction timings represent the minimum execution time in clock cycles for each instruction. The timings are based on the following assumptions:

- The opcode, along with any data or displacement required for execution of a particular instruction, has been prefetched and resides in the queue at the time it is needed.
- No wait states or bus HOLDS occur.
- All word-data is located on even-address boundaries.

All jumps and calls include the time required to fetch the opcode of the next instruction at the destination address. Any instructions which involve memory references can require one (and in some cases, two) additional clocks above the minimum timings shown. This is due to the asynchronous nature of the handshake between the BIU and EU.

2.3 DEVICE PIN DEFINITIONS

The following paragraphs present functional descriptions of all input/output signals and electrical descriptions of all of the input/output pins on the 80186 and 80188 40-pin DIP's.

2.3.1 Functional Description of All Signals

Figure 2-4 shows the 80186/80188 DIP pin assignments and Table 2-10 provides a complete functional description of each device pin signal and correlates the description to the pin number and associated signal symbol.

2.3.2 Electrical Description of Pins

The absolute maximum ratings for the 8086/8088 device are as follows.

Absolute Maximum Ratings

Ambient Temperature Under Bias	0°C to 70°C
Storage Temperature	−65°C to +150°C
Voltage on Any Pin with Respect to GND	−1.0 to +7V
Power Dissipation	3.0 Watt

Stresses above those listed above may cause permanent damage to the device. These values present stress ratings only and functional operation of the device at these or any other conditions above those indicated in the operational sections of the device specifications is not implied. Exposure to absolute maximum conditions for extended periods of time may affect the device reliability.

Table 2-11 presents the D.C. voltage characteristics of the 80186/188 CPU's. Tables 2-12 through 2-16 list the various A.C. characteristics timing requirements and timing responses for the 80186/188 CPU's. Figure 2-5 presents the major cycle timing waveforms for the 80186/80188 CPU's related to the preceding A.C. characteristics tables.

2.4 OPERATING MODES

The following paragraphs present the various operating modes of the 80186/188 CPU's and compare these to those of the 8086/88 CPU's described in Chapter 1. Refer to the 8086/88 operating mode discussion in paragraph 1.4.

2.4.1 8086/88-80186/188 Operating Mode Comparisons

The 80186/188 multiplexed address/data bus simultaneously supports both the 8086/88 minimum mode local bus and the maximum mode system bus. The 80186/188 provides both local bus controller outputs (RD*, WR*, ALE, DEN* and DT/R*) and the system status outputs (S0*, S1* and S2*) for use with the 8288 bus controller. This is different from the 8086/88 where local bus controller outputs (generated only in the minimum mode) are not available if the status outputs (generated only in the maximum mode) are required.

Because the 80186/188 simultaneously provides both local bus control signals and status outputs, many systems supporting both a system bus (MULTIBUS) and a local bus will not require two separate external bus controllers. The bus control signals may be used to control the local bus while the status signals are concurrently connected to the 8288 bus controller to drive the system bus control signals. The 80186/188 CPU's require an 8288 and an 8289 to interface with the MULTIBUS.

2.4.2 Queue Status Mode of Operation

When the RD* line is externally grounded during reset and remains grounded during processor operation, causes the 80186 to enter "queue status" mode. In this mode, the WR* and ALE signals become queue status outputs, reflecting the status of the internal pre-fetch queue during each clock cycle. These signals allow a processor extension (such as the Intel 8087 numeric data processor) to track execution of instructions within the 80186. The interpretation of QS0 (ALE) and QS1 (WR*) are given in Table 2-17. These signals change on the high-to-low clock

Table 2-9 Instruction Set Summary

FUNCTION	FORMAT				Clock Cycles	Comments
DATA TRANSFER						
MOV = Move:						
Register to Register/Memory	1 0 0 0 1 0 0 w	mod reg r/m			2/12	
Register/memory to register	1 0 0 0 1 0 1 w	mod reg r/m			2/9	
Immediate to register/memory	1 1 0 0 0 1 1 w	mod 0 0 0 r/m	data	data if w = 1	12–13	8/16-bit
Immediate to register	1 0 1 1 w reg	data	data if w = 1		3–4	8/16-bit
Memory to accumulator	1 0 1 0 0 0 0 w	addr-low	addr-high		9	
Accumulator to memory	1 0 1 0 0 0 1 w	addr-low	addr-high		8	
Register/memory to segment register	1 0 0 0 1 1 1 0	mod 0 reg r/m			2/9	
Segment register to register/memory	1 0 0 0 1 1 0 0	mod 0 reg r/m			2/11	
PUSH = Push:						
Memory	1 1 1 1 1 1 1 1	mod 1 1 0 r/m			16	
Register	0 1 0 1 0 reg				10	
Segment register	0 0 0 reg 1 1 0				9	
Immediate	0 1 1 0 1 0 s 0	data	data if s = 0		10	
PUSHA = Push All	0 1 1 0 0 0 0 0				36	
POP = Pop:						
Memory	1 0 0 0 1 1 1 1	mod 0 0 0 r/m			20	
Register	0 1 0 1 1 reg				10	
Segment register	0 0 0 reg 1 1 1	(reg ≠ 01)			8	
POPA = Pop All	0 1 1 0 0 0 0 1				51	
XCHG = Exchange:						
Register/memory with register	1 0 0 0 0 1 1 w	mod reg r/m			4/17	
Register with accumulator	1 0 0 1 0 reg				3	
IN = Input from:						
Fixed port	1 1 1 0 0 1 0 w	port			10	
Variable port	1 1 1 0 1 1 0 w				8	
OUT = Output to:						
Fixed port	1 1 1 0 0 1 1 w	port			9	
Variable port	1 1 1 0 1 1 1 w				7	
XLAT = Translate byte to AL	1 1 0 1 0 1 1 1				11	
LEA = Load EA to register	1 0 0 0 1 1 0 1	mod reg r/m			6	
LDS = Load pointer to DS	1 1 0 0 0 1 0 1	mod reg r/m	(mod ≠ 11)		18	
LES = Load pointer to ES	1 1 0 0 0 1 0 0	mod reg r/m	(mod ≠ 11)		18	
LAHF = Load AH with flags	1 0 0 1 1 1 1 1				2	
SAHF = Store AH into flags	1 0 0 1 1 1 1 0				3	
PUSHF = Push flags	1 0 0 1 1 1 0 0				9	
POPF = Pop flags	1 0 0 1 1 1 0 1				8	
SEGMENT = Segment Override:						
CS	0 0 1 0 1 1 1 0				2	
SS	0 0 1 1 0 1 1 0				2	
DS	0 0 1 1 1 1 1 0				2	
ES	0 0 1 0 0 1 1 0				2	

Shaded areas indicate instructions not available in iAPX 86, 88 microsystems.

Table 2-9 Instruction Set Summary (continued)

FUNCTION	FORMAT				Clock Cycles	Comments
ARITHMETIC						
ADD = Add:						
Reg/memory with register to either	0 0 0 0 0 0 d w	mod reg r/m			3/10	
Immediate to register/memory	1 0 0 0 0 0 s w	mod 0 0 0 r/m	data	data if s w = 01	4/16	
Immediate to accumulator	0 0 0 0 0 1 0 w	data	data if w = 1		3/4	8/16-bit
ADC = Add with carry:						
Reg/memory with register to either	0 0 0 1 0 0 d w	mod reg r/m			3/10	
Immediate to register/memory	1 0 0 0 0 0 s w	mod 0 1 0 r/m	data	data if s w = 01	4/16	
Immediate to accumulator	0 0 0 1 0 1 0 w	data	data if w = 1		3/4	8/16-bit
INC = Increment:						
Register/memory	1 1 1 1 1 1 1 w	mod 0 0 0 r/m			3/15	
Register	0 1 0 0 0 reg				3	
SUB = Subtract:						
Reg/memory and register to either	0 0 1 0 1 0 d w	mod reg r/m			3/10	
Immediate from register/memory	1 0 0 0 0 0 s w	mod 1 0 1 r/m	data	data if s w = 0 1	4/16	
Immediate from accumulator	0 0 1 0 1 1 0 w	data	data if w = 1		3/4	8/16-bit
SBB = Subtract with borrow:						
Reg/memory and register to either	0 0 0 1 1 0 d w	mod reg r/m			3/10	
Immediate from register/memory	1 0 0 0 0 0 s w	mod 0 1 1 r/m	data	data if s w = 0 1	4/16	
Immediate from accumulator	0 0 0 1 1 1 0 w	data	data if w = 1		3/4	8/16-bit
DEC = Decrement:						
Register/memory	1 1 1 1 1 1 1 w	mod 0 0 1 r/m			3/15	
Register	0 1 0 0 1 reg				3	
CMP = Compare:						
Register/memory with register	0 0 1 1 1 0 1 w	mod reg r/m			3/10	
Register with register/memory	0 0 1 1 1 0 0 w	mod reg r/m			3/10	
Immediate with register/memory	1 0 0 0 0 0 s w	mod 1 1 1 r/m	data	data if s w = 0 1	3/10	
Immediate with accumulator	0 0 1 1 1 1 0 w	data	data if w = 1		3/4	8/16-bit
NEG = Change sign	1 1 1 1 0 1 1 w	mod 0 1 1 r/m			3	
AAA = ASCII adjust for add	0 0 1 1 0 1 1 1				8	
DAA = Decimal adjust for add	0 0 1 0 0 1 1 1				4	
AAS = ASCII adjust for subtract	0 0 1 1 1 1 1 1				7	
DAS = Decimal adjust for subtract	0 0 1 0 1 1 1 1				4	
MUL = Multiply (unsigned):	1 1 1 1 0 1 1 w	mod 1 0 0 r/m				
Register-Byte					26–28	
Register-Word					35–37	
Memory-Byte					32–34	
Memory-Word					41–43	
IMUL = Integer multiply (signed):	1 1 1 1 0 1 1 w	mod 1 0 1 r/m				
Register-Byte					25–28	
Register-Word					34–37	
Memory-Byte					31–34	
Memory-Word					40–43	
IMUL = Integer immediate multiply (signed)	0 1 1 0 1 0 s 1	mod reg r/m	data	data if s = 0	22–25/29–32	
DIV = Divide (unsigned):	1 1 1 1 0 1 1 w	mod 1 1 0 r/m				
Register-Byte					29	
Register-Word					38	
Memory-Byte					35	
Memory-Word					44	

Shaded areas indicate instructions not available in iAPX 86, 88 microsystems.

Table 2-9 Instruction Set Summary (continued)

FUNCTION	FORMAT				Clock Cycles	Comments
ARITHMETIC (Continued):						
IDIV = Integer divide (signed):	1 1 1 1 0 1 1 w	mod 1 1 1 r/m				
Register-Byte					44–52	
Register-Word					53–61	
Memory-Byte					50–58	
Memory-Word					59–67	
AAM = ASCII adjust for multiply	1 1 0 1 0 1 0 0	0 0 0 0 1 0 1 0			19	
AAD = ASCII adjust for divide	1 1 0 1 0 1 0 1	0 0 0 0 1 0 1 0			15	
CBW = Convert byte to word	1 0 0 1 1 0 0 0				2	
CWD = Convert word to double word	1 0 0 1 1 0 0 1				4	
LOGIC						
Shift/Rotate Instructions:						
Register/Memory by 1	1 1 0 1 0 0 0 w	mod TTT r/m			2/15	
Register/Memory by CL	1 1 0 1 0 0 1 w	mod TTT r/m			5+n/17+n	
Register/Memory by Count	1 1 0 0 0 0 0 w	mod TTT r/m	count		5+n/17+n	
	TTT Instruction 0 0 0 ROL 0 0 1 ROR 0 1 0 RCL 0 1 1 RCR 1 0 0 SHL/SAL 1 0 1 SHR 1 1 1 SAR					
AND = And:						
Reg/memory and register to either	0 0 1 0 0 0 d w	mod reg r/m			3/10	
Immediate to register/memory	1 0 0 0 0 0 0 w	mod 1 0 0 r/m	data	data if w = 1	4/16	
Immediate to accumulator	0 0 1 0 0 1 0 w	data	data if w = 1		3/4	8/16-bit
TEST = And function to flags, no result:						
Register/memory and register	1 0 0 0 0 1 0 w	mod reg r/m			3/10	
Immediate data and register/memory	1 1 1 1 0 1 1 w	mod 0 0 0 r/m	data	data if w = 1	4/10	
Immediate data and accumulator	1 0 1 0 1 0 0 w	data	data if w = 1		3/4	8/16-bit
OR = Or:						
Reg/memory and register to either	0 0 0 0 1 0 d w	mod reg r/m			3/10	
Immediate to register/memory	1 0 0 0 0 0 0 w	mod 0 0 1 r/m	data	data if w = 1	4/16	
Immediate to accumulator	0 0 0 0 1 1 0 w	data	data if w = 1		3/4	8/16-bit
XOR = Exclusive or:						
Reg/memory and register to either	0 0 1 1 0 0 d w	mod reg r/m			3/10	
Immediate to register/memory	1 0 0 0 0 0 0 w	mod 1 1 0 r/m	data	data if w = 1	4/16	
Immediate to accumulator	0 0 1 1 0 1 0 w	data	data if w = 1		3/4	8/16-bit
NOT = Invert register/memory	1 1 1 1 0 1 1 w	mod 0 1 0 r/m			3	
STRING MANIPULATION:						
MOVS = Move byte/word	1 0 1 0 0 1 0 w				14	
CMPS = Compare byte/word	1 0 1 0 0 1 1 w				22	
SCAS = Scan byte/word	1 0 1 0 1 1 1 w				15	
LODS = Load byte/wd to AL/AX	1 0 1 0 1 1 0 w				12	
STOS = Stor byte/wd from AL/A	1 0 1 0 1 0 1 w				10	
INS = Input byte/wd from DX port	0 1 1 0 1 1 0 w				14	
OUTS = Output byte/wd to DX port	0 1 1 0 1 1 1 w				14	

Shaded areas indicate instructions not available in iAPX 86, 88 microsystems.

Table 2-9 Instruction Set Summary (continued)

FUNCTION	FORMAT			Clock Cycles	Comments
STRING MANIPULATION (Continued):					
Repeated by count in CX					
MOVS – Move string	1 1 1 1 0 0 1 0	1 0 1 0 0 1 0 w		8+8n	
CMPS – Compare string	1 1 1 1 0 0 1 z	1 0 1 0 0 1 1 w		5+22n	
SCAS – Scan string	1 1 1 1 0 0 1 z	1 0 1 0 1 1 1 w		5+15n	
LODS – Load string	1 1 1 1 0 0 1 0	1 0 1 0 1 1 0 w		6+11n	
STOS – Store string	1 1 1 1 0 0 1 0	1 0 1 0 1 0 1 w		6+9n	
INS – Input string	1 1 1 1 0 0 1 0	0 1 1 0 1 1 0 w		8+8n	
OUTS – Output string	1 1 1 1 0 0 1 0	0 1 1 0 1 1 1 w		8+8n	
CONTROL TRANSFER					
CALL = Call:					
Direct within segment	1 1 1 0 1 0 0 0	disp-low	disp-high	15	
Register memory indirect within segment	1 1 1 1 1 1 1 1	mod 0 1 0 r m		13/19	
Direct intersegment	1 0 0 1 1 0 1 0	segment offset		23	
		segment selector			
Indirect intersegment	1 1 1 1 1 1 1 1	mod 0 1 1 r m	(mod ≠ 11)	38	
JMP = Unconditional jump:					
Short/long	1 1 1 0 1 0 1 1	disp-low		14	
Direct within segment	1 1 1 0 1 0 0 1	disp-low	disp-high	14	
Register/memory indirect within segment	1 1 1 1 1 1 1 1	mod 1 0 0 r m		11/17	
Direct intersegment	1 1 1 0 1 0 1 0	segment offset		14	
		segment selector			
Indirect intersegment	1 1 1 1 1 1 1 1	mod 1 0 1 r m	(mod ≠ 11)	26	
RET = Return from CALL:					
Within segment	1 1 0 0 0 0 1 1			16	
Within seg adding immed to SP	1 1 0 0 0 0 1 0	data-low	data-high	18	
Intersegment	1 1 0 0 1 0 1 1			22	
Intersegment adding immediate to SP	1 1 0 0 1 0 1 0	data-low	data-high	25	

Shaded areas indicate instructions not available in iAPX 86, 88 microsystems.

Table 2-9 Instruction Set Summary (continued)

FUNCTION	FORMAT				Clock Cycles	Comments
CONTROL TRANSFER (Continued):						
JE/JZ = Jump on equal/zero	0 1 1 1 0 1 0 0	disp			4/13	13 if JMP taken 4 if JMP not taken
JL/JNGE = Jump on less/not greater or equal	0 1 1 1 1 1 0 0	disp			4/13	
JLE/JNG = Jump on less or equal/not greater	0 1 1 1 1 1 1 0	disp			4/13	
JB/JNAE = Jump on below/not above or equal	0 1 1 1 0 0 1 0	disp			4/13	
JBE/JNA = Jump on below or equal/not above	0 1 1 1 0 1 1 0	disp			4/13	
JP/JPE = Jump on parity/parity even	0 1 1 1 1 0 1 0	disp			4/13	
JO = Jump on overflow	0 1 1 1 0 0 0 0	disp			4/13	
JS = Jump on sign	0 1 1 1 1 0 0 0	disp			4/13	
JNE/JNZ = Jump on not equal/not zero	0 1 1 1 0 1 0 1	disp			4/13	
JNL/JGE = Jump on not less/greater or equal	0 1 1 1 1 1 0 1	disp			4/13	
JNLE/JG = Jump on not less or equal/greater	0 1 1 1 1 1 1 1	disp			4/13	
JNB/JAE = Jump on not below/above or equal	0 1 1 1 0 0 1 1	disp			4/13	
JNBE/JA = Jump on not below or equal/above	0 1 1 1 0 1 1 1	disp			4/13	
JNP/JPO = Jump on not par/par odd	0 1 1 1 1 0 1 1	disp			4/13	
JNO = Jump on not overflow	0 1 1 1 0 0 0 1	disp			4/13	
JNS = Jump on not sign	0 1 1 1 1 0 0 1	disp			4/13	
JCXZ = Jump on CX zero	1 1 1 0 0 0 1 1	disp			5/15	
LOOP = Loop CX times	1 1 1 0 0 0 1 0	disp			6/16	
LOOPZ/LOOPE = Loop while zero/equal	1 1 1 0 0 0 0 1	disp			6/16	JMP taken/ JMP not taken
LOOPNZ/LOOPNE = Loop while not zero/equal	1 1 1 0 0 0 0 0	disp			16	
					5	
ENTER = Enter Procedure	1 1 0 0 1 0 0 0	data-low	data-high	L		
L=0					15	
L=1					25	
L>1					22+16(n−1)	
LEAVE = Leave Procedure	1 1 0 0 1 0 0 1				8	
INT = **Interrupt:**						
Type specified	1 1 0 0 1 1 0 1	type			47	
Type 3	1 1 0 0 1 1 0 0				45	if INT. taken/ if INT. not taken
INTO = Interrupt on overflow	1 1 0 0 1 1 1 0				48/4	
IRET = Interrupt return	1 1 0 0 1 1 1 1				28	
BOUND = Detect value out of range	0 1 1 0 0 0 1 0	mod reg r/m			33–35	

Shaded areas indicate instructions not available in iAPX 86, 88 microsystems.

Table 2-9 Instruction Set Summary (continued)

FUNCTION	FORMAT	Clock Cycles	Comments
PROCESSOR CONTROL			
CLC = Clear carry	1 1 1 1 1 0 0 0	2	
CMC = Complement carry	1 1 1 1 0 1 0 1	2	
STC = Set carry	1 1 1 1 1 0 0 1	2	
CLD = Clear direction	1 1 1 1 1 1 0 0	2	
STD = Set direction	1 1 1 1 1 1 0 1	2	
CLI = Clear interrupt	1 1 1 1 1 0 1 0	2	
STI = Set interrupt	1 1 1 1 1 0 1 1	2	
HLT = Halt	1 1 1 1 0 1 0 0	2	
WAIT = Wait	1 0 0 1 1 0 1 1	6	if $\overline{test} = 0$
LOCK = Bus lock prefix	1 1 1 1 0 0 0 0	2	
ESC = Processor Extension Escape	1 1 0 1 1 T T T | mod LLL r/m (TTT LLL are opcode to processor extension)	6	

Shaded areas indicate instructions not available in iAPX 86, 88 microsystems.

FOOTNOTES

The effective Address (EA) of the memory operand is computed according to the mod and r/m fields:

if mod = 11 then r/m is treated as a REG field
if mod = 00 then DISP = 0*, disp-low and disp-high are absent
if mod = 01 then DISP = disp-low sign-extended to 16-bits, disp-high is absent
if mod = 10 then DISP = disp-high: disp-low

if r/m = 000 then EA = (BX) + (SI) + DISP
if r/m = 001 then EA = (BX) + (DI) + DISP
if r/m = 010 then EA = (BP) + (SI) + DISP
if r/m = 011 then EA = (BP) + (DI) + DISP
if r/m = 100 then EA = (SI) + DISP
if r/m = 101 then EA = (DI) + DISP
if r/m = 110 then EA = (BP) + DISP*
if r/m = 111 then EA = (BX) + DISP

DISP follows 2nd byte of instruction (before data if required)

*except if mod = 00 and r/m = 110 then EA = disp-high: disp-low.

NOTE:
EA CALCULATION TIME IS 4 CLOCK CYCLES FOR ALL MODES, AND IS INCLUDED IN THE EXECUTION TIMES GIVEN WHENEVER APPROPRIATE.

SEGMENT OVERRIDE PREFIX

0 0 1 reg 1 1 0

reg is assigned according to the following:

reg	Segment Register
00	ES
01	CS
10	SS
11	DS

REG is assigned according to the following table:

16-Bit (w = 1)	8-Bit (w = 0)
000 AX	000 AL
001 CX	001 CL
010 DX	010 DL
011 BX	011 BL
100 SP	100 AH
101 BP	101 CH
110 SI	110 DH
111 DI	111 BH

The physical addresses of all operands addressed by the BP register are computed using the SS segment register. The physical addresses of the destination operands of the string primitive operations (those addressed by the DI register) are computed using the ES segment, which may not be overridden.

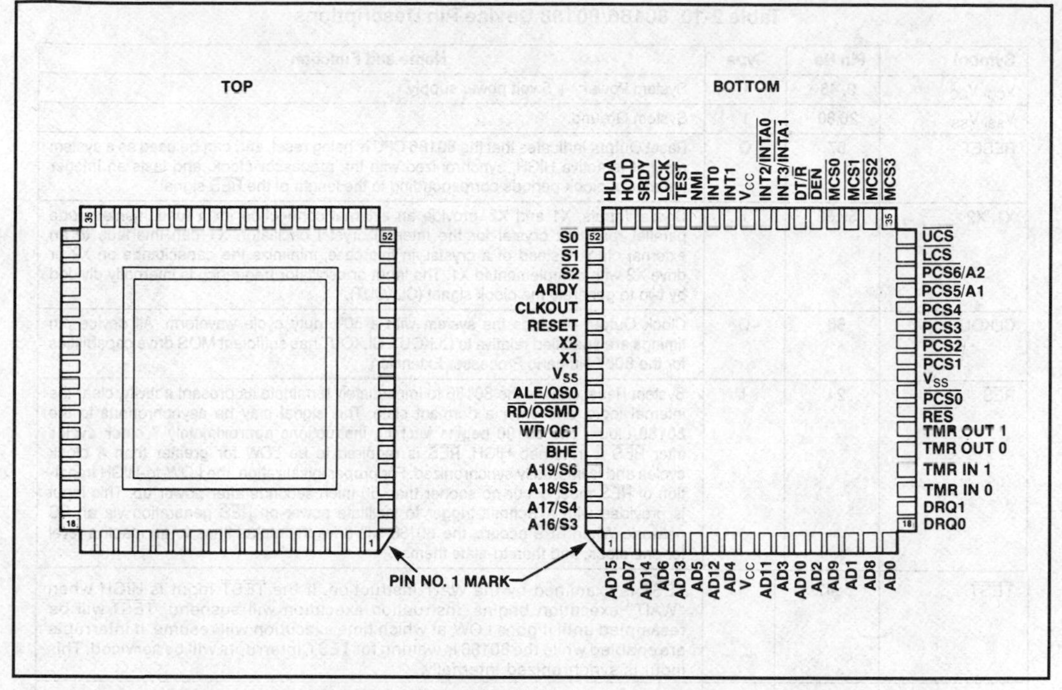

Figure 2-4 80186/80188 DIP Pin Assignments

transition, one clock phase earlier than on the 8086. Note that since execution unit operation is independent of bus interface unit operation, queue status lines may change in any T state.

Since the ALE, RD*, and WR* signals are not directly available from the 80186 when it is configured in queue status mode, these signals must be derived from the status lines S0*-S2* using an external 8288 bus controller. To prevent the 80186 from accidentally entering queue status mode during reset, the RD* line is internally provided with a weak pullup device. RD* is the ONLY tri-state or input pin on the 80186 which is pulled up (neither pullups nor pulldowns are used for any other 80186 tri-state or input pin).

2.4.3 Interrupt Controller Operating Modes

The integrated interrupt controller has two major modes of operation. These are the non-iRMX 86 mode (referred to as master mode) and the iRMX 86 mode. In master mode the integrated interrupt controller acts as the master interrupt controller for the system.

In iRMX 86 mode the controller operates as a slave to an external interrupt controller which operates as the master system interrupt controller. Some of the interrupt controller registers and interrupt controller pins change definitions between the two modes, but the basic function of the interrupt controller remains basically the same. The main difference between the two modes is that when in the master mode, the interrupt controller presents its input directly to the 80186 CPU and in the iRMX 86 mode the interrupt controller presents its interrupt input to an external controller. The external interrupt controller then presents the interrupt inputs to the CPU.

Placing the interrupt controller in the iRMX 86 mode is done by setting the iRMX mode bit in the peripheral control block relocation register. A description of the operation of the integrated interrupt controller in the iRMX 86 and non-iRMX 86 modes of operation is contained in paragraph 2.8.3.

2.5 BUS OPERATION

Bus operation in the 80186/188 and 8086/88 CPU's is basically the same. Before proceeding with this section review the 8086 Bus Operation discussion in paragraph 1.5.

In the 80186, bus cycles occur sequentially, but do not necessarily follow one after another; that is, the bus may remain idle for several T states (Ti) between each bus access initiated by the 80186. A bus idle occurs whenever the 80186 internal queue is full and no read/write cycles

Table 2-10 80186/80188 Device Pin Descriptions

<table>
<tr><th>Symbol</th><th>Pin No.</th><th>Type</th><th>Name and Function</th></tr>
<tr><td>V_{CC}, V_{CC}</td><td>9, 43</td><td>I</td><td>System Power: + 5 volt power supply.</td></tr>
<tr><td>V_{SS}, V_{SS}</td><td>26,60</td><td>I</td><td>System Ground.</td></tr>
<tr><td>RESET</td><td>57</td><td>O</td><td>Reset Output indicates that the 80186 CPU is being reset, and can be used as a system reset. It is active HIGH, synchronized with the processor clock, and lasts an integer number of clock periods corresponding to the length of the $\overline{RES}$ signal.</td></tr>
<tr><td>X1, X2</td><td>59,58</td><td>I</td><td>Crystal Inputs, X1 and X2, provide an external connection for a fundamental mode parallel resonant crystal for the internal crystal oscillator. X1 can interface to an external clock instead of a crystal. In this case, minimize the capacitance on X2 or drive X2 with complemented X1. The input or oscillator frequency is internally divided by two to generate the clock signal (CLKOUT).</td></tr>
<tr><td>CLKOUT</td><td>56</td><td>O</td><td>Clock Output provides the system with a 50% duty cycle waveform. All device pin timings are specified relative to CLKOUT. CLKOUT has sufficient MOS drive capabilities for the 8087 Numeric Processor Extension.</td></tr>
<tr><td>$\overline{RES}$</td><td>24</td><td>I</td><td>System Reset causes the 80186 to immediately terminate its present activity, clear the internal logic, and enter a dormant state. This signal may be asynchronous to the 80186 clock. The 80186 begins fetching instructions approximately 7 clock cycles after $\overline{RES}$ is returned HIGH. $\overline{RES}$ is required to be LOW for greater than 4 clock cycles and is internally synchronized. For proper initialization, the LOW-to-HIGH transition of $\overline{RES}$ must occur no sooner than 50 microseconds after power up. This input is provided with a Schmitt-trigger to facilitate power-on $\overline{RES}$ generation via an RC network. When $\overline{RES}$ occurs, the 80186 will drive the status lines to an inactive level for one clock, and then tri-state them.</td></tr>
<tr><td>$\overline{TEST}$</td><td>47</td><td>I</td><td>$\overline{TEST}$ is examined by the WAIT instruction. If the $\overline{TEST}$ input is HIGH when "WAIT" execution begins, instruction execution will suspend. $\overline{TEST}$ will be resampled until it goes LOW, at which time execution will resume. If interrupts are enabled while the 80186 is waiting for $\overline{TEST}$, interrupts will be serviced. This input is synchronized internally.</td></tr>
<tr><td>TMR IN 0,
TMR IN 1</td><td>20
21</td><td>I
I</td><td>Timer Inputs are used either as clock or control signals, depending upon the programmed timer mode. These inputs are active HIGH (or LOW-to-HIGH transitions are counted) and internally synchronized.</td></tr>
<tr><td>TMR OUT 0,
TMR OUT 1</td><td>22
23</td><td>O
O</td><td>Timer outputs are used to provide single pulse or continuous waveform generation, depending upon the timer mode selected.</td></tr>
<tr><td>DRQ0
DRQ1</td><td>18
19</td><td>I
I</td><td>DMA Request is driven HIGH by an external device when it desires that a DMA channel (Channel 0 or 1) perform a transfer. These signals are active HIGH, level-triggered, and internally synchronized.</td></tr>
<tr><td>NMI</td><td>46</td><td>I</td><td>Non-Maskable Interrupt is an edge-triggered input which causes a type 2 interrupt. NMI is not maskable internally. A transition from a LOW to HIGH initiates the interrupt at the next instruction boundary. NMI is latched internally. An NMI duration of one clock or more will guarantee service. This input is internally synchronized.</td></tr>
<tr><td>INT0, INT1,
INT2/$\overline{INTA0}$
INT3/$\overline{INTA1}$</td><td>45,44
42
41</td><td>I
I/O
I/O</td><td>Maskable Interrupt Requests can be requested by strobing one of these pins. When configured as inputs, these pins are active HIGH. Interrupt Requests are synchronized internally. INT2 and INT3 may be configured via software to provide active-LOW interrupt-acknowledge output signals. All interrupt inputs may be configured via software to be either edge- or level-triggered. To ensure recognition, all interrupt requests must remain active until the interrupt is acknowleged. When iRMX mode is selected, the function of these pins changes (see Interrupt Controller section of this data sheet).</td></tr>
<tr><td>A19/S6,
A18/S5,
A17/S4,
A16/S3</td><td>65
66
67
68</td><td>O
O
O
O</td><td>Address Bus Outputs (16–19) and Bus Cycle Status (3–6) reflect the four most significant address bits during T_1. These signals are active HIGH. During T_2, T_3, T_W, and T_4, status information is available on these lines as encoded below:<table><tr><th></th><th>Low</th><th>High</th></tr><tr><td>S6</td><td>Processor Cycle</td><td>DMA Cycle</td></tr></table>S3,S4, and S5 are defined as LOW during T_2–T_4.</td></tr>
<tr><td>AD15–AD0</td><td>10–17,
1–8</td><td>I/O</td><td>Address/Data Bus (0–15) signals constitute the time mutiplexed memory or I/O address (T_1) and data (T_2, T_3, T_W, and T_4) bus. The bus is active HIGH. A_0 is analogous to $\overline{BHE}$ for the lower byte of the data bus, pins D_7 through D_0. It is LOW during T_1 when a byte is to be transferred onto the lower portion of the bus in memory or I/O operations.</td></tr>
</table>

Table 2-10 80186/80188 Device Pin Descriptions (continued)

<table>
<tr><th>Symbol</th><th>Pin No.</th><th>Type</th><th>Name and Function</th></tr>
<tr><td>$\overline{BHE}$/S7</td><td>64</td><td>O</td><td>During T_1 the Bus High Enable signal should be used to determine if data is to be enabled onto the most significant half of the data bus, pins $D_{15}-D_8$. $\overline{BHE}$ is LOW during T_1 for read, write, and interrupt acknowledge cycles when a byte is to be transferred on the higher half of the bus. The S_7 status information is available during T_2, T_3, and T_4. S_7 is logically equivalent to $\overline{BHE}$. The signal is active LOW, and is tristated OFF during bus HOLD.
<table>
<tr><th colspan="3">$\overline{BHE}$ and A0 Encodings</th></tr>
<tr><th>$\overline{BHE}$ Value</th><th>A0 Value</th><th>Function</th></tr>
<tr><td>0</td><td>0</td><td>Word Transfer</td></tr>
<tr><td>0</td><td>1</td><td>Byte Transfer on upper half of data bus (D15–D8)</td></tr>
<tr><td>1</td><td>0</td><td>Byte Transfer on lower half of data bus (D_7-D_0)</td></tr>
<tr><td>1</td><td>1</td><td>Reserved</td></tr>
</table></td></tr>
<tr><td>ALE/QS0</td><td>61</td><td>O</td><td>Address Latch Enable/Queue Status 0 is provided by the 80186 to latch the address into the 8282/8283 address latches. ALE is active HIGH. Addresses are guaranteed to be valid on the trailing edge of ALE. The ALE rising edge is generated off the rising edge of the CLKOUT immediately preceding T_1 of the associated bus cycle, effectively one-half clock cycle earlier than in the standard 8086. The trailing edge is generated off the CLKOUT rising edge in T_1 as in the 8086. Note that ALE is never floated.</td></tr>
<tr><td>$\overline{WR}$/QS1</td><td>63</td><td>O</td><td>Write Strobe/Queue Status 1 indicates that the data on the bus is to be written into a memory or an I/O device. $\overline{WR}$ is active for T_2, T_3, and T_W of any write cycle. It is active LOW, and floats during "HOLD." It is driven HIGH for one clock during Reset, and then floated. When the 80186 is in queue status mode, the ALE/QS0 and $\overline{WR}$/QS1 pins provide information about processor/instruction queue interaction.
<table>
<tr><th>QS1</th><th>QS0</th><th>Queue Operation</th></tr>
<tr><td>0</td><td>0</td><td>No queue operation</td></tr>
<tr><td>0</td><td>1</td><td>First opcode byte fetched from the queue</td></tr>
<tr><td>1</td><td>1</td><td>Subsequent byte fetched from the queue</td></tr>
<tr><td>1</td><td>0</td><td>Empty the queue</td></tr>
</table></td></tr>
<tr><td>$\overline{RD}$/$\overline{QSMD}$</td><td>62</td><td>O</td><td>Read Strobe indicates that the 80186 is performing a memory or I/O read cycle. $\overline{RD}$ is active LOW for T_2, T_3, and T_W of any read cycle. It is guaranteed not to go LOW in T_2 until after the Address Bus is floated. $\overline{RD}$ is active LOW, and floats during "HOLD." $\overline{RD}$ is driven HIGH for one clock during Reset, and then the output driver is floated. A weak internal pull-up mechanism on the $\overline{RD}$ line holds it HIGH when the line is not driven. During $\overline{RESET}$ the pin is sampled to determine whether the 80186 should provide ALE, $\overline{WR}$ and $\overline{RD}$, or if the Queue-Status should be provided. $\overline{RD}$ should be connected to GND to provide Queue-Status data.</td></tr>
<tr><td>ARDY</td><td>55</td><td>I</td><td>Asynchronous Ready informs the 80186 that the addressed memory space or I/O device will complete a data transfer. The ARDY input pin will accept an asynchronous input, and is active HIGH. Only the rising edge is internally synchronized by the 80186. This means that the falling edge of ARDY must be synchronized to the 80186 clock. If connected to V_{CC}, no WAIT states are inserted. Asynchronous ready (ARDY) or synchronous ready (SRDY) must be active to terminate a bus cycle. If unused, this line should be tied LOW.</td></tr>
<tr><td>SRDY</td><td>49</td><td>I</td><td>Synchronous Ready must be synchronized externally to the 80186. The use of SRDY provides a relaxed system-timing specification on the Ready input. This is accomplished by eliminating the one-half clock cycle which is required for internally resolving the signal level when using the ARDY input. This line is active HIGH. If this line is connected to V_{CC}, no WAIT states are inserted. Asynchronous ready (ARDY) or synchronous ready (SRDY) must be active before a bus cycle is terminated. If unused, this line should be tied LOW.</td></tr>
<tr><td>$\overline{LOCK}$</td><td>48</td><td>O</td><td>$\overline{LOCK}$ output indicates that other system bus masters are not to gain control of the system bus while $\overline{LOCK}$ is active LOW. The $\overline{LOCK}$ signal is requested by the LOCK prefix instruction and is activated at the beginning of the first data cycle associated with the instruction following the LOCK prefix. It remains active until the completion of the instruction following the LOCK prefix. No prefetches will occur while $\overline{LOCK}$ is asserted. $\overline{LOCK}$ is active LOW, is driven HIGH for one clock during RESET, and then floated.</td></tr>
</table>

Table 2-10 80186/80188 Device Pin Descriptions (continued)

<table>
<tr><th>Symbol</th><th>Pin No.</th><th>Type</th><th>Name and Function</th></tr>
<tr><td>$\overline{S0}$,$\overline{S1}$,$\overline{S2}$</td><td>52–54</td><td>O</td><td>Bus cycle status $\overline{S0}$–$\overline{S2}$ are encoded to provide bus-transaction information:
<table>
<tr><th colspan="4">80186 Bus Cycle Status Information</th></tr>
<tr><th>$\overline{S2}$</th><th>$\overline{S1}$</th><th>$\overline{S0}$</th><th>Bus Cycle Initiated</th></tr>
<tr><td>0</td><td>0</td><td>0</td><td>Interrupt Acknowledge</td></tr>
<tr><td>0</td><td>0</td><td>1</td><td>Read I/O</td></tr>
<tr><td>0</td><td>1</td><td>0</td><td>Write I/O</td></tr>
<tr><td>0</td><td>1</td><td>1</td><td>Halt</td></tr>
<tr><td>1</td><td>0</td><td>0</td><td>Instruction Fetch</td></tr>
<tr><td>1</td><td>0</td><td>1</td><td>Read Data from Memory</td></tr>
<tr><td>1</td><td>1</td><td>0</td><td>Write Data to Memory</td></tr>
<tr><td>1</td><td>1</td><td>1</td><td>Passive (no bus cycle)</td></tr>
</table>
The status pins float during "HOLD."
$\overline{S2}$ may be used as a logical M/$\overline{IO}$ indicator, and $\overline{S1}$ as a DT/$\overline{R}$ indicator.
The status lines are driven HIGH for one clock during Reset, and then floated ntil a bus cycle begins.</td></tr>
<tr><td>HOLD (input)
HLDA (output)</td><td>50
51</td><td>I
O</td><td>HOLD indicates that another bus master is requesting the local bus. The HOLD input is active HIGH. HOLD may be asynchronous with respect to the 80186 clock. The 80186 will issue a HLDA (HIGH) in response to a HOLD request at the end of T_4 or T_1. Simultaneous with the issuance of HLDA, the 80186 will float the local bus and control lines. After HOLD is detected as being LOW, the 80186 will lower HLDA. When the 80186 needs to run another bus cycle, it will again drive the local bus and control lines.</td></tr>
<tr><td>$\overline{UCS}$</td><td>34</td><td>O</td><td>Upper Memory Chip Select is an active LOW output whenever a memory reference is made to the defined upper portion (1K–256K block) of memory. This line is not floated during bus HOLD. The address range activating $\overline{UCS}$ is software programmable.</td></tr>
<tr><td>$\overline{LCS}$</td><td>33</td><td>O</td><td>Lower Memory Chip Select is active LOW whenever a memory reference is made to the defined lower portion (1K–256K) of memory. This line is not floated during bus HOLD. The address range activating $\overline{LCS}$ is software programmable.</td></tr>
<tr><td>$\overline{MCS0-3}$</td><td>38,37,36,35</td><td>O</td><td>Mid-Range Memory Chip Select signals are active LOW when a memory reference is made to the defined mid-range portion of memory (8K–512K). These lines are not floated during bus HOLD. The address ranges activating $\overline{MCS0-3}$ are software programmable.</td></tr>
<tr><td>$\overline{PCS0}$
$\overline{PCS1-4}$</td><td>25
27,28,29,30</td><td>O
O</td><td>Peripheral Chip Select signals 0–4 are active LOW when a reference is made to the defined peripheral area (64K byte I/O space). These lines are not floated during bus HOLD. The address ranges activating $\overline{PCS0-4}$ are software programmable.</td></tr>
<tr><td>$\overline{PCS5}$/A1</td><td>31</td><td>O</td><td>Peripheral Chip Select 5 or Latched A1 may be programmed to provide a sixth peripheral chip select, or to provide an internally latched A1 signal. The address range activating $\overline{PCS5}$ is software programmable. When programmed to provide latched A1, rather than $\overline{PCS5}$, this pin will retain the previously latched value of A1 during a bus HOLD. A1 is active HIGH.</td></tr>
<tr><td>$\overline{PCS6}$/A2</td><td>32</td><td>O</td><td>Peripheral Chip Select 6 or Latched A2 may be programmed to provide a seventh peripheral chip select, or to provide an internally latched A2 signal. The address range activating $\overline{PCS6}$ is software programmable. When programmed to provide latched A2, rather than $\overline{PCS6}$, this pin will retain the previously latched value of A2 during a bus HOLD. A2 is active HIGH.</td></tr>
<tr><td>DT/$\overline{R}$</td><td>40</td><td>O</td><td>Data Transmit/Receive controls the direction of data flow through the external 8286/8287 data bus transceiver. When LOW, data is transferred to the 80186. When HIGH the 80186 places write data on the data bus.</td></tr>
<tr><td>$\overline{DEN}$</td><td>39</td><td>O</td><td>Data Enable is provided as an 8286/8287 data bus transceiver output enable. $\overline{DEN}$ is active LOW during each memory and I/O access. $\overline{DEN}$ is HIGH whenever DT/$\overline{R}$ changes state.</td></tr>
</table>

Table 2-11 D.C. Characteristics

D.C. CHARACTERISTICS ($T3_A = 0°–70°$, $V_{CC} = 5V \pm 10\%$)

Symbol	Parameter	Min.	Max.	Units	Test Conditions
V_{IL}	Input Low Voltage	− 0.5	+ 0.8	Volts	
V_{IH}	Input High Voltage (All except X1 and ($\overline{\text{RES}}$)	2.0	V_{CC} + 0.5	Volts	
V_{IH1}	Input High Voltage ($\overline{\text{RES}}$)		V_{CC} + 0.5	Volts	
V_{OL}	Output Low Voltage	3.0	0.45	Volts	I_a = 2.5 mA for $\overline{\text{SO}}$-$\overline{\text{S2}}$ I_a = 2.0 mA for all other outputs
V_{OH}	Output High Voltage	2.4		Volts	I_{oa} = − 400 μA
I_{CC}	Power Supply Current		550 450	mA	Max measured at T_A = 0°C T_A = 70°C
I_{LI}	Input Leakage Current		± 10	μA	OV < V_{IN} < V_{CC}
I_{LO}	Output Leakage Current		± 10	μA	0.45V < V_{OUT} < V_{CC}
V_{CLO}	Clock Output Low		0.6	Volts	I_a = 4.0 mA
V_{CHO}	Clock Output High	4.0		Volts	I_{oa} = −200 μA
V_{CLI}	Clock Input Low Voltage	−0.5	0.6	Volts	
V_{CHI}	Clock Input High Voltage	3.9	V_{CC} + 1.0	Volts	
C_{IN}	Input Capacitance		10	pF	
C_{IO}	I/O Capacitance		20	pF	

are being requested by the execution unit or integrated DMA unit. Recall that the bus interface unit fetches opcodes (including immediate data) from memory, while the execution unit actually executes the pre-fetched instructions. The number of clock cycles required to execute an 80186 instruction vary from 2 clock cycles for a register to register move to 67 clock cycles for an integer divide.

If a program contains many long instructions, program execution will be CPU limited, that is, the instruction queue will be constantly filled. Thus, the execution unit does not need to wait for an instruction to be fetched. If a program contains mainly short instructions or data move instructions, the execution will be bus limited. Here, the execution unit will be required to wait often for an instruction to be fetched before it continues its operation.

Although the amount of bus usage (i.e., the percentage of bus time used by the 80186 for instruction fetching and execution required for top performance) will vary considerably from one program to another, a typical instruction mix on the 80186 will require greater bus usage than the 8086. This is greater usage caused by the higher performance execution unit requiring instructions from the prefetch queue at a greater rate. This usage also means that the effect of wait states is more pronounced in an 80186 system than in an 8086 system. In all but a few cases, however, the performance degradation incurred by adding a wait state is less than might be expected because instruction fetching and execution are performed by separate units.

2.5.1 HALT Bus Cycle

The 80186 uses a HALT bus cycle to signal external circuits that the CPU has executed a HLT instruction. This bus cycle differs from a normal bus cycle in two important ways. First, since the processor is entering a halted state, none of the control lines (RD* or WR*) will be driven active. Address and data information will not be driven by the processor, and no data will be returned. Second, the S0*-S2* status lines go to their passive state (all high) during T2 of the bus cycle, well before they go to their passive state during a normal bus cycle. RD*, WR*, INTA*, DEN* will all go high (V_{OH}) and DT/R* will go low (V_{OL}). Like a normal bus cycle, ALE is driven active. Since no valid address information is present, the

Table 2-12 A.C. Characteristics Timing Requirements

A.C. CHARACTERISTICS (T_A = 0°–70°C, V_{CC} = 5V ± 10%)
80186 Timing Requirements All Timings Measured At 1.5 Volts Unless Otherwise Noted.
Applicable to 80186 (8 MHz) and 80186-6 (6 MHz)

Symbol	Parameter	Min.	Max.	Units	Test Conditions
TDVCL	Data in Setup (A/D)	20		ns	
TCLDX	Data in Hold (A/D)	10		ns	
TARYCHL	Asynchronous Ready inactive hold time	15		ns	
TARYHCH	Asynchronous Ready (AREADY) active setup time*	20		ns	
TARYLCL	AREADY inactive setup time	35		ns	
TCHARYX	AREADY hold time	15		ns	
TSRYCL	Synchronous Ready (SREADY) transition setup time	20		ns	
TCLSRY	SREADY transition hold time	15		ns	
THVCL	HOLD Setup*	25		ns	
TINVCH	INTR, NMI, $\overline{\text{TEST}}$, TIMERIN, Setup*	25		ns	
TINVCL	DRQ0, DRQ1, Setup*	25		ns	

*To guarantee recognition at next clock.

information strobed into the address latches should be ignored. However, this ALE pulse can be used to latch the HALT status from the S0*-S2* status lines.

Halting the processor does not interfere with the operation of any of the 80186 integrated peripheral units. Therefore, if a DMA transfer is pending while the processor is halted, the bus cycles associated with the DMA transfer will run. In fact, DMA latency time will improve while the processor is halted because the DMA unit will not be contending with the processor for access to the 80186 bus.

2.5.2 8086/80186 Bus Operation Differences

The 80186 bus was designed to be upward compatible with the 8086 bus. As a result, the 8086 bus interface components (the 8288 bus controller and the 8289 bus arbiter) may be used directly with the 80186. There are a few differences between the two processors, however, which must be considered. These are described in the following paragraphs.

CPU DUTY CYCLE AND CLOCK GENERATOR

The 80186 contains an integrated clock generator which provides a 50% duty cycle CPU clock. The 8086 differs by using an external clock generator (the 8284A) with a 33% duty cycle CPU clock (one-third of the time it is high, the other two-thirds of the time, it is low). These differences manifest themselves as follows:

1. No oscillator output is available from the 80186, as it is available from the 8284A clock generator.
2. The 80186 does not provide a PCLK (50% duty cycle, one-half CPU clock frequency) output as does the 8284A.
3. The clock low phase of the 80186 is narrower, and the clock high phase is wider than on the same speed 8086.
4. The 80186 does not internally factor AEN with RDY. Therefore, if both RDY inputs (ARDY and SRDY) are used, external logic must be used to prevent the RDY not connected to a certain device from being driven active during an access to this device (remember, only one RDY input needs to be active to terminate a bus cycle).
5. The 80186 concurrently provides both a single asynchronous ready input and a single synchronous ready input, while the 8284A provides either two synchronous ready inputs or two asynchronous ready inputs as a user-strapable option.
6. The CLOCKOUT (CPU clock output signal) drive capacity of the 80186 is less than the CPU clock drive capacity of the 8284A. Therefore, not as many high speed devices (e.g., Schottky TTL flip-flops) may be connected to this signal as can be used with the 8284A clock output.

Table 2-13 A.C. Characteristics Master Interface Timing Responses

Symbol	Parameters	80188 (8 MHz) Min.	Max.	80188-6 (6 MHz) Min.	Max.	Units	Test Conditions
T_{CLAV}	Address Valid Delay	5	55	5	63	ns	C_L = 20-200 pF all outputs
T_{CLAX}	Address Hold	10		10		ns	
T_{CLAZ}	Address Float Delay	T_{CLAX}	35	T_{CLAX}	44	ns	
T_{CHCZ}	Command Lines Float Delay		45		56	ns	
T_{CHCV}	Command Lines Valid Delay (after float)		55		76	ns	
T_{LHLL}	ALE Width	$T_{CLCL-35}$		$T_{CLCL-35}$		ns	
T_{CHLH}	ALE Active Delay		35		44	ns	
T_{CHLL}	ALE Inactive Delay		35		44	ns	
T_{LLAX}	Address Hold to ALE Inactive	$T_{CHCL-25}$		$T_{CHCL-30}$		ns	
T_{CLDV}	Data Valid Delay	10	44	10	55	ns	
T_{CLDOX}	Data Hold Time	10		10		ns	
T_{WHDX}	Data Hold after WR	$T_{CLCL-40}$		$T_{CLCL-50}$		ns	
T_{CVCTV}	Control Active Delay 1	5	70	5	87	ns	
T_{CHCTV}	Control Active Delay 2	10	55	10	76	ns	
T_{CVCTX}	Control Inactive Delay	5	55	5	76	ns	
T_{CVDEX}	$\overline{DEN}$ Inactive Delay (Non-Write Cycle)	10	70	10	87	ns	
T_{AZRL}	Address Float to $\overline{RD}$ Active	0		0		ns	
T_{CLRL}	$\overline{RD}$ Active Delay	10	70	10	87	ns	
T_{CLRH}	$\overline{RD}$ Inactive Delay	10	55	10	T_{CLCH}	ns	
T_{RHAV}	$\overline{RD}$ Inactive to Address Active	$T_{CLCL-40}$		$T_{CLCL-50}$		ns	
T_{CLHAV}	HLDA Valid Delay	5	50	5	67	ns	
T_{RLRH}	$\overline{RD}$ Width	$2T_{CLCL-50}$		$2T_{CLCL-50}$		ns	
T_{WLWH}	$\overline{WR}$ Width	$2T_{CLCL-40}$		$2T_{CLCL-40}$		ns	
T_{AVAL}	Address Valid to ALE Low	$T_{CLCH-25}$		$T_{CLCH-45}$		ns	
T_{CHSV}	Status Active Delay	10	55	10	T_{CHCL}	ns	
T_{CLSH}	Status Inactive Delay	10	65	10	T_{CLCH}	ns	
T_{CLTMV}	Timer Output Delay		60		75	ns	100 pF max
T_{CLRO}	Reset Delay		60		75	ns	
T_{CHQSV}	Queue Status Delay		35		44	ns	
T_{CHDX}	Status Hold Time	10		10		ns	
T_{AVCH}	Address Valid to Clock High	10		10		ns	

7. The crystal or external oscillator used by the 80186 is twice the CPU clock frequency, while the crystal or external oscillator used with the 8284A is three times the CPU clock frequency.

LOCAL BUS CONTROLLER AND CONTROL SIGNALS

The 80186 simultaneously provides both local bus controller outputs (RD*, WR*, ALE, DEN*, and DT/R*)

Table 2-14 A.C. Characteristics Chip-Select Timing Requirements

Symbol	Parameter	Min.	Max.	Min.	Max.	Units	Test Conditions
T_{CLCSV}	Chip-Select Active Delay		66		80	ns	
T_{CXCSX}	Chip-Selct Hold from Command Inactive	35		35		ns	
T_{CHCSX}	Chip-Select Inactive Delay	5	35	10	47	ns	

Table 2-15 A.C. Characteristics CLKIN Requirements

80186 CLKIN Requirements

		80186 (8 MHz)		80186-6 (6 MHz)			
Symbol	**Parameter**	**Min.**	**Max.**	**Min.**	**Max.**	**Units**	**Test Conditions**
TCKIN	CLKIN Period	62.5	250	83	250	ns	
TCKHL	CLKIN Fall Time		10		10	ns	3.5 to 1.0 volts
TCKLH	CLKIN Rise Time		10		10	ns	1.0 to 3.5 volts
TCLCK	CLKIN Low Time	25		33		ns	1.5 volts
TCHCK	CLKIN High Time	25		33		ns	1.5 volts

and status outputs (S0*, S1*, S2*) for use with the 8288 bus controller. This is different from the 8086 where the local bus controller outputs (generated only in minimum mode) are sacrificed if status outputs (generated only in maximum mode) are desired. These differences will manifest themselves in 8086 systems and 80186 systems as follows:

1. Because the 80186 can simultaneously provide local bus control signals and status outputs, many systems supporting both a system bus (e.g., a MULTIBUS) and a local bus will not require two separate external bus controllers, that is, the 80186 bus control signals may be used to control the local bus while the 80186 status signals are concurrently connected to the 8288 bus controller to drive the control signals of the system bus.

2. The ALE signal of the 80186 goes active a clock phase earlier on the 80186 then on the 8086 or the 8288. This timing minimizes address propagation time through the address latches, since typically the delay time through these latches from inputs valid is less than the propagation delay from the strobe input active.

3. The 80186 RD* input must be tied low to provide queue status outputs from the 80186 (see Figure 2-6). When so strapped into "queue status mode", the ALE and WR* outputs provide queue status information. Notice that this queue status information is available one clock phase earlier from the 80186 than from the 8086. See Figure 2-7.

HOLD/HLDA VERSUS RQ*/GT*

The 80186 uses a HOLD/HLDA type of protocol for exchanging bus mastership (like the 8086 in minimum mode) rather than the RQ*/GT* protocol used by the 8086 in maximum mode. This allows compatibility with Intel's new generation of bus master peripheral devices (for example the 82586 Ethernet controller or 82730 CRT controller).

STATUS INFORMATION

The 80186 does not provide S3-S5 status information. On the 8086, S3 and S4 provide information regarding the segment register used to generate the physical address of the currently executing bus cycle. S5 provides information concerning the state of the interrupt enable flip-flop. These status bits are always low on the 80186.

Status signal S6 is used to indicate whether the current bus cycle is initiated by either the CPU or a DMA device; subsequently, S6 is always low on the 8086. On the 80186, it is low whenever the current bus cycle is initiated by the 80186 CPU, and is high when the current bus cycle is initiated by the 80186 integrated DMA unit.

BUS DRIVE

The 80186 output drivers will drive 200pF loads. This is double that of the 8086 (100pF). This allows larger systems to be constructed without the need for bus buffers. It

Table 2-16 A.C. Characteristics CLKOUT Requirements

80186 CLKOUT Timing (200 pF load)

Symbol	**Parameter**	**Min.**	**Max.**	**Min.**	**Max.**	**Units**	**Test Conditions**
TCICO	CLKIN to CLKOUT Skew		50		62.5	ns	
TCLCL	CLKOUT Period	125	500	167	500	ns	
TCLCH	CLKOUT Low Time	½ TCLCL-7.5		½ TCLCL-7.5		ns	1.5 volts
TCHCL	CLKOUT High Time	½ TCLCL-7.5		½ TCLCL-7.5		ns	1.5 volts
TCH1CH2	CLKOUT Rise Time		15		15	ns	1.0 to 3.5 volts
TCL2CL1	CLKOUT Fall Time		15		15	ns	3.5 to 1. volts

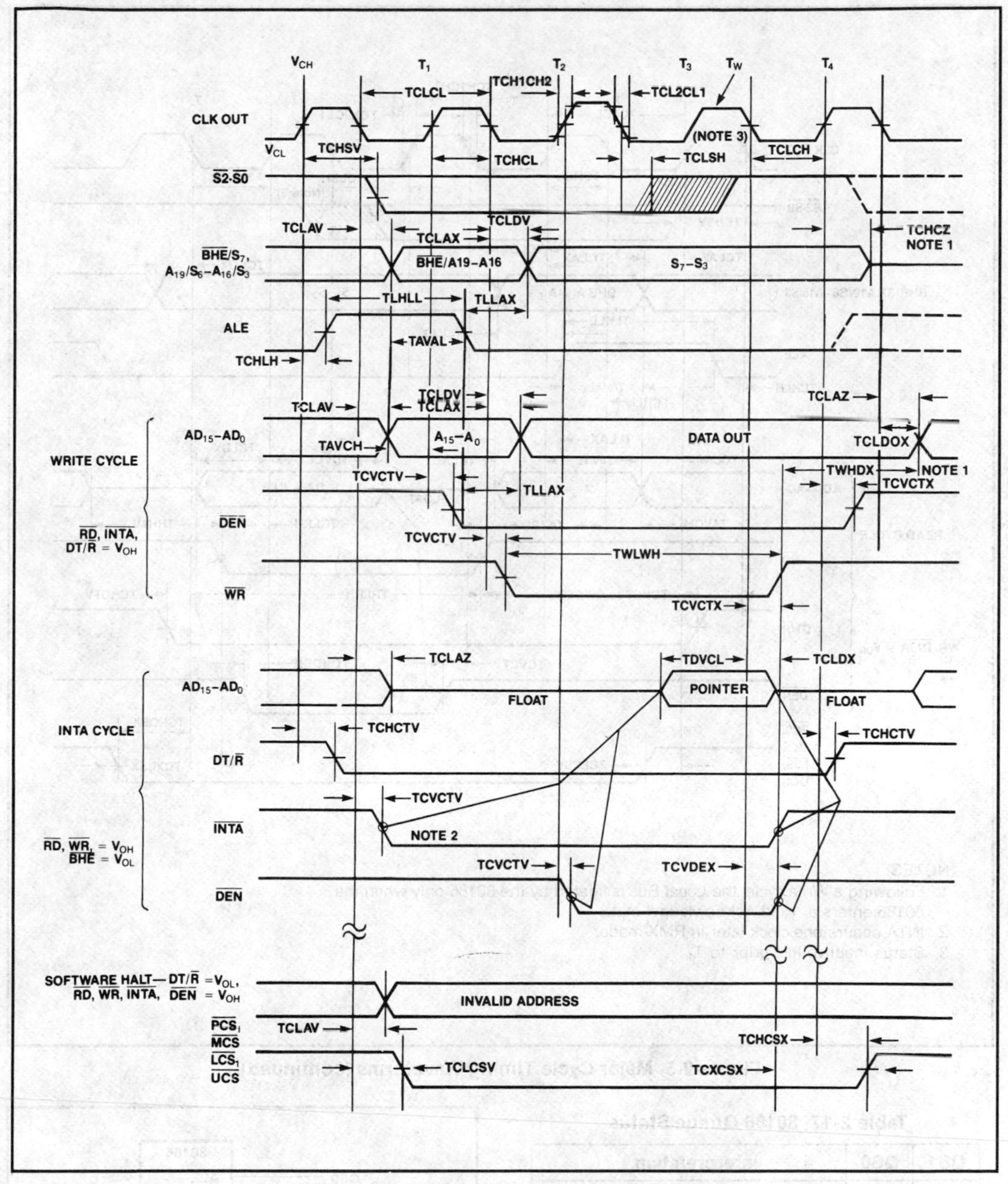

Figure 2-5 Major Cycle Timing Waveforms

also means that good grounds must be provided to the 80186, since its large drivers can discharge its outputs very quickly causing large current transients on the 80186 ground pins.

READ/WRITE SIGNALS

The 80186 does not provide early and late write signals, as does the 8288 bus controller. The WR* signal generated by the 80186 corresponds to the early write signal of

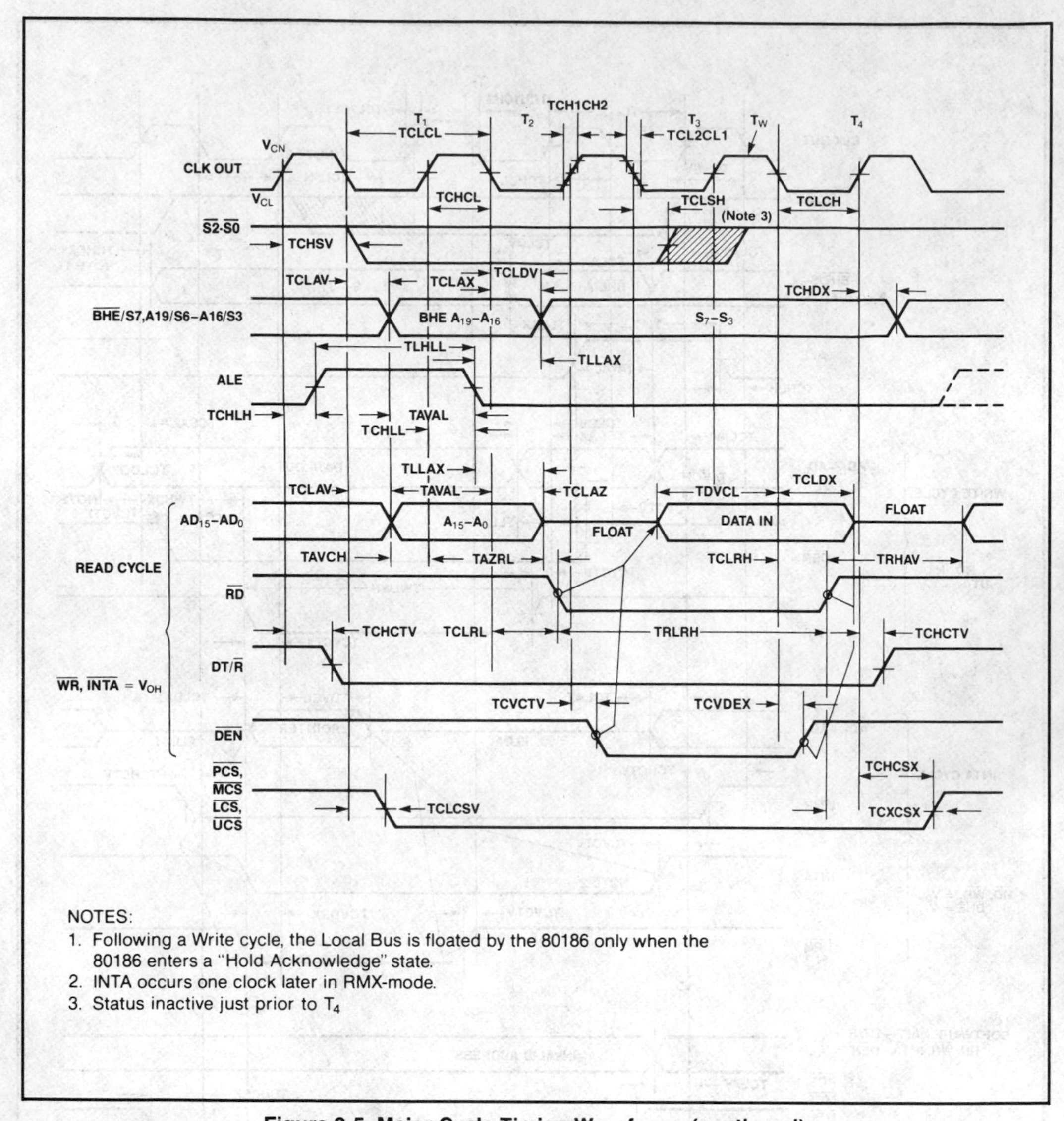

Figure 2-5 Major Cycle Timing Waveforms (continued)

Table 2-17 80186 Queue Status

QS1	QS0	Interpretation
0	0	no operation
0	1	first byte of instruction taken from queue
1	0	queue was reinitialized
1	1	subsequent byte of instruction taken from queue

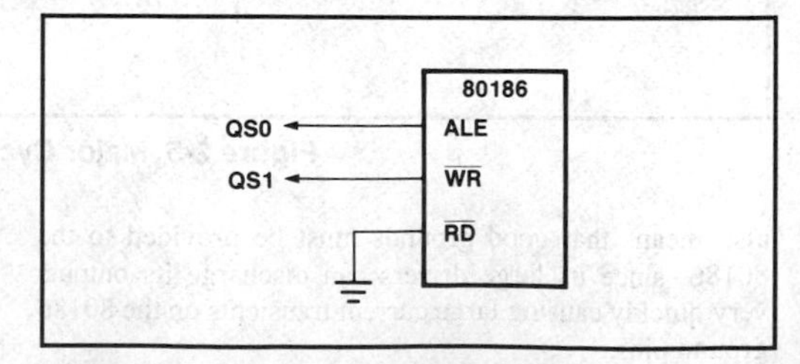

Figure 2-6 Generating Queue Status Information

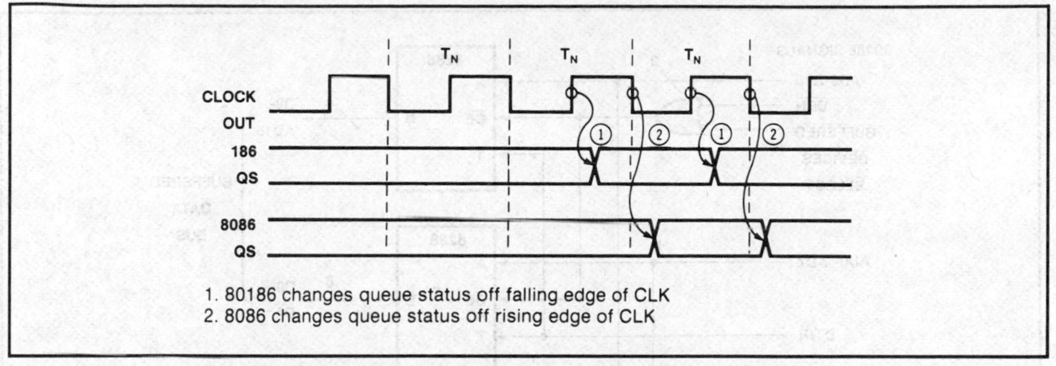

Figure 2-7 80186 and 8086 Queue Status Generation

the 8288. This means that data is not stable on the address/data bus when this signal is driven active.

The 80186 also does not provide differentiated I/O and memory ready and write command signals. If these signals are desired, an external 8288 bus controller may be used, or the S2* signal may be used to synthesize differentiated commands.

2.5.3 Multiplexed Address/Data Bus (186, 188)

Because of the bus drive capabilities of the 80186 (200pF, sinking 2mA, sourcing 400μA, roughly twice that of the 8086), this bus may not require additional buffering in many small systems. If data buffers are not used in the system, take steps to prevent bus contention between the 80186 and the devices directly connected to the 80186 data bus. Since the 80186 floats the address/data bus before activating any command lines, the only requirement on a directly connected device is that it floats its output drivers after a read *BEFORE* the 80186 begins to drive address information for the next bus cycle (consider the minimum time from RD* inactive until addresses active for the next bus cycle (t_{RHAV}) which has a minimum value of 85ns). If the memory or peripheral device cannot disable its output drivers in time, data buffers will be required to prevent both the 80186 and the peripheral or memory device from driving these lines concurrently. Note, this parameter is unaffected by the addition of wait states. Data buffers solve this problem because their output float times are typically much faster than the 80186 required minimum.

If buffers are required, the 80186 provides DEN* (Data ENable) and DT/R* (Data Transmit/Receive) signals to simplify buffer interfacing. The DEN* and DT/R* signals are activated during all bus cycles, whether or not the cycle addresses buffered devices. The DEN* signal is driven low whenever the processor is either ready to receive data (during a read) or when the processor is ready to send data (during a write); that is, any time during an active bus cycle when address information is not being generated on the address/data pins. In most systems, the DEN* signal should NOT be directly connected to the OE* input of buffers, since unbuffered devices (or other buffers) may be directly connected to the processor's address/data pins. If DEN* were directly connected to several buffers, contention would occur during read cycles, as many devices attempt to drive the processor bus. Rather, DEN* should be a factor (along with the chip selects for buffered devices) in generating the output enable input of a bi-directional buffer.

The DT/R* signal determines the direction of data propagation through the bi-directional bus buffers. It is high when ever data is being driven out from the processor, and is low whenever data is being read into the processor. Unlike the DEN* signal, DT/R* may be directly connected to bus buffers, since this signal does not usually directly enable the output drives of the buffer. See Figure 2-8 for an example data bus subsystem supporting both buffered and unbuffered devices. Observe the A side of the 8286 buffer is connected to the 80186, the B side to the external device. The B side of the buffer has greater drive capacity than the A side (since it is meant to drive much greater loads). The DT/R* signal can directly drive the T (transmit) signal of the buffer, since it has the correct polarity for this configuration.

CONTROL SIGNALS

The 80186 directly provides the control signals RD*, WR*, LOCK*, and TEST*. In addition, the 80186 provides the status signals S0*-S2* and S6 from which all other required bus control signals can be generated.

RD* AND WR*

The RD* and WR* signals strobe data to or from memory or I/O space. The RD* signal is driven low off the beginning of T2, and is driven high off the beginning of T4 during all memory and I/O reads (see Figure 2-9). RD*

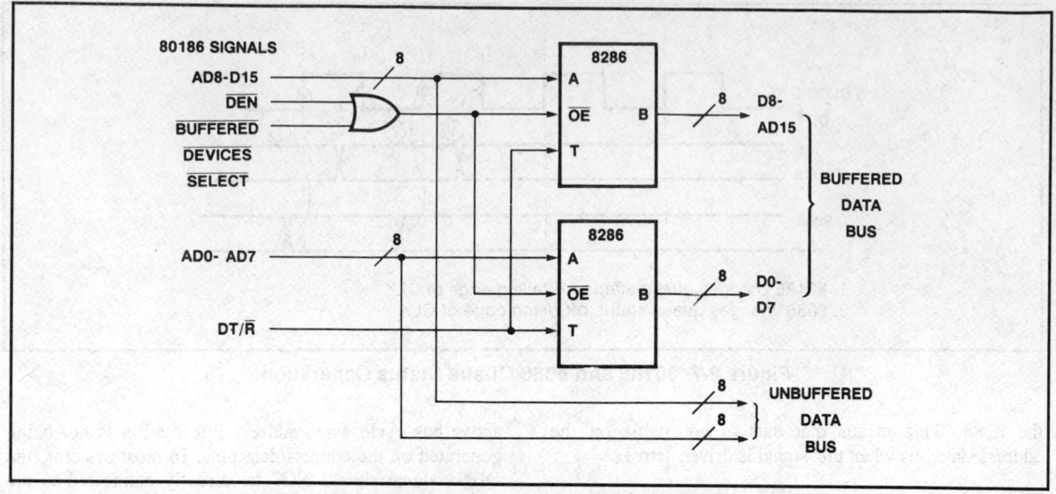

Figure 2-8 Example 80186 Buffered/Unbuffered Data Bus

will not become active until the 80186 has ceased driving address information on the address/data bus. Data is sampled into the processor at the beginning of T4. RD* will not go inactive until the processor's data hold time (10ns) has been satisfied.

Note that the 80186 does not provide separate I/O and memory RD* signals. If separate I/O read and memory read signals are required, they can be synthesized using the S2* signal (which is low for all I/O operations and high for all memory operations) and the RD* signal (see Figure 2-10). If this approach is used, the S2* signal will required latching, since the S2* signal (like S0* and S1*) goes to a passive state well before the beginning of T4 (where RD* goes inactive). If S2* was directly used for this purpose, the type of read command (I/O or memory) could change just before T4 as S2* goes to the passive state (high). The status signals may be latched using ALE in an identical fashion as is used to latch the address signals (often using the spare bits in the address latches).

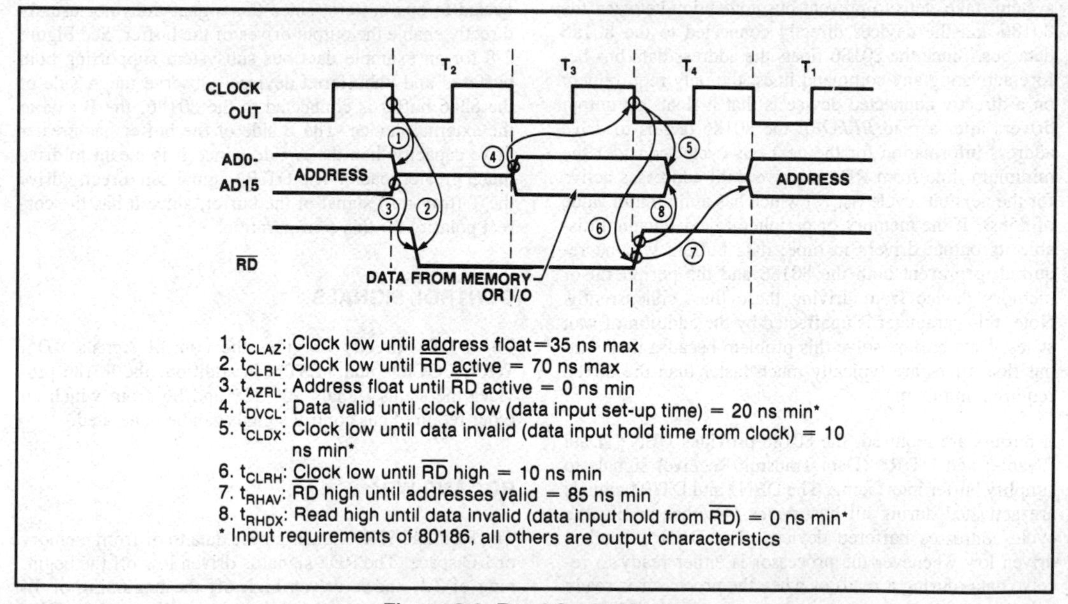

Figure 2-9 Read Cycle Timing

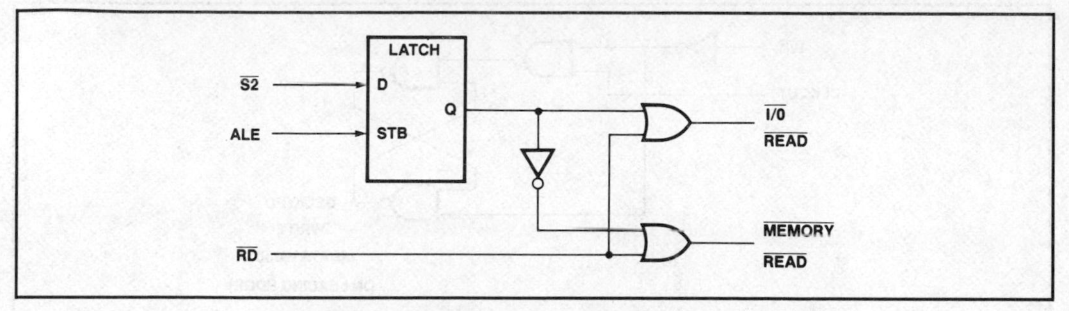

Figure 2-10 Generating I/O and Memory Read Signals

Often the lack of separate I/O and memory RD* signal is not important in an 80186 system. Each of the 80186 chip select signals will respond on only one of memory or I/O accesses (the memory chip selects respond only accesses to memory space; the peripheral chip selects can respond to accesses to either I/O or memory space, at programmer option). Therefore, the chip select signal enables the external device only during accesses to the proper address in the proper space.

The WR* signal is also driven low off the beginning of T2 and driven high off the beginning of T4. Like the RD* signal, the WR* signal is active for all memory and I/O writes, and also like the RD* signal, separate I/O and memory writes may be generated using the latched S2* signal along with the WR* signal (see Figure 2-11). More importantly, however, is the active going edge of write. At the time WR* makes its active (high to low) transition, valid write data is NOT present on the data bus. When using this signal as a write enable signal for DRAMs and iRAMs consider that both of these devices require that the write data be stable on the data bus at the time of the inactive to active transition of the WE* signal. In DRAM applications, a DRAM controller (such as the Intel 8207 or 8203) solves this problem while with iRAMs this problem may be solved by placing cross-coupled NAND gates (S-R latch) between the CPU and the iRAMs on the WR* line (see Figure 2-12). This S-R latch will delay the active going edge of the WR* signal to the iRAMs by a clock phase, allowing valid data to be driven onto the data bus.

STATUS LINES

The 80186 provides three status outputs which are used to that indicate the type of bus cycle currently being executed. These signals go from an inactive state (all high) to one of seven possible active states during the T state immediately preceding T1 of a bus cycle (see Figure 2-13). The possible status line encodings and their interpretations are given in Table 2-18. The status lines are driven to their inactive state in the T state (T3 or Tw) immediately preceding T4 of the current bus cycle.

The status lines may be directly connected to an 8288 bus controller, which can be used to provide local bus control

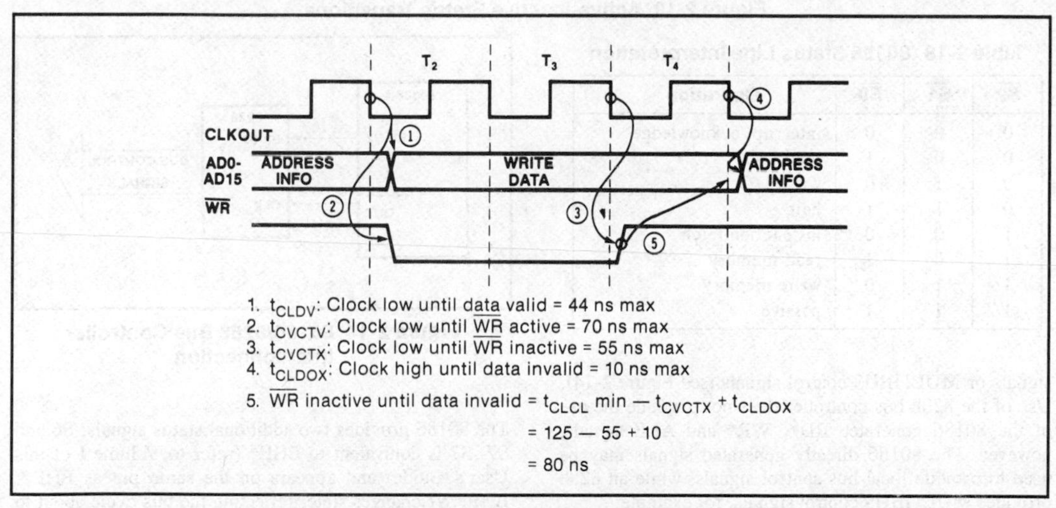

Figure 2-11 Write Cycle Timing

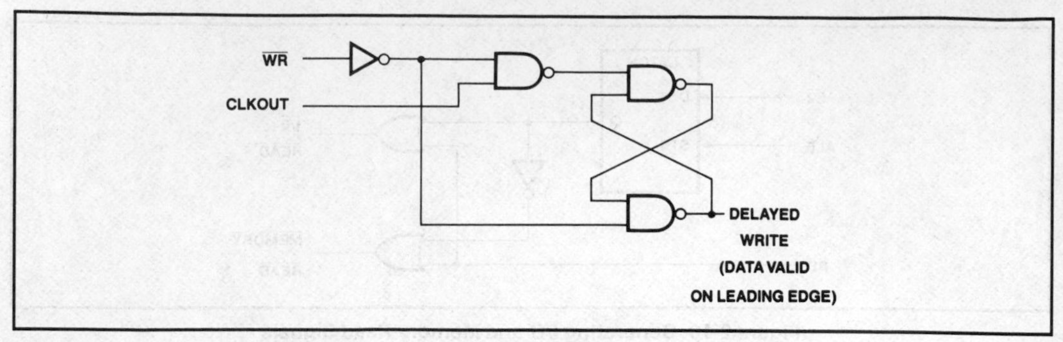

Figure 2-12 Synthesizing Delayed Write from the 80186

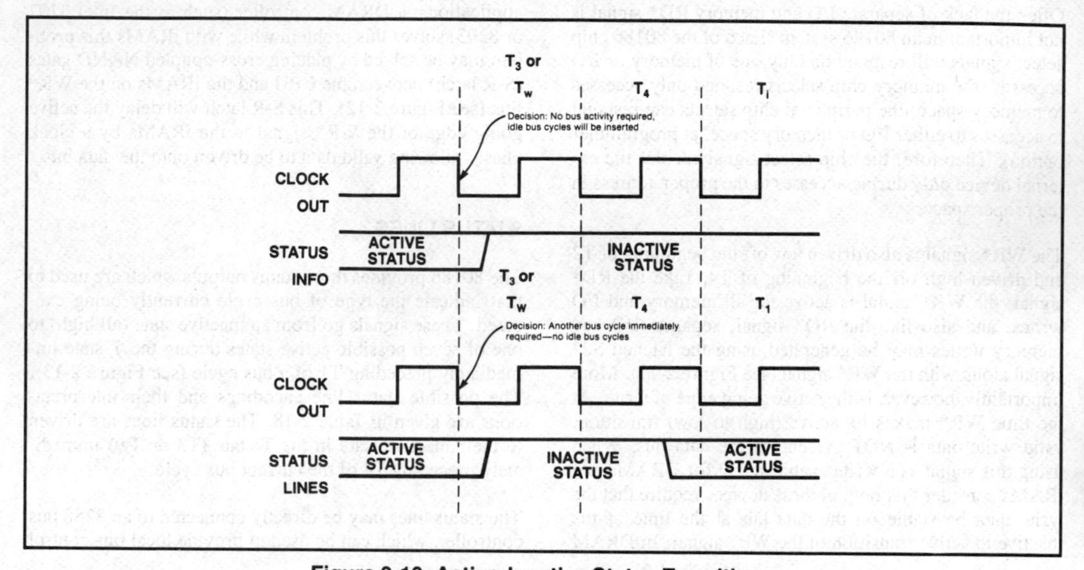

Figure 2-13 Active-Inactive Status Transitions

Table 2-18 80186 Status Line Interpretation

S2*	S1*	SØ*	Operation
0	0	0	interrupt acknowledge
0	0	1	read I/O
0	1	0	write I/O
0	1	1	halt
1	0	0	instruction fetch
1	0	1	read memory
1	1	0	write memory
1	1	1	passive

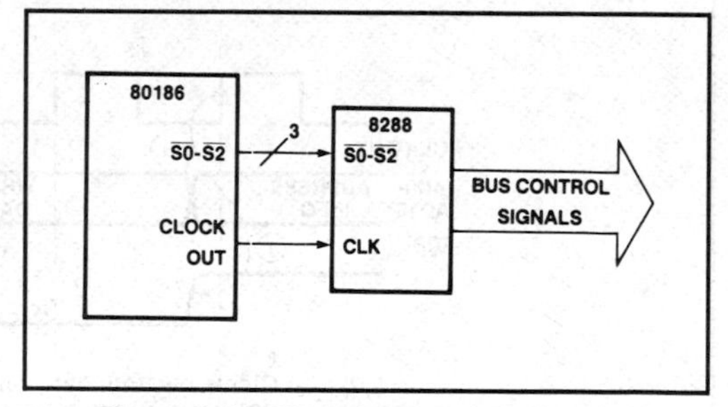

Figure 2-14 80186/8288 Bus Controller Interconnection

signals or MULTIBUS control signals (see Figure 2-14). Use of the 8288 bus controller does not preclude the use of the 80186 generated RD*, WR* and ALE signals, however. The 80186 directly generated signals may be used to provide local bus control signals, while an 8288 provides MULTIBUS control signals, for example.

The 80186 provides two additional status signals: S6 and S7. S7 is equivalent to BHE* (refer to Volume I of this User's Guide) and appears on the same pin as BHE*. BHE*/S7 changes state, reflecting the bus cycle about to be run, in the middle of the T state (T4 or Ti) immediately preceding T1 of the bus cycle. This timing means that BHE*/S7 does not need to be latched, i.e., it may be used directly as the BHE* signal. S6 provides information concerning the unit generating the bus cycle. It is time multiplexed with A19, and is available during T2, T3, T4, and Tw. In the 8086 family, all central processors (e.g., the 8086, 8088, and 8087) drive this line low, while all I/O processors (e.g., 8089) drive this line high during their respective bus cycles. Following this scheme, the 80186 drives this line low whenever the bus cycle is generated by the 80186 CPU, but drives it high when the bus cycle is generated by the integrated 80186 DMA unit. This process allows external devices to distinguish between bus cycles fetching data for the CPU from those transferring data for the DMA unit.

The three other status signals, S3, S4, and S5, available on the 8086 are not provided on the 80186. Together, S3 and S4 indicate the segment register from which the current physical address derives. S5 indicates the state of the interrupt flip-flop. On the 80186, these signals will always be low.

TEST* AND LOCK*

The 80186 provides a TEST* input and a LOCK* output. The TEST* input is used in conjunction with the processor WAIT instruction. TEST* is typically driven by a processor extension (like the 8087) to indicate whether it is busy. Then, by executing the WAIT (or FWAIT) instruction, the central processors may be forced to temporarily suspend program execution until the processor extension indicates that it is idle by driving the TEST* line low.

The CPU drives LOCK* output low whenever the data cycles of a LOCKED instruction are executed. A LOCKED instruction is generated whenever the LOCK prefix occurs immediately before an instruction. The LOCK prefix is active for the single instruction immediately following the LOCK prefix. This signal indicates to a bus arbiter (e.g., the 8289) that a series of locked data transfers is occurring. The bus arbiter should not release the bus while locked transfers are occurring. The 80186 will not recognize a bus HOLD, nor will it allow DMA cycles to be run by the integrated DMA controller during locked data transfers. Locked transfers are used in multiprocessor systems to access memory based semaphore variables which control access to shared system resources (refer to Intel Application Note AP-106, "Multiprogramming with the iAPX88 and iAPX86 Microsystems," by George Alexy, September 1980).

On the 80186, the LOCK* signal goes active during T1 of the first DATA cycle of the locked transfer. It is driven inactive three T states after the beginning of the last DATA cycle of the locked transfer. On the 8086, the LOCK* signal is activated immediately after the LOCK prefix is executed. The LOCK prefix may be executed well before the processor is prepared to perform the locked data transfer. This process activates the LOCK* signal before the first LOCKED data cycle is performed. Since LOCK* is active before the processor requires the bus for the data transfer, opcode pre-fetching can be LOCKED. However, since the 80186 does not activate the LOCK* signal until the processor is ready to actually perform the locked transfer, locked pre-fetching will not occur with the 80186.

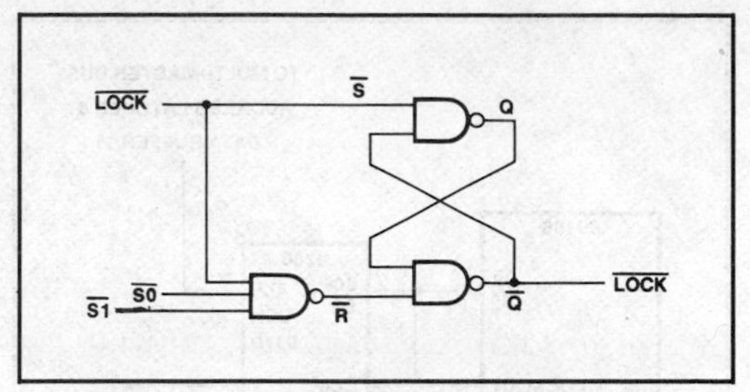

Figure 2-15 Circuit Holding LOCK* Active Until Ready is Returned

The LOCK* signal does not remain active until the end of the last data cycle of the locked transfer; this may cause problems in some systems if, for example, the processor requests memory access from a dual ported RAM array and is denied immediate access (because of a DRAM refresh cycle, for example). When the processor finally gains access to the RAM array, it may have already dropped its LOCK* signal. This allows the dual port controller to give the other port access to the RAM array instead. Figure 2-15 illustrates an example circuit which can be used to hold LOCK* active until a RDY has been received by the 80186.

MULTIBUS® APPLICATIONS

The 8288 and 8289 are the bus controlled and multimaster bus arbitration devices used with the 8086 and 8088. Because the 80186 bus is similar to the 8086 bus, they can be directly used with the 80186 (see Figure 2-16).

The 8288 bus controller generates control signals (RD*, WR*, ALE, DT/R*, DEN, etc.) for an 8086 maximum mode system. It derives its information by decoding status lines S0*-S2* of the processor. Because the 80186 and the 8086 drive the same status information on these lines, the 80186 can connect directly to the 8288 just as in an 8086 system. Using the 8288 with the 80186 does not prevent using the 80186 control signals directly. Many systems require both local bus control signals and system bus control signals. In this type of system, the 80186 lines could be used as the local signals, with the 8288 lines used as the system signals.

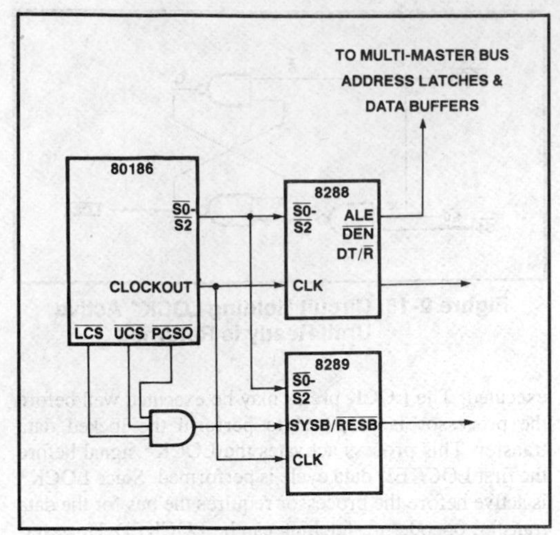

Figure 2-16 80186/8288/8289 Interconnection

NOTE

In an 80186 system, the 8288-generated ALE pulse occurs later than that of the 80186 itself.

In multi-master bus systems, use the 8288 ALE pulse to strobe the addresses into the system bus address latches to insure that the address hold times are met.

The 8289 bus arbiter arbitrates the use of a multi-master system bus among various devices each of which can become the bus master. This component also decodes status lines S0*-S2* of the processor directly to determine when the system bus is required. When the system bus is required, the 8289 forces the processor to wait until it has acquired control of the bus, then it allows the processor to drive address, data and control information onto the system bus. The system determines when it requires system bus resources by an address decode. Whenever the address being driven coincides with the address of an on-board resource, the system bus is not required and thus will not be requested. The circuit shown in Figure 2-16 factors the 80186 chip select lines to determine when the system bus should be required, or when the 80186 request can be satisfied using a local resource.

2.5.4 Data Transfer

During clock cycles T2, T3, Tw, and T4 of a bus cycle the multiplexed address/data bus becomes a 16-bit data bus. Data transfers on this bus may be either in bytes or in words. All memory is byte addressable. This means that the upper and lower byte of a 16-bit word each have a unique byte address by which they may be individually accessed, even though they share a common word address (see Figure 2-17).

All bytes with even addresses (A0 = 0) reside on the lower 8 bits of the data bus, and all bytes with odd addresses (A0 = 1) reside in the upper 8 bits of the data bus. Whenever an access is made to only an even byte, A0 is driven low, BHE* is driven high, and the data transfer occurs on D0-D7 of the data bus. Whenever an access is made to only an odd byte, BHE* is driven low, A0 is driven high, and the data transfer takes place on D8-D16 of the data bus. If a word access is performed to an even address, both A0 and BHE* are driven low and the data transfer takes place over the entire 16-bit data bus (D0-D15).

Word accesses are made to the addressed byte and the next higher numbered byte. Two byte accesses must be performed if a word access is performed to an odd address, the first to access the odd byte at the first word address on D8-D15, and the second to access the even byte at the next sequential word address on D0-D7. For example, byte 0 and byte 1 can be individually accessed (read or written) in two separate bus cycles (byte accesses) to byte addresses 0 and 1 at word address 0 (see Figure 2-17). They may also be accessed together in a single bus cycle (word access) to word address 0. However, two word access bus cycles are required to address 1. The first cycle accesses byte 1 at word address 0 (note byte 0 will not be accessed), and the second cycle accesses byte 2 at word address 2 (note byte 3 will not be accessed). Therefore, to maximize processor performance, all data should be located at even addresses.

When byte reads are made, the data returned on the half of the data bus not being accessed is ignored. When byte writes are made, the data driven on the half of the data bus not being written is indeterminate.

2.5.5 Memory and I/O Peripherals Interface

The 80186 uses the same techniques for interfacing memory (i.e., static RAM, dynamic RAM, EPROM, and ROM) as used for the 8086. Before continuing with this section, review the discussions regarding memory interface in paragraphs 1.5.4.

MEMORY INTERFACE

The 80186 includes a chip select unit that generates hardware chip select signals for memory and I/O accesses generated by the 80186 CPU and DMA units. This unit is programmable to fulfill the chip select requirements (in terms of memory device or bank size and speed) of most small and medium sized 80186 systems.

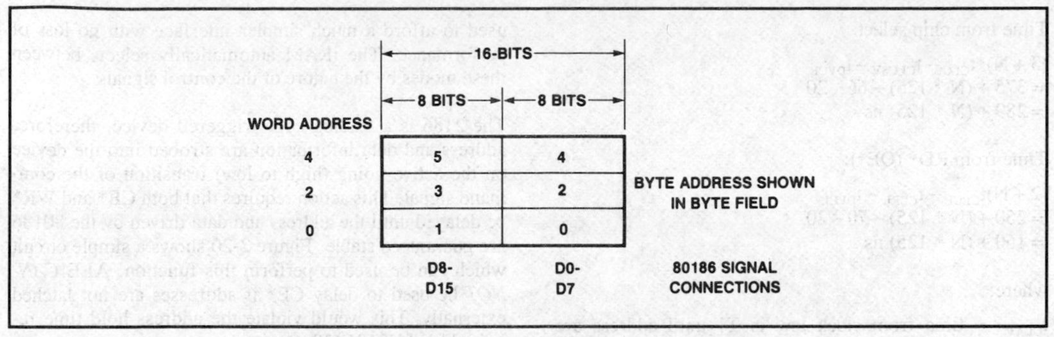

Figure 2-17 Physical Memory Byte/Word Addressing

Chip selects are driven for internally generated bus cycles only. Any cycles generated by an external unit (e.g., an external DMA controller) will not cause the chip selects to go active. Therefore, any external bus masters must be responsible for their own chip select generation. Also, during a bus HOLD, the 80186 does not float (i.e., tri-state) the chip-select lines. Therefore, logic must be included to enable the devices to which the external bus master wishes to access (see Figure 2-18).

ROM and EPROM Interface

The Intel 2764 EPROM provides one of the simplest memory interfaces to implement with the 80186. The address is latched using the address generation circuit (see Figure 2-19). The A0 line of each EPROM is connected to the A1 address line from the 80186, NOT to the A0 line. Also, A0 signals a data transfer on only the lower 8 bits of the 16-bit data bus. The EPROM outputs are connected directly to the address/data inputs of the 80186, and the 80186 RD* signal is used as the OE* for the EPROMs.

The chip select output of the 80186 drives the chip enable of the EPROM directly. For this configuration, access time for the EPROMs is calculated as follows:

Time from address:

$t_{CLAV} + (3 + N)*t_{CLCL} - t_{IVOV}(8282) - t_{DVCL}$
$= 375 + (N * 125) - 44 - 30 - 20$
$= 281 + (N * 125)$ ns

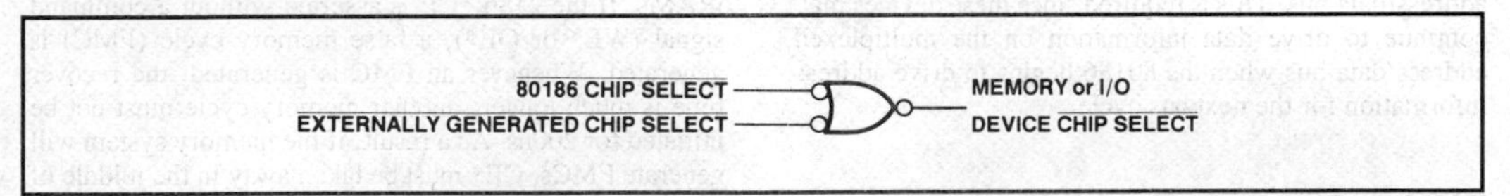

Figure 2-18 80186/External Chip Select/Device Chip Select Generation

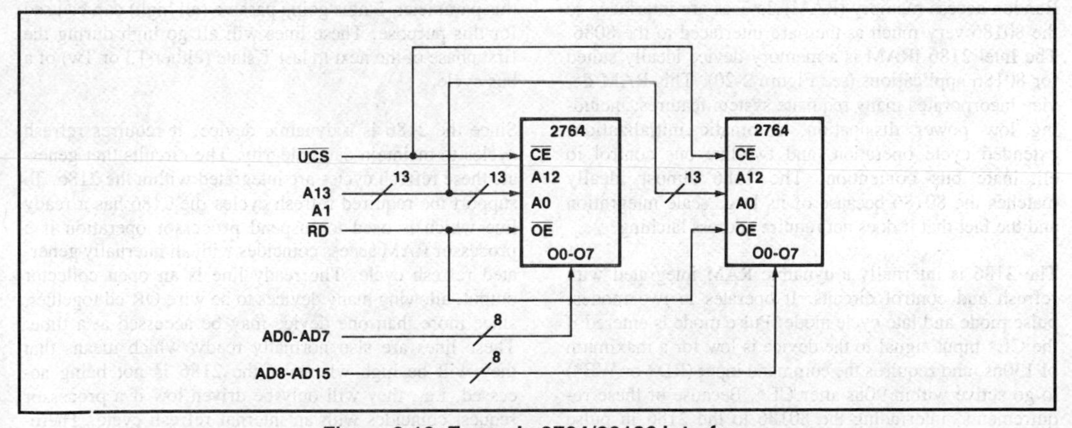

Figure 2-19 Example 2764/80186 Interface

Time from chip select:

$(3 + N)*t_{CLC} - t_{CLCSV} - t_{DVCL}$
$= 375 + (N * 125) - 66 - 20$
$= 289 + (N * 125)$ ns

Time from RD* (OE*):

$(2 + N)t_{CLCL} - t_{CLRL} - t_{DVCL}$
$= 250 + (N * 125) - 70 - 20$
$= 160 + (N * 125)$ ns

where:

t_{CLAV} = time from clock low in T1 until address are valid
t_{CLCL} = clock period of processor
t_{IVOV} = time from input valid of 8282 until output valid of 8282
t_{DVCL} = 186 data valid input setup time until clock low time of T4
t_{CLCSV} = time from clock low in T1 until chip selects are valid
t_{CLRL} = time from clock low in T2 until RD* goes low
N = number of wait states inserted

As indicated in the preceding calculations, 250ns EPROMs must be used for zero wait state operation. The only significant parameter not included in the preceding calculations is t_{RHAV}. This is the time from RD* inactive (high) until the 80186 begins driving address information. This parameter is typically 85ns to meet the 2764-25 (250ns speed selection) output float time requirement (85ns). If slower EPROMs are used, a discrete data buffer *MUST* be inserted between the EPROM data lines and the address/data bus. This is required since these devices may continue to drive data information on the multiplexed address/data bus when the 80186 begins to drive address information for the next bus cycle.

RAM Interface

Randon access memory (RAM) devices are interfaced to the 80186 very much as they are interfaced to the 8086. The Intel 2186 iRAM is a memory device ideally suited for 80186 applications (see Figure 2-20). This RAM device incorporates many requisite system features, including low power dissipation, automatic initialization, extended cycle operation, and two-line bus control to eliminate bus contention. The 2186 almost ideally matches the 80186 because of its large scale integration and the fact that it does not require address latching.

The 2186 is internally a dynamic RAM integrated with refresh and control circuits. It operates in two modes: pulse mode and late cycle mode. Pulse mode is entered if the CE* input signal to the device is low for a maximum of 130ns, and requires the command input (RD* or WE*) to go active within 90ns after CE*. Because of these requirements, interfacing the 80186 to the 2186 in pulse mode would be difficult. Instead, the late cycle mode is used to afford a much simpler interface with no loss of performance. The iRAM automatically selects between these modes by the nature of the control signals.

The 2186 is a leading edge triggered device, therefore, address and data information are strobed into the device on the active going (high to low) transition of the command signal. This action requires that both CE* and WR* be delayed until the address and data driven by the 80186 are guaranteed stable. Figure 2-20 shows a simple circuit which can be used to perform this function. ALE *CANNOT* be used to delay CE* if addresses are not latched externally. This would violate the address hold time required by the 2186 (30ns).

Since the 2186 devices are RAMs, data bus enables BHE* and A0 MUST be used to factor either the chip enables or write enables of the lower and upper bytes of the 16-bit RAM memory system. If this is not done, all memory writes, including single byte writes, will write to both the upper and lower bytes of the memory system. The example system shown in Figure 2-20 uses BHE* and A0 as factors to the 2186 CE* because both of these signals (A0 and BHE*) are valid when the address information is valid from the 80186.

The 2186 requires a certain amount of recovery time between the time chip enable goes inactive and the chip enable going active to insure proper operation. For a "normal" cycle (a read or write), this time is $t_{EHEL} = 40$ ns. The 80186 chip select lines go inactive soon enough at the end of a bus cycle to provide the required recovery time even if two consecutive accesses are made to the iRAMs. If the 2186 *CE is asserted without a command signal (WE* or OE*), a false memory cycle (FMC) is generated. Whenever an FMC is generated, the recover time is much longer; another memory cycle must not be initiated for 200ns. As a result, if the memory system will generate FMCs, CE* must be taken away in the middle of the T state (T3 or Tw) immediately preceding T4 to insure that two consecutive cycles to the iRAM will not violate this parameter. Status going passive (all high) can be used for this purpose. These lines will all go high during the first phase of the next to last T state (either T3 or Tw) of a bus cycle.

Since the 2186 is a dynamic device, it requires refresh cycles to maintain data integrity. The circuits that generate these refresh cycles are integrated within the 2186. To support the required refresh cycles the 2186 has a ready line which is used to suspend processor operation if a processor RAM access coincides with an internally generated refresh cycle. The ready line is an open collector output, allowing many devices to be wire OR'ed together, since more than one device may be accessed at a time. These lines are also normally ready, which means that they will be high whenever the 2186 is not being accessed, i.e., they will only be driven low if a processor request coincides with an internal refresh cycle. Therefore, the ready lines from the iRAM must be factored into

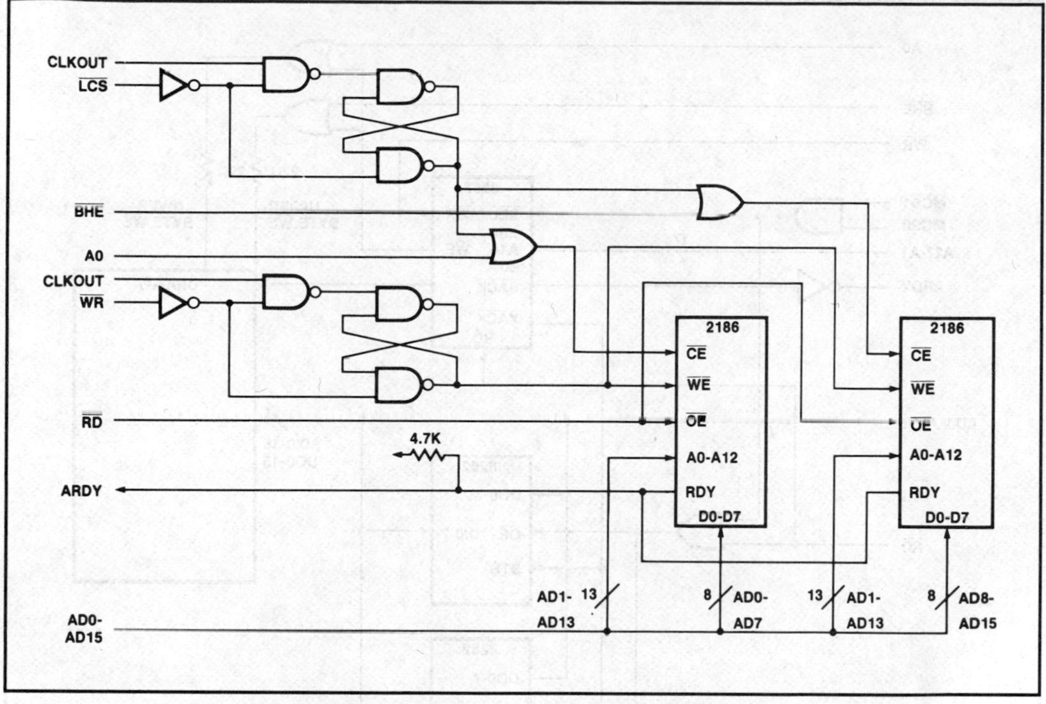

Figure 2-20 Example 2186/80186 Interface

the 80186 RDY circuit only during accesses to the iRAM itself. Since the 2186 refresh logic operates asynchronously to the 80186, this RDY line must be synchronized for proper operation with the 80186, either by the integrated ready synchronizer or by an external circuit. The example circuit uses the integrated synchronizer associated with the ARDY processor input.

The 2186 ready lines are active unless a processor access coincides with an internal refresh cycle. These lines must go inactive after a cycle is requested in time to insert wait states into the data cycle. The 2186 drives this line low within 50ns after CE* is received, which is early enough to force the 80186 to insert wait states if they are required. Of primary concern in this case is that the ARDY line be driven not active before its setup time in the middle of T2. This setup time is required by the nature of the 80186 asynchronous ready synchronization circuits. Since the 2186 RDY pulse may be as narrow as 50ns, if ready was returned after the first stage of the synchronizer, and subsequently changed states within the ready setup and hold time of the high to low going edge of the CPU clock at the end of T2, improper operation may occur.

The example interface shown in Figure 2-20 has a zero wait state RAM read access tie from CE* of:

$$3 * t_{CLCL} - t_{CLCSV} - (\text{TTL delay}) - t_{DVCL}$$
$$= 375 - 66 - 30 - 20\text{ns}$$
$$= 258 \text{ ns}$$

where:

t_{CLCL} = CPU clock cycle time
t_{CLCSV} = time from clock low in T1 until chip selects are valid
t_{DVCL} = 80186 data in setup time before clock low in T4

The data valid from OE* active is less than 100ns, and is therefore not an access time limiter in this interface. Additionally, the 2186 data float time from RD* inactive is less than the 85ns 80186 imposed maximum. The CE* generation circuit shown in Figure 2-20 provides an address setup time of at least 11ns, and an address hold time of at least 35ns (assuming a maximum two level TTL delay of less than 30ns).

Write cycle address setup and hold times are identical to the read cycle times. This circuit shown provides at least 11ns write data setup and 100ns data hold time from WE*, easily meeting the 0ns setup and 40ns hold times required by the 2186.

For more information concerning 2186 timing and interfacing refer to the 2186 data sheet in the Memory Components Handbook (Intel Order Number: 210830-004, or

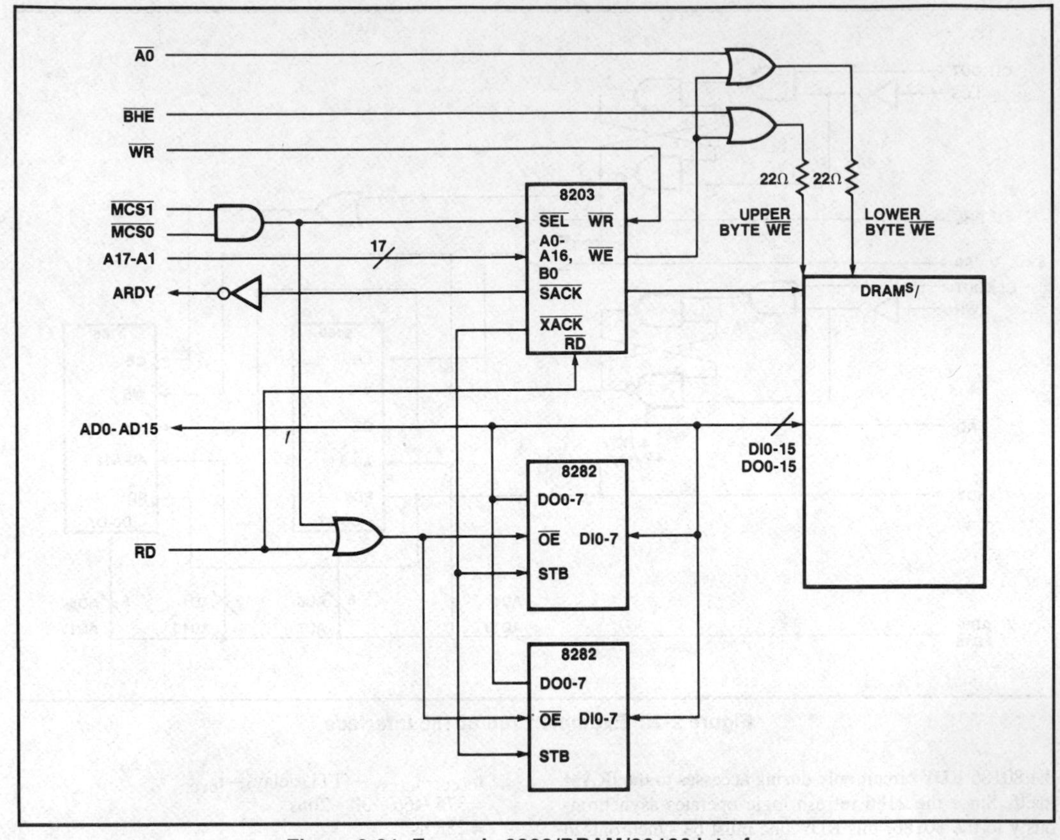

Figure 2-21 Example 8203/DRAM/80186 Interface

the Intel Application Note AP-132, "Designing Memory systems with the 8Kx8 iRAM" by John Fallin and William Righter (June 1982).

8203 Dynamic RAM Interface

The Intel 8203 Dynamic RAM Controller is designed specifically to provide all of the signals necessary (i.e., control, address multiplexing, and refresh generation) to use 2164, 2117 or 2118 dynamic RAMs in microcomputer systems. As such, it is ideally suited to 80186 applications. For an application example of an 80186 used with the 8203 and interfaced with 64K dynamic RAMs (see Figure 2-21).

All 8203 cycles are generated from control signals (RD* and WR*) provided by the 80186. These signals will not go active until T2 of the bus cycle. In addition, since the 8203 clock (generated by the internal crystal oscillator of the 8203) is asynchronous to the 80186 clock, all memory requests by the 80186 must be synchronized to the 8203 before the cycle will be run. To minimize this synchronization time, the 8203 should be used with the highest speed crystal that will maintain DRAM compatibility. Even if a 25 MHz crystal is used (the maximum allowed by the 8203), two wait states will be required by the example circuit when using 150ns DRAMs with an 8 MHz 80186, three wait states if 200ns DRAMs are used (see Figure 2-22).

The entire RAM array controlled by the 8203 can be selected by one or a group of the 80186 provided chip selects. These chip selects can also be used to insert the wait states required by the interface.

Since the 8203 is operating asynchronously to the 80186, the RDY output of the 8203 (used to suspend processor operation when a processor DRAM request coincides with a DRAM refresh cycle) must be synchronized to the 80186 (the 80186 ARDY line provides the necessary ready synchronization). The 8203 ready outputs operate in a normally not ready mode, that is, they are only driven active when an 8203 cycle is being executed, and a refresh cycle is not being run. This process differs fundamentally from the normally ready mode used by the 2186

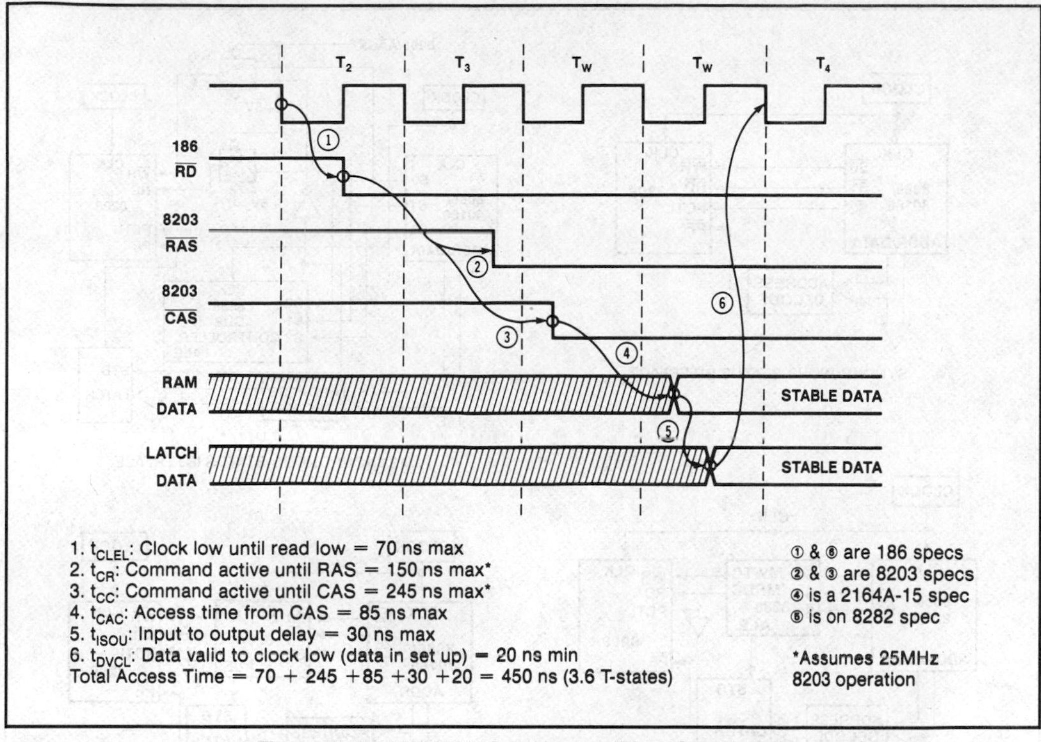

Figure 2-22 8203/2164A-15 Access Time Calculation

iRAMs. The 8203 SACK* signal is presented to the 80186 only when the DRAM is being accessed. Notice that the SACK* output of the 8203 is used, rather than the XACK* output. Since the 80186 will insert at least one full CPU clock cycle between the time RDY is sampled active, and the time data must be present on the data bus, using the XACK* signal would insert unnecessary additional wait states, since it does not indicate ready until valid data is available from the memory. (For more information about 8203/DRAM interfacing and timing, refer to the 8203 data sheet, or Intel Application Note AP97A, "Interfacing Dynamic RAM to iAPX86/88 Systems Using the Intel 8202A and 8203" by Brad May, April 1982).

8208 Dynamic RAM Interface

The Intel 8208 Dynamic RAM Controller is designed to address, refresh and directly drive 64K and 256K Dynamic RAM's in iAPX 186 and iAPX 188 systems. The 8208 contains the control circuits capable of supporting one of several possible interface bus structures (see Figure 2-23). It may be programmed to run synchronous or asynchrouous to the processor clock. The 8208 has been optimized to run synchronously with the 80186/188 and when programmed to run asynchronously it inserts the necessary synchronization circuits for RD*, WR*, PE*, and PCTL inputs.

The 8208 is capable of addressing 64K and 256K dynamic RAMs. It directly supports the 2164A RAM family or any RAM with similar timing requirements. Figure 2-24 shows the connection of the processor address bus to the 8208 using the different RAMs.

The 8208 divides memory into two banks with each bank having its own Row Address Strobe (RAS*) pair and Column Address Strobe (CAS*) pair. This organization permits RAM cycle interleaving. RAM cycle interleaving overlaps the start of the next RAM cycle with the RAM precharge period of the previous RAM cycle. Hiding the precharge period of one RAM cycle behind the data access period of the next RAM cycle optimizes memory bandwidth and is effective as long as successive RAM cycles occur in the alternate banks. Successive data accesses to the same bank cause the 8208 to wait for the precharge time of the previous RAM cycle. The exception to this is when the 8208 is programmed in an iAPX 186 synchronous configuration consecutive read cycles to the same bank do not result in additional wait states, zero wait state reads result.

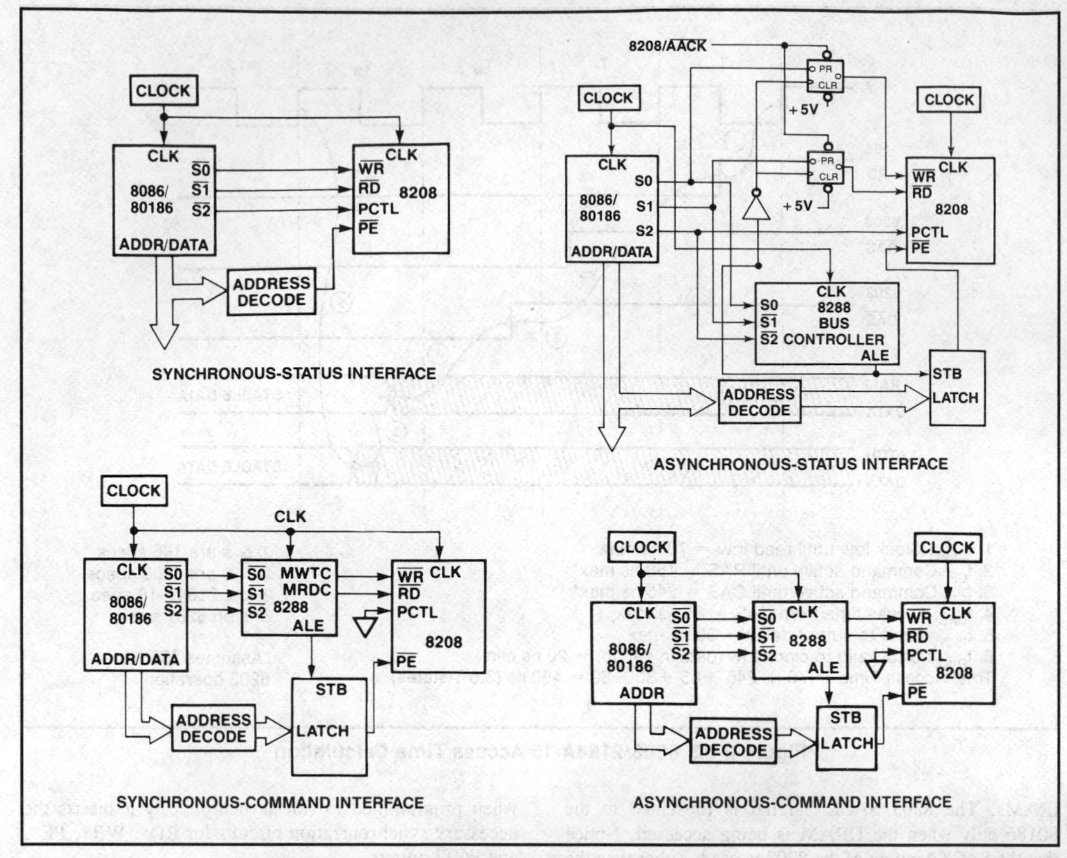

Figure 2-23 8208 Dynamic RAM Controller Interfaces

If all of the RAM banks are not occupied, the 8208 reassigns the RAS* and CAS* strobes to allow wider data words without increasing the loading on the RAS* and CAS* drivers. Table 2-19 shows the bank selection decoding and the horizontal word expansion, including RAS* and CAS* assignments. For example, if only one RAM bank is occupied, the two RAS* and CAS* strobes are activated with the same timing. Program bit RB is not used to check the bank select input BS. System design must protect from "illegal", non-existent banks of memory by deactivating the PE input when addressing an "illegal", non-existent bank of memory. The 8208 adjusts and optimizes either the fast or slow RAMS as programmed.

a. 8208 Memory Initialization

After programming is complete, the 8208 performs eight RAM "wake-up" cycles to prepare the dynamic RAM for proper device operation. During the "warm-up" some of the RAM interface parameters may not be met, but this should not harm the dynamic RAM array.

b. Refresh

The 8208 provides an internal refresh interval counter and a refresh address counter to allow the 8208 to refresh memory. It will refresh 128 rows every 2 milliseconds or 256 rows every 4 milliseconds. This allow RAM refresh options to be supported. Also, the 8208 has the ability to refresh 256 row address locations every 2 milliseconds via the Refresh Period programming option. the 8208 may be programmed for any of five refresh options. These are:

1. Internal refresh only;
2. External refresh with failsafe protection;
3. External refresh without failsafe protection;
4. Burst Refresh modes;
5. No Refresh.

The refresh time interval may be decreased by 10%, 20% or 30%. This option allows the 8208 to compensate for reduced clock frequencies. An additional 5% interval

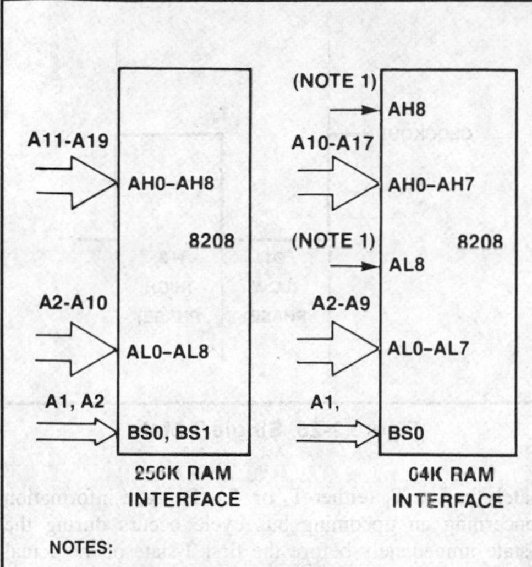

Figure 2-24 8208 Processor Address Interfaces

shortening is built-in in all refresh interval options to compensate for lock variations and non-immediate response to the internally generated refresh request.

c. External Refresh Requests After RESET

External refresh requests are not recognized by the 8208 until after it is finished programming and preparing memory for access. Memory preparation includes 8 RAM cycles to prepare and ensure proper dynamic RAM operation. The time it takes for the 8208 to recognize a request is shown as follows.

Table 2-19 Bank Selection Decoding and Word Expansion

Program Bit RB	Bank Input BS	8208 $\overline{RAS}/\overline{CAS}$ Pair Allocation
0	0	$\overline{RAS}_{0,1}$, $\overline{CAS}_{0,1}$ to Bank 0
0	1	Illegal
1	0	$\overline{RAS}_0$, $\overline{CAS}_0$ to Bank 0
1	1	$\overline{RAS}_1$, $\overline{CAS}_1$ to Bank 1

TRESP = PROG + TPREP

where:

TPROG = (40)(TCLCL) which is programming time
TPREP = (8)(32)(TCLCL) which is RAM warm-up time

if TCLCL = 125 nsec then TRESP = 37 usec

d. Reset

The 8208 uses the falling edge of the asynchronous RESET input to directly sample the logic levels of the PCTL, RFRQ, and PDI inputs. The internally synchronized falling edge of reset is used to begin programming operations (shifting the contents of the external shift register, if needed, into the PDI input).

The 8208 will register but not respond to command and status inputs until programming is completed. A simple means of preventing commands or status from occurring this period is to differentiate the system reset pulse to obtain a smaller reset pulse for the 8208. The total time of the 8208 reset pulse and the 8208 programming time must be less than the time before the first command the CPU issues in systems that alter default port synchronization programming bit (default is synchronous interface). Differentiated reset is unnecessary when the default synchronization programming is used.

The differentiated reset pulse would be shorter than the system reset pulse by at least the programming period required by the 8208. The differentiated reset pulse first resets the 8208, and system reset would reset the rest of the system. While the rest of the system is still in reset, the 8208 completes its programming. Figure 2-25 illustrates a circuit to accomplish this task. Within four clocks after RESET goes active, all the 8208 outputs will go high, except for AO0-2, which will go low.

2.5.6 Interpreting the 80186/80188 Bus Timing Diagrams

The 80186 bus and the 8086 bus are very similar in structure. Both include a multiplexed address/data bus, along with various control and status lines. Table 2-20 lists the 80186 bus signals by function and name. Each bus cycle requires a minimum of 4 CPU clock cycles along with any number of wait states required to accommodate the speed access limitations of external memory or peripheral devices. The bus cycles initiated by the 80186 CPU are identical to those initiated by the 80186 integrated DMA unit. The following paragraphs describe the 80186 bus timing with all timing values given for an 8MHz 80186. Any future speed selections for the 80186 may have different values for the various parameters.

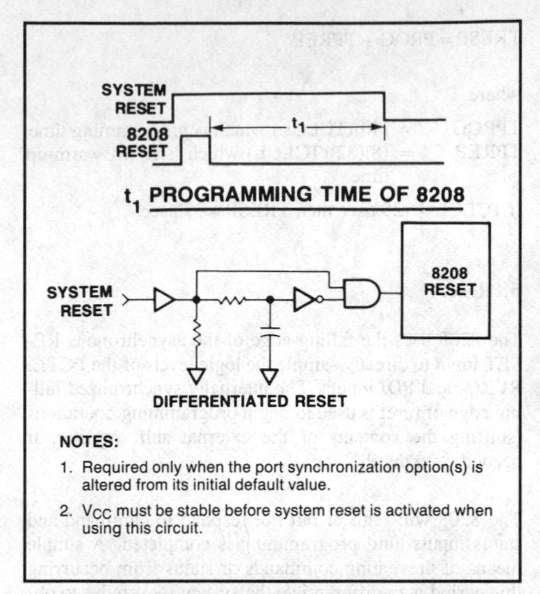

Figure 2-25 8208 Differentiated Reset Circuit

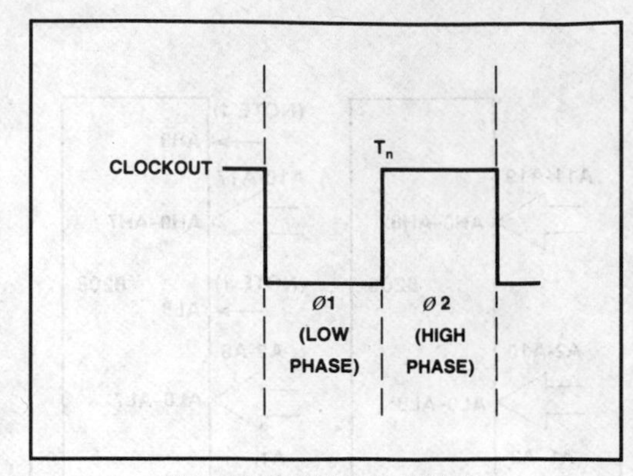

Figure 2-26 Single T-State

Each 80186 clock cycle (called "T" states) are numbered sequentially T_1, T_2, T_3, T_w and T_4. Additional idle T states (T_i) can occur between T_4 and T_1 when the processor requires no bus activity (instructions fetches, memory writes, I/O reads, etc.). The ready signals control the number of wait states (T_w) inserted in each bus cycle. This number can vary from zero to positive infinity.

The beginning of the T state is signaled by a high to low transition of the CPU clock. Each T state is divided into two phases, phase 1 (or the low phase) and phase two (or the high phase) which occur during the low and high levels of the CPU clock, respectively (see Figure 2-26).

Different types of bus activity occur during all of the T-states (see Figure 2-27). Address generation information occurs during T_1, data generation during T_2, T_3, T_w and T_4. The beginning of a bus cycle is signaled by the status lines of the processor going from a passive state (all high) to an active state in the middle of the T-state immediately before T_1 (either T_4 or T_i). Because information concerning an upcoming bus cycle occurs during the T-state immediately before the first T-state of the actual bus cycle, two different types of T_4 and T_i can be generated. One where the T-state is immediately followed by a bus cycle and one where the T-state is immediately followed by an idle T state.

During the first type of T_4 or T_i, status information concerning the upcoming bus cycle is generated. This information will be available no later than t_{CHSV} (55 ns) after the low-to-high transition of the 80186 clock in the middle of the T state. During the second type of T_4 or T_i, the status outputs remain inactive (high), since no bus cycle is to be started. This means that the decision per the nature of a T_4 or T_i state (i.e., whether it is immediately followed by a T_i or a T_1) is decided at the beginning of the T-state immediately preceding the T_4 or T_i (see Figure 2-13). This has consequences for the bus latency time.

Physical addresses are generated by the 80186 during T_1 of the bus cycle. Since the address and data lines are multiplexed on the same set of pins, addresses must be latched during T_1 if they are required to remain stable for the duration of the bus cycle. To facilitate latching of the physical address, the 80186 generates an active high ALE (Address Latch Enable) signal which can be directly connected to a transparent latch's strobe input.

Table 2-20 80186 Bus Signals

Function	Signal Name
address/data	AD0-AD15
address/status	$\overline{\text{A16/S3-A19-S6,BHE/S7}}$
co-processor control	$\overline{\text{TEST}}$
local bus arbitration	HOLD,HLDA
local bus control	ALE,$\overline{\text{RD}}$,$\overline{\text{WR}}$,DT/$\overline{\text{R}}$,$\overline{\text{DEN}}$
multi-master bus	$\overline{\text{LOCK}}$
ready (wait) interface	SRDY,ARDY
status information	$\overline{\text{S0-S2}}$

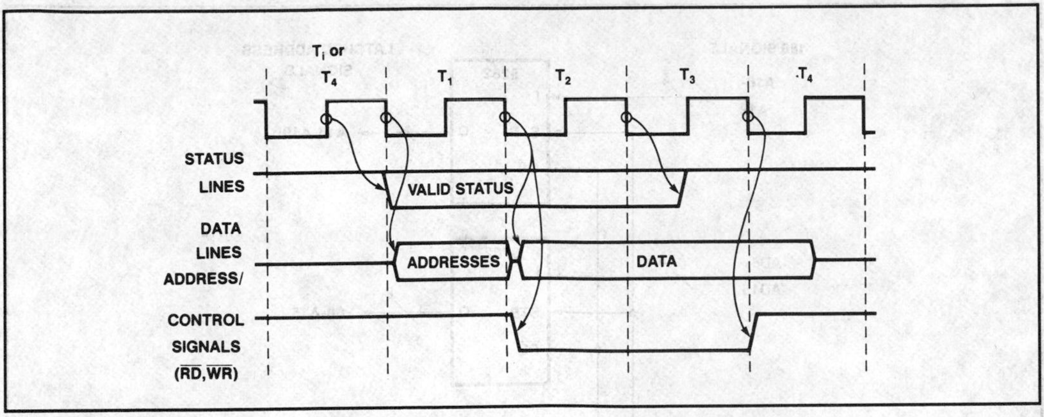

Figure 2-27 Example 80186 Bus Cycle

Addresses are guaranteed valid for no more than t_{CLAV} (44 ns) after the beginning of T_1, and will remain valid at least t_{CLAX} (10 ns) after the end of T_1. See Figure 2-28 for 80186 physical address generation parameters. The ALE signal is driven high in the middle of the T state (either T_4 or T_i) immediately preceding T_1 and is driven low in the middle of T_1, no sooner than t_{AVAL} (30 ns) after addresses become valid. This parameter (t_{AVAL}) is required to satisfy the address latch set-up times of address valid until strobe inactive. Addresses remain stable on the address/data bus at least t_{LLAX} (30 ns) after ALE goes inactive to satisfy address latch hold times of strobe inactive to address invalid.

Because ALE goes high long before addresses become valid, the delay through the address latches will be mainly the propagation delay through the latch rather than the delay from the latch strobe, which is typically longer than the propagation delay. For the Intel 8282 latch, this parameter is t_{IVOV}, the input valid to output valid delay when strobe is held active (high). Note that the 80186 drives ALE high one full clock phase earlier than either the 8086 or 8288 bus controller. The 80186 also keeps ALE high throughout the 8086 or 8288 ALE high time (i.e., the 80186 ALE pulse is wider).

A typical circuit for latching physical addresses (see Figure 2-29) uses three 8282 transparent octal non-inverting latches to demultiplex all 20 address bits provided by the 80186. Typically, the upper 4 address bits are used only to select among various memory components and subsystems, so when the integrated chip selects (see paragraph

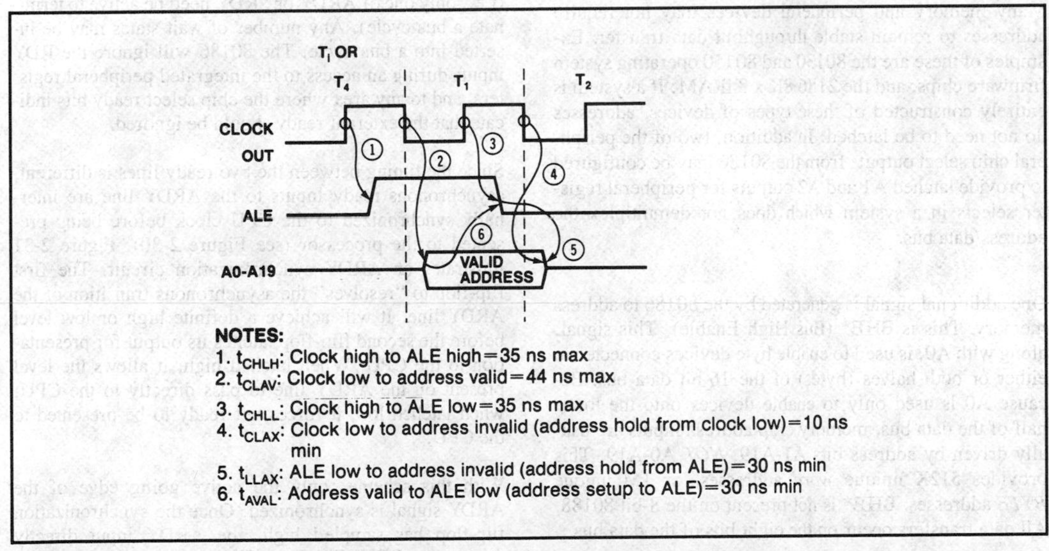

Figure 2-28 80186 Address Generation Timing

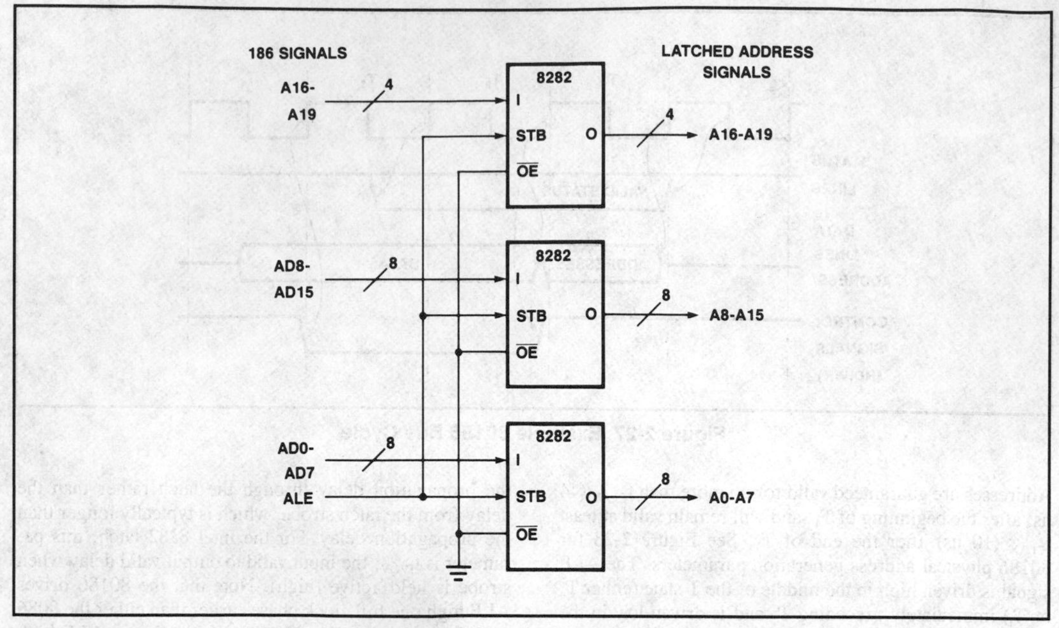

Figure 2-29 Demultiplexing the 80186 Address Bus

2.8.4) are used, these upper bits do not need to be latched. The worst case address generation time from the beginning of T_1 (including address latch propagation time t_{IVOV} of the Intel 8282) for the circuit is:

t_{CLAV} (44 ns) + t_{IVOV} (30 ns) = 74 ns

Many memory and peripheral devices may not require addresses to remain stable throughout data transfer. Examples of these are the 80130 and 80150 operating system firmware chips, and the 2186 8K x 8 iRAM. If a system is entirely constructed of these types of devices, addresses do not need to be latched. In addition, two of the peripheral chip select outputs from the 80186 may be configured to provide latched A1 and A2 outputs for peripheral register selects in a system which does not demultiplex the address/data bus.

One additional signal is generated by the 80186 to address memory. This is BHE* (Bus High Enable). This signal, along with A0, is used to enable byte devices connected to either or both halves (bytes) of the 16-bit data bus. Because A0 is used only to enable devices onto the lower half of the data bus, memory chip address inputs are usually driven by address bits A1-A19, *NOT* A0-A19. This provides 512K unique *word* addresses, or 1M unique *BYTE* addresses. BHE* is not present on the 8-bit 80188. All data transfers occur on the eight bits of the data bus.

2.5.7 Wait State Generator

The 80186 provides two ready lines, a synchronous ready (SRDY) line and an asynchronous ready (ARDY) line. These lines signal the processor to insert wait states (Tw) into a CPU bus cycle. Wait states allow slower devices to respond to CPU service requests (reads or writes). They are only inserted when both ARDY and SRDY are low (i.e., only one of ARDY or SRDY need be active to terminate a bus cycle). Any number of wait states may be inserted into a bus cycle. The 80186 will ignore the RDY inputs during an access to the integrated peripheral registers, and to any area where the chip select ready bits indicate that the external ready should be ignored.

Since the timing between the two ready lines is different, asynchronous ready inputs to the ARDY line are internally synchronized to the CPU clock before being presented to the processor (see Figure 2-30). Figure 2-31 illustrates an ARDY synchronization circuit. The first flip-flop to "resolves" the asynchronous transition of the ARDY line. It will achieve a definite high or low level before the second flip-flop latches its output for presentation to the CPU. When latched high, it allows the level present on the ARDY line to pass directly to the CPU; when latched low, it forces not ready to be presented to the CPU.

With this scheme, only the active going edge of the ARDY signal is synchronized. Once the synchronization flip-flop has sampled high, the ARDY input directly drives the RDY flip-flop. Since inputs to this RDY

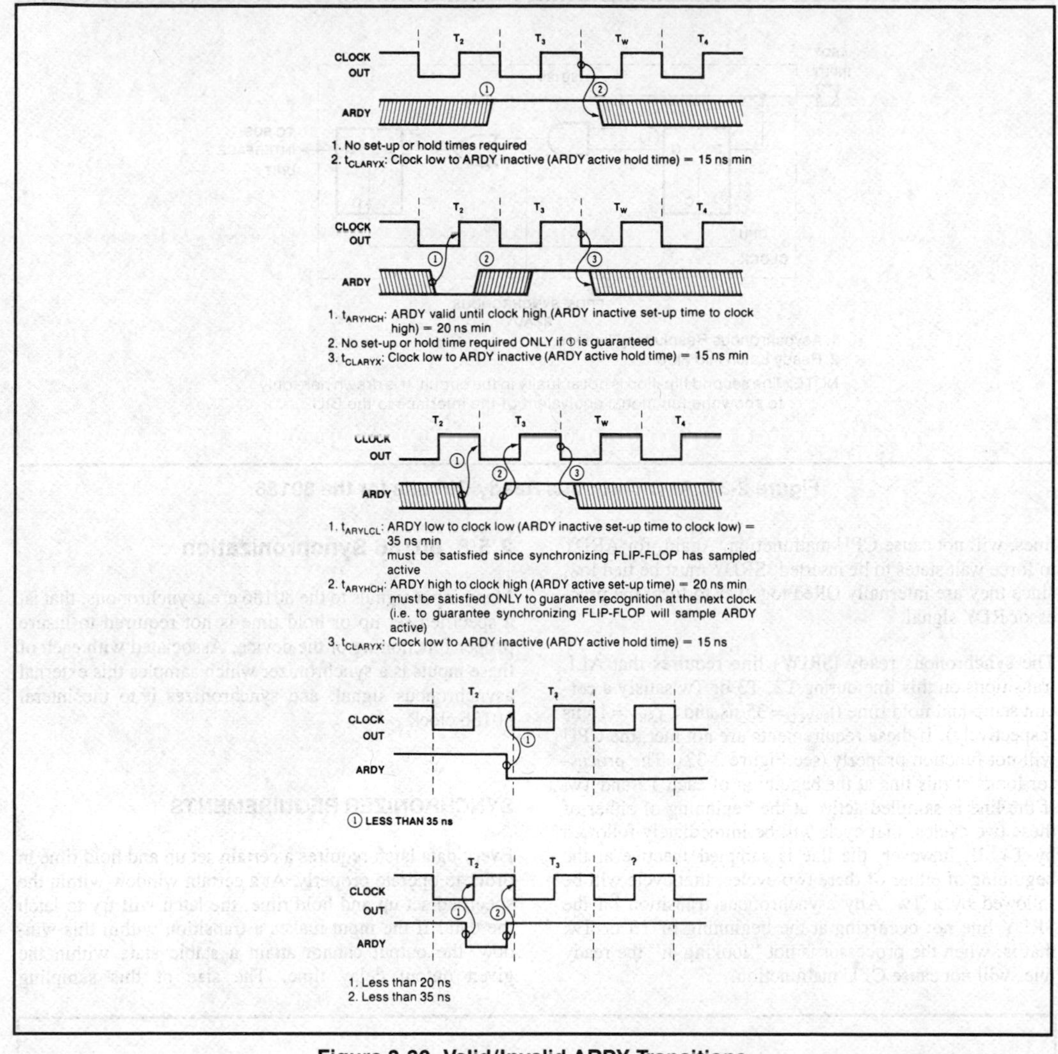

Figure 2-30 Valid/Invalid ARDY Transitions

flip-flop must satisfy certain setup and hold times, these setup and hold times (t_{ARYLCL} = 35ns and t_{CHARYX} = 15ns respectively) must be satisfied by any inactive going transition of the ARDY line. Used in this manner, ARDY allows a slow device the greatest amount of time to respond with a not ready after it has been selected. In a normally ready system, a slow device must respond with a not ready quickly after it has been selected to prevent the processor from continuing and accessing invalid data from the slow device. By implementing ARDY in the above manner, the slow device has an additional clock phase to respond with a not ready.

If RDY is sampled active into the RDY flip-flop at the beginning of T3 or Tw (meaning that ARDY was sampled high into the synchronization flip-flop in the middle of a T state, and has remained high until the beginning of the next T state), that T state will be immediately followed by T4. If RDY is sampled low into the RDY flip-flop at the beginning of T3 or T2 (meaning that either ARDY was sampled low into the synchronization flip-flop OR that ARDY was sampled high into the synchronization flip-flop, but has subsequently changed to low before the ARDY setup time) that T state will be immediately followed by a wait state (Tw). Any asynchronous transition on the ARDY line not occurring during the above times, that is, when the processor is not "looking at" the ready

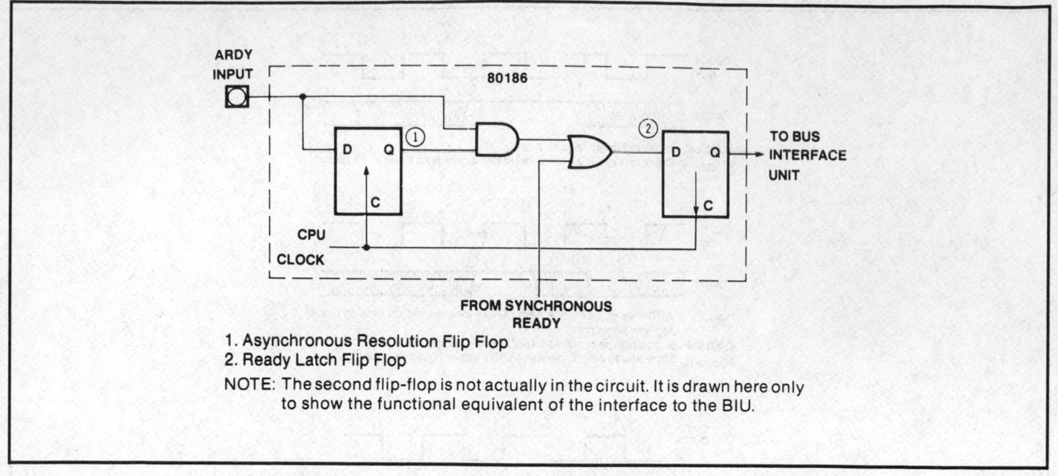

Figure 2-31 Asynchronous Ready Circuits for the 80186

lines, will not cause CPU malfunction. Again, for ARDY to force wait states to be inserted, SRDY must be tied low, since they are internally ORed together to form the processor RDY signal.

The synchronous ready (SRDY) line requires that ALL transitions on this line during T2, T3 or Tw satisfy a certain setup and hold time (t_{SRYCL} = 35 ns and t_{CLSRY} = 15 ns respectively). If these requirements are not met, the CPU will not function properly (see Figure 2-32). The processor looks at this line at the beginning of each T3 and Tw. If the line is sampled active at the beginning of either of these two cycles, that cycle will be immediately followed by T4. If, however, the line is sampled inactive at the beginning of either of these two cycles, that cycle will be followed by a Tw. Any asynchronous transition on the SRDY line not occurring at the beginning of T3 or Tw, that is, when the processor is not "looking at" the ready lines will not cause CPU malfunction.

2.5.8 80186 Synchronization

Many input signals to the 80186 are asynchronous, that is, a specified set up or hold time is not required to insure proper functioning of the device. Associated with each of these inputs is a synchronizer which samples this external asynchronous signal, and synchronizes it to the interal 80186 clock.

SYNCHRONIZER REQUIREMENTS

Every data latch requires a certain set up and hold time in order to operate properly. At a certain window within the specified set up and hold time, the latch will try to latch the data. If the input makes a transition within this window, the output cannot attain a stable state within the given output delay time. The size of this sampling

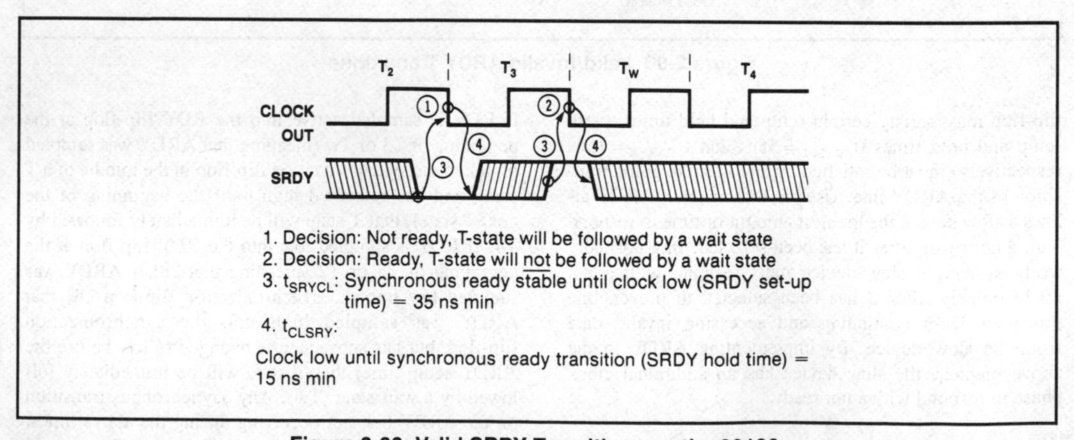

Figure 2-32 Valid SRDY Transitions on the 80186

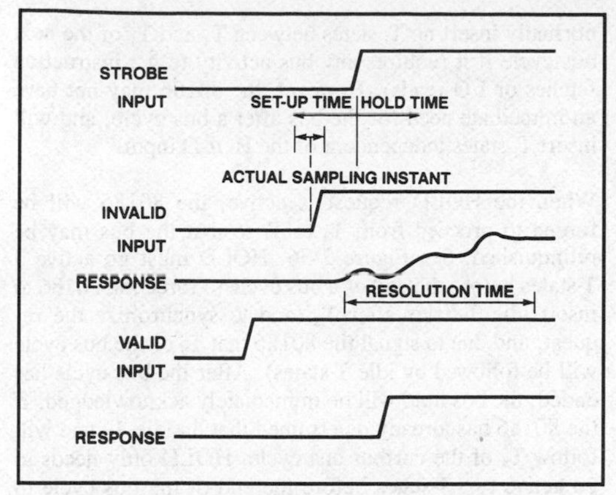

Figure 2-33 Valid & Invalid Latch Input Transitions & Responses

window is typically much smaller than the actual window specified by the data sheet specifications, however, part to part variation can move this actual window around within the specified window.

Even if the input to a data latch makes a transition while a data latch is attempting to latch this input, the output of the latch will attain a stable state after a certain amount of time—typically much longer than the normal strobe to output delay time (see Figure 2-33). Therefore, in order to synchronize an asynchronous signal, sample the signal into one data latch, wait a certain amount of time, then latch it into a second data latch. Since the time between the strobe into the first data latch and the strobe into the second data latch allows the first data latch to attain a steady state (or to resolve the asynchronous signal), the second data latch will be presented with an input signal which satisfies any set up and hold time requirements it may have. The output of this second latch is a synchronous signal with respect to its strobe input.

A synchronization failure can occur if the synchronizer fails to resolve the asynchronous transition within the time between the two latch's strobe signals. The rate of failure is determined by the actual size of the sampling window of the data latch, and by the amount of time between the strobe signals of the two latches. Obviously, as the sampling window gets smaller, the number of times an asynchronous transition will occur during the sampling window will drop. In addition, however, a smaller sampling window is also indicative of a faster resolution time for an input transition which manages to fall within the sampling window.

80186 SYNCHRONIZERS

The 80186 contains synchronizers on the RES*, TEST*, TmrIn0-1, DRQ0-1, NMI, INT0-3, ARDY, and HOLD input lines. Each of these synchronizers use the two stage synchronization technique described above (with some minor modifications for the ARDY line, refer to paragraph 2.5.1). The sampling window of the latches is designed to be in the tens of pico-seconds, and should allow operation of the synchronizers with a mean time between failures of over 30 years assuming continuous operation.

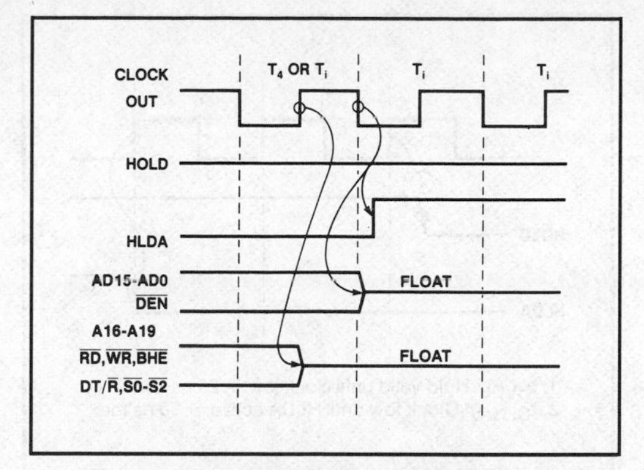

Figure 2-34 Signal Float/HLDA Timing

2.6 BUS EXCHANGE MECHANISMS

The 80186 uses a HOLD/HLDA bus exchange protocol. This protocol allows other asynchronous bus master devices (i.e., ones which drive address, data, and control information on the bus) to gain control of the bus to perform bus cycles (memory or I/O reads or writes).

2.6.1 HOLD Response

In the HOLD/HLDA protocol, a device requiring bus control (e.g., an external DMA device) raises the HOLD line. In response to this HOLD request, the 80186 will raise its HLDA line after it has finished its current bus activity. When the external device is finished with the bus, it drops its bus HOLD request. The 80186 responds by dropping its HLDA line and resuming bus operation.

When the 80186 recognizes a bus hold by driving HLDA high, it will float many of its signals (see Figure 2-34). AD0-AD15 (address/data 0-15) and DEN* (data enable) are floated within t_{CLAZ} (35 ns) after the same clock edge that caused HLDA to be driven active. A16-A19 (address 16-19), RD*, WR*, BHE* (Bus High Enable), DT/R* (Data Transmit/Receive*) and S0-S2 (status 0-2) are floated within t_{CHCZ} (45 ns) after the clock edge immediately before the clock edge on which HLDA becomes active.

Only the signals described in the previous paragraph float during bus HOLD. Signals that do not float during bus HOLD are mainly associated with peripheral

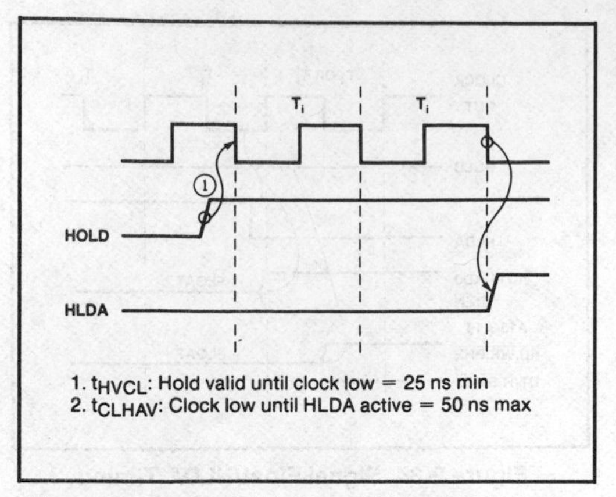

Figure 2-35 80186 Idle Bus HOLD/HLDA Timing

functionality or control bus devices, either directly or indirectly. These signals include TmrOut, ALE (Address Latch Enable) and the chip select lines (UCS*, LCS*, MCS0-3*, and PCS0-6*). The designer should be aware that the chip select circuits do not look at externally generated addresses. Discrete chip select and ready generation logic must be used for memory or peripheral devices that are addresses by external bus master devices.

2.6.2 HOLD/HLDA Timing and Bus Latency

The time required between HOLD going active and the 80186 driving HLDA active is known as bus latency. Many factors affect this latency, including synchronization delays, bus cycle times, locked transfer times and interrupt acknowledge cycles. Since the HOLD request line is internally synchronized by the 80186, and it may be an asynchronous signal. To guarantee recognition on a certain clock edge, it must satisfy a certain setup and hold time to the falling edge of the CPU clock. A full CPU clock cycle is required for this synchronization, that is, the internal HOLD signal is not presented to the internal bus arbitration circuits until one full clock cycle after it is latched from the HOLD input. If the bus is idle, HLDA will follow HOLD by two CPU clock cycles plus a small amount of setup and propagation delay time. The first clock cycle synchronizes the input and the second clock cycle signals the internal circuits to initiate a bus hold. (See Figure 2-35.)

Many factors influence the number of clock cycles between a HOLD request and a HLDA. These factors may make the latency longer than the best case shown above. One of the most important factors is that the 80186 will not relinquish the local bus until the bus is idle. An idle bus occurs whenever the 80186 is not performing any bus transfers. When the bus is idle the 80186 generates idle T-states. The bus can become idle only at the end of a bus cycle. Therefore, the 80186 can recognize HOLD only after the end of the current bus cycle. The 80186 will normally insert no T_i states between T_4 and T_1 of the next bus cycle if it requires any bus activity (e.g., instruction fetches or I/O reads). However, the 80186 may not have an immediate need for the bus after a bus cycle, and will insert T_i states independent of the HOLD input.

When the HOLD request is active, the 80186 will be forced to proceed from T_4 to T_i so that the bus may be relinquished. See Figure 2-36. HOLD must go active 3 T-states before the end of a bus cycle to force the 80186 to insert idle T-states after T_4 (and to synchronize the request, and one to signal the 80186 that T_4 of the bus cycle will be followed by idle T-states). After the bus cycle has ended, the bus hold will be immediately acknowledged. If the 80186 has already determined that an idle T-state will follow T_4 of the current bus cycle, HOLD only needs to go active two T-states before the end of the bus cycle to force the 80186 to relinquish the bus at the end of the current bus cycle. This is because the external HOLD request is not required to force the generation of idle T-states.

An external HOLD has a higher priority than both the 80186 CPU or the integrated DMA unit. However, an external HOLD will not separate the two cycles needed to perform a word access to an odd memory location. Also, an external HOLD will not separate the two-to-four bus cycle required to perform a DMA transfer using the integrated controller. Each of these factors will add additional bus cycle times to the bus latency of the 80186.

Another factor influencing bus latency is locked transfers. Whenever a locked transfer is occurring, the 80186 will not recognize external HOLDs. The 80186 will also not recognize internal DMA bus requests. Locked transfers are programmed by preceding an instruction with the LOCK prefix. Any transfers generated by such a prefixed instruction will be locked, and will not be separated by any external bus requesting device. String instructions may be locked. Since string transfers may require thousands of bus cycles, bus latency will suffer if they are locked.

The final factor affecting bus latency time is interrupt acknowledge cycles. When an external interrupt controller is used, or if the integrated interrupt controller is used in the iRMX86 mode the 80186 will run two interrupt acknowledge cycles back to back. These cycles are automatically "locked" and will never be separated by any bus HOLD, either internal or external.

2.6.3 End of HOLD Timing

After the 80186 recognizes that the HOLD input has gone inactive, it will drop its HLDA line in a single clock cycle. Figure 2-37 shows this timing. The 80186 will insert only two T_i after HLDA has gone inactive, assuming that the 80186 has internal bus cycles to run. During the last T_i, status information will go active concerning the bus

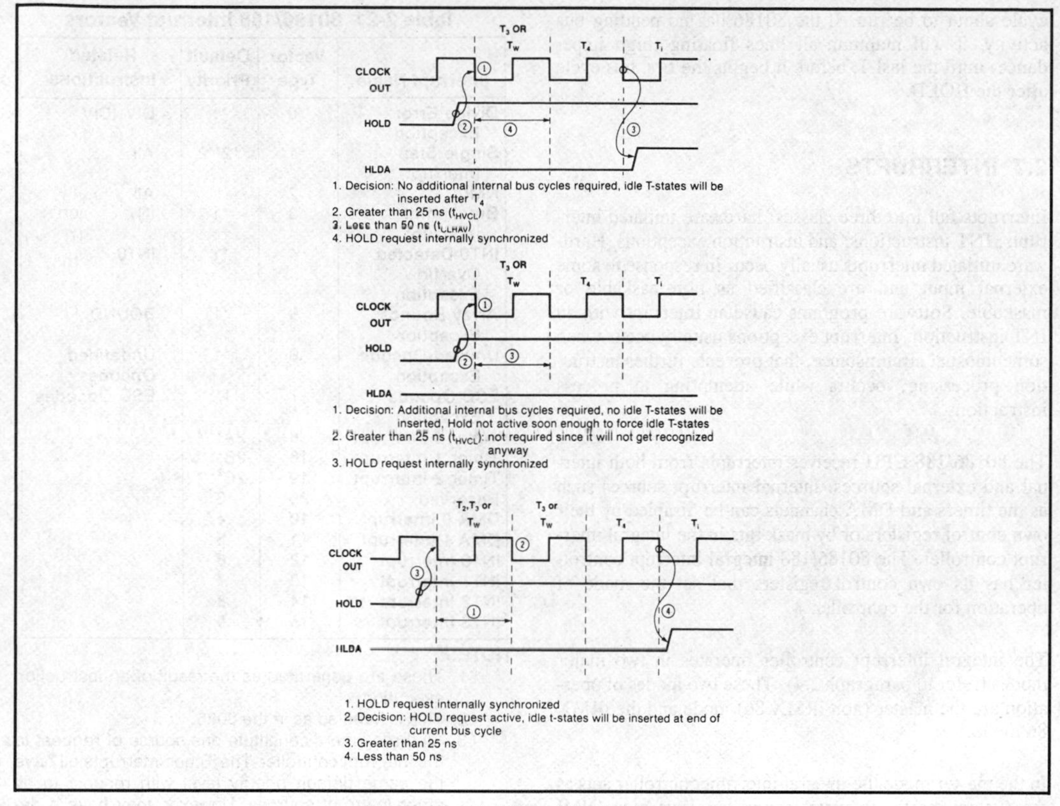

Figure 2-36 HOLD/HLDA Timing

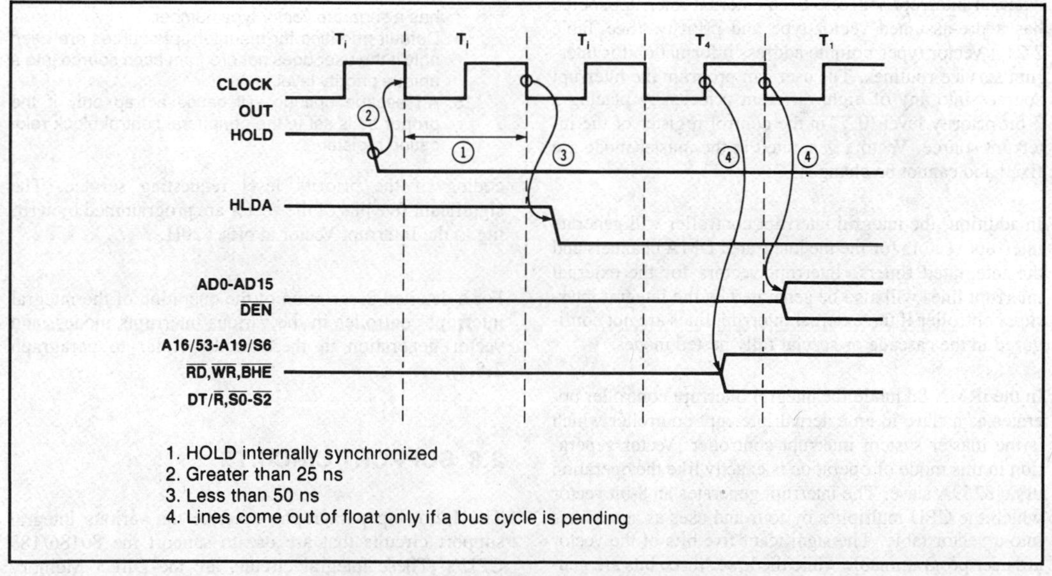

Figure 2-37 End of HOLD Timing Diagram

cycle about to be run. If the 80186 has no pending bus activity, it will maintain all lines floating (high impedance) until the last T_i before it begins the first bus cycle after the HOLD.

2.7 INTERRUPTS

Interrupts fall into three classes: hardware initiated interrupts; INT instructions; and instruction exceptions. Hardware initiated interrupts usually occur in response to some external input and are classified as non-maskable or maskable. Software programs cause an interrupt with an INT instruction. Interrupt exceptions usually occur when some unusual circumstance, that prevents further instruction processing, occurs while attempting to process instructions.

The 80186/188 CPU receives interrupts from both internal and external sources. Internal interrupt sources such as the timers and DMA channels can be disabled by their own control registers or by mask bits in the integral interrupt controller. The 80186/188 integral interrupt controller has its own control registers that set the mode of operation for the controller.

The integral interrupt controller operates in two major modes (refer to paragraph 2.4). These two modes of operation are the master (non-iRMX 86) mode and the iRMX 86 mode.

In the master mode the integral interrupt controller acts as the system master interrupt controller. Five pins (NMI and INT0-INT3) are provided in this interrupt mode for external interrupt sources. Each external interrupt source has a pre-assigned vector type and priority. (See Table 2-21.) Vector types point to address information for interrupt service routines. The user can program the interrupt sources into any of eight different priority by placing a 3-bit priority level (0-7) in the control register of the interrupt source. Vectors generated in the master mode are fixed and cannot be changed.

In addition, the integral interrupt controller will generate interrupt vectors for the the integrated DMA channels and the integrated timers. Interrupt vectors for the external interrupt lines will also be generated by the integral interrupt controller if the external interrupt lines are not configured in the cascade or special fully nested modes.

In the iRMX 86 mode the integral interrupt controller operates as a slave to an external interrupt controller which is the master system interrupt controller. Vector generation in this mode of operation is exactly like the operation of an 8259A slave. The interrupt generates an 8-bit vector which the CPU multiplies by four and uses as an address into a vector table. The significant five bits of the vector are user programmable while the lower three bits are generated by the priority logic. These bits represent the encoding of the priority level requesting service. The significant five bits of the vector are programmed by writing to the Interrupt Vector at offset 20H.

Table 2-21 80186/188 Interrupt Vectors

Interrupt Name	Vector Type	Default Priority	Related Instructions
Divide Error Exception	0	*1	DIV, IDIV
Single Step Interrupt	1	12**2	All
NMI	2	1	All
Breakpoint Interrupt	3	*1	INT
INT0 Detected Overflow Exception	4	*1	INT0
Array Bounds Exception	5	*1	BOUND
Unused-Opcode Exception	6	*1	Undefined Opcodes
ESC Opcode Exception	7	*1***	ESC Opcodes
Timer 0 Interrupt	8	2A****	
Timer 1 Interrupt	18	2B****	
Timer 2 Interrupt	19	2C****	
Reserved	9	3	
DMA 0 Interrupt	10	4	
DMA 1 Interrupt	11	5	
INT0 Interrupt	12	6	
INT1 Interrupt	13	7	
INT2 Interrupt	14	8	
INT3 Interrupt	15	9	

NOTES:

*1. These are generated as the result of an instruction execution.

**2. This is handled as in the 8086.

****3. All three timers constitute one source of request to the interrupt controller. The Timer interrupts all have the same default priority level with respect to all other interrupt sources. However, they have a defined priority ordering amongst themselves. (Priority 2A is higher priority than 2B.) Each Timer interrupt has a separate vector type number.

4. Default priorities for the interrupt sources are used only if the user does not program each source into a unique priority level.

***5. An escape opcode will cause a trap only if the proper bit is set in the peripheral control block relocation register.

For a detailed description of the operation of the integral interrupt controller in the various interrupts modes, and vector generation in these modes (refer to paragraph 2.8.4).

2.8 SUPPORT CIRCUITS

The following paragraphs describe the various integral support circuits that are use to support the 80186/188 CPU's. These integral circuits are the Direct Memory Access (DMA) Unit, the Timer Unit, the Interrupt

Controller Unit, the Chip Select Unit and the Clock Generator Unit. Paragraph 2.2.1 provides an overview of these integral circuits.

2.8.1 Direct Memory Access (DMA) Unit

The 80186 contains an integrated DMA unit with two independent high speed DMA channels. These channels operate independently of the CPU, and drive all integrated bus interface components (bus controller, chip selects, etc.) exactly as the CPU (see Figure 2-38). Therefore, bus cycles initiated by the DMA unit are exactly the same as bus cycles initiated by the CPU (except that S6 = 1 during all DMA initiated cycles, refer to paragraph 2.5). Therefore, interfacing with the DMA unit itself is very simple, since, except for the addition of the DMA request connection, it is exactly the same as interfacing to the CPU.

Data transfers can occur between memory and I/O spaces (e.g., Memory to I/O) or within the same space (e.g., Memory to Memory or I/O to I/O). Data can be transferred either in bytes (8 bits) or in words (16 bits) to or from even or odd addresses. Each DMA channel maintains both a 20-bit source and destination pointer which can be optionally incremented or decremented after each data transfer (by one or two depending on byte or word transfers). Each data transfer consumes two bus cycles (a minimum of eight clocks), one cycle to fetch data and the other to store data. This provides a maximum data transfer rate of one MW/sec (megaword/second) or two MBytes/sec.

PROGRAMMING THE DMA UNIT

Each of the two DMA channels contains several registers which are used to control the channel operations. These registers are included in the 80186 integrated peripheral control block. Registers included are the source and destination pointer registers, the transfer count register, and the control register. Layout and bit interpretations for these registers are shown in Figure 2-39.

The 20-bit source and destination pointers allow access to the complete 1 Mbyte address space of the 80186. All 20 bits are affected by the auto-increment or auto-decrement unit of the DMA (i.e., the DMA channels address the full 1 Mbyte address space of the 80186 as a flat, linear array without segments). When addressing I/O space, the upper 4 bits of the DMA pointer registers should be programmed to be 0. If these upper 4 bits are not programmed to 0, the programmed value (greater than 64K in *I/O space*) will be driven onto the address bus where it is not accessable to the CPU. However, the data transfer will take place correctly.

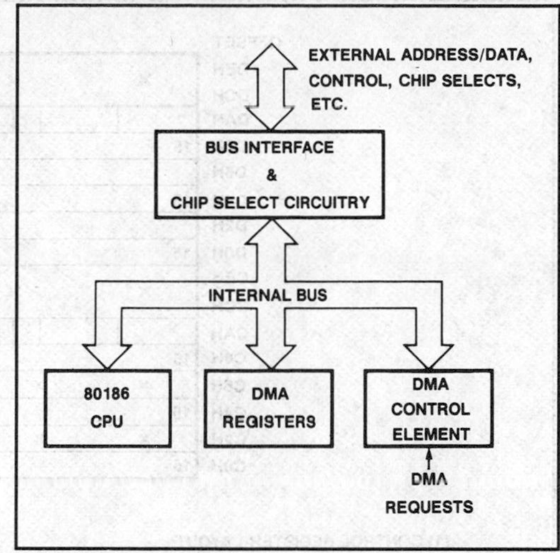

Figure 2-38 80186 CPU/DMA Channel Internal Model

After every DMA transfer the 16-bit DMA transfer count register is decremented by 1, whether a byte transfer or a word transfer has occurred. If the TC bit in the DMA control register is set, the DMA ST/STOP* bit (discussed later) will be cleared when this register goes to zero, causing DMA activity to cease. A transfer count of zero allows 65536 (2^{16}) transfers.

The DMA control register contains bits which control various channel characteristics. (See Figure 2-40.) This includes control bits for each of the data source and destination whether the pointer points to memory or I/O space, or whether the pointer will be incremented/decremented/left alone after each DMA transfer. The control register also contains a bit which selects between byte or word transfers. Two synchronization bits are used to determine the source of the DMA requests. The TC bit determines whether DMA activity will cease after a programmed number of DMA transfers. The INT bit is used to enable interrupts to the processor when this has occurred.

NOTE

An Interrupt will not be generated to the CPU when the count reaches zero unless both the INT bit and the TC bit are set.

The control register also contains a start/stop (ST/STOP*) bit. This bit is used to enable DMA transfers. Whenever this bit is set, the channel is "armed" and a DMA transfer will occur whenever a DMA request is made to the channel. If this bit is cleared, no DMA transfers will be performed by the channel. A companion bit, the CHG/NOCHG* bit, allows the contents of the DMA register to be changed without modifying the state of the start/stop bit. The ST/STOP* will only be modified if the CHG/

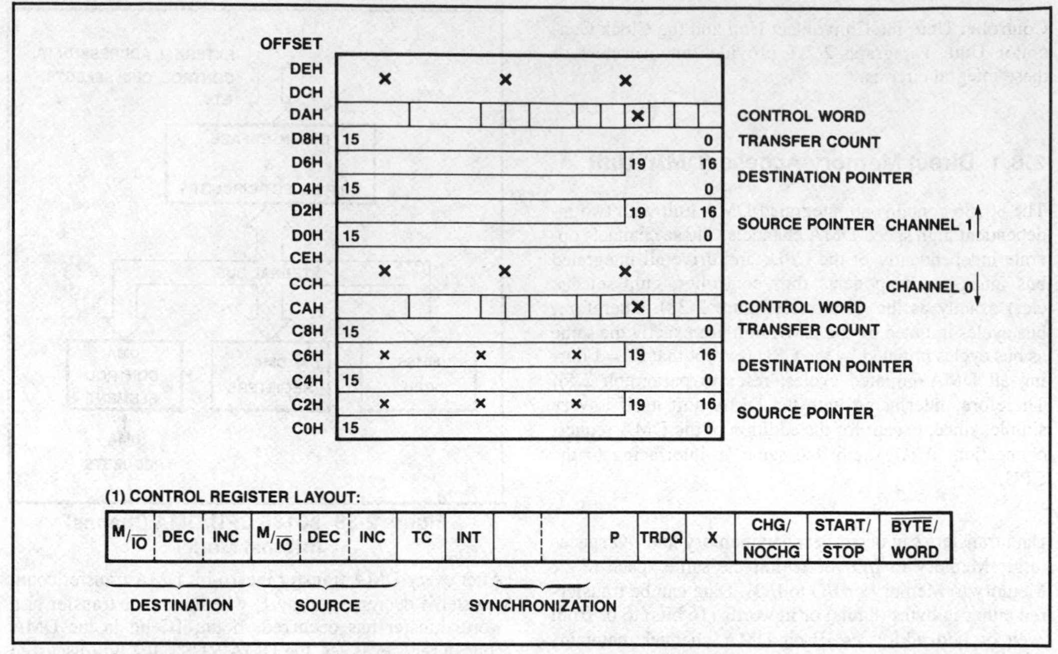

Figure 2-39 80186 DMA Register Layout

NOCHG* bit is also set during the write to the DMA control register. The CHG/NOCHG* bit is write only. This bit will always be read back as a '0'. Because DMA transfers could occur immediately after the ST/STOP* bit is set, this bit should only be set after all other DMA control registers have been programmed. This bit is automatically cleared when the transfer count reaches zero and the TC bit in the DMA control register is set. This bit is also cleared when the transfer count register reaches zero and unsynchronized DMA transfers are programmed (regardless of the state of the TC bit).

All DMA unit programming registers are directly accessable by the CPU. This means the CPU can, for example, modify the DMA source pointer register after 137 DMA transfers have occurred, and have the new pointer value used for the 138th DMA transfer. If more than one register in the DMA channel is being modified during the time when a DMA request may be generated, and the DMA channel is enabled (ST/STOP* bit set), the register programming values should be placed into memory locations and moved into the DMA registers using a locked string move instruction. This will prevent a DMA transfer from occurring after only half of the register values have changed. This also holds true if a read/modify/write type of operation is being performed (e.g., ANDing off bits in a pointer register in a single AND instruction to a pointer register mapped into memory space.

DMA TRANSFERS

Every DMA transfer in the 80186 consists of two independent bus cycles, the fetch cycle and the deposit cycle (see Figure 2-41). During the fetch cycle, the byte or word data is accessed from memory or I/O space using the address in the source pointer register. The data accessed is placed in an internal temporary register, which is not accessible by the CPU. During the deposit cycle, the byte or word data in this internal register is placed in

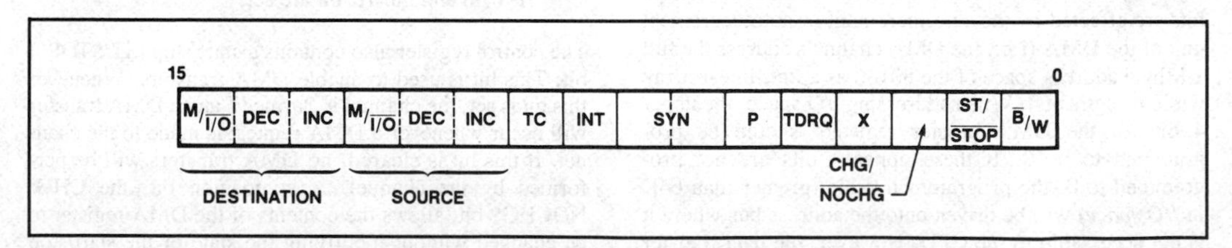

Figure 2-40 DMA Control Register

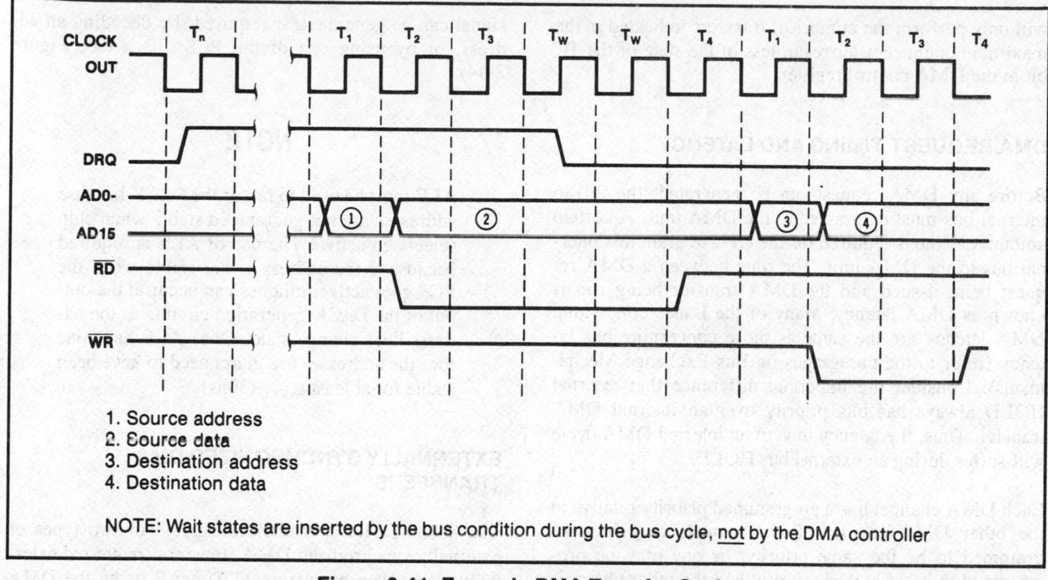

Figure 2-41 Example DMA Transfer Cycle

memory or I/O space using the address in the destination pointer register. These two bus cycles will not be separated by bus HOLD or by the other DMA channel, and one will never be run without the other except when the CPU is RESET. Notice that the bus cycles run by the DMA unit are exactly the same as memory or I/O bus cycles run by the CPU. The only difference between the two is the state of the S6 status line (which is multiplexed on the A19 line): on all CPU initiated bus cycles, this status line will be driven low; on all DMA initiated bus cycles, this status line will be driven high.

DMA REQUESTS

Each DMA channel has a single DMA request line by which an external device may request a DMA transfer. The synchronization bits in the DMA control register determine whether this line is interpreted to be connected to the source of the DMA data or the destination of the DMA data. All transfer requests on this line are synchronized to the CPU clock before being presented to internal DMA logic. Any asynchronous transitions of the DMA request line will not cause the DMA channel to malfunction. In addition to external requests, DMA requests may be generated whenever the internal Timer 2 times out, or continuously by programming the synchronization bits in the DMA control register to call for unsynchronized DMA transfers.

The 80186 DMA controller handles two types of internally synchronized DMA transfers: the first Timer 2 generates the DMA request, and the second where the DMA channel itself generates the DMA request. The DMA channel can be programmed to generate a DMA request whenever Timer 2 reaches its maximum count. Setting the TDRQ bit in the DMA channel control register selects this feature. A DMA request generated in this manner will be latched in the DMA controller, so that once the timer request has been generated, it cannot be cleared except by running the DMA cycle or by clearing the TDRQ bits in both DMA control registers. Before any DMA requests are generated in this mode, Timer 2 must be initiated and enabled.

A timer requested DMA cycle being run by either DMA channel will reset the timer request. Thus, if both channels are using the timer to request a DMA cycle, only one DMA channel will execute a transfer for every timeout of Timer 2. Another implication of having a single bit timer DMA request latch in the DMA controller is that if another Timer 2 timeout occurs before a DMA channel has a chance to run a DMA transfer, the first request will be lost (i.e., only a single DMA transfer will occur, even though the timer has timed out twice).

The DMA channel can also be programmed to provide its own DMA requests. In this mode, DMA transfer cycles will be run continuously at the maximum bus bandwidth, one after the other until the preprogrammed number of DMA transfers (in the DMA transfer count register) have occurred. This mode is selected by programming the synchronization bits in the DMA control register for unsynchronized transfers. In this mode, the DMA controller monopolizes the CPU bus (i.e., the CPU will not be able to perform opcode fetching, memory operations, etc., while the DMA transfers are occurring). Also, the DMA will only perform the number of transfers indicated in the maximum count register regardless of the state of the TC bit in the DMA control register.

DMA REQUEST TIMING AND LATENCY

Before any DMA request can be generated, the 80186 internal bus must be granted to the DMA unit. A certain amount of time is required for the CPU to grant this internal bus to the DMA unit. The time between a DMA request being issued and the DMA transfer being run is known as DMA latency. Many of the issues concerning DMA latency are the same as those concerning bus latency (refer to the paragraphs on Bus Exchange Mechanisms). Consider the important difference that external HOLD always has bus priority over an internal DMA transfer. Thus, the latency time of an internal DMA cycle will suffer during an external bus HOLD.

Each DMA channel has a programmed priority relative to the other DMA channel. Both channels may be programmed to be the same priority, or one may be programmed to be of higher priority than the other channel. If both channels are active, DMA latency will suffer on the lower priority channel. If both channels are active and both channels are of the same programmed priority, DMA transfer cycles will alternate between the two channels (i.e., the first channel will perform a fetch and deposit, followed by a fetch and deposit by the second channel, etc).

The DMA request (DRQ) is sampled four clock cycles before the beginning of a bus cycle to determine if any DMA activity will be required. A minimum of four CPU clock cycles must occur between the time DRQ goes active and the beginning of the first DMA cycle (see Figure 2-42). It takes at least four clock cycles for the request to propagate through the logic circuits (see Figure 2-43). This time is independent of the number of wait states inserted in the bus cycle. The maximum DMA latency is a function of other processor activity.

If DRQ is sampled active at point 1 in Figure 2-42, the DMA cycle will be executed, even if the DMA request goes inactive before the beginning of the first DMA cycle. If the BIU is busy and cannot run the cycle when DRQ goes active, DRQ must remain active for a minimum of four clock cycles before the time that it is possible to run the requested cycle. DMA requests are not permanently stored, therefore, if DRQ goes inactive after one clock, a zero will be propagated through the logic and no DMA cycles will be run.

DMA ACKNOWLEDGE

The 80186 does not generate an explicit DMA acknowledge signal. Instead, a read or write directly to the DMA requesting device is performed. A DMA acknowledge signal can be generated, if required, by decoding an address, or by using one of the PCS* lines (see Figure 2-44).

NOTE

ALE must be used to factor the DACK because addresses are not guaranteed stable when chip selects go active. The use of ALE is required because if the address is not stable when the PCS goes active, glitches can occur at the output of the DACK generation circuits as the address lines change state. Once ALE has gone low, the addresses are guaranteed to have been stable for at least t_{AVAL} (30ns).

EXTERNALLY SYNCHRONIZED DMA TRANSFERS

The 80186 DMA controller is capable of two types of externally synchronized DMA transfers (requested externally rather than by integrated Timer 2 or by the DMA channel itself (in unsynchronized transfers). These transfers are source synchronized and destination synchronized transfers and are selected by programming the synchronization bits in the DMA channel control register. Source synchronized and destination synchronized transfer differ in the time at which the DMA request pin is sampled to determine if another DMA transfer is immediately required after the currently executing DMA transfer. For source synchronized transfers, the DMA request is sampled such that two source synchronized DMA transfers may occur one immediately after the other. For destination synchronized transfers a certain amount of idle time is automatically inserted between two DMA transfers to allow time for the DMA requesting device to drive its DMA request inactive.

Source Synchronized DMA Transfers

In a source synchronized DMA transfer, the source of the DMA data requests the DMA cycle (for example, a floppy disk read from the disk to main memory). In this type of transfer, the device requesting the transfer is read during the fetch cycle of the DMA transfer. Since four CPU clock cycles elapse from the time DMA request is sampled to the time the DMA transfer is actually begun, and a bus cycle takes a minimum of four clock cycles, the earliest time the DMA request pin will be sampled for another DMA transfer will be at the beginning of the deposit cycle of a DMA transfer. This allows over three CPU clock cycles between the time the DMA requesting device receives an acknowledge to its DMA request (around the beginning of T2 of the DMA fetch cycle), and the time it must drive this request inactive (assuming no wait states) to insure that another DMA transfer is not performed if it is not desired (see Figure 2-45).

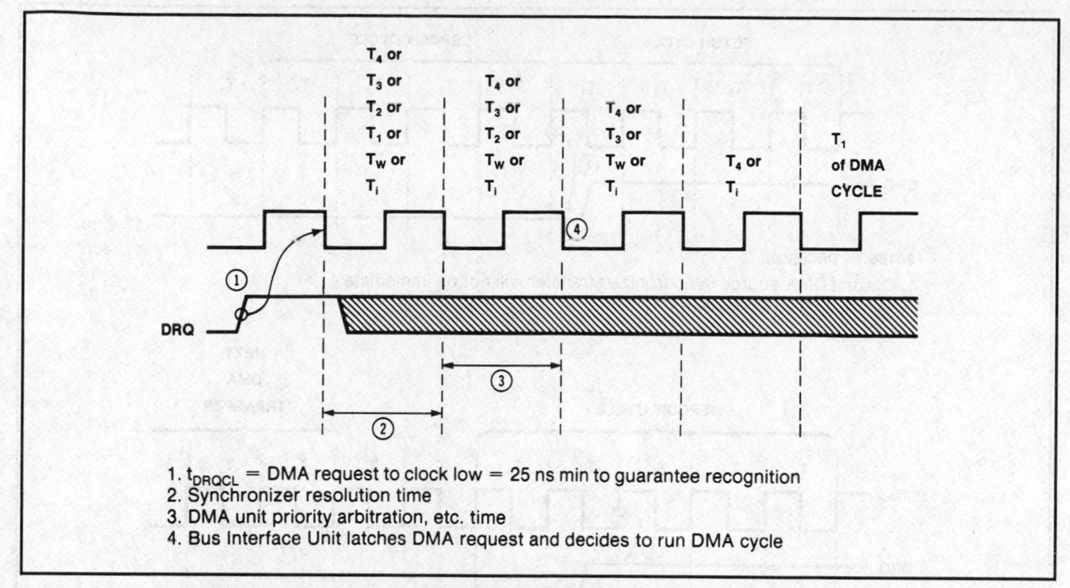

Figure 2-42 DMA Request Timing

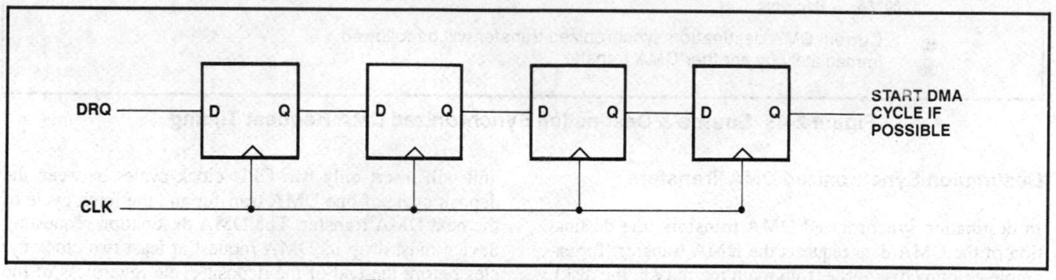

Figure 2-43 DMA Request Logic

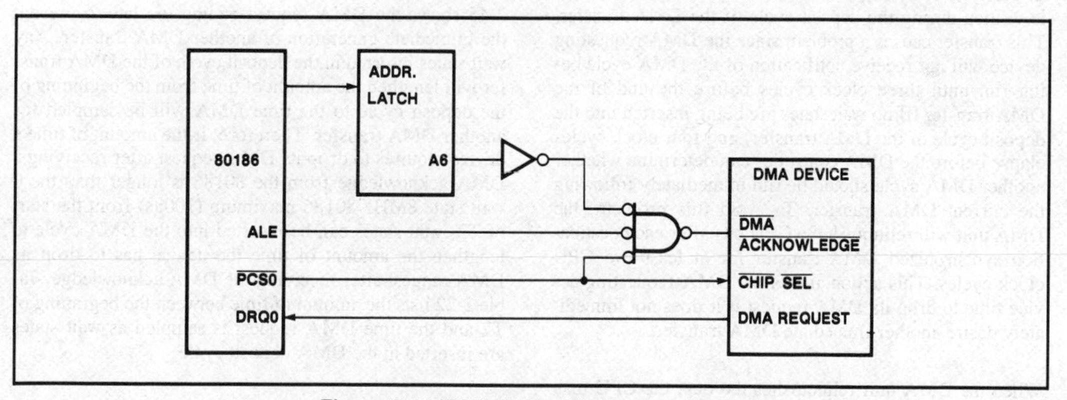

Figure 2-44 DMA Acknowledge Synthesis

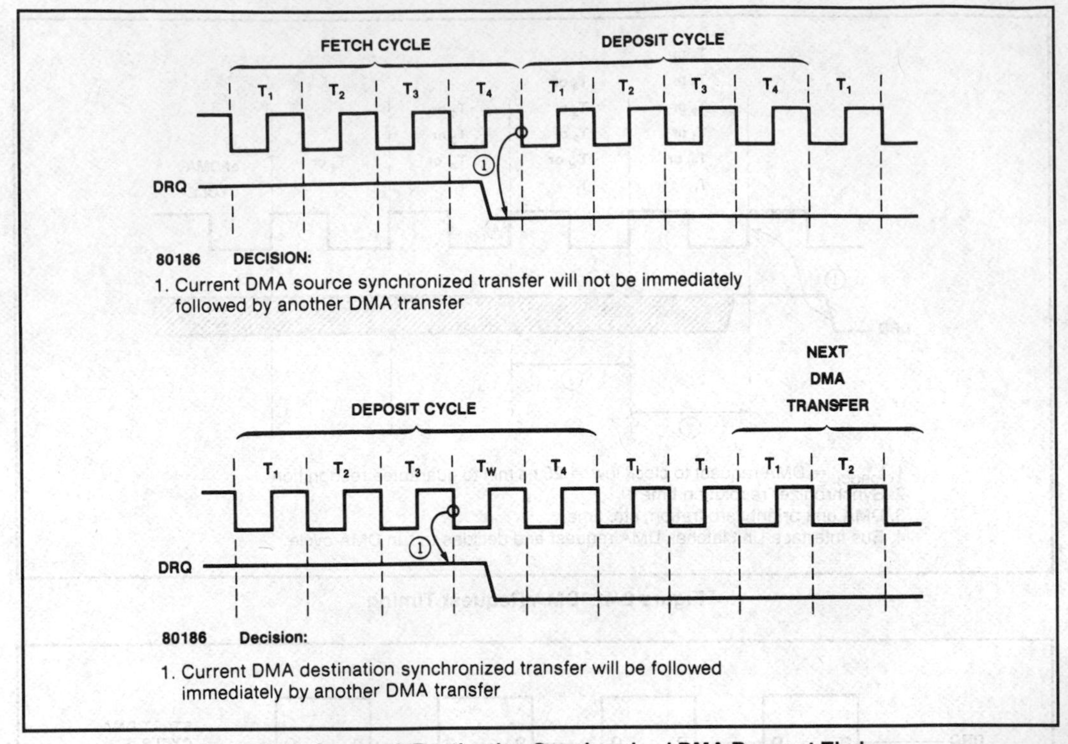

Figure 2-45 Source & Destination Synchronized DMA Request Timing

Destination Synchronized DMA Transfers

In destination synchronized DMA transfers, the destination of the DMA data requests the DMA transfer (for example a floppy disk write from main memory to the disk). In this type of transfer, the device requesting the transfer is written during the deposit cycle of the DMA transfer. This transfer causes a problem since the DMA requesting device will not receive notification of the DMA cycle being run until three clock cycles before the end of the DMA transfer (if no wait states are being inserted into the deposit cycle of the DMA transfer) and four clock cycles elapse before the DMA controller can determine whether another DMA cycle should be run immediately following the current DMA transfer. To avoid this problem, the DMA unit will relinquish the CPU bus after each destination synchronized DMA transfer for at least two CPU clock cycles. This action allows the DMA requesting device time to drop its DMA request if it does not immediately desire another immediate DMA transfer.

When the DMA unit relinquishes the bus, the CPU may resume bus operation (e.g., instruction fetching, memory or I/O reads or writes, etc.). Typically, a CPU initiated bus cycle will be inserted between each destination synchronized DMA transfer. If no CPU bus activity is required, however (and none can be guaranteed), the DMA unit will insert only two CPU clock cycles between the deposit cycle of one DMA transfer and the fetch cycle of the next DMA transfer. The DMA destination requesting device must drop its DMA request at least two clock cycles before the end of the deposit cycle regardless of the number of wait states inserted into the bus cycle. Figure 2-45 shows the DMA request ending too late to prevent the immediate generation of another DMA transfer. Any wait states inserted in the deposit cycle of the DMA transfer will lengthen the amount of time from the beginning of the deposit cycle to the time DMA will be sampled for another DMA transfer. Therefore, if the amount of time a device requires to drop its DMA request after receiving a DMA acknowledge from the 80186 is longer than the 0 wait state 8MHz 80186 maximum (100ns) from the start of T2, wait states can be inserted into the DMA cycle to lengthen the amount of time the device has to drop its DMA request after receiving the DMA acknowledge. Table 2-22 lists the amount of time between the beginning of T2 and the time DMA request is sampled as wait states are inserted in the DMA deposit cycle.

2.8.2 Timer Unit

The 80186 contains three internal 16-bit programmable timers (see Figure 2-46) two of which are connected to

Table 2-22 DMA Request Inactive Timing

WAIT STATES	MAXIMUM TIME (ns) 6MHz	8MHZ
0	141	100
1	308	225
2	475	350
3	641	475

Table 2-23 Timer Control Block Format

Register Name	Register Offset Tmr. 0	Tmr. 1	Tmr. 2
Mode/Control Word	56H	5EH	66H
Max Count B	54H	5CH	not present
Max Count A	52H	5AH	62H
Count Register	50H	58H	60H

four external pins (two pins per timer). These timers (Timers 0 and 1) can be used to count external events, time external events, generate non-repetitive waveforms, etc. The third timer is not directly accessible through dedicated pins. This timer is useful for real-time coding and time delay applications and may be used to prescale the other two timers (refer to Volume I of this User's Guide).

The timers are controlled by 11 16-bit registers in the internal peripheral control block (refer to Table 2-23). The count register contains the current value of the timer and it can be read or written at any time independent of whether the timer is running or not. The value of this register will be incremented for each timer event. Each of the timers contains a MAX COUNT register, which defines the maximum count the timer will reach. After reaching the MAX COUNT register value, the timer count value will reset to zero during that same clock (i.e., the maximum count value is never stored in the count register itself). Timers 0 and 1 contain, in addition, a second MAX COUNT register, which enables the timers to alternate their count between two different MAX COUNT values programmed by the user. If a single MAX COUNT register is used, the timer output pin switches LOW for a single clock, one clock after the maximum count value has been reached. In the dual MAX COUNT register mode, the output pin indicates which MAX COUNT register is currently in use, thus allowing nearly complete freedom in selecting waveform duty cycles. For the timers with two MAX COUNT registers, the RIU bit in the control register determines which is used for the comparison.

Each timer gets serviced every fourth CPU clock cycle. Therefore, the timers, whether clocked internally or externally can only operate at speeds up to one-quarter the internal clock frequency (one-eighth the crystal rate). This will be 2 MHz for an 8 MHz CPU clock. Due to internal synchronization and pipelining of the timer circuits, a timer output may take up to six clocks to respond to any individual clock or gate input. Since the count registers and the maximum count registers are all 16 bits wide, 16 bits of resolution are provided. However, any read or write access to the Timers will add one wait state to the minimum four-clock bus cycle. This is needed to synchronize and coordinate the internal data flows between the internal timers and the internal bus.

TIMER INPUT PIN OPERATION

Timers 0 and 1 each have individual timer input pins. All low-to-high transitions on these input pins are

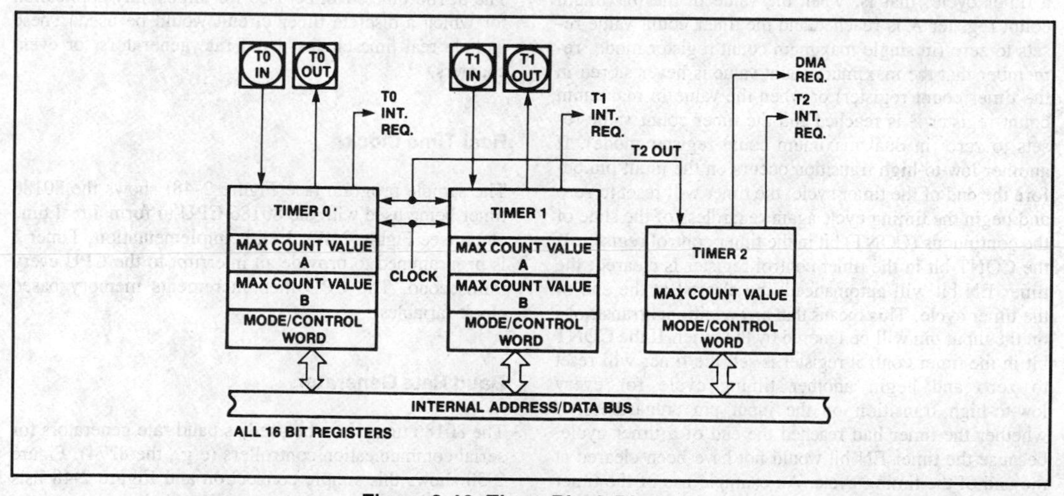

Figure 2-46 Timer Block Diagram

synchronized, latched, and presented to the counter element when the particular timer is being serviced by the counter element.

Signals on this input affect timer operation in three different ways. The way the pin signals are used is determined by the external (EXT) and retrigger (RTG) bits in the timer control register. If the EXT bit is set, transitions on the input pin cause the timer count value to increment if the timer is enabled (the timer control register enable bit is set). Thus, the timer counts external events. If the EXT bit is cleared, all timer increments are caused by either the CPU clock or by Timer 2 timing out. In this mode, the RTG bit determines whether the input pin will enable timer operation, or whether it will retrigger timer operation.

If the EXT bit is low and the RTG bit is also low, the timer will count internal timer events only when the timer input pin is high and the enable (EN) bit in the timer control register is set.

In this mode, the pin is level sensitive, not edge sensitive. A low-to-high transition on the timer input pin is not required to enable timer operation. If the input is tied high, the timer will be continually enabled. The time enable input signal is completely independent of the EN bit in the timer control register: both must be high for the timer to count. Example uses for the timer in this mode would be a real time clock or a baud rate generator.

If the EXT bit is low and the RTG bit is high, the timer will act as a digital one-shot. In this mode, every low-to-high transition on the timer input pin will cause the timer to reset to zero. If the timer is enabled (i.e., the EN bit in the timer control register is set) timer operation will begin and the timer will count CPU clock transitions or Timer 2 timeouts. Timer operation will cease at the end of a timer cycle, that is, when the value in the maximum count register A is reached and the timer count value resets to zero (in single maximum count register mode, remember that the maximum count value is never stored in the timer count register) or when the value in maximum count register B is reached and the timer count value resets to zero (in dual maximum count register mode). If another low-to-high transition occurs on the input pin before the end of the timer cycle, the timer will reset to zero and begin the timing cycle again regardless of the state of the continuous (CONT) bit in the timer control register. If the CONT bit in the timer control register is cleared, the timer EN bit will automatically be cleared at the end of the timer cycle. This means that any additional transitions on the input pin will be ignored by the timer. If the CONT bit in the timer control register is set, the timer will reset to zero and begin another timing cycle for every low-to-high transition on the input pin, regardless of whether the timer had reached the end of a timer cycle, because the timer EN bit would not have been cleared at the end of the timing cycle. An example use of the timer is this mode is an alarm clock time out signal or interrupt.

TIMER OUTPUT PIN OPERATION

Timers 0 and 1 each contain a single timer output pin. This pin can perform two functions at programmer option. The first is a single pulse indicating the end of a timing cycle. The second is a level indicating the maximum count register currently being used. The timer outputs operate as outlined below whether internal or external clocking of the timer is used. If external clocking is used, however, the user should remember that the time between an external transition on the timer input pin and the time this transition is reflected in the timer out pin will vary depending on when the input transition occurs relative to the timer's being serviced by the counter element.

When the timer is in single maximum count register mode (timer control register ALT bit cleared) the timer output pin goes low for a single CPU clock the clock after the timer is serviced by the counter element where maximum count is reached (see Figure 2-47). This mode is useful when using the timer as a baud rate generator.

When the timer is programmed in dual maximum count register mode (timer control register ALT bit set), the timer output pin indicates which maximum count register is being used. The pin is low if maximum count register B is being used for the current count, high if maximum count register A is being used. If the timer is programmed in continuous mode (the CONTinuous bit in the timer control register is set), this pin could generate a waveform of any duty cycle. For example, if maximum count register A contained 10 and maximum count register B contained 20, a 33% duty cycle waveform would be generated.

TIMER APPLICATIONS

The 80186 timers can be used for almost any application for which a discrete timer circuit would be used. These include real time clocks, baud rate generators, or event counters.

Real Time Clock

The sample program (see Figure 2-48) shows the 80186 timer being used with the 80186 CPU to form a real time clock (see Figure 2-49). In this implementation, Timer 2 is programmed to provide an interrupt to the CPU every millisecond. The CPU then increments memory based clock variables.

Baud Rate Generator

The 80186 timers can be used as baud rate generators for serial communication controllers (e.g., the 8274). Figure 2-50 shows this simple connection and Figure 2-48 lists the code to program the timer as a baud rate generator.

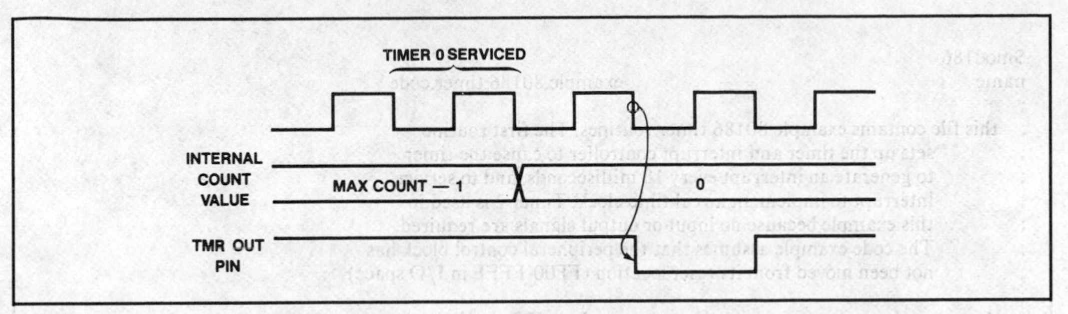

Figure 2-47 80186 Timer Out Signal

Event Counter

The 81086 timer can be used to count events. Figure 2-51 shows a hypothetical application in which the 80186 timer will count the interruptions in a light source. The number of interruptions can be read directly from the count register of the timer, since the timer counts up (i.e., each interruption in the light source will cause the timer count value to increase). Figure 2-48 lists the code to set up the 80186 timer in this mode.

2.8.3 Interrupt Controller

The 80186 integrated interrupt controller performs the tasks of an 8259A type interrupt controller in a typical microprocessor system. Figure 2-52 shows a block diagram of the integrated interrupt controller. These tasks include synchronizing and prioritizing interrupt requests, and request type vectoring in response to a CPU interrupt acknowledge. Nesting is provided so interrupt service routines for lower priority interrupts may themselves be interrupted by higher priority interrupts. The integrated controller has two major modes of operation, the iRMX-86 mode and the non-iRMX 86 (master) mode. In the master mode the integrated interrupt controller can be the master controller for up to two external Intel 8259A interrupt controllers allowing up to 128 interrupts. In the iRMX 86 mode it can be the slave to an external interrupt controller to allow compatibility with the iRMX86 operating system and the 80130/80150 operating system coprocessors (refer to Volume I of this User's Manual).

The 80186 can receive interrupts from a number of sources, both internal and external. The internal interrupt controller merges these requests on a priority basis, for individual service by the CPU.

Internal interrupt sources (Timers and DMA channels) are disabled by their own control registers or by mask bits within the interrupt controller. The 80186 interrupt controller has its own control registers that set the controller mode of operation.

The interrupt controller resolves priority among simultaneous requests. Nesting is provided so interrupt service routines for lower priority interrupts may themselves be interrupted by higher priority interrupts.

iRMX™ 86 MODE OPERATION

The iAPX186/188 integrated interrupt controllers have a special iRMX compatibility mode of operation that allows the use of the 80186/188 within the iRMX 86 operating system interrupt structure. To use this mode of operation, bit 14 in the peripheral control block relocation register must be set and special initilization software must be provided.

When the iRMX mode is used, the internal interrupt controller is used as a slave controller to an external interrupt controller. The internal 80186/188 resources are monitored through the internal interrupt controller, and the external interrupt controller functions as the system master interrupt controller. When an external interrupt controller (such as an 8259A) is used it requires additional control pins from the 80186. Therefore, some of the external interrupt pins are no longer used for external interrupt inputs. Since the external interrupt registers are no longer required, the unused registers can now be used by the timers. There are enough of these unused registers to dedicate one to each timer. Previously all of the timers shared one register. In this mode of operation each timer interrupt source has its own mask bit, IS bit and control word.

The iRMX 86 operating system requires peripherals to be assigned fixed priority levels. This is incompatible with the normal operation of the 80186/188 interrupt controller. Therefore the initialization software must program the proper priority for each source. The required priority levels for the internal interrupt sources in the iRMX 86 mode are shown in Table 2-24. These priority level assignments must remain fixed in the iRMX mode of operation.

The iRMX 86 mode of operation allows nesting of interrupt requests. The configuration of the 80186/188 with respect to an external 8259A master is shown in Figure

```
$mod186
name                                    example_80186_timer_code
;
;  this file contains example 80186 timer routines. The first routine
;           sets up the timer and interrupt controller to cause the timer
;           to generate an interrupt every 10 milliseconds, and to service
;           interrupt to implement a real time clock. Timer 2 is used in
;           this example because no input or output signals are required.
;           The code example assumes that the peripheral control block has
;           not been moved from its reset location (FF00-FFFF in I/O space).
;
arg1                 equu    word ptr [BP + 4]
arg2                 equ     word ptr [BP + 6]
arg3                 equ     word ptr [BP + 8]
timer_2int           equ     19                          ;  timer 2 has vector type 19
timer_2control       equ     0FF66h
timer_2max_ctl       equ     0FF62h
timer_int_ctl        equ     0FF32h                      ;  interrupt controller regs
eoi_register         equ     0FF22h
interrupt_stat       equ     0FF30h

data                 segment                             public 'data'
                     public  hour_,minute_,second_,msec_
msec_                db      ?
hour_                db      ?
minute_              db      ?
second_              db      ?
data                 ends

cgroup               group   code
dgroup               group   data

code                 segment                             public 'code'
                     public  set_time_
                     assume  cs:code,ds:dgroup
;
;  set_time(hour,minute,second) sets the time variables, initializes the
;          80186 timer2 to provide interrupts every 10 milliseconds, and
;          programs the interrupt vector for timer 2
;
set_time_            proc    near
                     enter   0,0                         ;  set stack addressability
                     push    AX                          ;  save registers used
                     push    DX
                     push    SI
                     push    DS

                     xor     AX,AX                       ;  set the interrupt vector
                                                         ;  the timers have unique
                                                         ;  interrupt
                                                         ;  vectors even though they share
                                                         ;  the same control register
                     mov     DS,AX

                     mov     SI,4 * timer2_int
```

Figure 2-48 Example Timer Interface Code (Sheet 1 of 4)

```
                          mov     DS:[SI],offset timer_2_interrupt_routine
                          inc     SI
                          inc     SI
                          mov     DS:[SI],CS
                          pop     DS

                          mov     AX,arg1                 ;  set the time values
                          mov     hour_,AL
                          mov     AX,arg2
                          mov     minute_,AL
                          mov     AX,arg3
                          mov     second_,AL
                          mov     msec_,0

                          mov     DX,timer2_max_ctl       ;  set the max count value
                          mov     AX,20000                ;  10 ms / 500 ns (timer 2 counts
                                                          ;  at 1/4 the CPU clock rate)
                          out     DX,AX
                          mov     DX,timer2_control       ;  set the control word
                          mov     AX,1110000000000001b    ;  enable counting
                                                          ;  generate interrupts on TC
                                                          ;  continuous counting
                          out     DX,AX

                          mov     DX,timer_int_ctl        ;  set up the interrupt controller
                          mov     AX,0000b                ;  unmask interrupts
                                                          ;  highest priority interrupt
                          out     DX,AX
                          sti                             ;  enable processor interrupts

                          pop     SI
                          pop     DX
                          pop     AX
                          leave
                          ret
set_time_                 endp

timer2_interrupt_routine  proc    far
                          push    AX
                          push    DX

                          cmp     msec_,99                ;  see if one second has passed
                          jae     bump_second             ;  if above or equal...
                          inc     msec_
                          jmp     reset_int_ctl
bump_second:
                          mov     msec_,0                 ;  reset millisecond
                          cmp     second_,59              ;  see if one minute has passed
                          jae     bump_minute
                          inc     second_
                          jmp     reset_int_ctl
bump_minute:
                          mov     second_,0
                          cmp     minute_,59              ;  see if one hour has passed
                          jae     bump_hour
                          inc     minute_
                          jmp     reset_int_ctl
```

Figure 2-48 Example Timer Interface Code (Sheet 2 of 4)

```
bump_hour:
                        mov     minute_,0
                        cmp     hour_,12                ;  see if 12 hours have passed
                        jae     reset_hour
                        inc     hour_
                        jmp     reset_int_ctl
reset_hour:
                        mov     hour_,1
reset_int_ctl:

                        mov     DX,eoi_register
                        mov     AX,8000h                ;  non-specific end of interrupt
                        out     DX,AX

                        pop     DX
                        pop     AX
                        iret
timer2_interrupt_routine endp
code                    ends
                        end
$mod186
name                    example_80186_baud_code
;
;  this file contains example 80186 timer routines. The second routine
;       sets up the timer as a baud rate generator. In this mode,
;       Timer 1 is used to continually output pulses with a period of
;       6.5 usec for use with a serial controller at 9600 baud
;       programmed in divide by 16 mode (the actual period required
;       for 9600 baud is 6.51 usec). This assumes that the 80186 is
;       running at 8 MHz. The code example also assumes that the
;       peripheral control block has not been moved from its reset
;       location (FF00-FFFF in I/O space).
;
timer1_control          equ     0FF5Eh
timer1_max_cnt          equ     0FF5Ah

code                    segment                         public 'code'
                        assume  cs:code
;
;  set_baud() initializes the 80186 timer1 as a baud rate generator for
;       a serial port running at 9600 baud
;
set_baud_               proc    near
                        push    AX                      ;  save registers used
                        push    DX

                        mov     DX,timer1_max_cnt       ;  set the max count value
                        mov     AX,13                   ;  500ns * 13 = 6.5 usec
                        out     DX,AX
                        mov     DX,timer1_control       ;  set the control word
                        mov     AX,1100000000000001b    ;  enable counting
                                                        ;  no interrupt on TC
                                                        ;  continuous counting
                                                        ;  single max count register
                        out     DX,AX
```

Figure 2-48 Example Timer Interface Code (Sheet 3 of 4)

```
                pop     DX
                pop     AX
                ret
set_baud_       endp
code            ends
                end
$mod186
name            example_80186_count_code
;
;  this file contains example 80186 timer routines. The third routine
;       sets up the timer as an external event counter. In this mode,
;       Timer 1 is used to count transitions on its input pin. After
;       the timer has been set up by the routine, the number of
;       events counted can be directly read from the timer count
;       register at location FF58H in I/O space. The timer will
;       count a maximum of 65535 timer events before wrapping
;       around to zero. This code example also assumes that the
;       peripheral control block has not been moved from its reset
;       location (FF00-FFFF in I/O space).
;
timer1_control  equu    0FF5Eh
timer1_max_cnt  equ     0FF5Ah
timer1_cnt_reg  equ     0FF58H

code            segment                         public 'code'
                assume  cs:code
;
;  set_count() initializes the 80186 timer1 as an event counter
;
set_count_      proc    near
                push    AX                      ; save registers used
                push    DX

                mov     DX,timer1_max_cnt       ; set the max count value
                mov     AX,0                    ; allows the timer to count
                                                ; all the way to FFFFH
                out     DX,AX
                mov     DX,timer1_control       ; set the control word
                mov     AX,1100000000000101b    ; enable counting
                                                ; no interrupt on TC
                                                ; continuous counting
                                                ; single max count register
                                                ; external clocking
                out     DX,AX

                xor     AX,AX                   ; zero AX
                mov     DX,timer1_cnt_reg       ; and zero the count in the timer
                out     DX,AX                   ; count register

                pop     DX
                pop     AX
                ret

set_count_      endp
code            ends
                end
```

Figure 2-48 Example Timer Interface Code (Sheet 4 of 4)

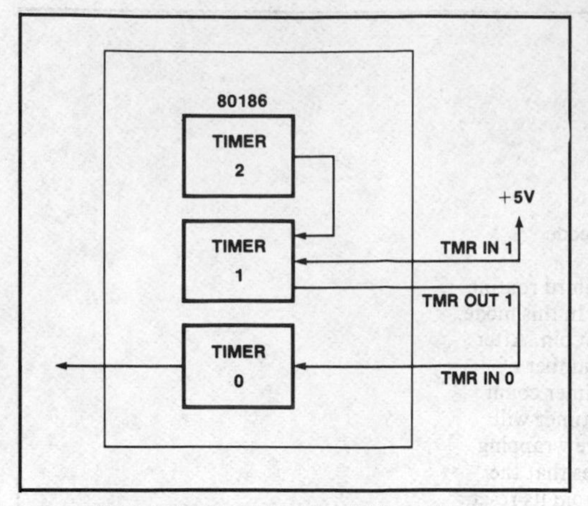

Figure 2-49 80186 Real Time Clock

2-53. The INT0 input is used as the 80186 CPU interrupt input. INT3 functions as an output to send the 80186 slave-interrupt-requests to one of the 8 master-PIC-inputs.

Correct master-slave interface requires decoding of the slave addresses (CAS0-2). Because of pin limitations, the 80186 slave address will have to be decoded externally. INT1* is used as a slave-select input. In this configuration the slave vector address is transferred internally, but the READY input must be supplied externally. INT2* is used as an acknowledge output, suitable to drive the INTA* input of an 8259A.

NON-iRMX™ 80 MODE

When configured in the non-iRMX 86 mode, the internal interrupt controller operates in one of three basic modes: the fully nested mode, the cascade mode, and the special

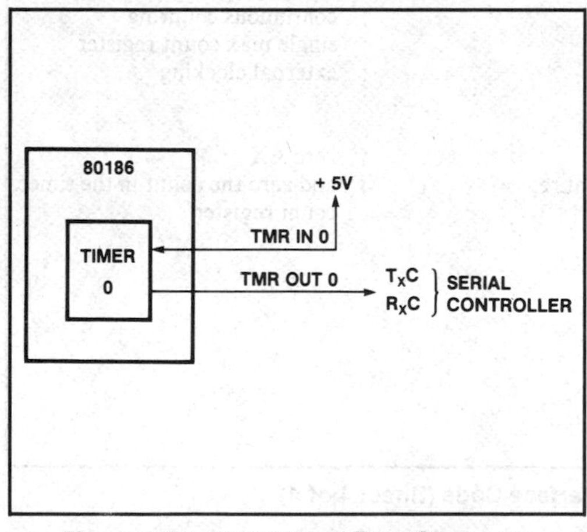

Figure 2-50 80186 Baud Rate Generator

fully nested modes of operation. Five pins are provided for external interrupt sources. One of these pins is dedicated to NMI. The other four (INT0-INT3) may be configured in three ways. The response to internal interrupts is identical in all three modes, but the function of the four external interrupt pins differs in each mode. The interrupt controller is set to one of these modes by programming the correct bits in the INT0 and INT1 control registers.

In the fully nested mode of operation, the four pins are configured as four interrupt input lines with internally generated interrupt vectors. In both the cascade and the special fully nested modes of operation the four interrupt input pins can be configured as either three interrupt input lines and interrupt acknowledge output, or two interrupt inputs lines and two dedicated interrupt acknowledge output lines. In the cascade mode of operation, when two interrupts are received from the same interrupt controller, one after the other, the internal controller will wait until the service routine for the first is complete before acknowledging the second internal interrupt. When this occurs in the special fully nested mode, the second interrupt from the same cascaded interrupt controller is assumed to be of higher priority and will be acknowledged before the first interrupt service routind is completed. These four interrupt inputs can be programmed in either edge-or level-trigger mode, as specified by the LTM bit in the source's control register.

The interrupt controller will generate interrupt vectors for the integrated DMA channels and the integrated timers. In addition, interrupt vectors for the external interrupt lines will be generated if they are not configured in cascade, or special fully nested mode.

Each interrupt source has a preassigned vector type (see Table 2-21). Vector types point to address information for interrupt service routines. The vectors generated are fixed and cannot be changed.

The user can program the interrupt sources into any of eight different priority levels. Programming is done by placing a 3-bit priority level (0-7) in the control register of each interrupt source. (A source priority of 4 has higher priority over all priority levels from 5-7. Priority registers containing values lower than 4 have higher priority.) All interrupt sources have preprogrammed default priority levels.

If two requests with the same programmed priority level are pending at once, the priority ordering scheme indicated in Table 2-21 is used. If the serviced interrupt routine reenables interrupts it allows other requests to be serviced.

CONTROL REGISTERS

The interrupt controller contains registers that control its operation (see Figure 2-54). Certain registers change

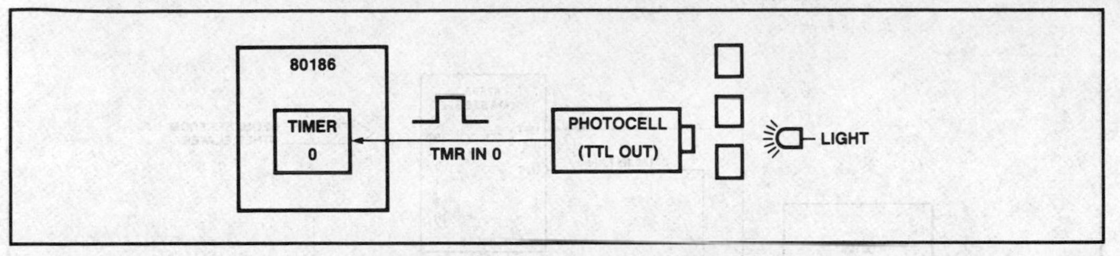

Figure 2-51 80186 Event Counter

Table 2-24 Internal Source Priority Level

Priority Level	Interrupt Source
0	Timer 0
1	(reserved)
2	DMA 0
3	DMA 1
4	Timer 1
5	Timer 2

their modes of operation between the two major modes of the interrupt controller: master mode and iRMX86 mode. These control registers include the Timer Register, two DMA registers, and four external input registers. The Timer and the DMA registers are used for interrupt controller interaction with the internal DMA and Timer units of the processor. Refer to Volume I of this User's Manual for full descriptions of these registers. The external input registers are of the greatest concern to the hardware designer.

The external input registers contain the control words for the four external interrupt input pins. See Figures 2-55 and 2-56. Figure 2-55 illustrates the format of the INT0 and the INT1 control registers; Figure 2-56 shows the format of the INT2 and INT3 registers. In cascade mode or special fully nested mode, the control words in the INT2 and INT3 registers are not used.

INTERRUPT SOURCES

The 80186 interrupt controller receives and arbitrates among many different interrupt request sources, both internal and external. Each interrupt source may be programmed to be a different priority level in the interrupt controller. Figure 2-57 shows an interrupt request generation flow chart. Such a flowchart would be followed independently by each interrupt source.

Internal Interrupt Sources

The 80186 internal interrupt sources include three timers and the two DMA channels. These sources operate independently of external devices as regards to interrupts to

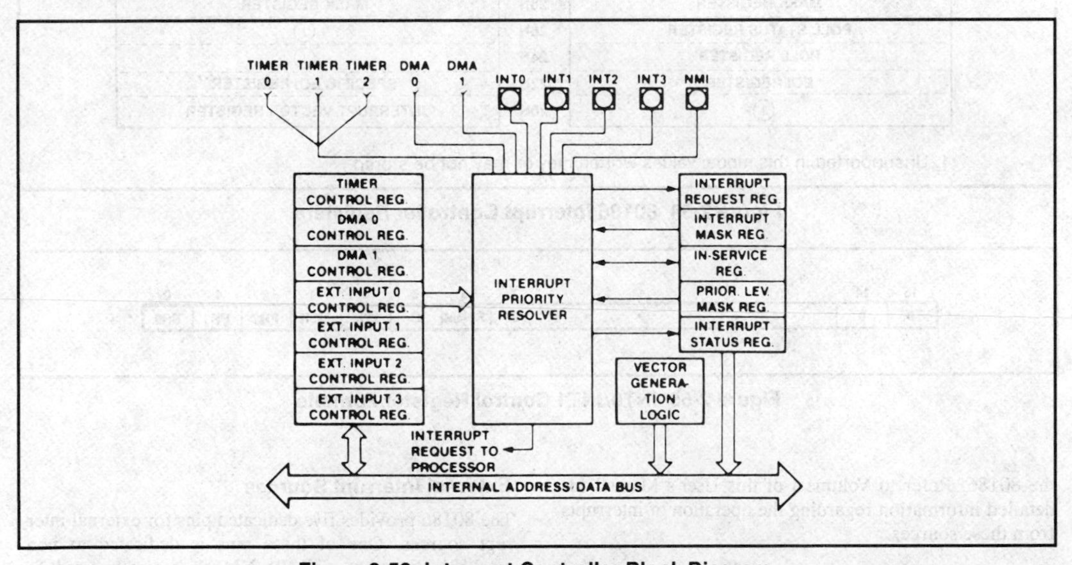

Figure 2-52 Interrupt Controller Block Diagram

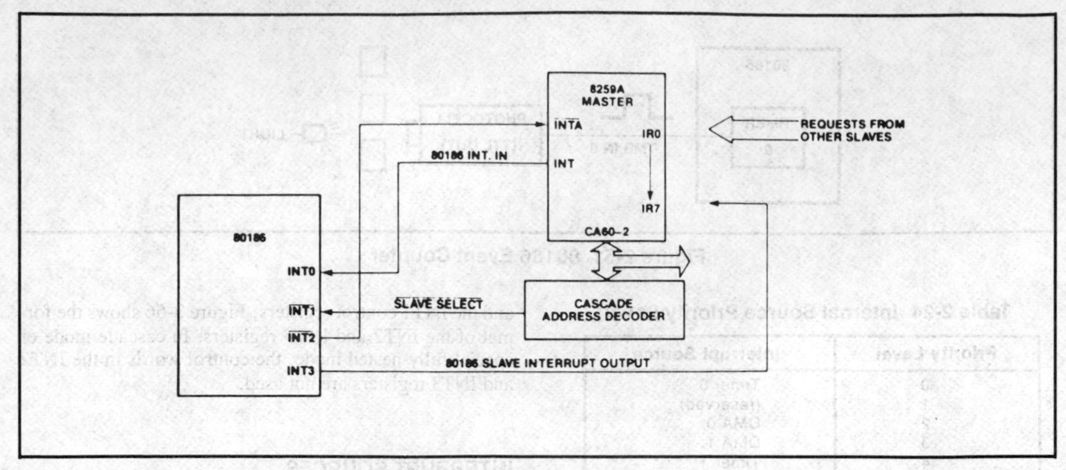

Figure 2-53 iRMX™ 86 Interrupt Controller Interconnection

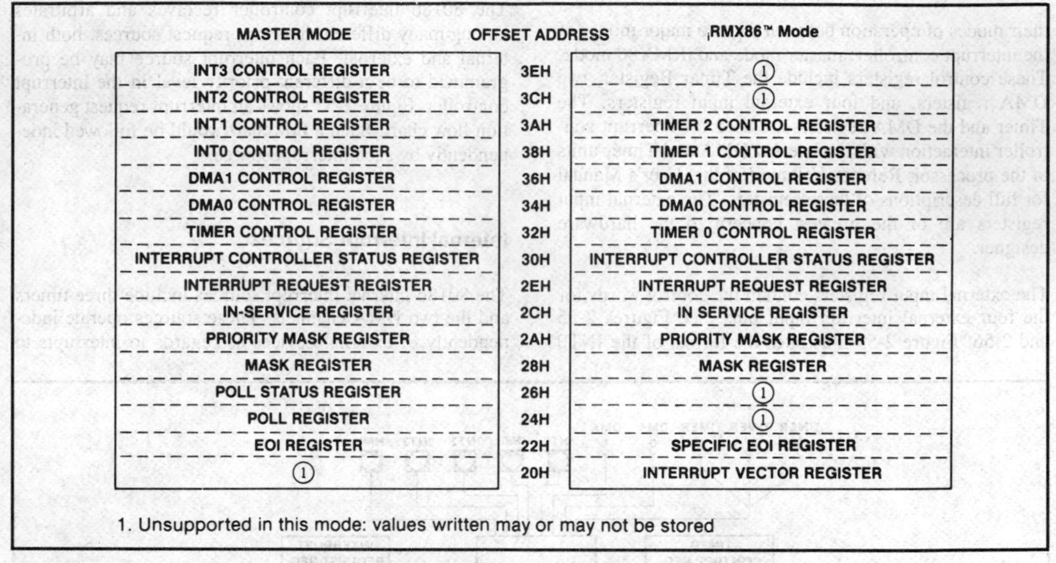

MASTER MODE	OFFSET ADDRESS	iRMX86™ Mode
INT3 CONTROL REGISTER	3EH	(1)
INT2 CONTROL REGISTER	3CH	(1)
INT1 CONTROL REGISTER	3AH	TIMER 2 CONTROL REGISTER
INT0 CONTROL REGISTER	38H	TIMER 1 CONTROL REGISTER
DMA1 CONTROL REGISTER	36H	DMA1 CONTROL REGISTER
DMA0 CONTROL REGISTER	34H	DMA0 CONTROL REGISTER
TIMER CONTROL REGISTER	32H	TIMER 0 CONTROL REGISTER
INTERRUPT CONTROLLER STATUS REGISTER	30H	INTERRUPT CONTROLLER STATUS REGISTER
INTERRUPT REQUEST REGISTER	2EH	INTERRUPT REQUEST REGISTER
IN-SERVICE REGISTER	2CH	IN SERVICE REGISTER
PRIORITY MASK REGISTER	2AH	PRIORITY MASK REGISTER
MASK REGISTER	28H	MASK REGISTER
POLL STATUS REGISTER	26H	(1)
POLL REGISTER	24H	(1)
EOI REGISTER	22H	SPECIFIC EOI REGISTER
(1)	20H	INTERRUPT VECTOR REGISTER

1. Unsupported in this mode: values written may or may not be stored

Figure 2-54 80186 Interrupt Controller Registers

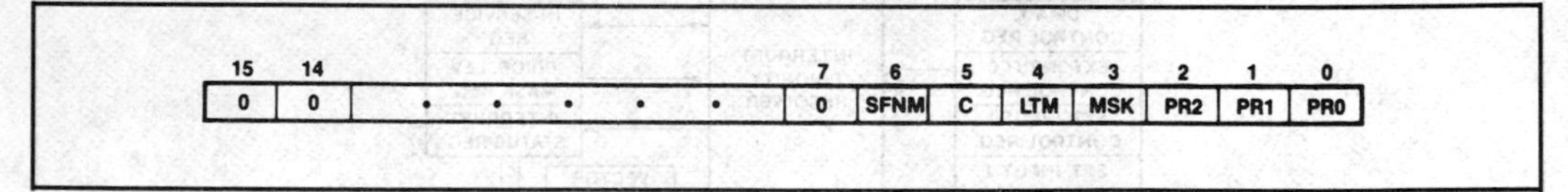

Figure 2-55 INT0/INT1 Control Register Formats

the 80186. Refer to Volume I of this User's Manual for detailed information regarding the operation of interrupts from these sources.

External Interrupt Sources

The 80186 provides five dedicated pins for external interrupt sources. One of these pins is dedicated to non-maskable interrupt, (NMI). NMI is typically used for

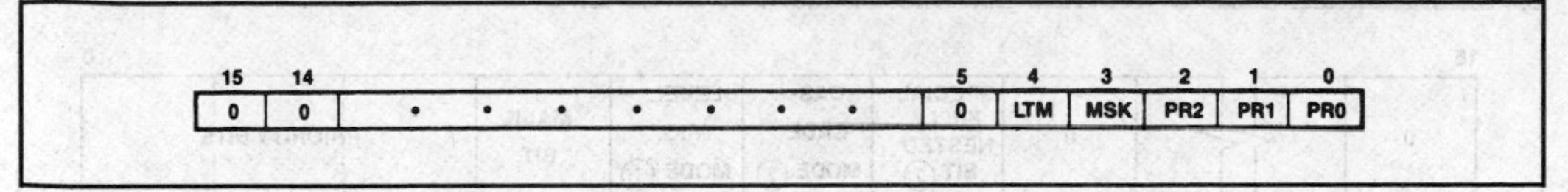

Figure 2-56 INT2/INT3 Control Register Format

power-fail interrupts, etc. The other four pins may function either as four interrupt input lines with internally generated interrupt vectors, as an interrupt line and an interrupt acknowledge line (called the "cascade mode") along with two other input lines with internally generated interrupt vectors, or as two interrupt input lines and two dedicated interrupt acknowledge output lines.

When programmed in master mode, the 80186 interrupt controller accepts external interrupt requests only. In this mode, the external pins associated with the interrupt controller may serve either as direct interrupt inputs, or as cascaded interrupt inputs from other interrupt controllers as a programmed option. These options are selected by programming the C and SFNM bits in the INT0 and INT1 control registers (see Figure 2-58).

When the interrupt lines are configured in cascade mode, the 80186 interrupt controller will not generate internal interrupt vectors for external sources. The interrupt

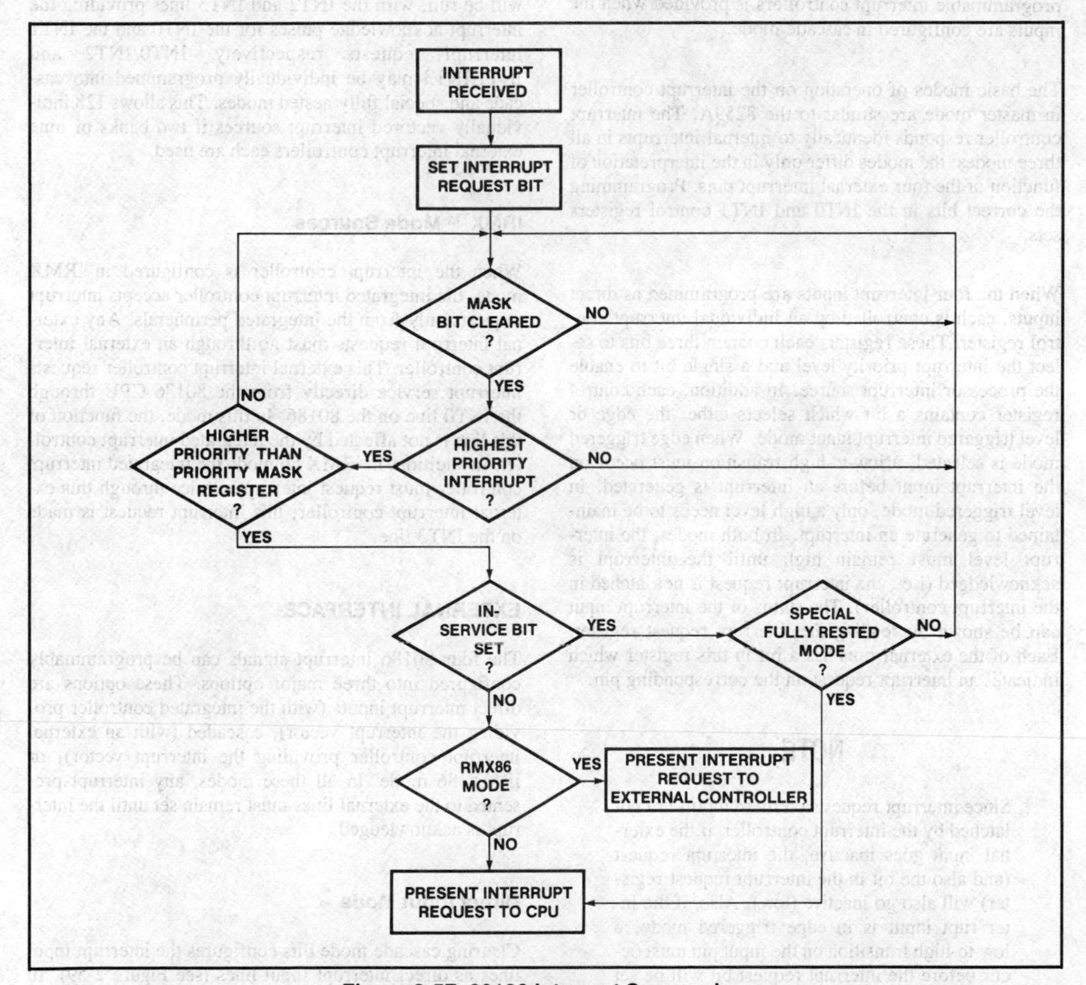

Figure 2-57 80186 Interrupt Sequencing

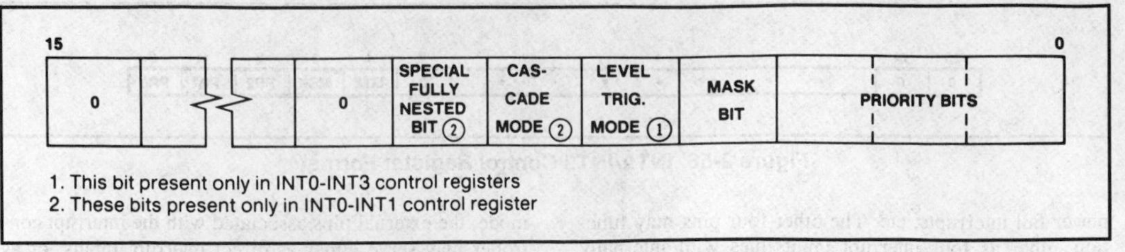

Figure 2-58 Interrupt Controller Control Register

controller will generate interrupt vectors for internal sources. External sources in the cascade mode use externally generated interrupt vectors. When an interrupt is acknowledged, the controller initiates two INTA* cycles and reads the vector into the 80186 on the second cycle. Therefore, the capability to interface to external 8259A programmable interrupt controllers is provided when the inputs are configured in cascade mode.

The basic modes of operation on the interrupt controller in master mode are similar to the 8259A. The interrupt controller responds identically to internal interrupts in all three modes: the modes differ only in the interpretation of function of the four external interrupt pins. Programming the correct bits in the INT0 and INT1 control registers sets.

When the four interrupt inputs are programmed as direct inputs, each is controlled by an individual interrupt control register. These registers each contain three bits to select the interrupt priority level and a single bit to enable the processor interrupt source. In addition, each control register contains a bit which selects either the edge or level triggered interrupt input mode. When edge triggered mode is selected, a low-to-high transition must occur on the interrupt input before an interrupt is generated. In level triggered mode, only a high level needs to be maintained to generate an interrupt. In both modes, the interrupt level must remain high until the interrupt is acknowledged (i.e., the interrupt request is not latched in the interrupt controller). The status of the interrupt input can be shown by reading the interrupt request register. Each of the external pins has a bit in this register which indicates an interrupt request on the corresponding pin.

NOTE

Since interrupt requests on these inputs are not latched by the interrupt controller, if the external input goes inactive, the interrupt request (and also the bit in the interrupt request register) will also go inactive (low). Also, if the inter rupt input is in edge triggered mode, a low-to-high transition on the input pin must occur before the interrupt request bit will be set in the interrupt request register.

If the C (Cascade) bits in the INT0 or INT1 control registers are set, the interrupt input is cascaded to an external interrupt controller. Whenever the interrupt presented to the INT0 or INT1 line is acknowledged in this mode, the integrated interrupt controller will not provide the interrupt type for the interrupt. Instead, two INTA bus cycles will be run, with the INT2 and INT3 lines providing the interrupt acknowledge pulses for the INT0 and the INT1 interrupt requests respectively. INT0/INT2 and INT1/INT3 may be individually programmed into cascade and special fully nested modes. This allows 128 individually vectored interrupt sources if two banks of nine external interrupt controllers each are used.

iRMX™ Mode Sources

When the interrupt controller is configured in iRMX mode, the integrated interrupt controller accepts interrupt requests only from the integrated peripherals. Any external interrupt requests must go through an external interrupt controller. This external interrupt controller requests interrupt service directly from the 80186 CPU through the INT0 line on the 80186. In this mode, the function of this line is not affected by the integrated interrupt controller. In addition, in iRMX 86 mode the integrated interrupt controller must request interrupt service through this external interrupt controller; this interrupt request is made on the INT3 line.

EXTERNAL INTERFACE

The four 80186 interrupt signals can be programmably configured into three major options. These options are direct interrupt inputs (with the integrated controller providing the interrupt vector), cascaded (with an external interrupt controller providing the interrupt vector), or iRMX 86 mode. In all these modes, any interrupt presented to the external lines must remain set until the interrupt is acknowledged.

Direct Input Mode

Clearing cascade mode bits configures the interrupt input lines as direct interrupt input lines (see Figure 2-59). In this mode an interrupt source (e.g., an 8272 floppy disk

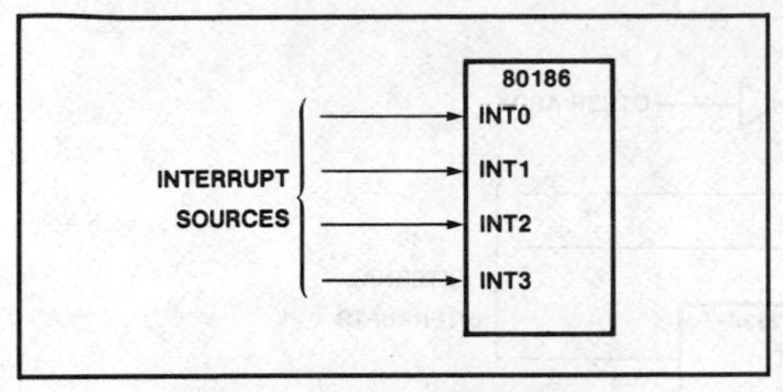

Figure 2-59 80186 Non-Cascaded Interrupt Connection

controller) may be directly connected to the interrupt input line. Whenever an interrupt is received on the input line, the integrated controller will do nothing unless the interrupt is enabled, and it is the highest priority pending interrupt. At this time, the interrupt controller will present the interrupt to the CPU and wait for an interrupt acknowledge. When the acknowledge occurs, it will present the interrupt vector address to the CPU. In this mode, the CPU will not run any interrupt acknowledge cycles. Also, in this mode, the SFNM bit in the interrupt control register is ignored.

Cascade Input Mode

Setting the cascade mode bit and clearing the SFNM bit configures the interrupt input lines in cascade mode. In this mode, the interrupt input line pairs with an interrupt acknowledge line. The INT2/INTA0* and INT3/INTA1* lines are dual purpose; they can function as direct input lines, or they can function as interrupt acknowledge outputs. INT2/INTA0* provides the interrupt acknowledge for an INT0 input, and INT3/INTA1* provides the interrupt acknowledge for an INT1 input (see Figure 2-60).

When programmed in this mode, in response to an interrupt request on the INT0 line, the 80186 will provide two interrupt acknowledge pulses. These pulses will be provided on the INT2/INTA0* line, and will also be reflected by interrupt acknowledge status being generated on the S0*-S2* status lines. On the second pulse, the interrupt type will be read in.

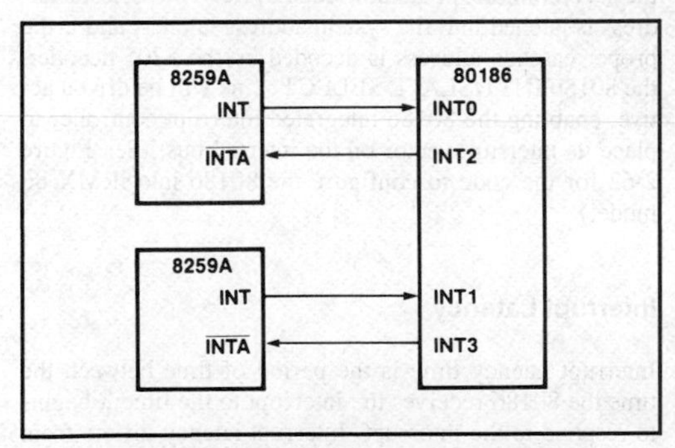

Figure 2-60 Cascade and Special Fully Nested Mode Interface

INT0/INT2/INTA0* and INT1/INT3/INTA1* may be individually programmed into interrupt request/acknowledge pairs, or programmed as direct inputs. Therefore, INT0/INT2/INTA0* may be programmed as an interrupt/acknowledge pair, while INT1 and INT3/INTA1* each provide separate internally vectored interrupt inputs.

When an interrupt is received on a cascaded interrupt, the priority mask bits and the in-service bits in the particular interrupt control register are set into the interrupt controller's mask and priority mask registers. This action prevents the controller from generating an 80186 CPU interrupt request from a lower priority interrupt.

As an example of the cascade mode, consider the 80186 interface to an 8259A (see Figure 2-61). The INT0 and the INT2 lines are used as direct interrupt input lines. (Figure 2-62 lists assembly code that may be used to initialize the 80186 interrupt controller.) This configuration provides ten external interrupt lines: two provided by the 80186 interrupt controller and eight from the 8259A. The 8259A, configured as the master controller, will only receive interrupt acknowledge pulses in response to an interrupt it has generated. It may be cascaded again with up to eight additional 8259A's (each configured as slaves).

NOTE

An interrupt ready signal must be returned to the 80186 to prevent the generation of undesired wait states in response to the interrupt acknowledge cycles.

Special Fully Nested Mode

When both the cascade mode bit and the SFNM bit are set, the interrupt input lines are configured in the Special Fully Nested Mode. In this mode the external interface is identical to the Cascade Mode. The Special Fully Nested Mode differs only in the conditions that allow an interrupt sent from the external interrupt controller to the integrated interrupt controller to interrupt the 80186 CPU.

When an interrupt is received from a Special Fully Nested Mode interrupt line, it will interrupt the 80186 CPU if it is the highest priority interrupt pending, regardless of the state of the in-service bit for the interrupt source in the interrupt controller. When an interrupt is acknowledged from a Special Fully Nested Mode interrupt line, in-serve bits in the particular interrupt control register will be set into the interrupt controller's in-service register. This will prevent the interrupt controller from generating an 80186

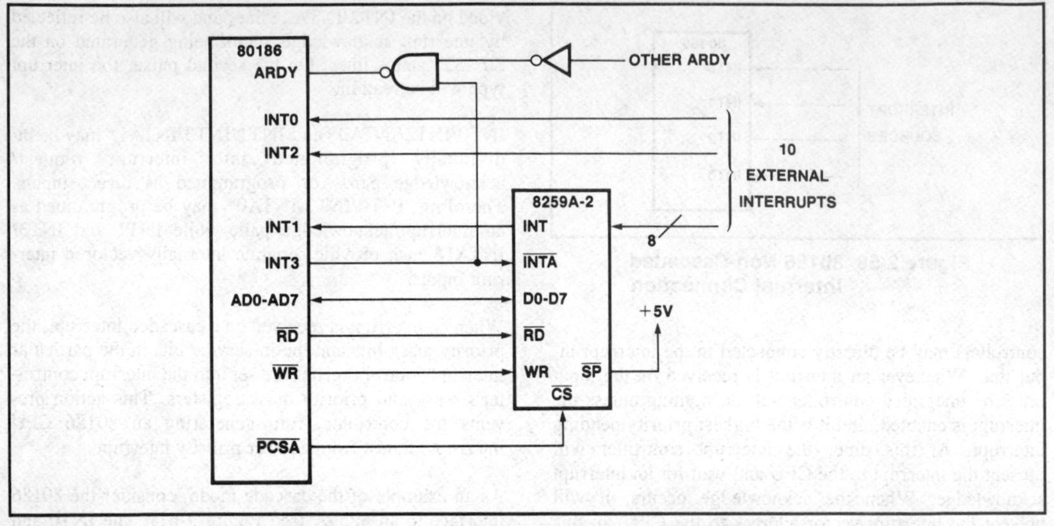

Figure 2-61 80186/8258A Interrupt Cascading

CPU interrupt request from a lower priority interrupt. Unlike cascade mode, however, the interrupt controller will not prevent additional interrupt requests generated by the same external interrupt controller from interrupting the 80186 CPU. If the external (cascaded) interrupt controller receives a higher priority interrupt request on one of its interrupt request lines and presents it to the integrated controller's interrupt request line, it may cause an interrupt to be generated to the 80186 CPU, regardless of the state of the in-service bit for the interrupt line.

If the SFNM mode bit is set, but the cascade mode bit is not set, the controller provides internal interrupt vectoring. The controller also ignores the state of the in-service bit in determining whether to present an interrupt request to the CPU. In other words, it uses the SFNM conditions of interrupt generation with an internally vectored interrupt response (i.e., if the interrupt pending is the highest priority type pending, it will cause a CPU interrupt regardless of the state of the in-service bit for the interrupt).

iRMX Mode

When the RMX bit in the peripheral relocation register is set, the interrupt controller is set into iRMX 86 mode. In this mode, all four interrupt controller input lines are used to perform the necessary handshaking with the external master interrupt controller (see Figure 2-63).

Because the integrated interrupt controller is a slave controller, it must be able to generate an interrupt input for an external interrupt controller. It also must be signaled when it has the highest priority pending interrupt to know when to place its interrupt vector on the bus. The INT3/ Slave Interrupt Output and INT1/Slave Select* lines, respectively supply these two signals. The external master interrupt controller must be able to interrupt the 80186 CPU, and needs to know when the interrupt request is acknowledged. The INT0 and INT2/INTA0* lines provide these functions.

In the iRMX86 mode (see Figure 2-64), the 80130 interrupt controller is the master interrupt controller of the system. The 80186 generates an interrupt request to the 80130 interrupt controller when one of the 80186 integrated peripherals has created an interrupt condition, and that condition is sufficient to generate an interrupt from the 80186 integrated interrupt controller. The 80130 decodes the interrupt acknowledge status directly from the 80186 status lines; thus, the INT2/INTA0* line of the 80186 need not be connected to the 81030. The circuit illustrated by Figure 2-64 uses this interrupt acknowledge signal to enable the cascade address decoder. The 80130 drives the cascade address on AD8-AD10 during T1 of the second interrupt acknowledge cycle. This cascade address is latched into the system address latches, and if the proper cascade address is decoded by the 8205 decoder, the 80186 INT1/SLAVE SELECT* line will be driven active, enabling the 80186 integrated interrupt controller to place its interrupt vector on the internal bus. (See Figure 2-62 for the code to configure the 80186 into iRMX 86 mode.)

Interrupt Latency

Interrupt latency time is the period of time between the time the 80186 receives the interrupt to the time it begins to respond to the interrupt. Interrupt latency differs from interrupt response time, which is the time from when the processor actually begins processing the interrupt to when

```
$mod186
name                example_80186_interrupt_code
;
;   This routine configures the 80186 interrupt controller to provide
;       two cascaded interrupt inputs (through an external 8259A
;       interrupt controller on pins INT0/INT2) and two direct
;       interrupt inputs (on pins INT1 and INT3). The default priority
;       levels are used. Because of this, the priority level programmed
;       into the control register is set the 111, the level all
;       interrupts are programmed to at reset.
;
int0_control        equu    0FF38H
int_mask            equ     0FF28H
;
code                segment                         public 'code'
                    assume  CS:code
set_int_            proc    near
                    push    DX
                    push    AX

                    mov     AX,0100111B             ; cascade mode
                                                    ; interrupt unmasked
                    mov     DX,int0_control
                    out     DX,AX

                    mov     AX,01001101B            ; now unmask the other external
                                                    ; interrupts
                    mov     DX,int_mask
                    out     DX,AX
                    pop     AX
                    pop     DX
                    ret
set_int_            endp
code                ends
                    end
$mod186
name                example_80186_interrupt_code
;
;   This routine configures the 80186 interrupt controller into iRMX 86
;       mode. This code does not initialize any of the 80186
;       integrated peripheral control registers, nor does it initialize
;       the external 8259A or 80130 interrupt controller.
;
relocation_reg      equ     0FFFEH
;
code                segment                         public 'code'
                    assume  CS:code
set_rmx_            proc    near
                    push    DX
                    push    AX

                    mov     DX,relocation_reg
                    in      AX,DX                   ; read old contents of register
                    or      AX,0100000000000000B    ; set the RMX mode bit
                    out     DX,AX
```

Figure 2-62 Example Interrupt Controller Interface Code

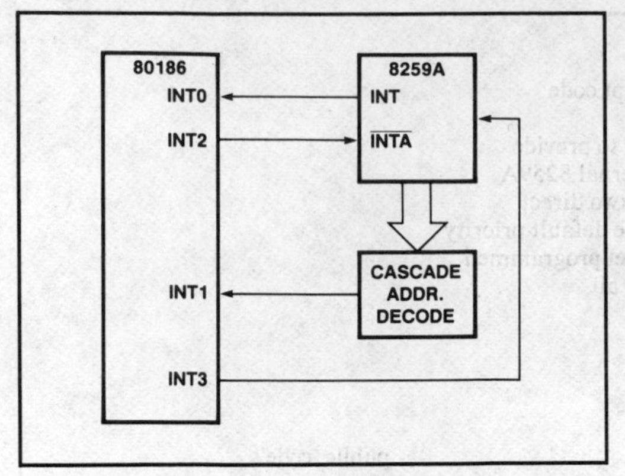

Figure 2-63 80186 iRMX™ 86 Mode Interface

it actually executes the first instruction of the interrupt service routine. The factors affecting interrupt latency are the instruction being executed and the state of the interrupt enable flip-flop. Interrupts will be acknowledged only if the interrupt enable flip-flop in the CPU is set. Therefore, interrupt latency will be very long indeed if interrupts are never enabled by the processor!

When interrupts are enabled in the CPU, the interrupt latency is a function of the instructions being executed. Only repeated instructions will be interrupted before being completed, and those only between their respective iterations. Therefore, the interrupt latency time could be as long as 69 CPU clocks—the time it takes the processor to execute an integer divide instruction (with a segment override prefix) the longest single instruction on the 80186.

Other factors can affect interrupt latency. An interrupt will not be accepted between the execution of a prefix (such as segment override prefixes and lock prefixes) and the instruction. In addition, an interrupt will not be accepted between an instruction which modifies any of the segment registers and the instruction immediately following the instruction. This interrupt denial is required to allow the stack to be changed. If the interrupt were accepted, the return address from the interrupt would be placed on a stack which was not valid (the Stack Segment register would have been modified but the Stack Pointer register would not have been). Finally, an interrupt will not be accepted between the execution of the WAIT instruction and the instruction immediately following it if the TEST* input is active. If the WAIT sees the TEST* input inactive, however, the interrupt will be accepted, and the WAIT will be re-executed after the interrupt

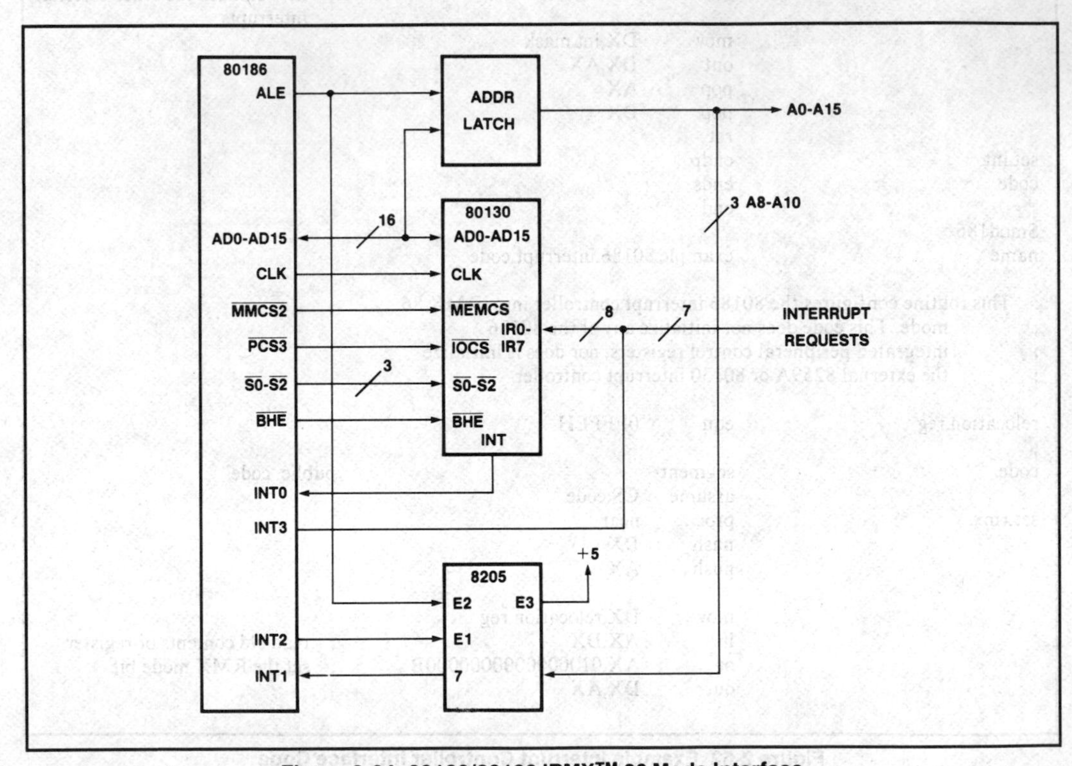

Figure 2-64 80186/80130 iRMX™ 86 Mode Interface

Table 2-25 80186 Interrupt Vector Types

Interrupt Name	Vector Type	Default Priority
timer 0	8	0a
timer 1	18	0b
timer 2	19	0c
DMA 0	10	2
DMA 1	11	3
INT 0	12	4
INT 1	13	5
INT 2	14	6
INT 3	15	7

return. Re-executing WAIT is required, since the WAIT is used to prevent execution by the 80186 of an 8087 instruction while the 8087 is busy.

INTERRUPT RESPONSE TIMING

The 80186 can respond to an interrupt in two different ways. The first will occur if the internal controller is providing the interrupt vector information with the controller in master mode. The second will occur if the CPU reads interrupt type information from an external interrupt controller or if the interrupt is in the iRMX 86 mode. In both of these instances the interrupt vector information driven by the 80186 integrated interrupt controller is not available outside the 80186 microprocessor.

In each interrupt mode the interrupt controller will automatically set the in-service bit when the integrated interrupt controller receives an interrupt response, and reset the interrupt request bit in the integrated controller. The priority mask bits are set by writing to the register only (except on RESET when they are set to 7). The priority mask bits will remain one value and prevent lower priority interrupts from occurring until the programmer resets or changes the register.

In addition, unless the interrupt control for the interrupt is set in Special Fully Nested Mode, the interrupt controller will prevent any interrupts from occurring from the same interrupt line until the in-service bit for that line has been cleared.

Internal Vectoring, Master Mode

In the master mode of operation, the interrupt types associated with all interrupt sources are fixed and unalterable (see Table 2-25). In response to an internal CPU interrupt acknowledge the interrupt controller will generate the vector address instead of the interrupt type. On the 80186, as with the 8086, the interrupt vector address is the interrupt type multiplied by 4. This speeds up the interrupt response time.

In master mode, the integrated interrupt controller is the master system interrupt controller. Therefore, no external interrupt controller needs to be informed when the integrated controller is providing an interrupt vector or when interrupt acknowledge is taking place. As a result, no interrupt acknowledge bus cycles will be generated. The first external indication that an interrupt has been acknowledged will be the processor reading the interrupt vector from the interrupt vector table to low memory.

Since the two interrupt acknowledge are not run, and the interrupt vector address does not need to be calculated, interrupt to an internally vectored interrupt is 42 clocks cycles, which is faster than the interrupt response when external vectoring is required, or the interrupt controller is run in the iRMX 86 mode.

If two interrupts of the same programmed priority occur, the default priority scheme (see Table 2-25) is used.

Internal Vectoring, iRMX™ 86 Mode

In the iRMX mode of operation the interrupt types associated with the various interrupt sources can be changed. The upper 5 most significant bits are taken from the interrupt vector register, and the lower 3 significant bits are taken from the priority level of the device causing the interrupt. Since the interrupt type, instead of the interrupt vector address, is given by the interrupt controller in this mode the interrupt vector address must be calculated by the CPU before servicing the interrupt.

In this mode of operation the integrated interrupt controller will present the interrupt type to the CPU in response to the two interrupt acknowledge bus cycles run by the processor. During the first interrupt acknowledge cycle, the external master interrupt controller determines which slave interrupt controller will be allowed to place its interrupt vector on the microprocessor bus. During the second interrupt acknowledge cycle, the processor reads the interrupt vector from its bus. Therefore, these two interrupt acknowledge cycles must be run since the integrated controller will present the interrupt type information only when the external interrupt controller signal the integrated controller that it has the highest pending interrupt request (see Figure 2-65). The 80186 samples the SLAVE SELECT* line during the falling edge of the clock at the beginning of T_3 of the second interrupt acknowledge cycle. This input must be stable 20ns before and 10ns after this edge.

These two interrupt acknowledge cycles will be run back to back, and will be LOCKED with the LOCK* (see paragraph 2.5.3) output active (meaning that DMA requests and HOLD requests will not be honored until both cycles have been run). Note that the two interrupt acknowledge cycles will always be separated by two idle T state, and that the wait states will be inserted into the interrupt acknowledge cycle if a ready is not returned by the

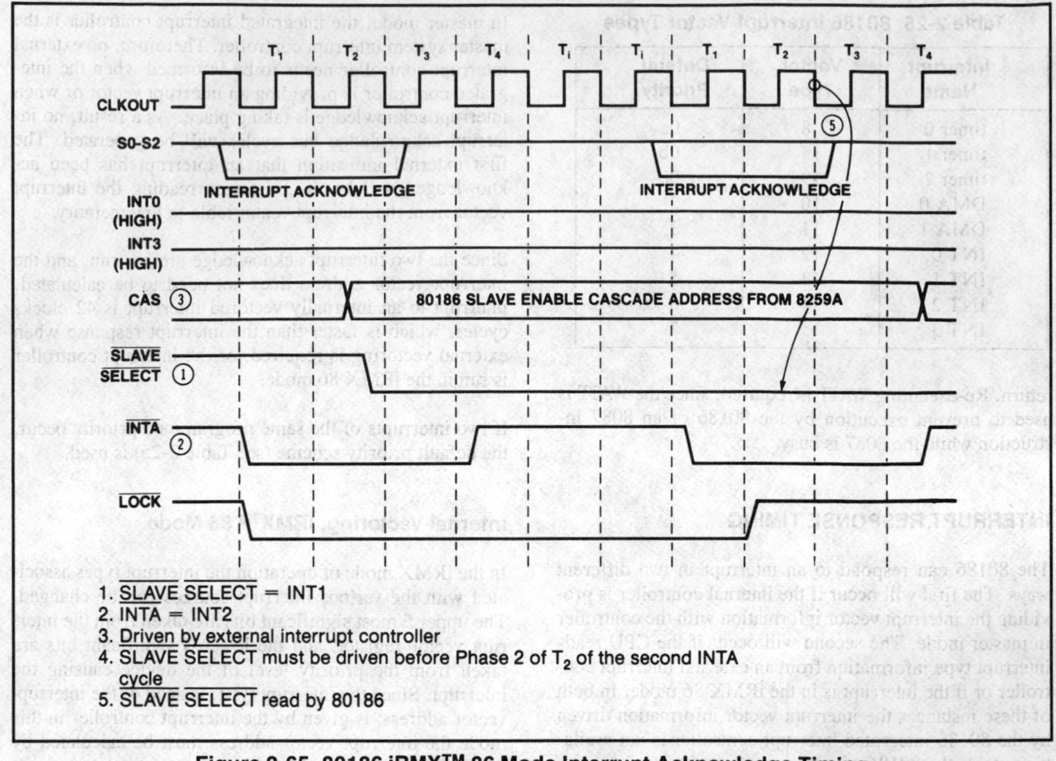

Figure 2-65 80186 iRMX™ 86 Mode Interrupt Acknowledge Timing

processor bus interface. The two idle T states are inserted to allow compatibility with the timing requirements of an external 8259A interrupt controller.

Because the interrupt acknowledge cycles must be run in iRMX 86 mode, even for internally generated vectors, and the integrated controller presents an interrupt type rather than a vector address, the interrupt response time here is the same as if an externally vectored interrupt was required, in other words 55 clocks.

External Vectoring

External interrupt vectoring occurs whenever the 80186 interrupt controller is placed in the cascade mode, special fully nested mode, or iRMX 86 mode (and the integrated controller is not enabled by the external master interrupt controller). In this mode, the 80186 generates two interrupt acknowledge cycles, reading the interrupt type off the lower 8 bits of the address/data bus on the second interrupt acknowledge cycle (see Figure 2-66). This interrupt response is exactly the same as the 8086, so that the 8259A interrupt controller can be used exactly as it would in an 8086 system. Notice that the two interrupt acknowledge cycles are LOCKED, and that two idle T-states are always inserted between the two interrupt acknowledge bus cycles, and that wait states will be inserted in the interrupt acknowledge cycle if a ready is not returned to the processor. Also notice that the 80186 provides two interrupt acknowledge signal, one for interrupts signaled by the INT0 line, and one for interrupts signaled by the INT1 line (on INT2/INTA0* and INT3/INTA1* lines, respectively). These two interrupt acknowledge signals are mutually exclusive. Interrupt acknowledge status will be driven on the status lines (S0*-S2*) when either INT2/INTA0* or INT3/INTA1* signal an interrupt acknowledge.

2.8.4 Chip Select/Wait State Generation Unit

The 80186/188 CPU contains an integrated chip select unit which provides programmable chip-select generation logic for both the memories and peripherals. This unit can also be programmed to provide WAIT state (READY) generation and can provide latched address bits A1 and A2. The chip select lines are active for all memory and I/O cycles in their programmed areas, whether the cycles are generated by the CPU of the integrated DMA unit.

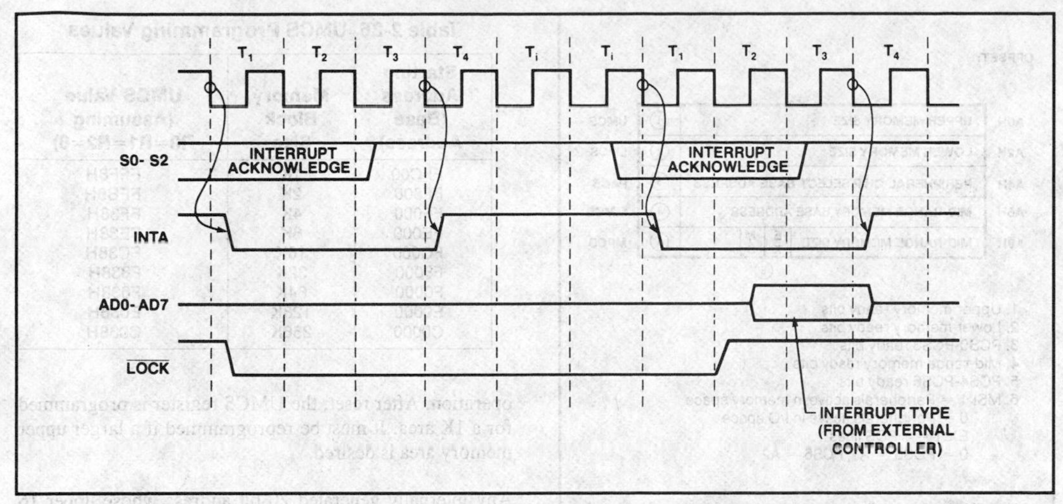

Figure 2-66 80186 Cascaded Interrupt Acknowledge Timing

MEMORY CHIP SELECTS

The 80186 provides six discrete chip select lines which connect to memory components in an iAPX186 system. These lines (see Figure 2-67) output signals for three memory areas: upper memory (UCS*), lower memory (LCS*), and mid-range memory (MCS0-3*).

The range for each chip select is user-programmable and can be set to 2K, 4K, 8K, 16K, 32K, 64K, 128K (plus 1K and 256K for upper and lower chip selects). In addition, the beginning or base address of the mid-range memory

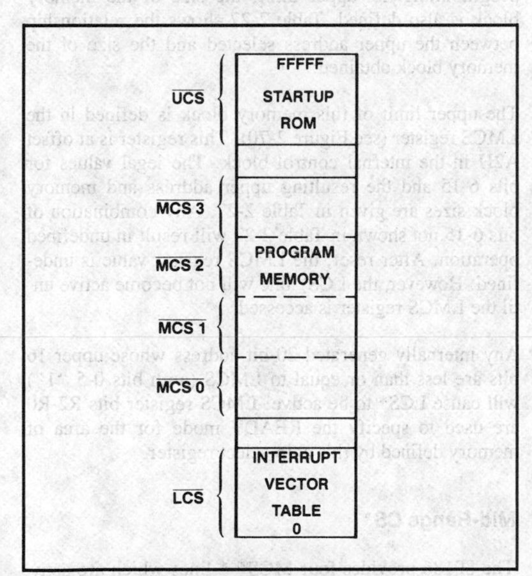

Figure 2-67 80186 Memory Areas and Chip Selects

chip select may also be selected. Only one chip select may be programmed to be active for any memory location at a time. All chip select sizes are in bytes, whereas iAPX 186 memory is arranged in words. For example, if 16 64K x 1 memories are used, the memory block size will be 128K, not 64K. The upper limit of UCS* and the lower limit of LCS* are fixed at FFFFFH and 0H in memory space, respectively. The other limit of these is set by the memory size programmed into the control register for the chip select line. Mid-range memory allows both the base address and the block size of the memory area to be programmed. The only limitation is that the base address must be programmed to be an integer multiple of the total block size. For example, if the block size was 128K bytes (four 32K byte blocks) the base address could be 0 or 20000H, but not 10000H.

Four registers in the peripheral control block (see Figure 2-68) control the memory chip selects. These selects include one each for UCS* and LCS*, the values of which determine the size of the memory blocks addressed by these two lines. The other two registers control the size and base address of the mid-range memory block.

On reset, only UCS* is active. Reset programs it to be active for the top 1K memory block, to insert three wait states to all memory fetches, and to factor external ready for every memory fetch. All other chip select registers assume indeterminate states after reset, but none of the other chip select lines will be active until all necessary registers for a chip select have been accessed (not necessarily written, a read to an uninitialized register will enable the chip select function controlled by that register).

Generally, the chip selects of the 80186 should not be programmed such that any two areas overlap. In addition, none of the programmed chip select areas should overlap

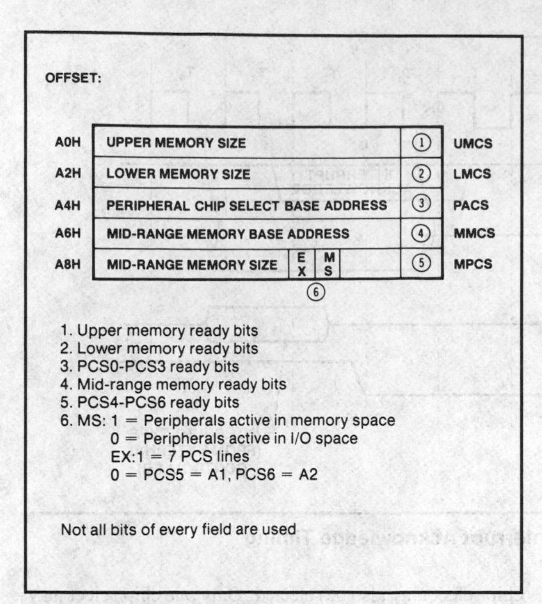

Figure 2-68 80186 Chip Select Control Registers

any of the locations of the integrated 256-byte control register block. If such an overlap condition exists, whenever two chip select lines are programmed to respond to the same area, both will become active during any access to that area. When programmed as such, the ready bits for both areas *must* be programmed to the same value. If not programmed in this manner, the processor response to an access in this area is indeterminate. If any of the chip select areas overlap the integrated 256-byte control register block, the timing on the chip select line is altered. As always, the CPU ignores any values returned on the external bus from this access.

Upper Memory CS*

The 80186 provides a chip select, called UCS*, for the top of memory. The top of memory is usually used as the system memory because, after reset, the 80186 begins executing at memory location FFFF0H.

The upper limit of memory defined by this chip select is always FFFFFH, while the lower limit is programmable. By programming the lower limit, the size of the select block is also defined. Table 2-26 shows the relationship between the base address selected and the size of the memory block obtained.

The lower limit of this memory block is defined in the UMCS register (see Figure 2-69). This register is at offset A0H in the internal control block. The legal values for bits 6-13 and the resulting starting address and memory block sizes are given in Table 2-26. Any combination of bits 6-13 not shown in Table 2-26 will result in undefined

Table 2-26 UMCS Programming Values

Starting Address (Base Address)	Memory Block Size	UMCS Value (Assuming R0=R1=R2=0)
FFC00	1K	FFF8H
FF800	2K	FFB8H
FF000	4K	FF38H
FE000	8K	FE38H
FC000	16K	FC38H
F8000	32K	F838H
F0000	64K	F038H
E0000	128K	E038H
C0000	256K	C038H

operation. After reset, the UMCS register is programmed for a 1K area. It must be reprogrammed if a larger upper memory area is desired.

Any internally generated 20-bit address whose upper 16 bits are greater than or equal to UMCS (with bits 0-5 "0") will cause UCS to be activated. UMCS bits R2-R0 are used to specify READY mode for the area of memory defined by this chip-select register.

Lower Memory CS*

The 80186 provides a chip select for low memory called LCS*. The bottom of memory contains the interrupt vector table, starting at location 00000H.

The lower limit of memory defined by this chip select is always 0h, while the upper limit is programmable. By programming the upper limit, the size of the memory block is also defined. Table 2-27 shows the relationship between the upper address selected and the size of the memory block obtained.

The upper limit of this memory block is defined in the LMCS register (see Figure 2-70). This register is at offset A2H in the internal control block. The legal values for bits 6-15 and the resulting upper address and memory block sizes are given in Table 2-27. Any combination of bits 6-15 not shown in Table 2-27 will result in undefined operation. After reset, the LMCS register value is undefined. However, the LCS* line will not become active until the LMCS register is accessed.

Any internally generated 20-bit address whose upper 16 bits are less than or equal to LMCS (with bits 0-5 "1") will cause LCS* to be active. LMCS register bits R2-R0 are used to specify the READY mode for the area of memory defined by this chip-select register.

Mid-Range CS*

The 80186 provides four MCS® * lines which are active within a user-locatable memory block. This block can be

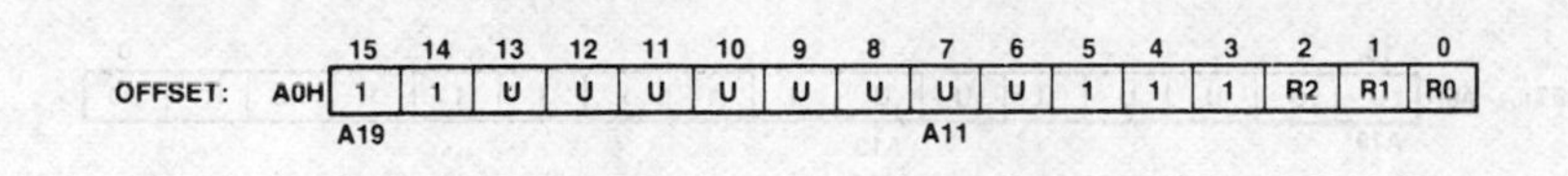

Figure 2-69 UMCS Register

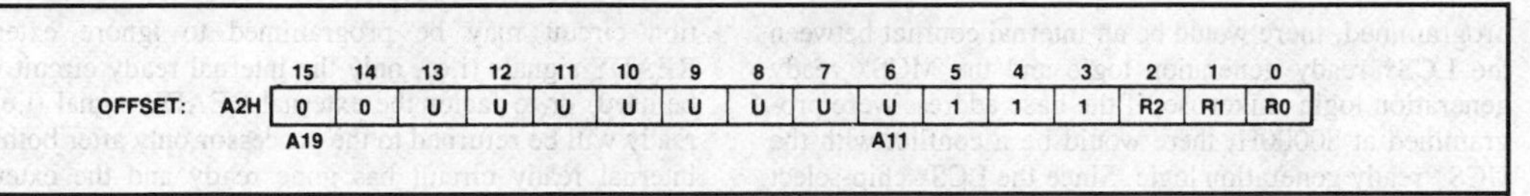

Figure 2-70 LMCS Register

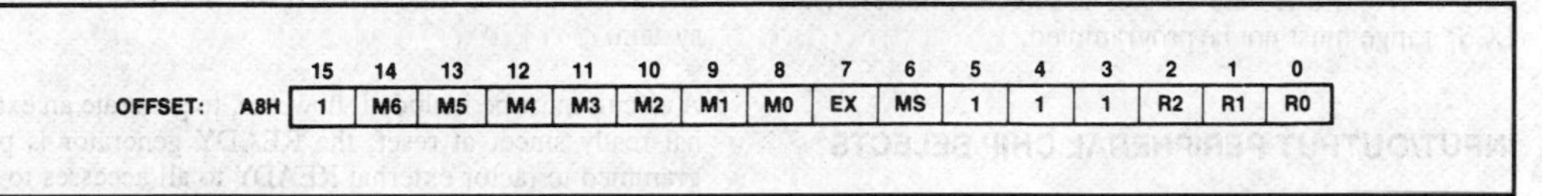

Figure 2-71 MPCS Register

located anywhere within the iAPX 186 1M byte memory address space exclusive of the areas defined by UCS* and LCS*. Both the base address and size of this memory block are programmable.

The size of the memory block defined by the mid-range select lines (refer to Table 2-28), is determined by bits 8-14 of the MPCS register (see Figure 2-71).

Table 2-27 LMCS Programming Values

Upper Address	Memory Block Size	LMCS Value (Assuming R0=R1=R2=0)
003FFH	1K	0038H
007FFH	2K	0078H
00FFFH	4K	00F8H
01FFFH	8K	01F8H
03FFFH	16K	03F8H
07FFFH	32K	07F8H
0FFFFH	64K	0FF8H
1FFFFH	128K	1FF8H
3FFFFH	256K	3FF8H

Table 2-28 MPCS Programming Values

Total Block Size	Individual Select Size	MPCS Bits 14–8
8K	2K	0000001B
16K	4K	0000010B
32K	8K	0000100B
64K	16K	0001000B
128K	32K	0010000B
256K	64K	0100000B
512K	128K	1000000B

NOTE

This register is located at A8H in the internal control block. Only one of bits 8-14 must be set at a time or unpredict able operation of the MCS* lines will otherwise occur.

Each of the four chip-select lines is active for one of the four equal contiguous divisions of the mid-range block. Therefore, if the total block size is 32K, each chip select is active for 8K of memory with MCS0* being active for the first range and MCS3* being active for the last range.

The base address of the mid-range memory block is defined 15-9 of the MMCS register (see Figure 2-72) located at offset A6H in the internal control block. These bits correspond to bits A19-A13 of the 20-bit memory address. Bits A12-A0 of the base address are always 0. The base address may be set at any integer multiple of the size of the total memory block selected. For example, if the mid-range block size is 32K (or the size of the block for which each MCS* line is active is 8K), the block could ocated at 10000H or 18000H, but not at 14000H, since the first few integer multiples of a 32K memory block are 0H, 8000H, 10000H, 18000H, etc. After reset, the contents of both of these registers is undefined. However, none of the MCS* lines will be active until both the MMCS and MPCS registers are accessed.

MMCS bits R2-R0 specify READY mode of operation for all mid-range chip selects. All devices in mid-range memory must use the same number of WAIT states.

The 512K block size for the mid-range memory chip selects is a special case. When using 512K, the base address would have to be at either locations 0H or 80000H. If it were to be programmed at 0H when the LCS* line was

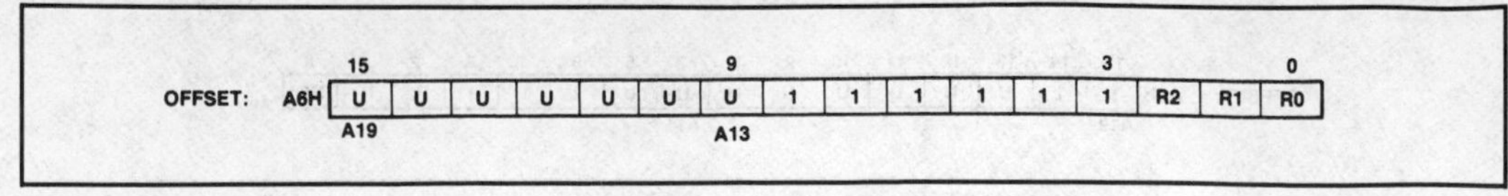

Figure 2-72 MMCS Register

programmed, there would be an internal conflict between the LCS* ready generation logic and the MCS* ready generation logic. Likewise, if the base address were programmed at 80000H, there would be a conflict with the UCS* ready generation logic. Since the LCS* chip-select line does not become active until programmed, while the UCS* line is active at reset the memory base can be set only at 0H. If this base address is selected, however, the LCS* range must not be programmed.

INPUT/OUTPUT PERIPHERAL CHIP SELECTS

Since 80186 memory interfacing is similar to the 8086, the two processors are also similar when interfacing to I/O peripherals. The 80186 contains integral interfacing logic that provides seven discrete chip select lines (PCS0-6*). These seven chip select lines are intended for connection to I/O peripherals in an iAPX86 system. The signals on these lines, PCS0-6*, go active for one of seven contiguous 128-byte areas in memory or I/O space above a programmed base address.

Two registers in the internal peripheral control block (see Figure 2-68) control the peripheral chip selects. These registers allow the base address of the peripherals to be set, and allow the peripherals to be mapped into memory or I/O space. Both registers must be accessed before any of the peripheral chip selects become active.

A bit in the memory/peripheral chip select (MPCS) register allows PCS5* and PCS6* to become latched when outputs A1 and A2 occur. When this option is selected, PCS5* and PCS6* indicate the state of A1 and A2 throughout the bus cycle. These outputs provide for external peripheral register selection in a system where the address is not latched. On reset, these lines are driven high and only indicate the state of A1 and A2 after both PACS and MPCS have been accessed (and are programmed to provide A1 and A2—refer to Volume I of this User's Guide).

READY/WAIT STATE GENERATION

The 80186/188 generates an internal READY signal for each of the memory or peripheral chip select (CS*) lines. From 0 to 3 WAIT states may be inserted by the internal ready generation unit for each access to any memory or I/O areas to which the chip select circuits respond. Table 2-29 shows how the ready control bits should be programmed to provide this. In addition, the READY generation circuit may be programmed to ignore external READY signals (i.e., only the internal ready circuit will be used) or to factor the external READY signal (i.e., a ready will be returned to the processor only after both the internal ready circuit has gone ready and the external ready has gone ready). Also, when a memory access occurs where there is no programmed chip select, ARDY and SRDY may be used to insert wait states as in the 8086 system.

A circuit must be included, however, to generate an external ready since, at reset, the READY generator is programmed to factor external READY to all accesses to the top 1K byte memory block. If a READY was not returned on one of the external ready lines (ARDY or SRDY) the processor would wait indefinitely to fetch the first instruction.

READY control consists of 3 bits for each CS* line or group of lines. This allows independent ready generation for each of upper memory, lower memory, mid-range memory, peripheral devices 0-3 and peripheral devices 4-6. The ready bits control an integrated WAIT State Generator that allows a programmable number of WAIT states to be automatically inserted whenever an access is made to the area of memory associated with a chip select area. Each set of ready bits includes a bit which determines whether the internal ready signals (ARDY or SRDY) are used or ignored (i.e., the bus cycle terminates even though a ready has not been returned on the external pins).

When the externally generated READY is used (R2 = 0), the internal ready generator operates in parallel with the external READY. For example, if the internal ready generator is set to insert two Wait states, but activity on the external READY lines inserts four WAIT states, only four WAIT states will be inserted by the processor. This is because the two WAIT states generated by the internal

Table 2-29 80186 WAIT State Programming

R2	R1	R0	Number of Wait States
0	0	0	0 + external ready
0	0	1	1 + external ready
0	1	0	2 + external ready
0	1	1	3 + external ready
1	0	0	0 (no external ready required)
1	0	1	1 (no external ready required)
1	1	0	2 (no external ready required)
1	1	1	3 (no external ready required)

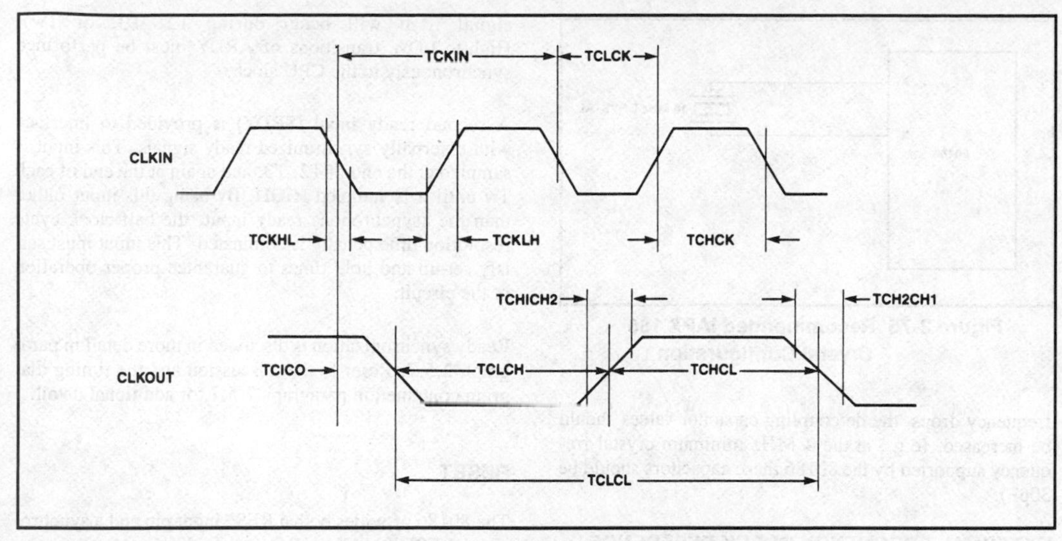

Figure 2-73 Clock In/Clock Out Timing

generator overlapped the first two WAIT states generated by the external READY signal. The external ARDY and SRDY lines are always ignored during cycles accessing internal peripherals.

2.8.5 Clock Generator/Reset/Ready

The 80186 clock generator produces the main clock signal (see Figure 2-73) for all 80186 integrated components, and all CPU synchronous devices in the 80186 system (see Figure 2-74). This clock generator includes a crystal oscillator, a divide-by-two counter, reset circuits, and ready generation logic.

The clock generator generates the 50% duty cycle processor clock for the iAPX 186 by dividing the output of a crystal oscillator by two to form the symmetrical clock signal. If an external oscillator is used, the state of the clock generator will change on the falling edge of the oscillator signal. The CLKOUT pin provides the processor clock signal for use outside the iAPX 186 and may be used to drive other system components. All timings are referenced to the output clock.

CRYSTAL CLOCK REFERENCE

The 80186 oscillator circuit is designed to be used with a parallel resonant fundamental mode crystal (see Figure 2-75) as the time base. The crystal frequency selected should be double the intended CPU clock frequency. Do not use an LC or RC circuit with this oscillator. If an external oscillator is used, connect it directly to input pin X1 in lieu of a crystal (input pin X2 may be left to float). The output of the oscillator is not directly available outside the 80186.

The crystal oscillator is a parallel resonant, Pierce oscillator designed to be used as shown in Figure 2-76 (the capacitor values shown are approximate). As the crystal

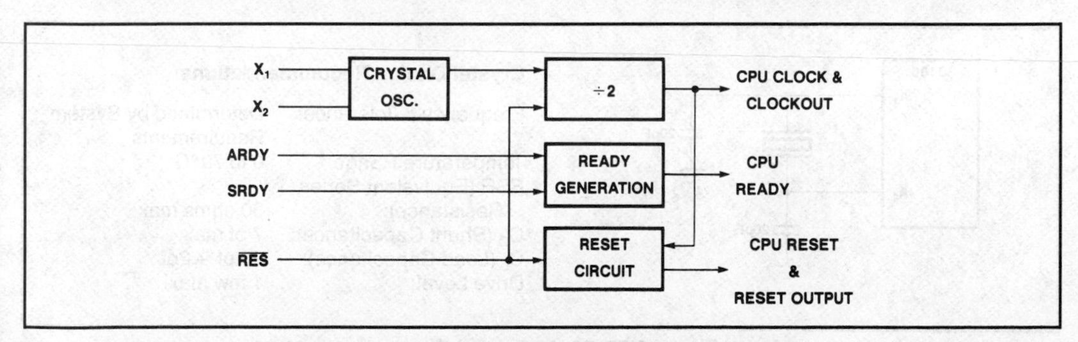

Figure 2-74 80186 Clock Generator Block Diagram

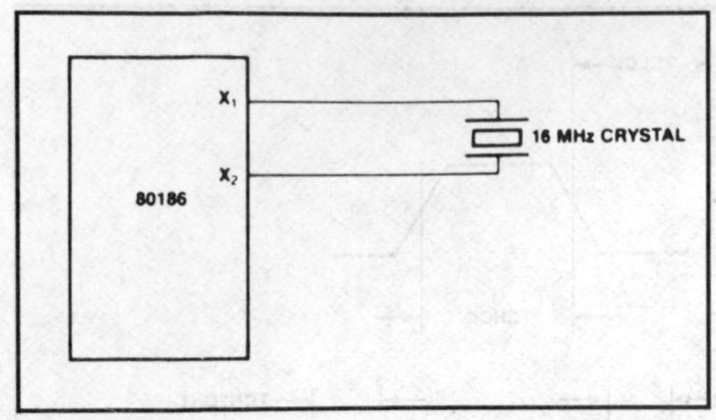

Figure 2-75 Recommended iAPX 186 Crystal Configuration

frequency drops, the de-coupling capacitor values should be increased, (e.g., at the 4 MHz minimum crystal frequency supported by the 80186 these capacitors should be 30pF).

EXTERNAL FREQUENCY CLOCK REFERENCE

The 80186 can use an external clock frequency standard (similar to the 8086 when used in conjunction with the 8284A). The external frequency input (EFI) signal connects directly to the X1 input of the oscillator (X2 is left open). This oscillator input drives an internal divide-by-two counter to generate the CPU clock. The external frequency reference can thus be virtually any duty cycle, as long as the minimum high and low times for the signal are consistent with those specified for the 80186 (refer to the Intel iAPX186 data sheet).

READY SYNCHRONIZATION

The 80186 provides both synchronous and asynchronous ready inputs. Asynchronous ready synchronization is accomplished by circuits which samples ARDY in the middle of T2, T3, and again in the middle of each Tw until ARDY is sampled HIGH. One-half CLKOUT cycle of resolution time is used and full synchronization is performed only on the rising edge of ARDY (i.e., the falling edge of ARDY must be synchronized to the CLKOUT signal if it will occur during T2, T3, or Tw). High-to-LOW transitions of ARDY must be performed synchronously to the CPU clock.

A second ready input (SRDY) is provided to interface with externally synchronized ready signals. This input is sampled at the end of T2, T3, and again at the end of each Tw until it is sampled HIGH. By using this input rather than the asynchronous ready input, the half-clock cycle resolution time penalty is eliminated. This input must satisfy set-up and hold times to guarantee proper operation of the circuit.

Ready synchronization is discussed in more detail in paragraph 2.5.7. Refer to that discussion and the timing diagram contained in paragraph 2.5.7 for additional detail.

RESET

The 80186 provides both a RES* input pin and a synchronized RESET output pin for use with other system components. The RES* input pin is provided with hysteresis to allow a power-on reset signal generated from an RC network. RES* is required to be low for greater than four clock cycles and must occur no sooner than 50 microseconds after power-up. RESET is guaranteed to remain active for at least five clocks, given a RES* input lasting at least six clocks. RESET may be delayed from RES* up to 2.5 clocks.

The reset input signal also resets the divide-by-two counter. A one clock cycle internal clear pulse is generated when the RES* input signal first goes active. This clear pulse goes active beginning on the first low-to-high transition of the X1 input after RES* goes active, and goes inactive on the next low-to-high transition of the X1 input. In order to insure that the clear pulse is generated on the next EFI cycle, the RES* input signal must satisfy a 25ns setup time to the high-to-low EFI input signal (see Figure 2-77). During this clear, clockout will be high. On the next high-to-low transition of X1, clockout will go low, and will change state on every subsequent high-to-low transition of EFI.

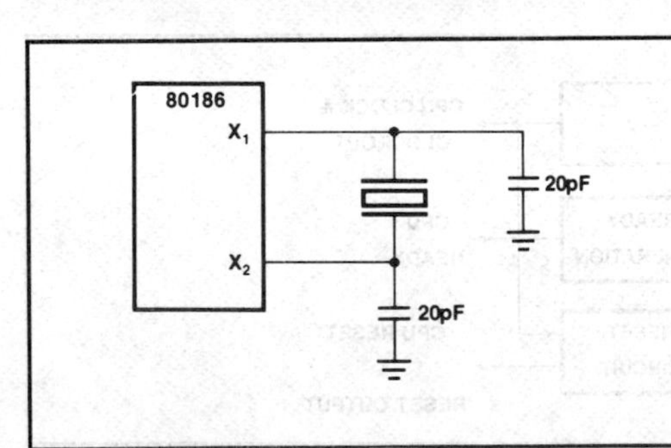

Crystal Choice Recommendations:

Frequency & Tolerance:	Determined by System Requirements
Temperature Range:	0 to 70°C
ESR (Equivalent Series Resistance):	30 ohms max
C_O (Shunt Capacitance):	7 pf max
C_L (Load Capacitance):	20 pf ±2pf
Drive Level:	1 mw max

Figure 2-76 80186 Crystal Connection

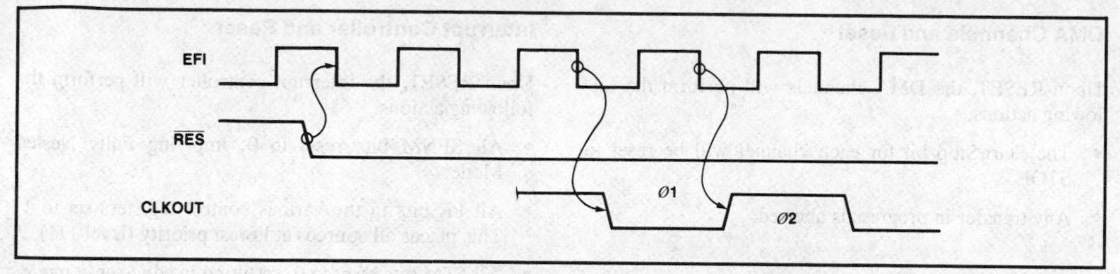

Figure 2-77 80186 Clock Generator Reset

The high-to-low transition of the clockout signal of the 80186 synchronizes the reset signal presented to the rest of the 80186, and also the signal present on the RESET output pin of the 80186. This signal remains active as long as the RES* input also remains active. After the RES* input goes inactive, the 80186 will begin to fetch its first instruction (at memory location FFFF0H) after six and a half CPU clock cycles (i.e., T1 of the first fetch will occur six and a half clock cycles later). To insure that the RESET output will go inactive on the next CPU clock cycle, the inactive going edge of the RES* input must satisfy certain hold and setup times to the low-to-high edge of the clockout signal of the 80186 (see Figure 2-78).

Initialization and Processor Reset

Processor initialization or startup is accomplished by driving the RES* input pin LOW. RES* forces the 80186 to terminate all execution and local bus activity. No instruction or bus activity will occur as long as RES* is active. After RES* becomes inactive and an internal processing interval elapses, the 80186 begins execution with the instruction at physical location FFFF0H. RES* also sets some registers to predefined values (see Table 2-30).

Local Bus Controller and Reset

Upon receipt of a RESET pulse from the RES* input, the local bus controller will perform the following actions:

- Drive DEN*, RD*, and WR* HIGH for one clock cycle, then float.

NOTE

RD* is also provided with an internal pull-up device to prevent the processor from inadvertently entering Queue Status mode during reset.

- Drive S0* – S2* to the passive state (all HIGH) and then float.
- Drive LOCK* HIGH and then float.

Table 2-30 80186 Initial Register State After RESET

Register	Value
Status Word	F002(H)
Instruction Pointer	0000(H)
Code Segment	FFFF(H)
Data Segment	0000(H)
Extra Segment	0000(H)
Stack Segment	0000(H)
Relocation Register	20FF(H)
UMCS	FFFB(H)

- Tristate AD0 – 15, A16 – 19, BHE*, DT/T*.
- Drive ALE LOW (ALE is never floated).
- Drive HLDA LOW.

Chip Select/Ready Logic and Reset

Upon reset, the Chip-Select/Ready logic will perform the following actions:

- All chip-select outputs will be driven high.
- Upon leaving RESET, the UCS* line will be programmed to provide chip select to a 1k block with the accompanying READY control bits set at 011 to allow the maximum number of internal wait states in conjunction with external Ready consideration (i.e., UMCS resets to FFFBH).
- No other chip select or READY control registers have any predefined values after RESET. They will not become active until the CPU accesses their control registers. Both the PACS and MPCS registers must be accessed before the PCS* lines will become active.

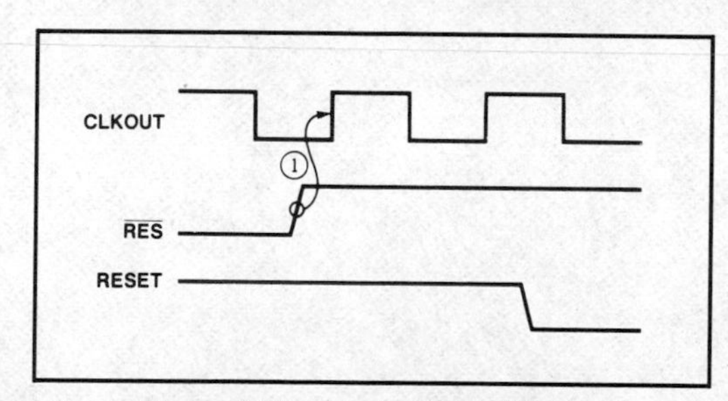

Figure 2-78 Coming Out of Reset

DMA Channels and Reset

Upon RESET, the DMA channels will perform the following actions:

- The Start/Stop bit for each channel will be reset to STOP.
- Any transfer in progress is aborted.

Timers and Reset

Upon RESET, the Timers will perform the following actions:

- All EN (Enable) bits are reset preventing timer counting.
- 11 SEL (Select) bits are reset to zero. This selects MAX COUNT register A, resulting in the Timer Out pins going HIGH upon RESET.

Interrupt Controller and Reset

Upon RESET, the interrupt controller will perform the following actions:

- All SFNM bits reset to 0, implying Fully Nested Mode.
- All PR bits in the various control registers set to 1. This places all sources at lowest priority (level 111).
- All LTM bits reset to 0, resulting in edge-sense mode.
- All Interrupt Service bits reset to 0.
- All Interrupt Request bits reset to 0.
- All MSK (Interrupt Mask) bits are set to 1 (mask).
- All C (Cascade) bits reset to 0 (non-cascade).
- All PRM (Priority Mask) bits set to 1, implying no levels masked.
- Initialized to non-iRMX 86 mode.

8087 Numeric Processor Extension

3

CHAPTER 3
8087 NUMERIC PROCESSOR EXTENSION

3.1 INTRODUCTION

This chapter provides specific hardware design information on the operation and functions of INTEL's 8087 Numeric Processor Extension (NPX). General information on the NPX coprocessor and its applications is presented, along with a component overview of the architectural and software considerations, and individual device pin functional signal definitions. Detailed descriptions of the NPX operating modes, general operation with the iAPX 86/186 host CPU's, and bus operation and timing are also presented. In addition, an explanation of the protocols supporting local bus transfers to the host CPU's, and a description of interrupt operation are also provided. For more specific information of any of the 8086 family support circuits, refer to the Microsystem Component Handbook (Order Number: 230843-002).

3.1.1 iAPX 86, 88, 186, 188 Base

The 8087 Numeric Processor Extension (NPX) is based on the iAPX86/ 88/186/188 family of microprocessors. These microprocessors are general purpose devices, designed for general data processing applications that require fast, efficient data movement and control instructions. The actual arithmetic performed on data values is fairly simple in data applications. The iAPX 86 family of microprocessors fills this need in an effective, low cost manner. However, some applications require more powerful arithmetic instructions and data types than provided by a general purpose data processor. Since the real world deals in fractional values and requires arithmetic operations like square root, sine and logarithms, integer data types and their operations may not meet the needed accuracy, speed, and ease of use requirements.

These advanced functions are not simple to implement and are not inexpensive. General data processors do not provide these features because of their cost to other less-complex applications that do not require such sophisticated features. Therefore a special, easy to use processor which has a high level of hardware and software support is required to implement these functions.

The 8087 (NPX) provides these features and supports the data types and operations needed. The NPX allows use of all of the current hardware and software support that is available for the iAPX 86/10, iAPX 88/10, iAPX 186/10 and iAPX 188/10 microprocessors. The following paragraphs present some typical applications for microprocessors using the NPX. In addition, a discussion of the use of the special hardware component, the 8087 NPX, and its software based 8087 emulator is also included. Both the component and the software emulator add extra data types and operations to the iAPX 86/10 family of microprocessors. The hardware component and the software emulator are completely compatible.

NUMERIC PROCESSOR EXTENSION APPLICATIONS

The versatility and performance of the 8087 NPX make it appropriate for a broad array of numerically-oriented applications. Generally, any application that exhibits the following characteristics will benefit by implementing numeric processing on the 8087:

1. Numeric data vary over a wide range of values or include non- integral values; non-integral values;
2. Algorithms produce very large or very small intermediate results;
3. Computations must be very precise, i.e., a large number of significant digits must be maintained;
4. Performance requirements exceed the capacity of traditional microprocessors;
5. Consistently safe, reliable results must be delivered using a programming staff that is not expert in numeric techniques.

The 8087 can also reduce software development costs and improve the performance of systems that do not use real numbers, but operate on multi-precision binary or decimal integer values.

A few examples, which show how the 8087 might be used in specific numerics applications, are described in the following list. In the past, these types of systems have typically been implemented with minicomputers. The advent of the 8087 brings the size and cost savings of microprocessor technology to these applications for the first time.

1. Business data processing — The NPX's ability to accept decimal operands and produce exact decimal results up to 18 digits greatly simplifies accounting programming. Financial calculations which use power functions can take advantage of the 8087's exponentiation and logarithmic instructions.
2. Process control — the 8087 solves dynamic range problems auto matically, and its extended precision allows control functions to be fine-tuned for more accurate and efficient performance. Control algorithms implemented with the NPX also contribute to improved reliability and safety, while the 8087's speed can be exploited in real-time operations.

3. Numeric control — The 8087 can move and position machine tool heads with extreme accuracy. Axis positioning also benefits from the hardware trigonometric support provided by the 8087.
4. Robotics — Coupling small size and modest power requirements with powerful computational abilities, the NPX is ideal for on-board six-axis positioning.
5. Navigation — Very small, light weight, and accurate inertial guidance systems can be implemented with the 8087. Its built-in trigonometric functions can speed and simplify the calculation of position from bearing data.
6. Graphics terminals — The 8087 can be used in graphics terminals to locally perform many functions which normally demand the attention of a main computer; these include rotation, scaling, and interpolation. By also including an 8089 Input/Output Processor to perform high speed data transfers, very powerful and highly self-sufficient terminals can be built from a relatively small number of 8086/88 family components.
7. Data acquistion — The 8087 can be used to scan, scale and reduce large quantities of data as it is collected. This lowers the storage requirements as well as the time required to process the data for analysis.

These examples are all oriented toward the "traditional" numerics applications. There are, however, many other types of systems that do not appear to the end user as "computational", but can employ the 8087 to advantage. The 8087 presents the imaginative system designer with an opportunity similar to that created by the introduction of the microprocessor itself. Many applications can be viewed as numerically-based if sufficient computational power is available to support this view. This is analogous to the thousands of successful products that have been built around"buried" microprocessors, even though the products themselves bear little resemblance to computers.

8087 EMULATOR VERSUS COMPONENT USE

Two basic implementations of the Numeric Data Processor Extension (NPX) are available. One is using the 8087 component and the other is with its software emulator (E8087). Whether the emulator or the component is used has no effect on programs at the source level. All instructions, data types and features are used in the same way at the source level.

All numeric instruction opcodes must be replaced with an interrupt instruction when the emulator is used. This replacement is performed by the LINK86 program. Interrupt vectors in the hosts interrupt vector table will point to numeric instruction emulation routines in the 8087 software emulator.

```
8087 BASED LINK/LOCATE COMMANDS

LINK86 :F1:PROG.OBJ, IO.LIB, 8087.LIB TO
       :F1:PROG.LNK
LOC86  :F1:PROG.LNK TO :F1:PROG

SOFTWARE EMULATOR BASED
LINK/LOCATE COMMANDS

LINK86 :F1:PROG.OBJ,  IO.LIB, E8087.LIB,
        E8087 TO :F1:PROG.LNK
LOC86  :F1:PROG.LNK TO :F1:PROG
```

Figure 3-1 Submit file Example

When the emulator is used, the linker changes all the 2-byte wait-escape, nop-escape, wait-segment override, or nop-segment override sequences generated by an assembler or compiler for the 8087 component with a 2-byte interrupt instruction. Any remaining bytes of the numeric instruction are left unchanged.

The host executes software interrupt instructions formed by the linker when it encounters numeric and emulated instructions. The interrupt vector table directs the host to the proper entry point in the 8087 emulator. The host then decodes any remaining part of the numeric instruction using the interrupt return address and CPU register set, performs the indicated operation, and returns to the next instruction following the emulated numeric instruction. One copy of the 8087 emulator can be shared by all programs in the host.

The decision to use the 8087 or the software emulator is made at link time, when all software modules are brought together. Depending on whether an 8087 or its software emulator is used, a different group of library modules are included for linking with the program.

If the 8087 component is used, the libraries do not add any code to the program, they just satisfy external references made by the assembler or compiler. Using the emulator will not increase the size of individual modules, however, other modules requiring about 16K bytes that implement the emulator will be automatically added.

Selecting between the emulator or the 8087 can be very easy. Different versions of submit files performing the link operation can be used to specify the different set of library modules needed. See Figure 3-1 for an example of the two different submit files for the same program using the NPX with an 8087 or the 8087 emulator.

3.1.2 8087 Mobility In Any iAPX 86, 88, 186 Design

The design of any maximum mode iAPX 86/1X, 88/1X, 186/1X or 188/1X system can be easily upgraded with an

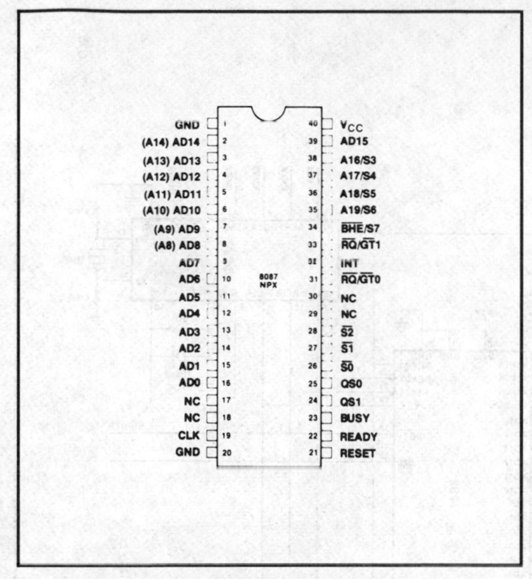

Figure 3-2 8087 Numeric Data Processor Pin Diagram

8087. Such a system would then be designated an 86/2X, 88/2X, 186/2X or 188/2X. See Figure 3-2 for 8087 DIP pin assignments, Figure 3-3 for local bus interconnections of a typical iAPX 86/20 (or iAPX 88/20) system, and Figure 3-4 for local bus interconnects of a typical iAPX 186/2X (or iAPX 188/2X) system. The 8087 shares the maximum mode host's multiplexed address/data bus, status signals, queue status signals, ready status signals, clock and reset signal. Two dedicated signals, BUSY and INT, are used to inform the host of the 8087's status. To ensure that the host will always see a "not busy" status if an 8087 is not installed, a 10K pull-down resistor should be installed on the BUSY signal line.

Adding the 8087 to an iAPX 86/88/186/188 design has a minor effect on the system timing. Installing the 8087 adds 15 pF to the total capacitive loading on the shared address/data and status signals. The 8087 can drive a total capacitive load of 100 pF above its own self load and sink 2.0 mA of DC current on its pins. This AC and DC drive is sufficient for an iAPX 86/21 system consisting of two sets of data transceivers, address latches, and bus controllers for two separate busses, an on-board bus and an off-board MULTIBUS using the 8289 bus arbiter. Refer to paragraphs 3.8 and 3.7 in this chapter for additional information on connecting the 8087 INT and RQ/GT pins.

A prewired 40-pin socket for the 8087 component can be left on a CPU board. Then, adding the 8087 to such a system would be as easy as plugging in the device. In this case, if a program attempts to execute any numeric instructions when the 8087 is not installed, the instruction will be treated as a NOP instruction by the host. Software can test for the existence of the 8087 by initializing it and then storing the control word. A program segment that illustrates this technique is shown in Figure 3-5.

When no CPU board space has been left for the 8087 component (or memory space for its software emulator), a maximum mode iAPX 86/1X system can be upgraded to a numeric processor using the iSBC 337 MULTIMODULE. The iSBC 337 MULTIMODULE is designed for just such a function. The iSBC 337 provides a socket for the host microprocessor and an 8087. A 40-pin plug is provided on the underside of the 337 to plug into the original host's socket (see Figure 3-6). Two other pins on the underside of the MULTIMODULE allow easy connection to the 8087 INT and RQ/GT1 pins.

3.2 COMPONENT OVERVIEW

The 8087 Numeric Data Processor Extension (NPX) provides arithmetic and logical instruction support for a variety of numeric data types in iAPX 86/20, 88/20 systems. The 8087 executes instructions as a coprocessor to a maximum mode 8086 or 8088 and effectively extends the register and instruction set of (including the addition of several new data types) an iAPX 86/10 or 88/10 based system. The 8087 is an extension to the iAPX 86/10 or 88/10 that provides enhanced register, data types, control, and instruction capabilities at the hardware level.

The 8087 extends the capability of an iAPX186/188 system when interfaced to an 80186 or 80188 through the Intel 82188 Integrated Bus Controller. When interfaced to the 80186/88, the combination of components form an iAPX186(188)/20 system.

3.2.1 Architecture Overview

The 8087 is internally comprised of two processing elements (see Figure 3-7), the Control Unit and the Numeric Execution Unit. The numeric execution unit executes all numeric instructions, while the control unit receives and decodes instructions, reads and writes memory operands and executes NPX control instructions. These two elements operate independently of one another; this allows the control unit to maintain synchronization with the CPU while the numeric execution unit is busy processing numeric instructions.

CONTROL UNIT

The control unit keeps the 8087 synchronized with its host CPU. 8087 instructions intermix with host CPU instructions in a single instruction stream (the CPU fetches all instructions from memory). By monitoring the status signals (S0*-S2*, S6) of the CPU, the NPX control unit de-

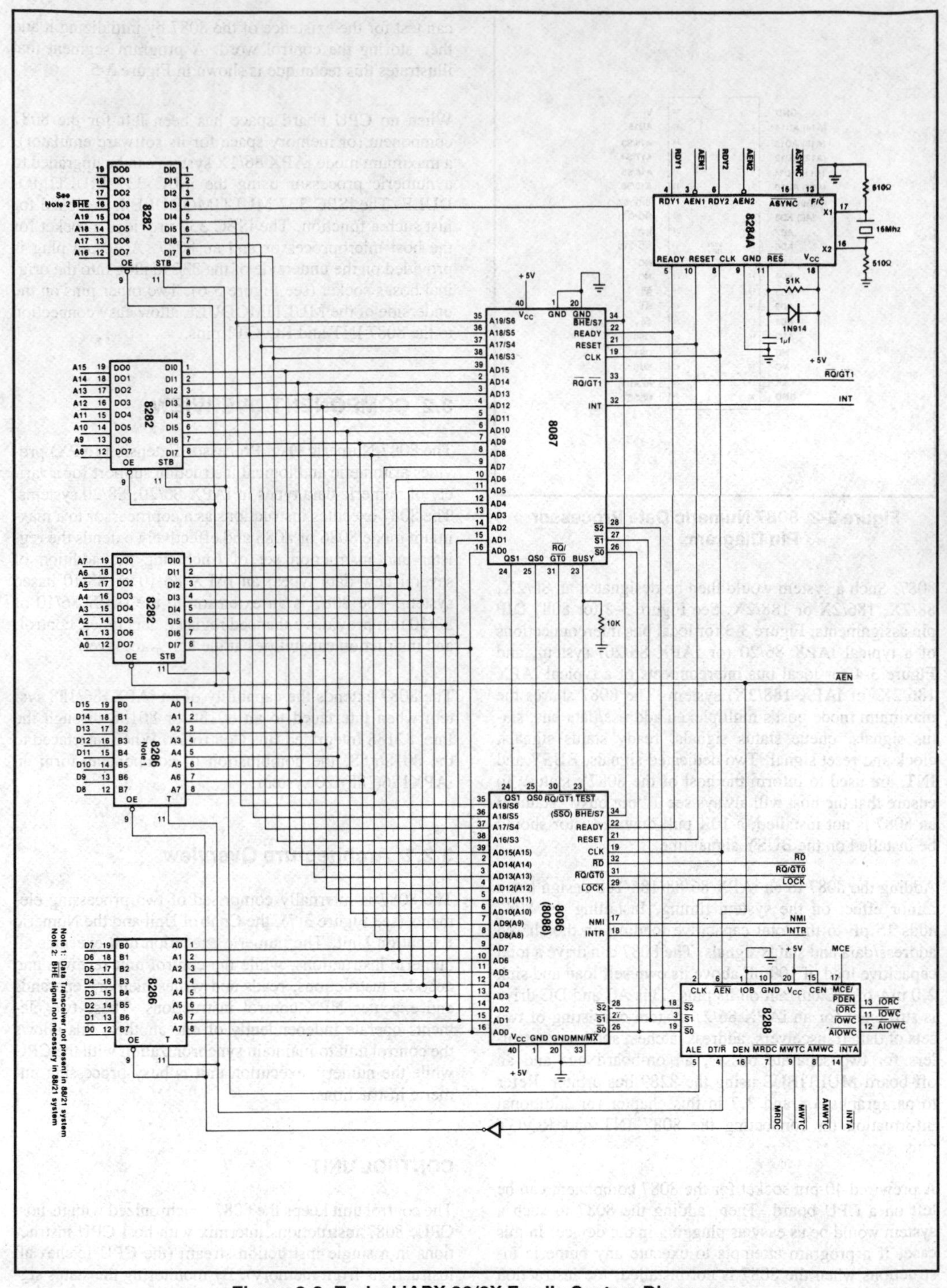

Figure 3-3 Typical iAPX 86/2X Family System Diagram

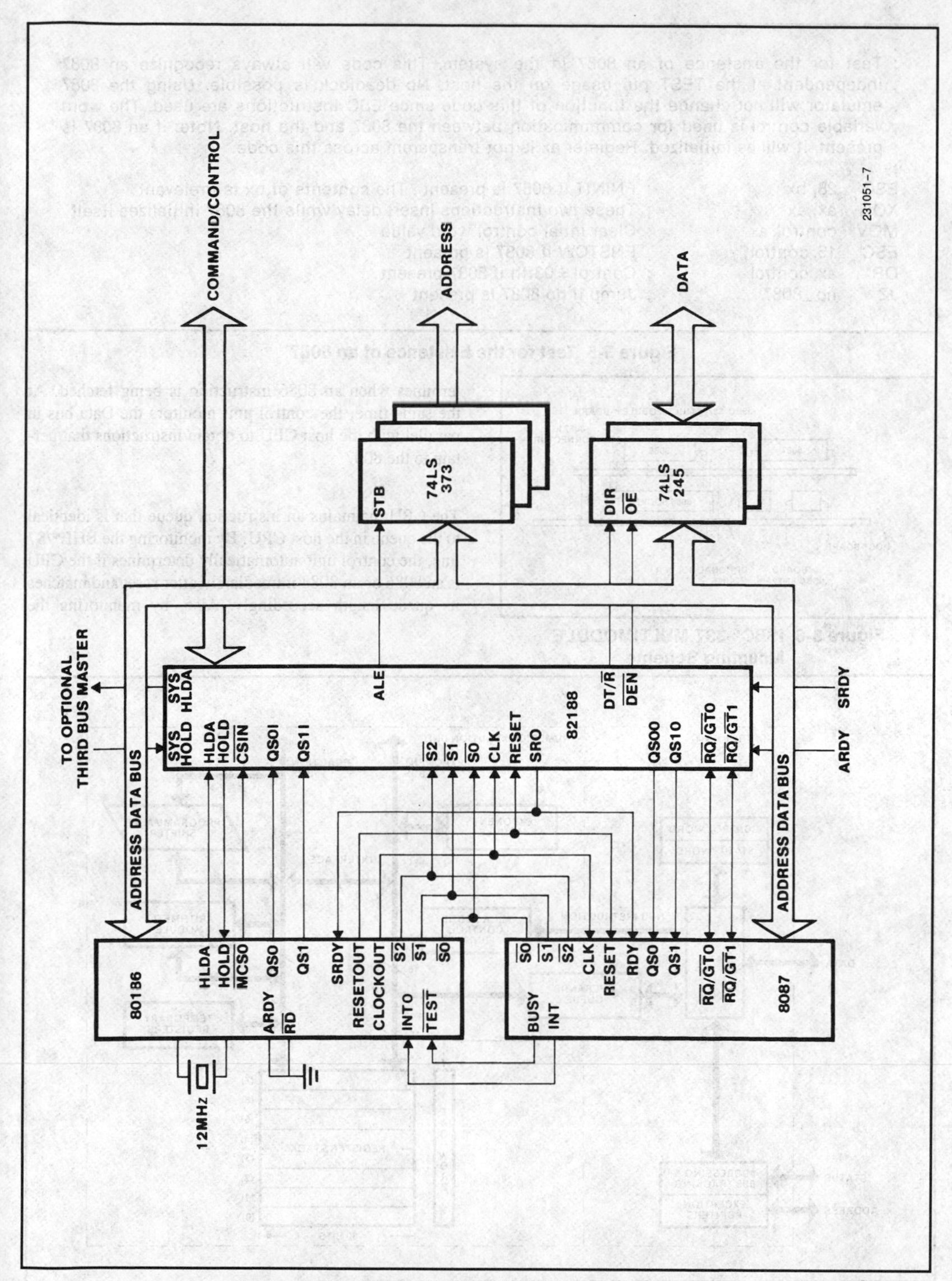

Figure 3-4 Typical iAPX 186/2X Family System Diagram

```
;
; Test for the existence of an 8087 in the system. This code will always recognize an 8087
; independent of the TEST pin usage on the host. No deadlock is possible. Using the 8087
; emulator will not change the function of this code since ESC instructions are used. The word
; variable control is used for communication between the 8087 and the host. Note: if an 8087 is
; present, it will be initialized. Register ax is not transparent across this code.
;
ESC   28, bx          ; FNINIT if 8087 is present . The contents of bx is irrelevant
XOR   ax, ax          ; These two instructions insert delay while the 8087 initializes itself
MOV   control, ax     ; Clear intial control word value
ESC   15, control     ; FNSTCW if 8087 is present
OR    ax, control     ; Control = 03ffh if 8087 present
JZ    no_8087         ; Jump if no 8087 is present
```

Figure 3-5 Test for the Existence of an 8087

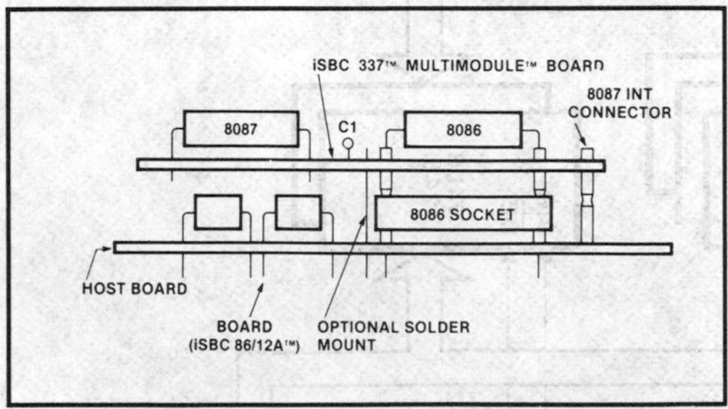

Figure 3-6 iSBC® 337 MULTIMODULE Mounting Scheme

termines when an 8086 instruction is being fetched. At the same time, the control unit monitors the Data bus in parallel with the host CPU to obtain instructions that pertain to the 8087.

The CPU maintains an instruction queue that is identical to the queue in the host CPU. By monitoring the BHE*/S7 line, the control unit automatically determines if the CPU is an 8086 or an 8088 immediately after reset and matches its queue length accordingly. Also, by monitoring the

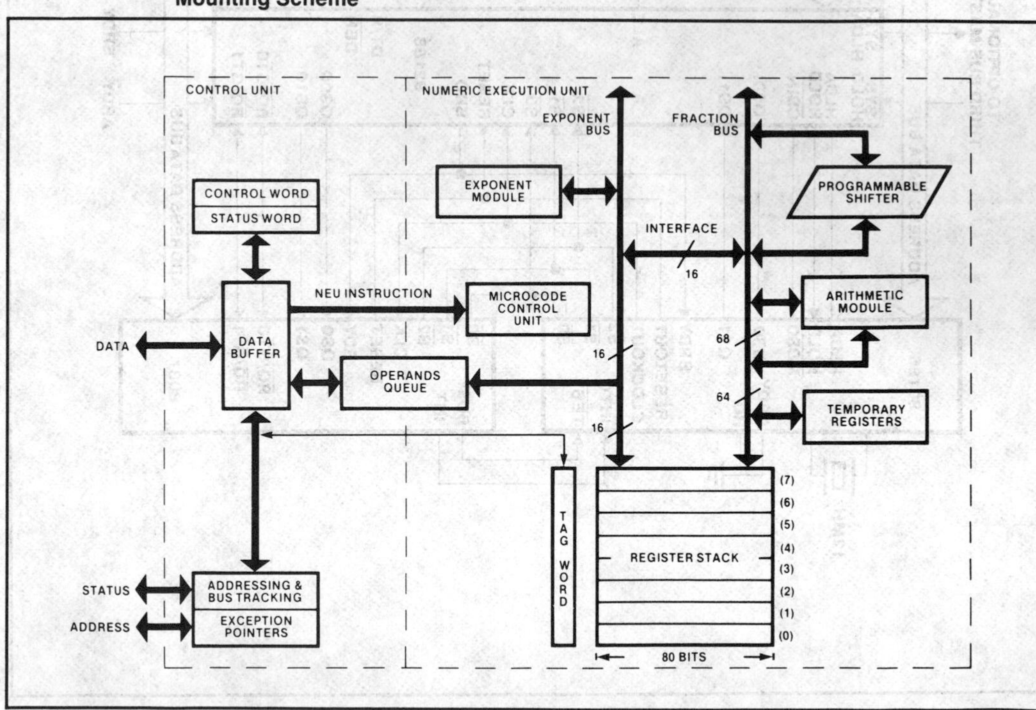

Figure 3-7 8087 Numeric Processor Extension Block Diagram

CPU's queue status lines (QS0, QS1), the control unit obtains and decodes instructions from the queue synchronously with the CPU.

A numeric instruction for the 8087 appears as an ESCAPE instruction to the 8086 or 8088 CPU; both the CPU and the NPX decode and execute the ESCAPE instruction together. Only the 8087, however, recognizes the numeric instructions. The start of a numeric operation begins when the CPU executes the ESCAPE instruction (the instruction may or may not identify a memory operand).

The CPU does, however, distinguish between ESCAPE instructions that refer to memory operands and those that do not. If the instruction refers to a memory operand, the CPU calculates the operand's address using any one of its available addressing modes, and then performs a "dummy read" of the word at that location. (Any location with the 1M byte address space is allowed.) This read cycle is normal except that the CPU ignores the data it receives. If the ESCAPE instruction does not contain a memory reference (e.g., an 8087 stack operation), the CPU simply proceeds to the next instruction.

An 8087 instruction can have one of three memory reference options:

1. not reference memory;
2. load an operand word from memory into the 8087;
3. store an operand word from the 8087 into memory.

If the 8087 requires no memory reference, the numeric execution unit simply executes its instruction. If the 8087 does require a memory reference, the control unit uses the "dummy read" cycle initiated by the host CPU to capture and save the address that the CPU places on the bus. If the instruction specifies a register load, the control unit also captures the data word when it becomes available on the local data bus. If the 8087 requires data longer than one word, the control unit immediately obtains the bus from the CPU using the request/grant protocol and reads in the rest of the information in consecutive bus cycles. In a store operation, the control unit captures and saves the store address as in a register load operation, and ignores the data word that follows in the "dummy read" cycle. When the 8087 is ready to perform the store, the control unit obtains the bus from the CPU and writes the operand starting at the specified address.

NUMERIC EXECUTION UNIT

The 8087 executes all instructions that involve the numeric register stack. These instructions include arithmetic, logical, transcendental, constant and data transfer operations. The numeric execution unit in the NPX has a 80-bit wide data path (64 fraction bits, 15 exponent bits and a sign bit) that allows internal operand transfers to be performed at very high speeds.

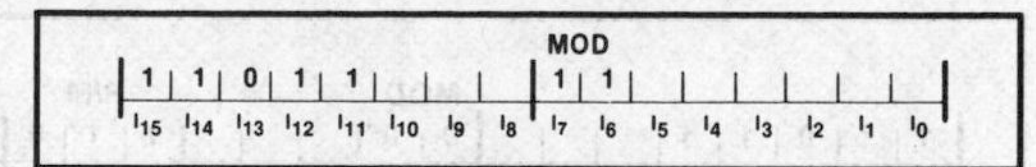

Figure 3-8 Non-Memory Reference Escape Instruction Form

When the numeric execution unit begins executing an instruction, it activates the 8087 BUSY signal. This signal can be used in conjunction with the CPU WAIT instruction to resynchronize both processors when the numeric execution unit has completed its current instruction.

3.2.2 Software Overview

The following paragraphs discuss the ESCAPE instruction format and discuss the use of the ESCAPE instruction with custom coprocessors. The constraints which the designer must exercise when designing this type of circuit are also discussed.

ESCAPE INSTRUCTION FORMAT

There are two basic forms of the ESCAPE instructions. These are the non-memory form (see Figure 3-8) and the memory reference form (see Figure 3-9). All ESCAPE instructions start with the high order 5-bits of the instruction being 11011. The non-memory form of the ESCAPE instruction initiates some activity in the coprocessor using the nine available bits of the ESCAPE instruction to indicate which action to perform.

The memory reference forms of the ESCAPE instruction allow the host to point out a memory operand to the coprocessor using any host memory addressing mode. Six bits are available in this form to identify what to do with the memory operand. Note that the coprocessor may not recognize all possible ESCAPE instructions. In this case the coprocessor ignores the unrecognized ESCAPE instructions.

In the memory reference forms of the ESCAPE instructions bits 7 and 6 of the byte follow the ESCAPE opcode. These two bits are the MOD field of the 8086 or 8088 effective address calculation. Together with R/M field bits 2 through 0, bits 7 and 6 determine the addressing mode and how many subsequent bytes still remain in the instruction.

The 8086 or 8088 ESCAPE instructions provide 64 memory reference opcodes and 512 non-memory reference opcodes. The 8087 only uses 57 of the memory reference opcodes and 406 of the non-memory reference opcodes. Refer to Figure 3-10 for a list of the ESCAPE instructions not used by the 8087.

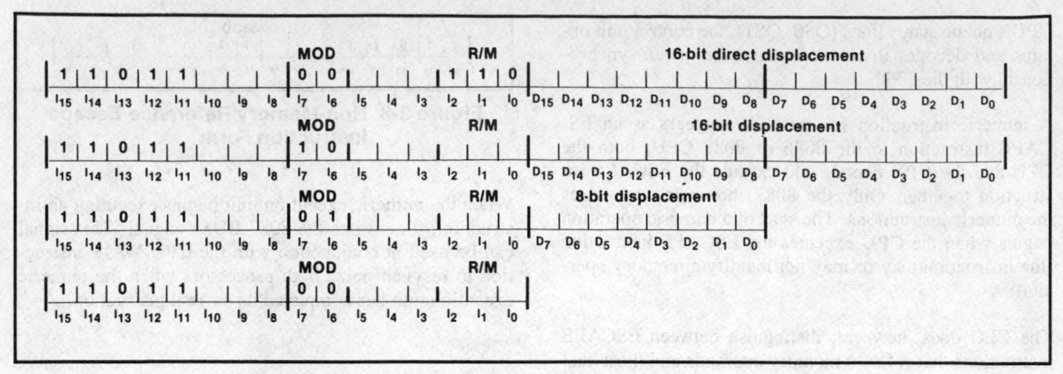

Figure 3-9 Memory Reference Escape Instruction Form

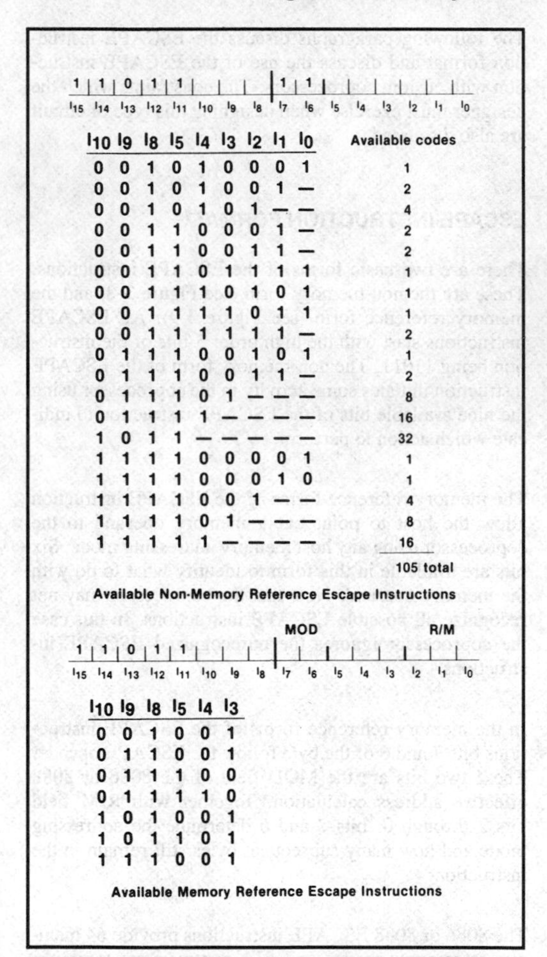

I_{10}	I_9	I_8	I_5	I_4	I_3	I_2	I_1	I_0	Available codes
0	0	1	0	1	0	0	0	1	1
0	0	1	0	1	0	0	1	—	2
0	0	1	0	1	0	1	—	—	4
0	0	1	1	0	0	0	1	—	2
0	0	1	1	0	0	1	1	—	2
0	0	1	1	0	1	1	1	1	1
0	0	1	1	1	0	1	0	1	1
0	0	1	1	1	1	0	1	1	1
0	0	1	1	1	1	1	1	—	2
0	1	1	1	0	0	1	0	1	1
0	1	1	1	0	0	1	1	—	2
0	1	1	1	0	1	—	—	—	8
0	1	1	1	1	—	—	—	—	16
1	0	1	1	—	—	—	—	—	32
1	1	1	1	0	0	0	0	1	1
1	1	1	1	0	0	0	1	0	1
1	1	1	1	0	0	1	—	—	4
1	1	1	1	0	1	—	—	—	8
1	1	1	1	1	—	—	—	—	16
									105 total

Available Non-Memory Reference Escape Instructions

I_{10}	I_9	I_8	I_5	I_4	I_3
0	0	1	0	0	1
0	1	1	0	0	1
0	1	1	1	0	0
0	1	1	1	1	0
1	0	1	0	0	1
1	0	1	1	0	1
1	1	1	0	0	1

Available Memory Reference Escape Instructions

Figure 3-10 ESCAPE Instructions Not Used By the 8087 NPX

USING THE 8087 WITH CUSTOM COPROCESSORS

When designing numeric processors with custom coprocessors, the designer should limit the use of ESCAPE instructions to only those not used by the 8087. Using only the unused ESCAPE instructions with custom coprocessors is necessary to prevent ambiguity as to whether any specific ESCAPE instruction is intended for the numeric or custom coprocessor. Note that using any escape instruction for a custom coprocessor may conflict with opcodes chosen for future Intel coprocessors.

Using the 8087 together with other custom coprocessors under the following constraints:

1. All 8087 errors are masked. The 8087 will update its opcode and instruction address registers for the unused opcodes. Unused memory references instructions will also update the operand address value. These changes make software-defined error handling in the 8087 impossible.

2. If the coprocessors provide a BUSY signal, they must be ORed together for connection to the host TEST pin. When the host executes a WAIT instruction, it does not know which coproces sor will be effected by the following ESCAPE instruction. Typically, all coprocessors must be idle before executing the ESCAPE instruction.

3.3 DEVICE PIN ASSIGNMENTS

A complete functional description of each device pin signal is provided Table 3-1. This table correlates the description to the pin number and associated signal symbol.

3.4 OPERATING MODES

The following paragraphs describe the operation of the 8087 NPX in conjunction with the 8086(88) and

Table 3-1 8087 Device Pin Descriptions

Symbol	Type	Name and Function
AD15–AD0	I/O	**Address Data:** These lines constitute the time multiplexed memory address (T_1) and data (T_2, T_3, T_W, T_4) bus. A0 is analogous to $\overline{BHE}$ for the lower byte of the data bus, pins D7–D0. It is LOW during T_1 when a byte is to be transferred on the lower portion of the bus in memory operations. Eight-bit oriented devices tied to the lower half of the bus would normally use A0 to condition chip select functions. These lines are active HIGH. They are input/output lines for 8087 driven bus cycles and are inputs which the 8087 monitors when the 8086/8088 is in control of the bus. A15-A8 do not require an address latch in an iAPX 88/20. The 8087 will supply an address for the T_1-T_4 period.
A19/S6, A18/S5, A17/S4, A16/S3	I/O	**Address Memory:** During T_1 these are the four most significant address lines for memory operations. During memory operations, status information is available on these lines during T_2, T_3, T_W, and T_4. For 8087 controlled bus cycles, S6, S4, and S3 are reserved and currently one (HIGH), while S5 is always LOW. These lines are inputs which the 8087 monitors when the 8086/8088 is in control of the bus.
BHE/S7	I/O	**Bus High Enable:** During T_1 the bus high enable signal ($\overline{BHE}$) should be used to enable data onto the most significant half of the data bus, pins D15–D8. Eight-bit oriented devices tied to the upper half of the bus would normally use $\overline{BHE}$ to condition chip select functions. $\overline{BHE}$ is LOW during T_1 for read and write cycles when a byte is to be transferred on the high portion of the bus. The S7 status information is available during T_2, T_3, T_W, and T_4. The signal is active LOW. S7 is an input which the 8087 monitors during 8086/8088 controlled bus cycles.
$\overline{S2}$, $\overline{S1}$, $\overline{S0}$	I/O	**Status:** For 8087 driven bus cycles, these status lines are encoded as follows: $\overline{S2}$ — $\overline{S1}$ — $\overline{S0}$ 0 (LOW) X X Unused 1 (HIGH) 0 0 Unused 1 0 1 Read Memory 1 1 0 Write Memory 1 1 1 Passive Status is driven active during T_4, remains valid during T_1 and T_2, and is returned to the passive state (1, 1, 1) during T_3 or during T_W when READY is HIGH. This status is used by the 8288 Bus Controller to generate all memory access control signals. Any change in $\overline{S2}$, $\overline{S1}$, or $\overline{S0}$ during T_4 is used to indicate the beginning of a bus cycle, and the return to the passive state in T_3 or T_W is used to indicate the end of a bus cycle. These signals are monitored by the 8087 when the 8086/8088 is in control of the bus.
$\overline{RQ}/\overline{GT0}$	I/O	**Request/Grant:** This request/grant pin is used by the NPX to gain control of the local bus from the CPU for operand transfers or on behalf of another bus master. It must be connected to one of the two processor request/grant pins. The request grant sequence on this pin is as follows: 1. A pulse one clock wide is passed to the CPU to indicate a local bus request by either the 8087 or the master connected to the 8087 $\overline{RQ}/\overline{GT1}$ pin. 2. The 8087 waits for the grant pulse and when it is received will either initiate bus transfer activity in the clock cycle following the grant or pass the grant out on the $\overline{RQ}/\overline{GT1}$ pin in this clock if the initial request was for another bus master. 3. The 8087 will generate a release pulse to the CPU one clock cycle after the completion of the last 8087 bus cycle or on receipt of the release pulse from the bus master on $\overline{RQ}/\overline{GT1}$.

Table 3-1 8087 Device Pin Descriptions (continued)

Symbol	Type	Name and Function
$\overline{RQ}/\overline{GT}1$	I/O	**Request/Grant:** This request/grant pin is used by another local bus master to force the 8087 to request the local bus. If the 8087 is not in control of the bus when the request is made the request/grant sequence is passed through the 8087 on the $\overline{RQ}/\overline{GT0}$ pin one cycle later. Subsequent grant and release pulses are also passed through the 8087 with a two and one clock delay, respectively, for resynchronization. $\overline{RQ}/\overline{GT}1$ has has an internal pullup resistor, and so may be left unconnected. If the 8087 has control of the bus the request/grant sequence is as follows: 1. A pulse 1 CLK wide from another local bus master indicates a local bus request to the 8087 (pulse 1). 2. During the 8087's next T_4 or T_1 a pulse 1 CLK wide from the 8087 to the requesting master (pulse 2) indicates that the 8087 has allowed the local bus to float and that it will enter the "RQ/GT acknowledge" state at the next CLK. The 8087's control unit is disconnected logically from the local bus during "RQ/GT acknowledge." 3. A pulse 1 CLK wide from the requesting master indicates to the 8087 (pulse 3) that the "RQ/GT" request is about to end and that the 8087 can reclaim the local bus at the next CLK. Each master-master exchange of the local bus is a sequence of 3 pulses. There must be one dead CLK cycle after each bus exchange. Pulses are active LOW.
QS1, QS0	I	**QS1, QS0:** QS1 and QS0 provide the 8087 with status to allow tracking of the CPU instruction queue. **QS1 QS0** 0 (LOW) 0 No Operation 0 1 First Byte of Op Code from Queue 1 (HIGH) 0 Empty the Queue 1 1 Subsequent Byte from Queue
INT	O	**Interrupt:** This line is used to indicate that an unmasked exception has occurred during numeric instruction execution when 8087 interrupts are enabled. This signal is typically routed to an 8259A. INT is active HIGH.
BUSY	O	**Busy:** This signal indicates that the 8087 NEU is executing a numeric instruction. It is connected to the CPU's $\overline{TEST}$ pin to provide synchronization. In the case of an unmasked exception BUSY remains active until the exception is cleared. BUSY is active HIGH.
READY	I	**Ready:** READY is the acknowledgment from the addressed memory device that it will complete the data transfer. The RDY signal from memory is synchronized by the 8284A Clock Generator to form READY. This signal is active HIGH.
RESET	I	**Reset:** RESET causes the processor to immediately terminate its present activity. The signal must be active HIGH for at least four clock cycles. RESET is internally synchronized.
CLK	I	**Clock:** The clock provides the basic timing for the processor and bus controller. It is asymmetric with a 33% duty cycle to provide optimized internal timing.
V_{CC}		**Power:** V_{CC} is the +5V power supply pin.
GND		**Ground:** GND are the ground pins.

NOTE:
For the pin descriptions of the 8086 and 8088 CPU's reference those respective data sheets (iAPX 86/10, iAPX 88/10).

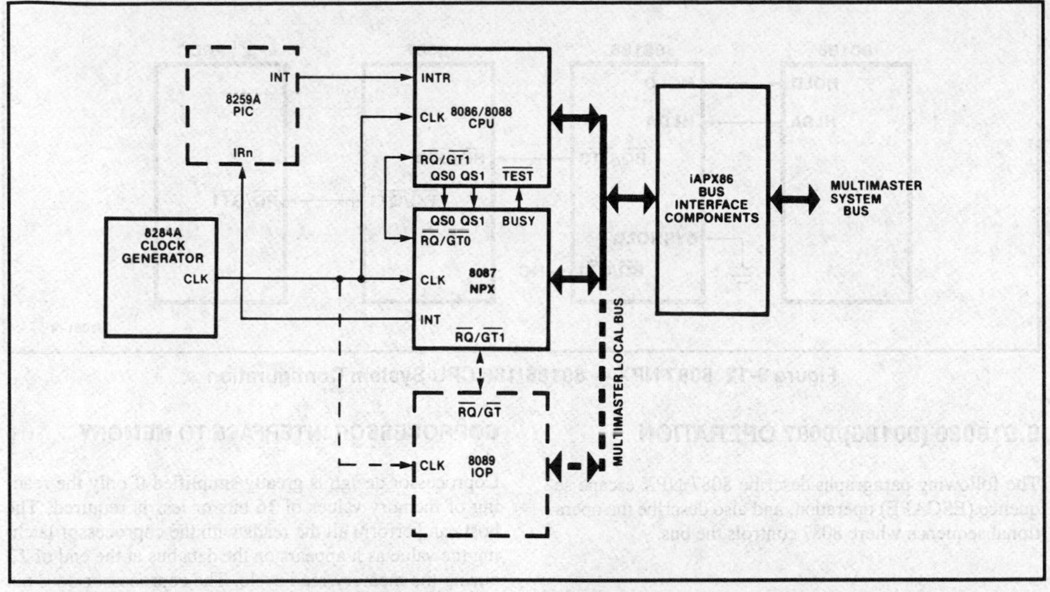

Figure 3-11 8087 NPX — 8086/88 CPU System Configuration

80186(188) microprocessors, describe the overall electrical interface and present design considerations relate to the interface.

3.4.1 8087/8086(88) Interface

When installed as a coprocessor to the 8086 or 8088, the 8087 connects in parallel with the CPU (see Figure 3-11). The CPU's status lines (S0*-S2*) and queue status lines (QS0-QS1) allow the 8087 to monitor and decode instructions in synchronization with the CPU and without any CPU overhead. The 8087 can process instructions in parallel with and independent of the host CPU. For resynchronization, the NPX's BUSY signal informs the CPU that the 8087 is executing an instruction; the CPU WAIT instruction tests this signal to insure that the NPX is ready to execute subsequent instructions. The NPX can interrupt the CPU when it detects an error or exception. The 8087's interrupt request line is typically routed to the CPU through an 8259A Programmable Interrupt Controller (see Figure 3-2) for 8087 pinout information.

The 8087 uses one of the request/grant lines of the iAPX86 architecture to obtain control of the local bus for data transfers. The other request/grant line is available for general system use (e.g., an I/O processor in LOCAL mode). A bus master can also be connected to the 8087's RQ*/GT1* line. In this configuration the 8087 will pass the request/grant handshake signals between the CPU and the attached master when the 8087 is in control. Therefore, two additional masters can be configured in an iAPX 86/20 or an 88/20 system; one master will share the 8086 bus with the 8087 on a first come first serve basis, and the second master will be guaranteed to be higher in priority than the 8087. All processors use the same clock generator and system bus interface components (bus controller, latches, transceivers, and bus arbiter — see Figure 3-11).

3.4.2 8087/80186(88) Interface

The iAPX186/20 system operates similar to the iAPX86/20. The 80186 contains integral controller devices (refer to Chapter 2) which result in device pin assignments and functions that differ from the 8086. To simplify iAPX186/20 system configuration, Intel provides the 82188 Integrated Bus Controller which enables communication between the 80186 and the 8087 without the need for random logic (see Figure 3-12).

The 82188 converts the ARDY and SRDY signals of the 80186 to RDY for the 8087; similarly, it converts HOLD/HLDA of the 80186 to RQ/GT0,1 for the 8087. When configured into an iAPX186/20 system, RD* (pin 62) of the 80186 must be grounded. The 82188 supplies the command and control signals to the devices on the system bus that the 80186 would otherwise provide. These signals include:

ARDY	DEN*
SRDY	DT/R*
RD*	CS OUT*
WR*	HOLD
ALE	HLDA

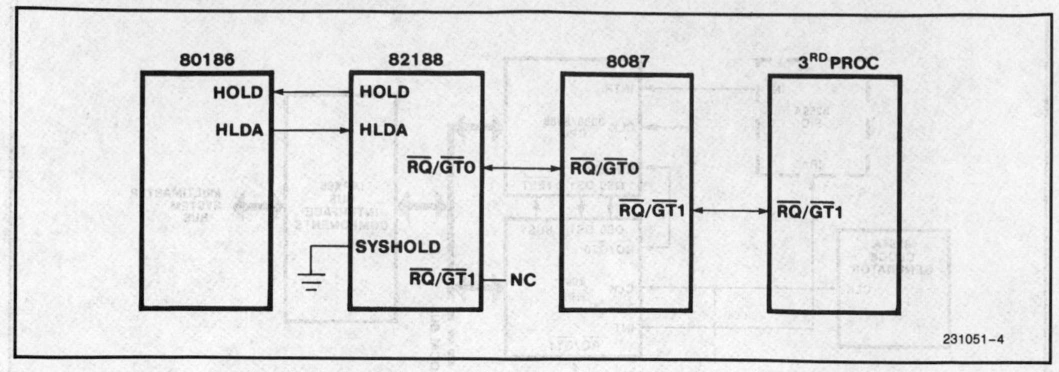

Figure 3-12 8087 NPX — 80186/188 CPU System Configuration

3.5 8086 (80186)/8087 OPERATION

The following paragraphs describe 8087 NPX escape sequence (ESCAPE) operation, and also describe the operational sequence where 8087 controls the bus.

3.5.1 Decoding Escape Instructions

The coprocessor must examine all instructions executed by the host to recognize ESCAPE instructions. When the host fetches an instruction byte from its internal queue, the coprocessor must also fetch an instruction byte.

The queue status state, fetch opcode byte, identifies when an opcode byte is being examined by the host. At the same time, the coprocessor will check if the byte fetched from its internal instruction queue is an ESCAPE opcode. If the instruction is not an ESCAPE, the coprocessor will ignore it. The queue status signals for fetch subsequent byte and flush queue let the coprocessor track the host's queue without knowledge of the length and function of host instructions and addressing modes.

HOST ESCAPE INSTRUCTION PROCESSING

The host performs one of two possible actions when an ESCAPE instruction occurs. The host may either do nothing or read a word value beginning at that address. The host ignores the value of the word read. ESCAPE instructions change none of the registers in the host except for advancing IP. Therefore, the ESCAPE instruction will effectively be a NOP to the host if no coprocessor exists, or the coprocessor ignores the ESCAPE instruction. Except for calculating a memory address and reading a word of memory, the host makes no other assumptions regarding coprocessor activity.

Memory reference ESCAPE instructions have two purposes. One identifies a memory operand and the other is, for certain instructions, to transfer a word from memory to the coprocessor.

COPROCESSOR INTERFACE TO MEMORY

Coprocessor design is greatly simplified if only the reading of memory values of 16 bits or less is required. The host can perform all the reads with the coprocessor latching the value as it appears on the data bus at the end of T3 during the memory read cycle. The coprocessor does not need to become a local bus master to read or write additional information.

If the coprocessor must write information to memory, or deal with data values longer than one word, it must save the memory address and be able to become the local bus master. The read operation performed by the host when executing the ESCAPE instruction places the 20-bit physical address of the operand on the address/data pins during T1 of the memory cycle. The coprocessor can latch the address at this time. If the coprocessor instruction also requires reading a value, it will appear on the data bus during T3 of the memory read. All other memory bytes are addressed relative to this starting physical address.

Whether the coprocessor becomes a bus master or not, it must be able to identify the memory read performed by the host in the course of executing an ESCAPE instruction if it has memory reference instruction forms. Identifying the memory read requires the following conditions be met:

1. A MOD value of 00, 01 or 10 in the second byte of the ESCAPE instruction executed by the host.
2. This action must be the first data read memory cycle performed by the host after it encountered the ESCAPE instruction (i.e., S2-S0 will be 101 and S6 will be 0).

The coprocessor must continue to track the host's instruction queue while it calculates the memory address and reads the memory value. This simply requires following the fetch subsequent byte status commands that occur on the queue status pins.

The coprocessor must be aware of the host bus characteristics that determine how the host will read the word operand of a memory reference ESCAPE instruction. An 8088 host will always perform two byte reads at sequential addresses, but an 8086 can perform either single word read or two byte reads to sequential addresses. The 8086 places no restrictions on the alignment of word operands in memory. It will automatically perform two byte operations for word operands at an odd address. These two operations are necessary because the two bytes of operand exist in two different memory words. The coprocessor must be able to accept the two possible methods of reading a word value on the 8086.

The coprocessor determines whether an 8086 performs one or two memory cycles as a part of the current ESCAPE instruction execution. During T1 of the first memory read by the host, the AD0 pin tells the coprocessor if this is the only read to be performed as part of the ESCAPE instruction. If AD0 is a 1 during T1 of the memory cycle, the 8086 immediately follows this memory read cycle with another one at the next byte address.

3.5.2 Concurrent Execution of Host and Coprocessor

After the coprocessor has started its operation, the host may continue on with the program, executing it in parallel while the coprocessor performs the function started earlier. The parallel operation of the coprocessor does not normally affect that of the host unless the coprocessor must reference memory or I/O-based operands. When the host releases the local bus to the coprocessor, the host may continue to execute from its internal instruction queue. However, the host must stop when it also needs the local bus currently in use by the coprocessor. Except for the stolen memory cycle, the operation of the coprocessor is transparent to the host.

This parallel operation of the host and coprocessor is called concurrent execution. Concurrent execution of instructions requires less total time than a strictly sequential execution would. System performance will be higher with concurrent execution of instructions between the host and coprocessor.

SYNCHRONIZATION

In exchange for the higher system performance made available by concurrent execution, programs must synchronize the coprocessor with the host. Synchronization is necessary whenever the host and coprocessor must use information available from the other. Synchronization involves either the host or coprocessor waiting for the other to finish an operation currently in progress. Since the host executes the program, and has program control instructions like jumps, it is given the responsibility for synchronization. To meet this need, a special host instruction exists to synchronization host operation with a coprocessor.

A more detailed discussion of the effects of instruction execution synchronization between the host CPU and the 8087 coprocessor is contained in the following paragraphs under "Instruction Synchronization".

COPROCESSOR CONTROL

The host has the responsibility for overall program control. Coprocessor operation is initiated by special "ESCAPE" instructions encountered by the host. When the host encounters an ESCAPE instruction, the coprocessor is expected to perform the action indicated by the instruction.

The host's coprocessor interface requires the coprocessor to recognize when the host has encountered an ESCAPE instruction. Whenever the host begins executing a new instruction, the coprocessor must look to see if it is an ESCAPE instruction. Since only the host fetches instructions and executes them, the coprocessor must monitor the instructions being executed by the host.

3.5.3 Instruction Synchronization

Instruction synchronization is required because the 8087 can only perform one numeric operation at a time. Before any numeric operation is started, the 8087 must have completed all activity from previous instructions. When executing a typical NPX instruction, the CPU will complete the ESC long before the 8087 finishes interpretation of the same machine instruction. Upon completion of the ESC, the CPU will decode and execute the next instruction, and the NPX's control unit, tracking the CPU, will do the same. (The NPX "executes" a CPU instruction by ignoring it.) If the CPU has work to do that does not effect the NPX, it can proceed with a series of instructions while the NPX is executing in parallel. The NPX's control unit will ignore these CPU-only instructions as they do not contain the 8087 escape code. This asynchronous execution of the processors can substantially improve the performance of systems that can be designed to exploit it.

Two cases, however, make it necessary to synchronize the execution of the CPU to the NPX:

1. An NPX instruction that is executed by the numeric execution unit must not be started if the execution unit is still busy executing a previous instruction.

2. The CPU should not execute an instruction that accesses a memory operand being referenced by the NPX until the NPX has actually accessed the location.

The host coprocessor synchronization instruction (WAIT) uses the TEST pin of the host. The coprocessor can signal that it is still busy to the host via this pin. Whenever the host executes a wait instruction, it will stop program execution while the TEST input is active. When the TEST pin becomes inactive, the host will resume program execution with the next instruction following the WAIT. While waiting on the TEST pin, the host can be interrupted at 5 clock intervals; however, after the TEST pin becomes inactive, the host will immediately execute the next instruction, ignoring any pending interrupts between the WAIT and the following instruction.

The WAIT instruction allows software to synchronize the CPU to the NPX so that the CPU will not execute the following instruction until the NPX is finished with its current (if any) instruction.

Whenever the 8087 is executing an instruction, it activates its BUSY line. This signal is wired to the CPU's TEST* input as shown in Figure 3-11. The NPX ignores the WAIT instruction, and the CPU executes it. The CPU interprets the WAIT instruction as "wait while TEST* is active." The CPU examines the TEST* pin every 5 clocks. If TEST* is inactive, execution proceeds with the instruction following the WAIT. If TEST* is active, the CPU examines the pin again. Therefore, the effective execution time of a WAIT can stretch from 3 clocks (3 clocks are required for decoding and setup) to infinity, as long as TEST* remains active. The purpose of the WAIT instruction is to prevent the CPU from decoding the next instruction until the 8087 is not busy. The instruction following a WAIT is decoded simultaneously by both processors.

To satisfy the first synchronization case, every 8087 instruction that affects the numeric execution unit should be preceded by a WAIT to ensure that the execution unit is ready. All instructions except the processor control class affect the numeric execution unit. To simplify programming, the 8086 family language translators provide the WAIT automatically, therefore, when an assembly language programmer codes:

```
FMUL    ;(multiply)
FDIV    ;(divide)
```

The assembler produces *four* machine instructions, as if the programmer had written:

```
WAIT
FMUL    ;(multiply)
WAIT
FDIV    ;(divide)
```

This ensures that the multiply runs to completion before the CPU and the 8087 control unit decode the divide.

To satisfy the second synchronization case, the programmer must explicitly code the FWAIT instruction immediately before a CPU instruction that accesses a memory operand read or written by a previous 8087 instruction. This will ensure that the 8087 has read or written the memory operand before the CPU attempts to use it. (The FWAIT mnemonic causes the assembler to create a CPU WAIT instruction that can be eliminated at link time if the program is run on an 8087 emulator.)

A typical sequence of instructions that illustrates the effect of the WAIT instruction and parallel execution of the NPX with a CPU is shown in Figure 3-13). The first two instructions in the sequence (FMUL and FSQRT) are 8087 instructions that illustrate the ASM-86 assembler's automatic generation of a preceding WAIT, and the effect of the WAIT when the NPX is, and is not, busy.

Since the NPX is not busy when the first WAIT is encountered, the CPU executes it and immediately proceeds to the next instruction, and the NPX ignores the WAIT. The next instruction is decoded simultaneously by both processors. The NPX starts the multiplication and raises its BUSY line. The CPU executes the ESC and then the second WAIT. Since TEST* is active (it is tied to BUSY), the CPU effectively stretches execution of the multiply by lowering BUSY. The next instruction is interpreted as a square root by the NPX and another escape by the CPU. The CPU finishes the ESC well before the NPX completes the FSQRT. This time, instead of waiting, the CPU executes three instructions (CMP, JG and MOV) while the 8087 is working on the FSQRT. The 8087 ignores these CPU-only instructions. The CPU then encounters the third WAIT, generated by the assembler immediately preceding the FIST (store stack top into integer word). When the NPX finished the FSQRT, both processors proceed to the next instruction, FIST to the NPX and ESC to the CPU. The CPU completes the escape quickly and then executes an explicit programmer-coded FWAIT to ensure that the 8087 has updated BETA before it moves BETA's new value to the register AX (refer to Figure 3-13).

The 8087 control unit can execute most processor control instructions by itself regardless of what the numeric execution unit is doing. Therefore, in these cases the 8087 can potentially execute two instruction at once. The ASM-86 assembler provides separate"wait" and "no wait" mnemonics for these instructions. For example, the instruction that sets the 8087 interrupt enable mask, and therefore disables interrupts, can be coded as FDISI or FNDISI. The assembler does not generate a WAIT if the second form is coded, so that the interrupts can be disabled while the numeric execution unit is busy with a previous instruction. The no-wait forms are principally used in exception handlers and operating systems.

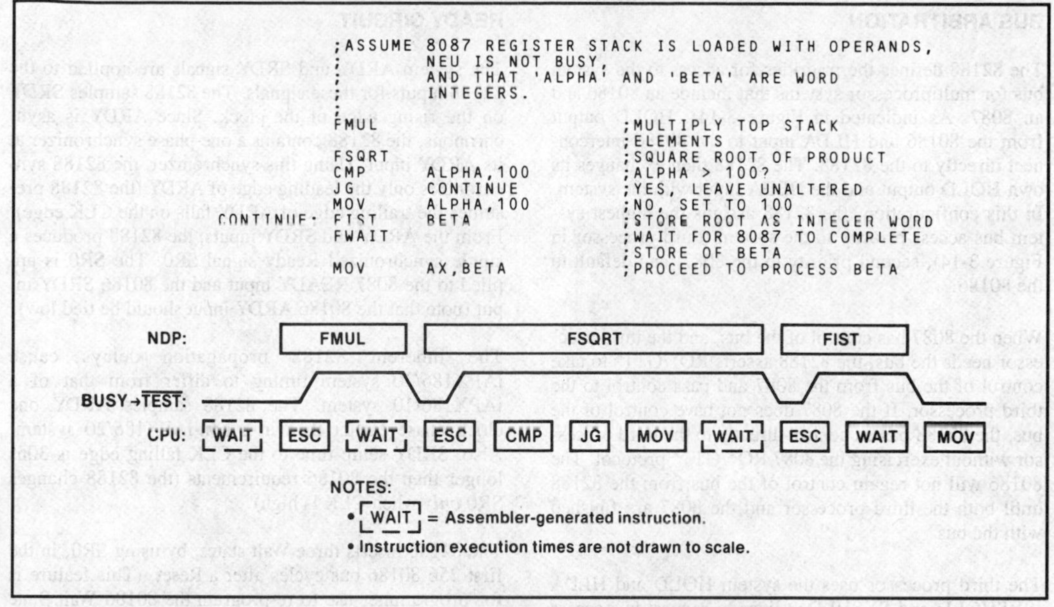

Figure 3-13 Synchronizing Execution With WAIT

3.6 BUS OPERATION

Connecting the 8087 in tandem with an 8086 (iAPX86/20) or with an 80186 (iAPX186/20), does not change system bus operation from the normal operation of the bus in a iAPX86/10 or iAPX186/10 system. However, some minor differences exist between the iAPX86/20 and the iAPX186/20 systems, primarily due the requirement for a 82188 Interface chip in the iAPX186/20 system. For additional information on the 82188 Integrated Bus Controller refer to the Preliminary Data Sheet Revision 1.2. The following paragraphs describe the operation and timing of the bus in the various configurations.

3.6.1 iAPX86/20 Bus Operation

Operation and timing for the 8087 bus structure are identical to all other processors in the maximum mode configuration iAPX 86, 88 series and the iAPX 186, 188 series. The address time-multiplexes with the data on the first 16/8 lines of the address/data bus. A16 through A19 are time-multiplex with four status lines S3-S6. Lines S3, S4, and S6 are always high (logical 1) for 8087 driven bus cycles while S5 is always low (logical 0). When the 8087 is monitoring CPU bus cycles (passive mode), the 8087 monitors S6 to discriminate between 8086/8088 activity and that of a local I/O processor or any other local bus master.

NOTE

The 8086/8088 must be the only processor on the local bus to drive S6 low.

Line S7 multiplexes with BHE* and has the same value as BHE* for all 8087 bus cycles. When an 8288 Bus Controller is used, status lines S0*-S2* are used to determine the type of bus cycle being run, as shown in the following list:

S2*	S1*	S0*	
0	X	X	Unused
1	0	0	Unused
1	0	1	Memory Data Read
1	1	0	Memory Data Write
1	1	1	Passive (no bus cycle)

3.6.2 iAPX186/20 Bus Operation

The 82188 Interface chip provides a local bus arbitration function for an 80186 system consisting of an 80186, an 8087 and a third processor with a HOLD-HLDA type bus exchange protocol. The 82188 also provides the bus control signals otherwise supplied to the system by the 80186 and contains ARDY and SRDY signals to its own integral Ready circuit (refer to paragraph 3.4.2).

The 82188 also has an integral queue status circuit which inserts a one-phase delay on the queue status signals to meet the 8087 Queue-Status timing requirements (refer to paragraph 3.4.2).

BUS ARBITRATION

The 82188 defines the priorities for access to the system bus for multiprocessor systems that include an 80186 and an 8087. As indicated in Figure 3-14), HOLD output from the 80186 and HLDA input to the 80186 interconnect directly to the 82188. The 82188 then exchanges its own HOLD output and the HLDA input with the system. In this configuration, the 82188 assigns the highest system bus access priority to the system (third processor in Figure 3-14), second priority to the 8087, and default to the 80186.

When the 8087 has control of the bus, and the third processor needs the bus, the 82188 asserts RQ*/GT1* to take control of the bus from the 8087 and pass control to the third processor. If the 8087 does not have control of the bus, the 82188 passes control directly to the third processor without exercising the 8087 RQ*/GT1* protocol. The 80186 will not regain control of the bus from the 82188 until both the third processor and the 8087 are finished with the bus.

The third processor uses the system HOLD and HLDA (SYSHOLD and SYSHLDA) lines to request bus access from the 82188. Similarly, the 82188 uses the 80186 HOLD and HLDA lines to gain bus control from and return bus control to the 80186. The 82188 also uses the RQ*/GT0* lines from the 8087 for NPX bus control.

NOTE

The 82188 contains weak pull-up devices to set both RQ*/GT1* and RQ*/GT0* high if the 82188 is configured in a system with out an 8087.

BUS CONTROL SIGNALS

Status line outputs from the 80186 and the 8087 (see Figure 3-12) are sent to the 82188. The 82188 decodes these signal lines and generates bus control signals that would otherwise be generated and output directly by an 80186. The signals decoded by the 82188 include:

ALE
RD*
WR*
DT/R*
DEN*

The 82188 also contains the AEN* input which enables the system command lines. This signal provides the hardware designer with the ability to tri-state RD*, WR*, and DEN* by asserting AEN* high S0*, S1* and S2* decode exactly the same as for the 8086 and the 80186.

READY CIRCUIT

The system ARDY and SRDY signals are applied to the 82188 inputs for these signals. The 82188 samples SRDY on the rising edge of the clock. Since ARDY is asynchronous, the 82188 contains a one-phase synchronizer at its ARDY input. Using this synchronizer, the 82188 synchronizes only the leading edge of ARDY (the 82188 presumes the trailing edge of ARDY falls on the CLK edge). From the ARDY and SRDY inputs, the 82188 produces a single synchronized Ready signal SR0. The SR0 is applied to the 8087 READY input and the 80186 SRDY input (note that the 80186 ARDY input should be tied low).

The inherent 82188 propagation delays cause iAPX186/20 system timing to differ from that of a iAPX186/10 system. The 82188 samples ARDY one clock phase earlier than in a non-iAPX186/20 system. Also, SRDY setup time to the CLK falling edge is 30ns longer than the 80186 requirements (the 82188 changes SR0 *only* when CLK is high).

The 82188 inserts three Wait states, by using SR0, in the first 256 80186 bus cycles after a Reset. (This feature is for programmer use to re-program the 80186 Wait State generator to 0 Wait states.)

3.7 BUS EXCHANGE MECHANISM

Two basic decisions must be made when connecting the 8087 to a system: 1.) interconnection of the RQ/GT signals of all of the local bus masters; and 2.) connecting the Interrupt (INT) signal pin. The decision on where to connect the RQ/GT signal that is made at this point affects the response time needed to service local bus requests from other local bus masters, such as an 8089 IOP or other coprocessor. The interrupt connection affects the response time to service an interrupt request and how user-interrupt handlers are written. The implications of how these pins are connected concern both the hardware designer and programmer and must be understood by both. The following paragraphs provide information on making the decision where to connect the RQ/GT signal. Refer to paragraph 3.8 for the discussion on interconnection of the Interrupt (INT) signal.

3.7.1 8087 RQ/GT Function

The presence of the 8087 in the RQ/GT path from the IOP to the host has little effect on the maximum wait time seen by the IOP when requesting the local bus. The 8087 adds two clocks of delay to the basic time required by the host. This low delay is achieved due to a preemptive protocol implemented by the 8087 on RQ/GT1.

The 8087 always gives higher priority to a request for the local bus from a device attached to its RQ/GT1 pin than to a request generated internally by the 8087. If the 8087

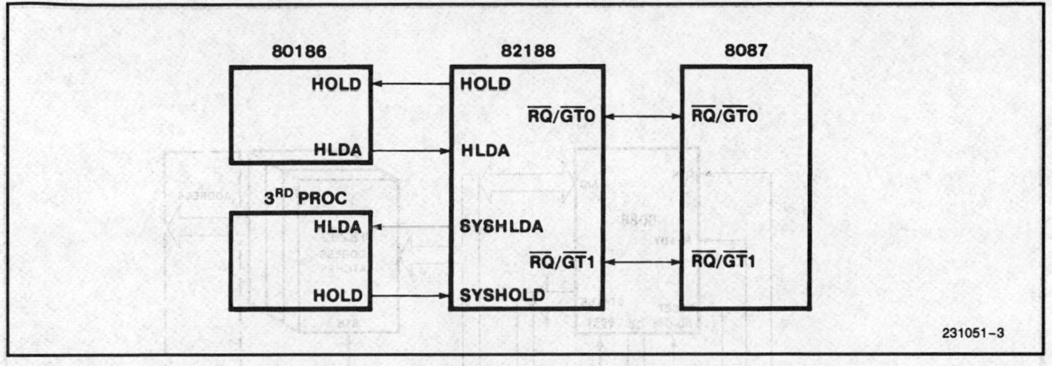

Figure 3-14 Three Processor System Bus Signal Connections

currently owns the local bus and a request is made to its RQ/GT1 pin, the 8087 will finish the current memory cycle and release the local bus to the requestor. If the request from the devices arrives when the 8087 does not own the local bus, the 8087 will then pass the request on to the host via its RQ/GT0 pin.

The RQ/GT issue can be broken into three general catagories depending on system configuration: 86/20 or 88/20, 86/21 or 88/21, and 86/22 or 88/22. Remote operation of an IOP is not effected by the 8087 RQ/GT connection.

iAPX 86/20, 88/20 SYSTEM CONFIGURATION

For an 86/20, 88/20 just connect the RQ/GT0 of the 8087 to RQ/GT0 (1) of the host (see Figure 3-3).

iAPX 86/21, 88/21 SYSTEM CONFIGURATION

For an 86/21 or 88/21, connect RQ/GT0 of the 8087 to RQ/GT0(1) of the host and connect RQ/GT of the 8089 to RQ/GT1 of the 8087 (see Figure 3-15).

The RQ/GT1 pin of the 8087 exists to provide one I/O processor with a low maximum wait time for the local bus. The maximum wait times to gain control of the local bus for a device attached to RQ/GT1 of an 8087 for an 8086 or 8088 host are shown in Table 3-2. These numbers are all dependent on when the host will release the local bus to the 8087.

Three factors determine when the host will release the local bus (see Table 3-2):

1. Type of host;
2. Current instruction being executed;
3. Use of the lock prefix.

An 8086 host will not release the local bus between the two consecutive byte operations performed for odd-aligned word operands. In contrast, the 8088 will never release the local bus between two bytes of a word transfer, independent of its byte alignment. Host operations such as acknowledging an interrupt will not release the local bus for several bus cycles. Using a lock prefix in front of a host instruction prevents the host from releasing the local during the execution of that instruction.

iAPX 86/22, 88/22 SYSTEM CONFIGURATION

An 86/22 system offers two alternatives in regards to which IOP to connect to an I/O device. Each IOP will offer a different maximum delay time to service an I/O request. (See Figure 3-16.)

The second 8089 (IOPA) must use the RQ/GT0 pin of the host. When using two IOP's the designer must decide which IOP services which I/O devices. This decision is determined by the maximum wait time allowed between the time an I/O device requests IOP service and when the IOP can respond. Since the maximum service delay times of the two IOP's can be very different, it makes very little difference which of the two host RQ/GT pins are used.

The different wait times are due to the non-preemptive nature of bus grants between the two host RQ/GT pins. IOPA and the 8087/IOPB combination cannot communicate about the need to use the local bus. Any request for the local bus by the IOPA must wait (worst case) for the host, the 8087, and the IOPB to finish their longest sequence of memory cycles. IOPB must wait in the worst case for the host and IOPA to finish their longest sequence of memory cycles. The 8087 has little effect on the maximum wait time of IOPB.

3.7.2 Delay Effects of the 8087

The delay effects of the 8087 on IOPA can be significant. When executing special instructions (FSAVE, FNSAVE,

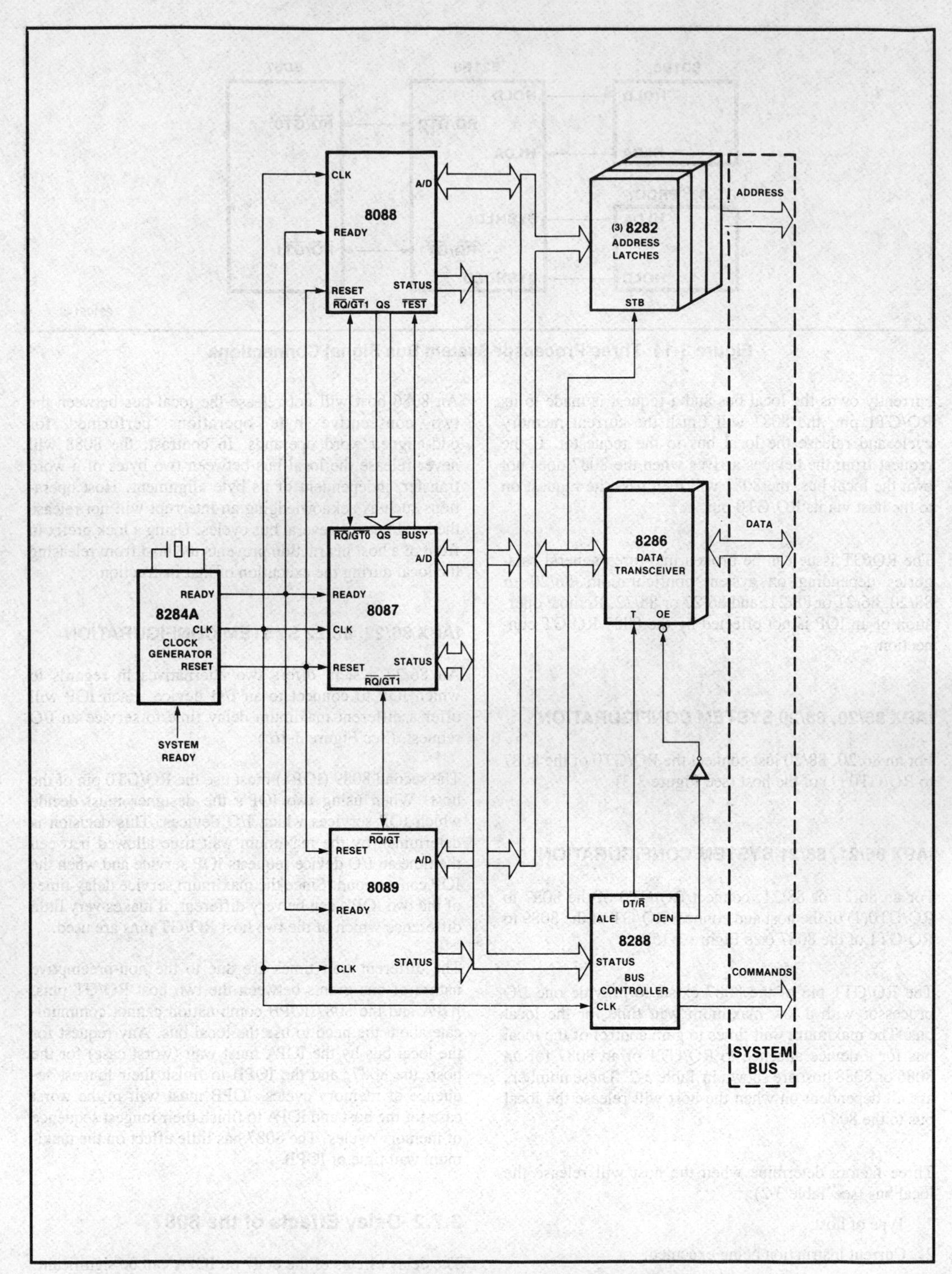

Figure 3-15 iAPX 88/21 System Configuration

Table 3-2 Worst Case Local Bus Request Wait Times In Clocks

System Configuration	No Locked Instructions	Only Locked Exchange	Other Locked Instructions
iAPX 86/21 even aligned words	15_1	35_1	max (15_1, *)
iAPX 86/21 odd aligned words	15_1	43_2	max (43_2, *)
iAPX 88/21	15_1	43_2	max (43_2, *)

Notes: 1. Add two clocks for each wait state inserted per bus cycle
2. Add four clocks for each wait state inserted per bus cycle
* Execution time of longest locked instruction

FRSTOR), the 8087 can perform 50 or 96 consecutive memory cycles with an 8086 or 8088 host, respectively. These instructions do not affect response time to local bus requests seen by an IOPB.

If the 8087 is performing a series of memory cycles while executing these instructions, and IOPB requests the local bus, the 8087 will stop its current memory activity, then release the local bus to IOPB. The 8087 cannot release the bus IOPA since it cannot know that IOPA wants to use the local bus, like it can for IOPB.

3.7.3 Reducing 8087 Delay Effects

For 86/22 or 88/22 systems requiring lower maximum wait times for IOPA, it is possible to reduce worst case bus usage. If three 8087 instructions are never executed (namely FSAVE, FNSAVE, or FRSTOR) the maximum number of consecutive memory cycles performed by the 8087 is 10 or 16 for an 8086 or 8088 host respectively. The function of these instructions can be emulated with other 8087 instructions.

There are alternative techniques for switching the numeric context without using the FSAVE/FNSAVE or FRSTOR instructions. These alternative techniques are slower than those using these instructions, but they reduce the worst case continuous local bus usage of the 8087. Only an iAPX 86/22 or iAPX 88/22 systems derive any real benefit from these alternatives. By replacing all FSAVE/FNSAVE instructions, the worst case local bus usage of the 8087 will be 6 or 10 consecutive bus cycles for the 8086 or 8088 host, respectively.

Instead of saving and loading the entire numeric context in one long series of memory transfers, these alternative routines use the FSTENV/FNSTENV/FLDENY instructions and separate numeric register load/store instructions. Using separate load/store instructions for the numeric registers forces the 8087 to release the local bus after each numeric load/save instruction. The longest series of back-to-back transfers required by these instructions are 8/12 memory cycles (8086/8088 host, respectively). The FSAVE/FNSAVE/FRSTOR instructions, in contrast, perform 50/94 back-to-back memory cycles for an 8086 or 8088 host.

COMPATIBILITY WITH FSAVE/FNSAVE

This technique produces a context area of the same format produced by the FSAVE/FNSAVE instructions. Other software modules expecting this type of format will not be affected. All of the same interrupt and deadlock considerations that apply to FSAVE and FNSAVE also apply to FSTENV and FNSTENV. With the exception that the numeric environment is 7 words rather than the 47 words of the numeric context, all factors concerning the use of the FSAVE/FNSAVE also apply.

The state of the NPX registers must be saved in memory in the same as used with the FSAVE/FNSAVE instructions. The program example (see Figure 3-17) starting at the label SMALL_BLOCK_NPX_SAVE illustrates a software loop that will store their contents into memory in the same top relative order as that of FSAVE/FNSAVE.

To save the registers the FSTP instructions, the FSTP instructions must be tagged valid, zero, or special. This function will force all the registers to be tagged valid, independent of their contents or old tag, and then save them. No problems will arise if the tag value conflicts with the register's content for the FSTP instruction. Saving empty registers insures compatibility with the FSAVE/FNSAVE instructions. After saving all the numeric registers, they will all be tagged empty, the same as if an FSAVE/FNSAVE instruction had been executed.

COMPATIBILITY WITH FRSTOR

Restoring numeric context reverses the procedure described in the preceding paragraphs. This is shown by the code starting at SMALL_BLOCK_NPX_RESTORE (see Figure 3-18). All eight registers are reloaded in the reverse order. With each register load, a tag value will be assigned to each register. The tags assigned by the register load do not since the tag word will be overwritten when the environment is reloaded later with FLDENV.

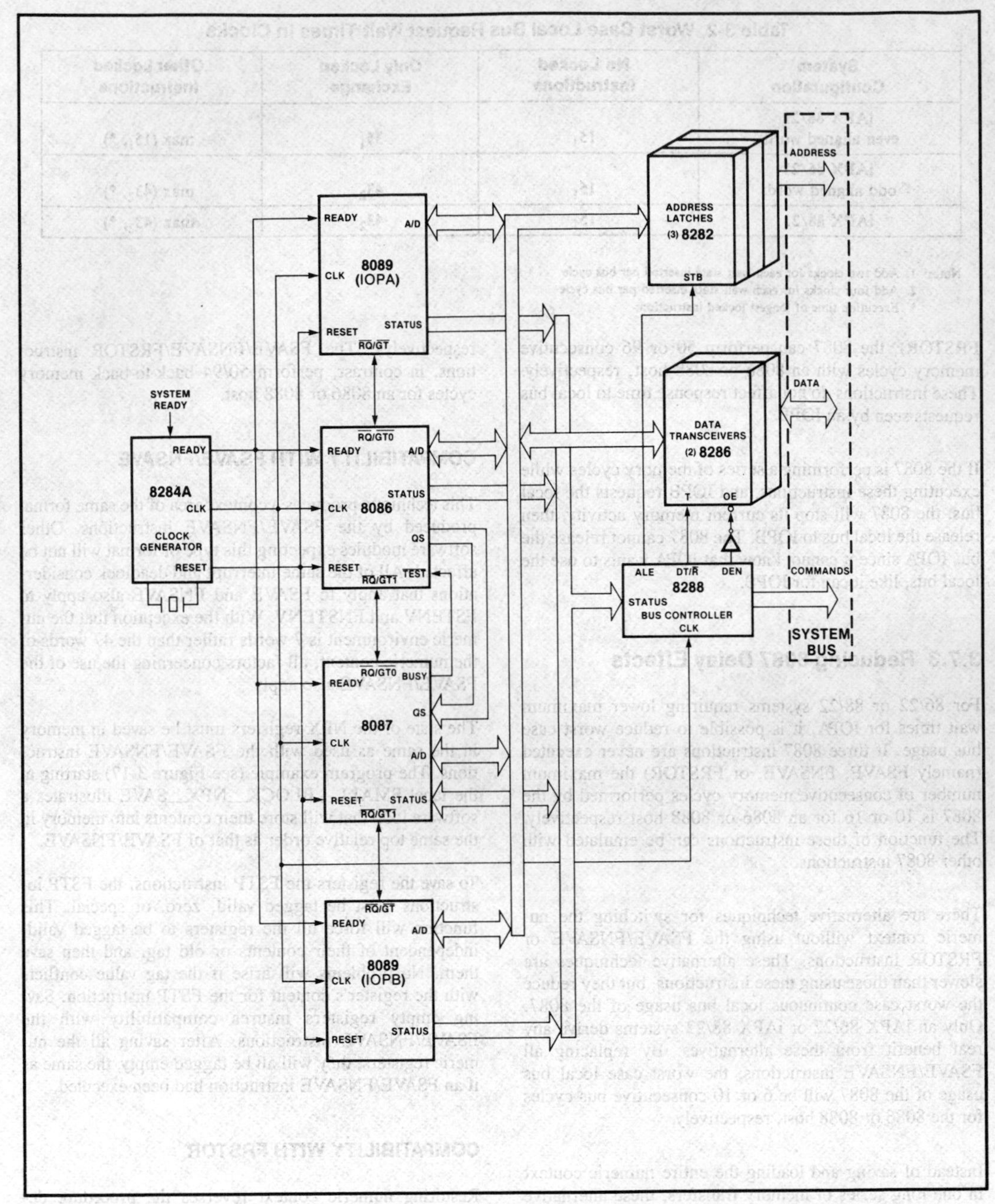

Figure 3-16 iAPX 86/22 System

Two assumptions are required for the correct operation of the restore function. First, all numeric registers must be empty, and second, the TOP field must be the same as that in the context being restored. These assumptions will be satisfied if a matched set of pushes and pops were performed between saving the numeric context and reloading it. If these assumptions cannot be met, the code example (see Figure 3-19) starting at NPX_CLEAN shows how

```
;
; Save the NPX context independent of NDP interrupt state. Avoid using the FSAVE instruction to
; limit the worst case memory bus usage of the 8087. The NPX context area formed will appear the
; same as if an FSAVE instruction had written into it. The variable save_area will hold the NPX
; context and must be 47 words long. The registers ax, bx, and cx will not be transparent.
;
small_block_NPX_save:
        FNSTCW  save_area               ; Save current IEM bit
        NOP                             ; Delay while 8087 saves control register
        FNDISI                          ; Disable 8087 BUSY signal
        MOV     ax, save_area           ; Get original control word
        MOV     cx, 8                   ; Set numeric register count
        XOR     bx, bx                  ; Tag field value for stamping all registers as valid
        FSTENV  save_area               ; Save NPX environment
        FWAIT                           ; Wait for the store to complete
        XCHG    save_area + 4, bx       ; Get original tag value and set new tag value
        FLDENV  save_area               ; Force all register tags as valid. BUSY is still masked. No data
        MOV     save_area, ax           ; synchronization needed. Put original control word into NPX
        MOV     save_area + 4, bx       ; environment. Put original tag word into NPX environment
        XOR     bx, bx                  ; Set initial register index
reg_store_loop:
        FSTP    saved_reg [bx]          ; Save register
        ADD     bx, type saved_reg      ; Bump pointer to next register
        LOOP    reg_store_loop
                                        ; All done
```

Figure 3-17 SMALL_BLOCK_NPX_SAVE

to force all the NPX registers empty and set the TOP of field in the status word.

These improvements do have a cost. This is the increased execution time of 427 or 747 additional clocks for an 8086 or 8088, respectively, for the equivalent save and restore operations. These operations appear in time-critical context-switching functions of an operating system or interrupt handler. This technique has no affect on the maximum wait time seen by IOPB or wait time seen by IOPA due to IOPB.

```
;
; Restore the NPX context without using the FRSTOR instruction. Assume the NPX context is in the
; same form as that created by an FSAVE/FNSAVE instruction, all the registers are empty, and that
; the TOP field of the NPX matches the TOP field of the NPX context. The variable save_area must
; be an NPX context save area, 47 words long. The registers bx and cx will not be transparent.
;
small_block_NPX_restore:
        MOV     cx, 8                   ; Set register count
        MOV     bx, type saved_reg*7    ; Starting offset of ST(7)
reg_load_loop:
        FLD     saved_reg [bx]          ; Get the register
        SUB     bx, type saved_reg      ; Bump pointer to next register
        LOOP    reg_load_loop
        FLDENV  save_area               ; Restore NPX context
                                        ; All done
```

Figure 3-18 SMALL_BLOCK_NPX_RESTORE

```
;
; Force the NPX into a clean state with TOP matching the TOP field stored in the NPX context and all
; numeric registers tagged empty. Save_area must be the NPX environment saved earlier.
; Temp_env is a 7 word temporary area used to build a prototype NPX environment. Register ax will
; not be transparent.
;

NPX_clean:
        FINIT                           ; Put NPX into known state
        MOV     ax, save_area+2         ; Get original status word
        AND     ax, 3800H               ; Mask out the top field
        FSTENV  temp_env                ; Format a temporary environment area with all registers
                                        ; stamped empty and TOP field=0.
        FWAIT                           ; Wait for the store to finish.
        OR      temp_env+2, ax          ; Put in the desired TOP value.
        FLDENV  temp_env                ; Setup new NPX environment.
                                        ; Now enter small_block_NPX_restore
```

Figure 3-19 NPX_CLEAN Code Example

Which IOP to connect to which I/O device in an 86/22 or 88/22 system will depend on how quickly an I/O request by the device must be serviced by the IOP. This maximum time must be greater than the sum of the maximum delay of the IOP and the maximum wait time to gain control of the local bus by the IOP.

3.8 INTERRUPTS

One of the most important decisions to make in adding the 8087 to an 8086 or 8088 system is where to attach the 8087 Interrupt (INT) signal. The 8087 INT pin provides an external indication of software-selected numeric errors. This causes the numeric program to stop until something is done about the error. A numeric error occurs in the NPX whenever an operation is attempted with invalid operand or attempts to produce a result which cannot be represented. Deciding where to connect the INT signal can have important consequences on other interrupt handlers.

3.8.1 Recommended Interrupt Configurations

Five categories cover most of the uses of the 8087 interrupt in fixed priority interrupt systems. The following presents an interrupt configuration for each of these categories.

1. All errors on the 8087 are always masked. Numeric interrupts are not possible. Leave the 8087 INT signal disconnected.
2. The 8087 is the only interrupt in the system. Connect the 8087 INT signal directly to the host's INTR input (see Figure 3- 20). A bus driver supplies interrupt vector 10_{16} for compatibility with Intel supplied software.
3. The 8087 interrupt is a stop everything event. Choose a high priority interrupt input that will terminate all numerics related activity. This is a special case since the interrupt handler may never return to the point of interruption (i.e., reset the system and restart rather than attempt to continue operation).
4. Numeric exceptions or numeric programming errors are expected and all interrupt handlers either do not use the 8087 or only use it with all errors masked. Use the lowest priority interrupt input. The 8087 interrupt handler should allow further interrupts by higher priority events. The PIC's priority system will automatically prevent the 8087 from disturbing other interrupts without adding extra code to them.
5. Case 4 holds except that interrupt handlers may also generate numeric interrupts. Connect the 8087 INT signal to multiple interrupt inputs. One input would still be the lowest priority input as in case 4. Interrupt handlers that may generate a numeric interrupt may require another 8087 INT connection to the next highest priority interrupt. Normally the higher priority numeric interrupt inputs would be masked and the low priority numeric interrupt enabled. The higher priority interrupt would be unmasked only when servicing an interrupt which requires 8087 exception handling.

All of these configurations hide the 8087 from all interrupt handlers which do not use the 8087. Only those interrupt handlers that use the 8087 are required to perform any special 8087 related interrupt control activities.

A conflict can arise between the desired PIC interrupt input and the required interrupt vector of 10_{16} for compatibility with Intel software for numeric interrupts. A simple solution is to use more than one interrupt vector for numeric interrupts, all pointing at the same 8087 interrupt handler. Design the numeric interrupt handler so that it

```
;
; Disable any possible numeric interrupt from the 8087. This code is safe to place in any
; procedure. If an 8087 is not present, the ESCAPE instructions will act as nops. These
; instructions are not affected by the TEST pin of the host. Using the 8087 emulator will not
; convert these instructions into interrupts. A word variable, called control, is required to hold
; the 8087 control word. Control must not be changed until it is reloaded into the 8087.
;
ESC  15, control          ; (FNSTCW) Save current 8087 control word
NOP                       ; Delay while 8087 saves current control
NOP                       ; register value
ESC  28,cx                ; (FNDISI) Disable any 8087 interrupts
                          ; Set IEM bit in 8087 control register
                          ; The contents of cx is irrelevant
                          ; Interrupts can now be enabled

                 (Your Code Here)
;
; Reenable any pending interrupts in the 8087. This instruction does not disturb any 8087 instruction
; currently in progress since all it does is change the IEM bit in the control register.
;
TEST control, 80H         ; Look at IEM bit
JNZ  $+4                  ; If IEM = 1 skip FNENI
ESC  28,ax                ; (FNENI) reenable 8087 interrupts
```

Figure 3-20 Inhibit/Enable 8087 Interrupts

does not need to know what the interrupt vector was (i.e., do not use specific EOI commands). If an interrupt system uses rotating interrupt priorities, it does not matter which interrupt is used.

8089 Input/Output Processor

4

CHAPTER 4
8089 INPUT/OUTPUT PROCESSOR

4.1 INTRODUCTION

This chapter contains specific hardware design information on the operations and functions of INTEL's 8089 Input/Output Processor (IOP) when used with the iAPX 86,88 and iAPX 186,188 family of microprocesssors. The chapter contains general information on the IOP, along with a component overview presenting architectural and software considerations, and individual device pin functional signal definitions. Detailed descriptions of the IOP's operating modes, bus operation, bus exchange mechanisms and a description of interrupt operation are also provided. For more specific information of any of the 8086 family support circuits, refer to the Microsystems Components Handbook (Order Number 230843-002).

4.2 COMPONENT OVERVIEW

The 8089 Input/Output Processor (IOP) is an intelligent DMA controller that is used with the Intel iAPX 86,88 and iAPX 186,188 family of microprocessors. The processing power of the 8089 IOP can remove I/O overhead from the 8086, 8088, 80186 or 80188 microprocessors. In addition, it may operate concurrently with a CPU, giving improved performance in I/O intensive applications over an iAPX 86,88 or iAPX 186,188 system operating without an 8089. The 8089 provides two I/O channels, each supporting a transfer rate of up to 1.25 megabytes per second at the standard clock frequency of 5 MHz. Memory based communication between the IOP and CPU enhances system flexibility and encourages software modularity for more reliable, easier to develop systems.

The 8089 IOP combines the functions of a DMA controller with the processing capabilities of a microprocessor. In addition to the normal DMA function of transferring data, the 8089 dynamically translates and compares data as it is transferred. The IOP also supports a number of terminate conditions, including byte count, data compare or miscompare, and the occurrence of an external event. Each of the two separate DMA channels contains its own register set. Depending on the established priorities (both inherent and program determined), the two channels can alternate (interleave) their respective operations.

The 8089 has transfer flexibility integrally designed into it. It will perform routine transfers between an I/O peripheral and memory, and, in addition, transfer data between two I/O devices or between two areas of memory. The 8089 automatically handles transfers between dissimilar bus widths. When the 8089 transfers data from an 8-bit peripheral bus to a 16-bit memory bus, it reads two bytes from the peripheral, assembles the bytes into a 16-bit word and then writes the single word to the addressed memory location. Both 8-and 16-bit peripherals can reside on the same (16-bit) bus because the IOP transfers bytes with the 8-bit peripheral,and transfers words with the 16-bit peripheral.

4.2.1 Architectural Overview

The 8089 IOP is internally divided into the functional units described in the following paragraphs (see Figure 4-1). These functional units are connected by a 20-bit data path to obtain maximum internal transfer rates.

COMMON CONTROL UNIT (CCU)

IOP operations (instructions, DMA transfer cycles, channel attention responses, etc.) are composed of sequences called internal cycles. A single bus cycle takes one internal cycle, therefore, the execution of an instruction may require several internal cycles. There are 23 different types of internal cycles. Each of these take from two to eight clocks to execute, not including possible wait states and bus arbitration resolving.

The Common Control Unit (CCU) coordinates IOP activities by allocating internal cycles to the various processor units, i.e., the CCU determines which unit will execute the next internal cycle. For example, when both channels are active, the CCU determines which channel has priority and lets that channel run; if the channels have equal priority, the CCU "interleaves" their execution. The CCU also initializes the processor.

ARITHMETIC/LOGIC UNIT (ALU)

The Arithmetic/Logic Unit (ALU) can perform unsigned binary arithmetic on 8-and 16-bit binary numbers. The results of this arithmetic may be up to 20 bits in length. Available arithmetic instructions include addition, increment and decrement. Logical operations ("and," "or" and "not") may be performed on either 8-or 16-bit quantities.

ASSEMBLY/DISASSEMBLY REGISTERS

All data entering the chip flows through the Assembly/Dissassembly registers. When data is being transferred between different width buses, the 8089 uses the assembly/disassembly registers to effect the transfer in the fewest possible bus cycles. During a DMA transfer from an 8-bit peripheral to 16-bit memory, for example,

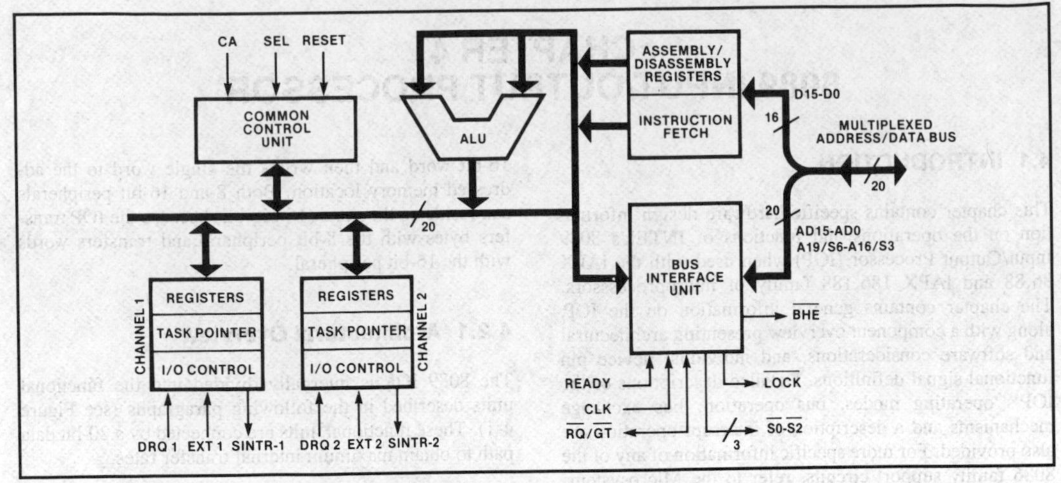

Figure 4-1 8089 Simplified Functional Block Diagram

the IOP runs two bus cycles, picking up eight bits in each cycle. It then assembles a 16-bit word and transfers the word to memory in a single bus cycle. (The first and last cycles of a transfer may be performed differently to accommodate odd-addressed words; the IOP automatically adjusts for this condition.)

INSTRUCTION FETCH UNIT

The instruction fetch unit controls instruction fetching for the executing channel (one channel actually runs at a time). If the bus over which the instructions are being fetched is eight bits wide, the instructions are obtained one byte at a time, and each fetch requires one bus cycle. If the instructions are being fetched over a 16-bit bus, the instruction fetch unit automatically employs a 1-byte queue to reduce the number of bus cycles. Each channel has its own queue, and the activity of one channel does not affect the other's queue.

BUS INTERFACE UNIT (BIU)

The Bus Interface Unit (BIU) controls all the bus cycles. It transfers instructions and data between the IOP and external memory or peripherals. Every bus access is associated with a register tag bit. These tag bits indicate to the BIU whether the system or I/O space is to be addressed. The BIU outputs the type of bus cycle (instruction fetch from I/O space, data store into system space, etc.) on status lines S0*, S1*, and S2*. An 8288 Bus Controller decodes these lines and provides signals that selectively enable one bus or the other.

The BIU also distinguishes between the physical and the logical widths of system and I/O buses. The physical widths of the buses are fixed. These are communicated to the BIU during initialization. In the local configuration, both buses must be the same width (either 8-or 16-bits), matching the width of the host CPU bus. In the remote configuration, the IOP system bus must be the same physical width as the bus it shares with the CPU. The width of the IOP's I/O bus (local to the 8089) may be selected independently. If any 16-bit peripherals are located in the I/O space, a 16-bit I/O bus must be used. If only 8-bit devices reside on the I/O bus, either an 8-or 16-bit I/O bus may be selected. A 16-bit I/O bus has the advantage of easy accommodation of future 16-bit devices and fewer instruction fetches if channel programs are placed in the I/O space.

For any given DMA transfer, a channel program specifies the logical width of the system and the I/O buses. Each channel specifies logical bus widths independently. The logical width of an 8-bit physical bus can only be eight bits. However, a 16-bit physical bus can be used as either an 8-or 16-bit logical bus. This allows both 8-and 16-bit devices to be accessed over a single 16-bit physical bus. The permissible physical and logical bus widths for both locally and remotely configured IOPs are listed in Table 4-1. Logical bus width pertains to DMA transfers only.

Table 4-1 Physical/Logical Bus Combinations

Configuration	System Bus Physical:Logical	I/O Bus Physical:Logical
Local	8:8 16:8/16	8:8 16:8/16
Remote	8:8 16:8/16 16:8/16 8:8	8:8 16:8/16 8:8 16:8/16

The physical bus width determines whether instructions are fetched and operands are read and written in bytes or words.

The BIU, in addition to performing transfers, is responsible for local bus arbitration. In the local configuration, the BIU uses the RQ*/GT* (request/grant) line to obtain the bus from the CPU and to return it after a transfer has been performed. In the remote configuration, the BIU uses RQ*/GT* to coordinate use of the local I/O bus with another IOP or a local CPU, if present. System bus arbitration in the remote configuration is performed by an 8289 Bus Arbiter that operates invisibly to the IOP. The BIU automatically asserts the LOCK* (bus lock) signal during execution of a TSL (test and set lock) instruction and, if specified by the channel program, can assert the LOCK* signal for the duration of a DMA transfer.

CHANNELS

Although the 8089 is a single processor, it is useful to consider it as two independent channels under most circumstances. A channel may perform DMA transfers and execute channel programs, or it may also be idle. The following paragraphs describe the hardware features that support these operations.

I/O Control

Each channel contains an I/O control section that controls the operation of the channel during DMA transfers. If the transfer is source (destination) synchronized, the channel waits for a signal on the DMA request line (DRQ) before performing the next fetch-store (store) sequence in the transfer. If the transfer is to be terminated by an external signal, the channel monitors its external terminate line (EXT) and stops the transfer when this line goes active. Between the fetch and store cycles (when the data is in the IOP) the channel optionally counts, translates, and scans the data, and may terminate the transfer based on the results of these operations. Each channel also has a system interrupt line (SINTR) that can be activated by software to issue an interrupt request to the CPU.

Registers

Each channel has an independent set of registers (see Figure 4-2) that are not accessible to the other channel. Most of the registers assume different roles depending whether a channel program is being executed or a DMA transfer is being performed. Channel programs must be careful to save these registers in memory prior to a DMA transfer if their values are needed following the transfer. Table 4-2 provides a brief summary of each of the channel registers. Refer to Chapter 7 of the iAPX 86/88,186/188 User's Manual Programmers Reference for a detailed description of the channel registers.

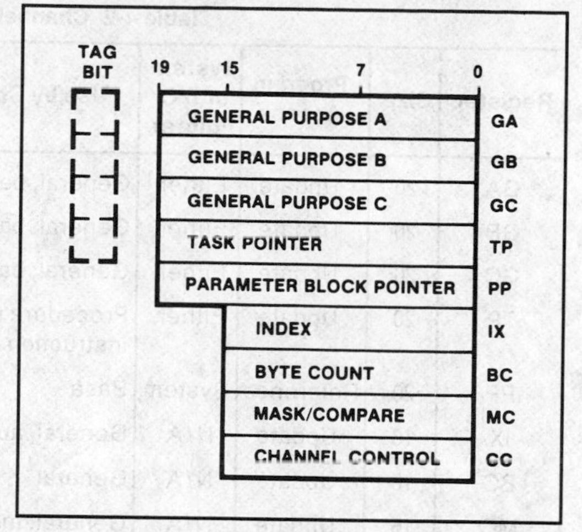

Figure 4-2 Channel Register Set

Task Pointer

The CCU loads the task pointer from the parameter block when it starts or resumes a channel program. The task pointer is used as an instruction pointer or program counter. During program execution, the channel automatically updates the task pointer to point to the next instruction to be executed. Program transfer instructions (JMP, CALL, etc.) update the task pointer to cause nonsequential execution. A procedure (subroutine) returns to the calling program by loading the task pointer with an address previously saved by the CALL instruction. The task pointer is fully accessible to channel programs and can be used as a general register or as a base register. This is not recommended, however, since it can make programs very difficult to understand.

4.2.2 Software Overview

This section provides a summary of the 8089 IOP's instruction set and also provides information on the machine-level encoding and decoding of these instructions.

INSTRUCTION SET SUMMARY

The IOP's 53 instructions are divided into five functional categories:

1. data transfer;
2. arithmetic;
3. logic and bit manipulation;
4. program transfer; and
5. processor control.

Table 4-2 Channel Register Summary

Register	Size	Program Access	System or I/O Pointer	Use by Channel Programs	Use in DMA Transfers
GA	20	Update	Either	General, base	Source/destination pointer
GB	20	Update	Either	General, base	Source/destination pointer
GC	20	Update	Either	General, base	Translate table pointer
TP	20	Update	Either	Procedure return, instruction pointer	Adjusted to reflect cause of termination
PP	20	Reference	System	Base	N/A
IX	16	Update	N/A	General, auto-increment	N/A
BC	16	Update	N/A	General	Byte counter
MC	16	Update	N/A	General, masked compare	Masked compare
CC	16	Update	N/A	Restricted use recommended	Defines transfer options

The following paragraphs provide a brief functional description of each instruction category and how they are used in channel programs. Instruction set reference data tables list every instruction alphabetically and show the execution time, encoded length and a sample of the ASM-89 coding for each permissable operand combination. Additional information on the 8089 instruction set is contained in volume 1 of this manual.

Data Transfer Instructions

Data transfer instructions move data between memory and the channel registers. The move word variable (MOV), move byte variable (MOVB), move word immediate (MOVI) and move byte immediate (MOVBI) instructions provide standard byte and word moves (including memory-to-memory). Refer to Figure 4-3 for the effect of these instructions on the register operands.

Two additional special instructions are provided, move pointer (MOVP) and load pointer with doubleword (LDP). These instructions load addresses into pointer registers and update tag bits in the process are available.

Arithmetic Instructions

Arithmetic instructions interpret all operands as unsigned 8, 16 or 20 bit binary numbers. Signed values are represented in standard two's complement notation with the high order bit representing the sign (0 = positive, 1 = negative). The processor has no way of detecting an overflow into the sign bit, therefore the software must provide for this possibility.

The 8089 performs arithmetic operations on values of up to 20 significant bits sign-extending byte and word operands to 20 bits. To accomplish this, bit 7 of a byte operand is propagated through bits 8-19 of an internal register. Sign extension does not affect the magnitude of the operand. The arithmetic operation is then performed and the 20-bit result is returned to the destination operand. High-order bits are truncated as necessary to fit the result in the available space. A carry out of, or borrow into the high-order bit of the result is not detected. If the destination is a register that is larger than the source operand, carries will be reflected in the upper register bits, up to the size of the register (see Figure 4-4).

Logical and Bit Manipulation Instructions

The logical instructions include the boolean operators AND, OR and NOT. Two bit manipulation instructions are provided for setting or clearing a single bit in memory or in an I/O device register. The logical operations always leave the upper four bits of the 20-bit destination registers undefined (see Figure 4-5). These bits should not be assumed to contain reliable values, or the same values from one operation to the next. When a register is specified as the destination register for a byte operation, bits 8-15 are overwritten by bit 7 of the result. Bits 8-15 can be preserved in AND and OR instructions by using word operations where the upper byte of the source operand is FFH or 00H, respectively.

Program Transfer Instructions

Register TP controls the sequence in which channel program instructions are executed. As each instruction is executed, the length of the instruction is added to TP so that

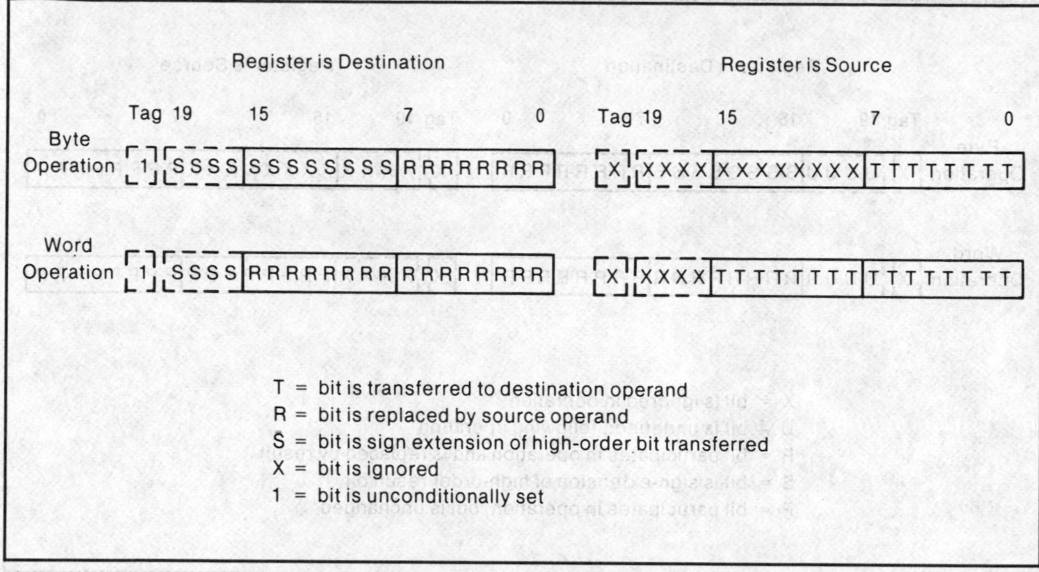

Figure 4-3 Register Operands in MOV Instructions

it points to the next sequential instruction. Program transfer instructions can alter this sequential instruction execution by adding a signed displacement value to TP. The displacement is contained in the program transfer instruction and may be either 8 or 16 bits long. The displacement is encoded in two's complement notation with the high-order bit indicating the displacement sign (0 = positive, 1 = negative). The range for an 8-bit displacement is −128 through +127 bytes from the end of the transfer instruction. The range for a 16-bit displacement is −32,768 through +32,767 bytes from the end of the transfer instruction. An instruction containing an 8-bit displacement is called a short transfer, and an instruction containing a 16-bit displacement is called a long transfer.

Each program transfer instruction has an alternate mnemonic. The alternate mnemonic begins with an "L". This

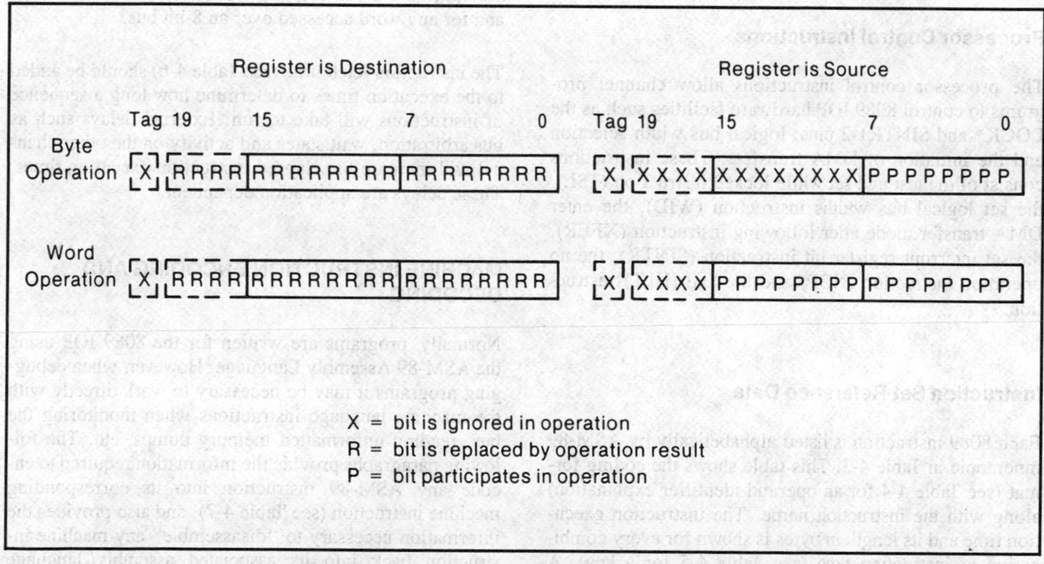

Figure 4-4 Register Operands in Arithmetic Instructions

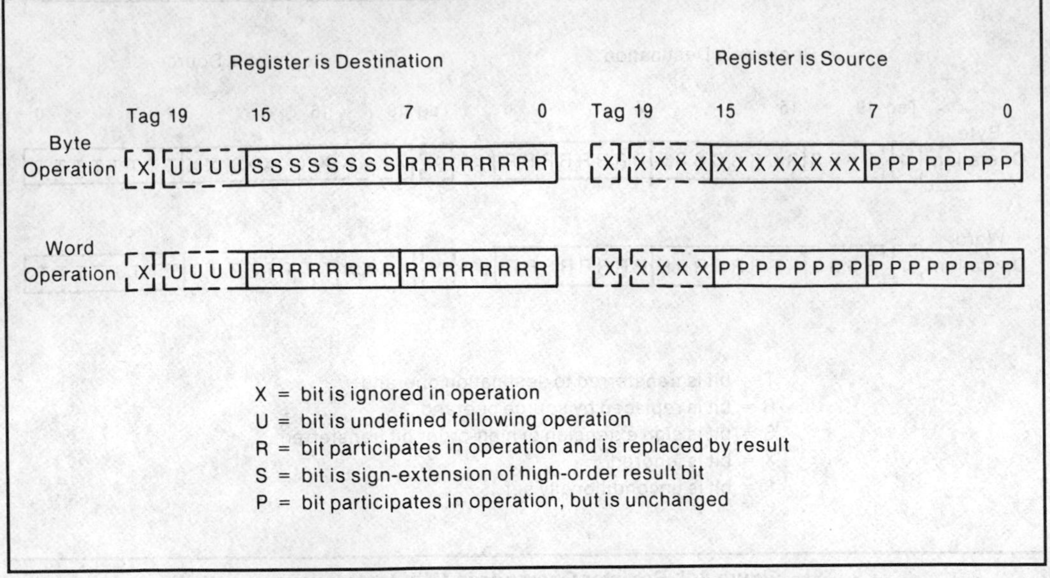

Figure 4-5 Register Operands in Logical Instructions

indicates the transfer is long and that the distance to the transfer target is expressed as a 16-bit displacement regardless of how far away the target location is located. If the instruction mnemonic does not begin with an "L" the ASM-89 assembler determines whether the transfer is long or short. Refer to Volume 1 of this manual for additional information on this function.

Processor Control Instructions

The processor control instructions allow channel programs to control 8089 IOP hardware facilities such as the LOCK* and SINTR1-2 pins, logical bus width selection and the initiation of DMA transfers. These instructions consist of the test and set while locked instruction (TSL), the set logical bus widths instruction (WID), the enter DMA transfer mode after following instruction (XFER), the set interrupt register bit instruction (SINTR), the no operation instruction (NOP) and the halt (HLT) instruction.

Instruction Set Reference Data

Each 8089 instruction is listed alphabetically by ASM-89 mnemonic in Table 4-3. This table shows the coding format (see Table 4-4 for an operand identifier explanation) along with the instruction name. The instruction execution time and its length in bytes is shown for every combination of instruction type (see Table 4-5 for a key). A coding example is also shown.

Instruction timing figures are given as the number of clock periods that are required to execute the instruction with a given combination of operands. When the CPU is operating at 5MHz, one clock period is 200ns, at 8MHz one clock period is 125ns. When an instruction operates on a memory word, two timings are provided. The first figure indicates execution time when the word is aligned on an even address and is accessed over a 16-bit bus. The second figure is for odd-addressed words on 16-bit buses and for any word accessed over an 8-bit bus.

The instruction fetch time (see Table 4-6) should be added to the execution times to determine how long a sequence of instructions will take to run. External delays such as bus arbitration, wait states and activity on the other channel will increase the elapsed instruction execution times. These delays are application dependent.

MACHINE INSTRUCTION ENCODING AND DECODING

Normally, programs are written for the 8089 IOP using the ASM-89 Assembly Language. However, when debugging programs it may be necessary to work directly with the machine language instructions when monitoring the bus, reading unformatted memory dumps, etc. The following paragraphs provide the information required to encode any ASM-89 instruction into its corresponding machine instruction (see Table 4-7), and also provides the information necessary to "disassemble" any machine instruction back into its associated assembly language equivalent (see Table 4-8).

Table 4-3 Instruction Set Reference Data

ADD destination, source — Add Word Variable

Operands	Clocks	Bytes	Coding Example
register, mem16	11/15	2-3	ADD BC, [GA].LENGTH
mem16, register	16/26	2-3	ADD [GB], GC

ADDB destination, source — Add Byte Variable

Operands	Clocks	Bytes	Coding Example
register, mem8	11	2-3	ADDB GC, [GA].N_CHARS
mem8, register	16	2-3	ADDB [PP].ERRORS, MC

ADDBI destination, source — Add Byte Immediate

Operands	Clocks	Bytes	Coding Example
register, immed8	3	3	ADDBI MC,10
mem8, immed8	16	3-4	ADDBI [PP+IX+].RECORDS, 2CH

ADDI destination, source — Add Word Immediate

Operands	Clocks	Bytes	Coding Example
register, immed16	3	4	ADDI GB, 0C25BH
mem16, immed16	16/26	4-5	ADDI [GB].POINTER, 5899

AND destination, source — Logical AND Word Variable

Operands	Clocks	Bytes	Coding Example
register, mem16	11/15	2-3	AND MC, [GA].FLAG_WORD
mem16, register	16/26	2-3	AND [GC].STATUS, BC

ANDB destination, source — Logical AND Byte Variable

Operands	Clocks	Bytes	Coding Example
register, mem8	11	2-3	AND BC, [GC]
mem8, register	16	2-3	AND [GA+IX].RESULT, GA

ANDBI destination, source — Logical AND Byte Immediate

Operands	Clocks	Bytes	Coding Example
register, immed8	3	3	GA, 01100000B
mem8, immed8	16	3-4	[GC+IX], 2CH

Table 4-3 Instruction Set Reference Data (continued)

ANDI destination, source — Logical AND Word Immediate

Operands	Clocks	Bytes	Coding Example
register, immed16	3	4	IX, 0H
mem16, immed16	16/26	4-5	[GB+IX].TAB, 40H

CALL TPsave, target — Call

Operands	Clocks	Bytes	Coding Example
mem24, label	17/23	3-5	CALL [GC+IX].SAVE, GET_NEXT

CLR destination, bit select — Clear Bit To Zero

Operands	Clocks	Bytes	Coding Example
mem8, 0-7	16	2-3	CLR [GA], 3

DEC destination — Decrement Word By 1

Operands	Clocks	Bytes	Coding Example
register	3	2	
mem16	16/26	2-3	DEC [PP].RETRY

DECB destination — Decrement Byte By 1

Operands	Clocks	Bytes	Coding Example
mem8	16	2-3	DECB [GA+IX+].TAB

HLT (no operands) — Halt Channel Program

Operands	Clocks	Bytes	Coding Example
(no operands)	11	2	HLT

INC destination — Increment Word by 1

Operands	Clocks	Bytes	Coding Example
register	3	2	INC GA
mem16	16/26	2-3	INC [GA].COUNT

INCB destination — Increment Byte by 1

Operands	Clocks	Bytes	Coding Example
mem8	16	2-3	INCB [GB].POINTER

Table 4-3 Instruction Set Reference Data (continued)

JBT source, bit-select, target — Jump if Bit True (1)

Operands	Clocks	Bytes	Coding Example
mem8, 0-7, label	14	3-5	JBT [GA].RESULT_REG, 3, DATA_VALID

JMCE source, target — Jump if Masked Compare Equal

Operands	Clocks	Bytes	Coding Example
mem8, label	14	3-5	JMCE [GB].FLAG, STOP_SEARCH

JMCNE source, target — Jump if Masked Compare Not Equal

Operands	Clocks	Bytes	Coding Example
mem8, label	14	3-5	JMCNE [GB+IX], NEXT_ITEM

JMP target — Jump Unconditionally

Operands	Clocks	Bytes	Coding Example
label	3	3-4	JMP READ_SECTOR

JNBT source, bit-select, target — Jump if Bit Not True (0)

Operands	Clocks	Bytes	Coding Example
mem8, 0-7, label	14	3-5	JNBT [GC], 3, RE_READ

JNZ source, target — Jump if Word Not Zero

Operands	Clocks	Bytes	Coding Example
register, label	5	3-4	JNZ BC, WRITE_LINE
mem16, label	12/16	3-5	JNZ [PP].NUM_CHARS, PUT_BYTE

JNZB source, target — Jump if Byte Not Zero

Operands	Clocks	Bytes	Coding Example
mem8, label	12	3-5	JNZB [GA], MORE_DATA

JZ source, target — Jump if Word is Zero

Operands	Clocks	Bytes	Coding Example
register, label	5	3-4	JZ BC, NEXT_LINE
mem16, label	12/16	3-5	JZ [GC+IX].INDEX, BUF_EMPTY

Table 4-3 Instruction Set Reference Data (continued)

JZB source, target — Jump if Byte Zero

Operands	Clocks	Bytes	Coding Example
mem8, label	12	3-5	JZB [PP].LINES_LEFT, RETURN

LCALL TPsave, target — Long Call

Operands	Clocks	Bytes	Coding Example
mem24, label	17/23	4-5	LCALL [GC].RETURN_SAVE, INIT_8279

LJBT source, bit-select, target — Long Jump if Bit True (1)

Operands	Clocks	Bytes	Coding Example
mem8, 0-7, label	14	4-5	LJBT [GA].RESULT, 1, DATA_OK

LJMCE source, target — Long jump if Masked Compare Equal

Operands	Clocks	Bytes	Coding Example
mem8, label	14	4-5	LJMCE [GB], BYTE_FOUND

LJMCNE source, target — Long jump if Masked Compare Not Equal

Operands	Clocks	Bytes	Coding Example
mem8, label	14	4-5	LJMCNE [GC+IX+], SCAN_NEXT

LJMP target — Long Jump Unconditional

Operands	Clocks	Bytes	Coding Example
label	3	4	LJMP GET_CURSOR

LJNBT source, bit-select, target — Long Jump if Bit Not True (0)

Operands	Clocks	Bytes	Coding Example
mem8, 0-7, label	14	4-5	LJNBT [GC], 6, CRCC_ERROR

LJNZ source, target — Long Jump if Word Not Zero

Operands	Clocks	Bytes	Coding Example
register, label	5	4	LJNZ BC, PARTIAL_XMIT
mem16, label	12/16	4-5	LJNZ [GA+IX].N_LEFT, PUT_DATA

Table 4-3 Instruction Set Reference Data (continued)

LJNZB source, target — Long Jump if Byte Not Zero

Operands	Clocks	Bytes	Coding Example
mem8, label	12	4-5	LJNZB [GB+IX+].ITEM, BUMP_COUNT

LJZ source, target — Long Jump if Word Zero

Operands	Clocks	Bytes	Coding Example
register, label	5	4	LJZ IX, FIRST_ELEMENT
mem16, label	12/16	4-5	LJZ [GB].XMIT_COUNT, NO_DATA

LJZB source, target — Long Jump if Byte Zero

Operands	Clocks	Bytes	Coding Example
mem8, label	12	4-5	LJZB [GA], RETURN_LINE

LPD destination, source — Load Pointer With Doubleword Variable

Operands	Clocks	Bytes	Coding Example
ptr-reg, mem32	20/28*	2-3	LPD GA, [PP].BUF_START

*20 clocks if operand is on even address; 28 if on odd address

LPDI destination, source — Load Pointer With Doubleword Immediate

Operands	Clocks	Bytes	Coding Example
ptr-reg, immed32	12/16*	6	LPDI GB, DISK_ADDRESS

*12 clocks if instruction is on even address; 16 if on odd address

MOV destination, source — Move Word

Operands	Clocks	Bytes	Coding Example
register, mem16	8/12	2-3	MOV IX, [GC]
mem16, register	10/16	2-3	MOV [GA].COUNT, BC
mem16, mem16	18/28	4-6	MOV [GA].READING, [GB]

MOVB destination, source — Move Byte

Operands	Clocks	Bytes	Coding Example
register, mem8	8	2-3	MOVB BC, [PP].TRAN_COUNT
mem8, register	10	2-3	MOVB [PP].RETURN_CODE, GC
mem8, mem8	18	4-6	MOVB [GB+IX+], [GA+IX+]

MOVBI destination, source — Move Byte Immediate

Operands	Clocks	Bytes	Coding Example
register, immed8	3	3	MOVBI MC, 'A'
mem8, immed8	12	3-4	MOVBI [PP].RESULT, 0

Table 4-3 Instruction Set Reference Data (continued)

MOVI destination, source — Move Word Immediate

Operands	Clocks	Bytes	Coding Example
register, immed16	3	4	MOVI BC, 0
mem16, immed16	12/18	4-5	MOVI [GB], 0FFFFH

MOVP destination, source — Move Pointer

Operands	Clocks	Bytes	Coding Example
ptr-reg, mem24	19/27*	2-3	MOVP TP, [GC+IX]
mem24, ptr-reg	16/22*	2-3	MOVP [GB].SAVE__ADDR, GC

*First figure is for operand on even address; second is for odd-addressed operand.

NOP (no operands) — No Operation

Operands	Clocks	Bytes	Coding Example
(no operands)	4	2	NOP

NOT destination/destination, source — Logical NOT Word

Operands	Clocks	Bytes	Coding Example
register	3	2	NOT MC
mem16	16/26	2-3	NOT [GA].PARM
register, mem16	11/15	2-3	NOT BC, [GA+IX].LINES__LEFT

NOTB destination/destination, source — Logical NOT Byte

Operands	Clocks	Bytes	Coding Example
mem8	16	2-3	NOTB [GA].PARM__REG
register, mem8	11	2-3	NOTB IX, [GB].STATUS

OR destination, source — Logical OR Word

Operands	Clocks	Bytes	Coding Example
register, mem16	11/15	2-3	OR MC, [GC].MASK
mem16, register	16/26	2-3	OR [GC], BC

ORB destination, source — Logical OR Byte

Operands	Clocks	Bytes	Coding Example
register, mem8	11	2-3	ORB IX, [PP].POINTER
mem8, register	16	2-3	ORB [GA+IX+], GB

ORBI destination, source — Logical OR Byte Immediate

Operands	Clocks	Bytes	Coding Example
register, immed8	3	3	ORBI IX, 00010001B
mem8, immed8	16	3-4	ORBI [GB].COMMAND, 0CH

Table 4-3 Instruction Set Reference Data (continued)

ORI destination, source		Logical OR Word Immediate	
Operands	**Clocks**	**Bytes**	**Coding Example**
register, immed16 mem16,immed16	3 16/26	4 4-5	ORI MC, 0FF0DH ORI [GA], 1000H

SETB destination, bit-select		Set Bit to 1	
Operands	**Clocks**	**Bytes**	**Coding Example**
mem8, 0-7	16	2-3	SETB [GA].PARM REG, 2

SINTR (no operands)		Set Interrupt Service Bit	
Operands	**Clocks**	**Bytes**	**Coding Example**
(no operands)	4	2	SINTR

TSL destination, set-value, target		Test and Set While Locked	
Operands	**Clocks**	**Bytes**	**Coding Example**
mem8, immed8, short-label	14/16*	4-5	TSL [GA].FLAG, 0FFH, NOT_READY

*14 clocks if destination ≠ 0; 16 clocks if destination = 0

WID source-width, dest-width		Set Logical Bus Widths	
Operands	**Clocks**	**Bytes**	**Coding Example**
8/16, 8/16	4	2	WID 8, 8

XFER (no operands)		Enter DMA Transfer Mode After Next Instruction	
Operands	**Clocks**	**Bytes**	**Coding Example**
(no operands)	4	2	XFER

Table 4-4 Operand Identifiers Definitions

IDENTIFIER	USED IN	EXPLANATION
destination	data transfer, arithmetic, bit manipulation	A register or memory location that may contain data operated on by the instruction, and which receives (is replaced by) the result of the operation.
source	data transfer, arithmetic, bit manipulation	A register, memory location, or immediate value that is used in the operation, but is not altered by the instruction.
target	program transfer	Location to which control is to be transferred.
TPsave	program transfer	A 24-bit memory location where the address of the next sequential instruction is to be saved.
bit-select	bit manipulation	Specification of a bit location within a byte; 0=least-significant (rightmost) bit, 7=most-significant (leftmost) bit.
set-value	TSL	Value to which destination is set if it is found 0.
source-width	WID	Logical width of source bus.
dest-width	WID	Logical width of destination bus.

Table 4-5 Operand Type Definitions

IDENTIFIER	EXPLANATION
(no operands)	No operands are written
register	Any general register
ptr-reg	A pointer register
immed8	A constant in the range 0-FFH
immed16	A constant in the range 0-FFFFH
mem8	An 8-bit memory location (byte)
mem16	A 16-bit memory location (word)
mem24	A 24-bit memory location (physical address pointer)
mem32	A 32-bit memory location (doubleword pointer)
label	A label within −32,768 to +32,767 bytes of the end of the instruction
short-label	A label within −128 to +127 bytes of the end of the instruction
0-7	A constant in the range: 0-7
8/16	The constant 8 or the constant 16

Table 4-6 Instruction Fetch Timings (Clock Periods)

INSTRUCTION LENGTH (BYTES)	BUS WIDTH		
	8	16	
		(1)	(2)
2	14	7	11
3	18	14	11
4	22	14	15
5	26	18	15

(1) First byte of instruction is on an even address.

(2) First byte of instruction is on an odd address. Add 3 clocks if first byte is not in queue (e.g., first instruction following program transfer).

Almost all 8089 machine instructions consist of from two to five bytes (see Figure 4-6). The only exceptions to this rule are the LPDI and memory-to-memory forms of the MOV and MOVB instructions which are six bytes long. The first two bytes are always present and are generally formatted as shown in Figure 4-6. See Table 4-7 for the exact encoding of every instruction.

The first byte of the instruction has four fields. Bits 5 through 7 comprise the R/B/P field. This field identifies a register, bit select or pointer register (see Table 4-9).

Bits 3 and 4 are the WB field. This field indicates how many displacement/data bytes are present in the instruction (see Table 4-10). The displacement bytes are used in program transfers. One byte is present for short transfers, while long transfers contain two-byte (word) displacement. The displacement is stored on two's complement notation with the high-order bit indicating the sign. Data bytes contain the value of an immediate constant operand. A byte immediate instruction (MOVBI) will have one data byte, and a word immediate instruction (ADDI) will have two bytes (a word) of immediate data. An instruction may contain either displacement or data bytes, but not both (the TSL instruction is an exception and contains one byte of displacement and one byte of data). If an offset byte is present, the displacement/data byte(s) always follow the offset byte.

The AA field specifies the addressing mode that the processor should use to construct the effective address of a memory operand. Four additional address modes are available (see Table 4-11).

The zero bit in the first instruction indicates whether the instruction operates on a byte (W = 0) or a wore (W = 1).

In the second instruction byte, bits 7 through 2 specify the instruction opcode (see Table 4-8 for a list of every assembly language instruction in hexadecimal order). The opcode, in conjunction with the W field of the first byte, identifies the instruction. For example, the opcode "111011" is the decrement instruction. If W = 0, the assembly language instruction for this opcode would be DECB. If W = 1, the instruction is DEC.

The MM field in the second byte (bits 0 and 1) indicate which pointer (base) register should be used to construct the effective address of a memory operand. See Table 4-12 for MM field encoding.

When the AA field value is "01" (base register + offset addressing), the third byte of the instruction contains the offset value. This unsigned value is added to the content of the base register by the MM field to from the effective address of the memory operand.

When the AA field is "10", the IX register value is added to the content of the base register specified by the MM field to provide a 64k range of effective addresses. The upper four bits of the IX register are not signed.

When the AA field value is "11", the IX register value is added to the base register value to form the effective address as described for the AA field value of "10". In this addressing mode the IX register value is incremented by one after every byte accessed.

Table 4-7 8089 Instruction Encoding

DATA TRANSFER INSTRUCTIONS

MOV = Move word variable	7 6 5 4 3 2 1 0	7 6 5 4 3 2 1 0	7 6 5 4 3 2 1 0	7 6 5 4 3 2 1 0	7 6 5 4 3 2 1 0	7 6 5 4 3 2 1 0
Memory to register	R R R 0 0 A A 1	1 0 0 0 0 0 M M	offset if AA=01			
Register to memory	R R R 0 0 A A 1	1 0 0 0 0 1 M M	offset if AA=01			
Memory to memory	0 0 0 0 0 A A 1	1 0 0 1 0 0 M M	offset if AA=01	0 0 0 0 0 A A 1	1 1 0 0 1 1 M M	offset if AA=01

Table 4-7 8089 Instruction Encoding (continued)

DATA TRANSFER INSTRUCTIONS (Cont'd.)

Instruction	7 6 5 4 3 2 1 0	7 6 5 4 3 2 1 0	7 6 5 4 3 2 1 0	7 6 5 4 3 2 1 0	7 6 5 4 3 2 1 0	7 6 5 4 3 2 1 0
MOVB = Move byte variable						
Memory to register	R R R 0 0 A A 0	1 0 0 0 0 0 M M	offset if AA=01			
Register to memory	R R R 0 0 A A 0	1 0 0 0 0 1 M M	offset if AA=01			
Memory to memory	0 0 0 0 0 A A 0	1 0 0 1 0 0 M M	offset if AA=01	0 0 0 0 0 A A 0	1 1 0 0 1 1 M M	offset if AA=01
MOVBI = Move byte immediate						
Immediate to register	R R R 0 1 0 0 0	0 0 1 1 0 0 0 0	data-8			
Immediate to memory	0 0 0 0 1 A A 0	0 1 0 0 1 1 M M	offset if AA=01	data-8		
MOVI = Move word immediate						
Immediate to register	R R R 1 0 0 0 1	0 0 1 1 0 0 0 0	data-lo	data-hi		
Immediate to memory	0 0 0 1 0 A A 1	0 1 0 0 1 1 M M	offset if AA=01	data-lo	data-hi	
MOVP = Move pointer						
Memory to pointer register	P P P 0 0 A A 1	1 0 0 0 1 1 M M	offset if AA=01			
Pointer register to memory	P P P 0 0 A A 1	1 0 0 1 1 0 M M	offset if AA=01			
LPD = Load pointer with doubleword variable	P P P 0 0 A A 1	1 0 0 0 1 0 M M	offset if AA=01			
LPDI = Load pointer with doubleword immediate	P P P 1 0 0 0 1	0 0 0 0 1 0 0 0	offset-lo	offset-hi	segment-lo	segment-hi

ARITHMETIC INSTRUCTIONS

Instruction	7 6 5 4 3 2 1 0	7 6 5 4 3 2 1 0	7 6 5 4 3 2 1 0	7 6 5 4 3 2 1 0	7 6 5 4 3 2 1 0
ADD = Add word variable					
Memory to register	R R R 0 0 A A 1	1 0 1 0 0 0 M M	offset if AA=01		
Register to memory	R R R 0 0 A A 1	1 1 0 1 0 0 M M	offset if AA=01		
ADDB = Add byte variable					
Memory to register	R R R 0 0 A A 0	1 0 1 0 0 0 M M	offset if AA=01		
Register to memory	R R R 0 0 A A 0	1 1 0 1 0 0 M M	offset if AA=01		
ADDI = Add word immediate					
Immediate to register	R R R 1 0 0 0 1	0 0 1 0 0 0 0 0	data-lo	data-hi	
Immediate to memory	0 0 0 1 0 A A 1	1 1 0 0 0 0 M M	offset if AA=01	data-lo	data-hi

Table 4-7 8089 Instruction Encoding (continued)

ARITHMETIC INSTRUCTIONS (Cont'd.)

Instruction	7 6 5 4 3 2 1 0	7 6 5 4 3 2 1 0	7 6 5 4 3 2 1 0	7 6 5 4 3 2 1 0	7 6 5 4 3 2 1 0	7 6 5 4 3 2 1 0
ADDBI = Add byte immediate						
Immedaite to register	R R R 0 1 0 0 0	0 0 1 0 0 0 0 0	data-8			
Immediate to memory	0 0 0 0 1 A A 0	1 1 0 0 0 0 M M	offset if AA=01	data-8		
INC = Increment word by 1						
Register	R R R 0 0 0 0 0	0 0 1 1 1 0 0 0				
Memory	0 0 0 0 0 A A 1	1 1 1 0 1 0 M M	offset if AA=01			
INCB = Increment byte by 1	0 0 0 0 0 A A 0	1 1 1 0 1 0 M M	offset if AA=01			
DEC = Decrement word by 1						
Register	R R R 0 0 0 0 0	0 0 1 1 1 1 0 0				
Memory	0 0 0 0 0 A A 1	1 1 1 0 1 1 M M	offset if AA=01			
DECB = Decrement byte by 1	0 0 0 0 0 A A 0	1 1 1 0 1 1 M M	offset if AA=01			

LOGICAL AND BIT MANIPULATION INSTRUCTIONS

Instruction	Byte 1	Byte 2	Byte 3	Byte 4	Byte 5
AND = AND word variable					
Memory to register	R R R 0 0 A A 1	1 0 1 0 1 0 M M	offset if AA=01		
Register to memory	R R R 0 0 A A 1	1 1 0 1 1 0 M M	offset if AA=01		
ANDB = AND byte variable					
Memory to register	R R R 0 0 A A 0	1 0 1 0 1 0 M M	offset if AA=01		
Register to memory	R R R 0 0 A A 0	1 1 0 1 1 0 M M	offset if AA=01		
ANDI = AND word immediate					
Immediate to register	R R R 1 0 0 0 1	0 0 1 0 1 0 0 0	data-lo	data-hi	
Immediate to memory	0 0 0 1 0 A A 1	1 1 0 0 1 0 M M	offset if AA=01	data-lo	data-hi
ANDBI = AND byte immediate					
Immediate to register	R R R 0 1 0 0 0	0 0 1 0 1 0 0 0	data-8		
Immediate to memory	0 0 0 0 1 A A 0	1 1 0 0 1 0 M M	offset if AA=01	data-8	
OR = OR word variable					
Memory to register	R R R 0 0 A A 1	1 0 1 0 0 1 M M	offset if AA=01		
Register to memory	R R R 0 0 A A 1	1 1 0 1 0 1 M M	offset if AA=01		

Table 4-7 8089 Instruction Encoding (continued)

LOGICAL AND BIT MANIPULATION INSTRUCTIONS (Cont'd.)

Instruction	7 6 5 4 3 2 1 0	7 6 5 4 3 2 1 0	7 6 5 4 3 2 1 0	7 6 5 4 3 2 1 0	7 6 5 4 3 2 1 0	7 6 5 4 3 2 1 0
ORB = OR byte variable						
Memory to register	R R R 0 0 A A 0	1 0 1 0 0 1 M M	offset if AA=01			
Register to memory	R R R 0 0 A A 0	1 1 0 1 0 1 M M	offset if AA=01			
ORI = OR word immediate						
Immediate to register	R R R 1 0 0 0 1	0 0 1 0 0 1 0 0	data-lo	data-hi		
Immediate to memory	0 0 0 1 0 A A 1	1 1 0 0 0 1 M M	offset if AA=01	data-lo	data-hi	
ORBI = OR byte immediate						
Immediate to register	R R R 0 1 0 0 0	0 0 1 0 0 1 0 0	data-8			
Immediate to memory	0 0 0 0 1 A A 0	1 1 0 0 0 1 M M	offset if AA=01	data-8		
NOT = NOT word variable						
Register	R R R 0 0 0 0 0	0 0 1 0 1 1 0 0				
Memory	0 0 0 0 0 A A 1	1 1 0 1 1 1 M M	offset if AA=01			
Memory to register	R R R 0 0 A A 1	1 0 1 0 1 1 M M	offset if AA=01			
NOTB = NOT byte variable						
Memory	0 0 0 0 0 A A 0	1 1 0 1 1 1 M M	offset if AA=01			
Memory to register	R R R 0 0 A A 0	1 0 1 0 1 1 M M	offset if AA=01			
SETB = Set bit to 1	B B B 0 0 A A 0	1 1 1 1 0 1 M M	offset if AA=01			
CLR = Clear bit to 0	B B B 0 0 A A 0	1 1 1 1 1 0 M M	offset if AA=01			
PROGRAM TRANSFER INSTRUCTIONS						
***CALL** = Call	1 0 0 0 1 A A 1	1 0 0 1 1 1 M M	offset if AA=01	disp-8		
LCALL = Long call	1 0 0 1 0 A A 1	1 0 0 1 1 1 M M	offset if AA=01	disp-lo	disp-hi	
***JMP** = Jump unconditional	1 0 0 0 1 0 0 0	0 0 1 0 0 0 0 0	disp-8			
LJMP = Long jump unconditional	1 0 0 1 0 0 0 1	0 0 1 0 0 0 0 0	disp-lo	disp-hi		

*The ASM-89 Assembler will automatically generate the long form of a program transfer instruction when the target is known to be beyond the byte-displacement range.

Table 4-7 8089 Instruction Encoding (continued)

PROGRAM TRANSFER INSTRUCTIONS (Cont'd.)

Instruction		7 6 5 4 3 2 1 0	7 6 5 4 3 2 1 0	7 6 5 4 3 2 1 0	7 6 5 4 3 2 1 0	7 6 5 4 3 2 1 0	7 6 5 4 3 2 1 0
***JZ** = Jump if word is 0							
	Label to register	R R R 0 1 0 0 0	0 1 0 0 0 1 0 0	disp-8			
	Label to memory	0 0 0 0 1 A A 1	1 1 1 0 0 1 M M	offset if AA=01	disp-8		
LJZ = Long jump if word is 0							
	Label to register	R R R 1 0 0 0 0	0 1 0 0 0 1 0 0	disp-lo	disp-hi		
	Label to memory	0 0 0 1 0 A A 1	1 1 1 0 0 1 M M	offset if AA=01	disp-lo	disp-hi	
***JZB** = Jump if byte is 0		0 0 0 0 1 A A 0	1 1 1 0 0 1 M M	offset if AA=01	disp-8		
LJZB = Long jump if byte is 0		0 0 0 1 0 A A 0	1 1 1 0 0 1 M M	offset if AA=01	disp-lo	disp-hi	
***JNZ** = Jump if word not 0							
	Label to register	R R R 0 1 0 0 0	0 1 0 0 0 0 0 0	disp-8			
	Label to memory	0 0 0 0 1 A A 1	1 1 1 0 0 0 M M	offset if AA=01	disp-8		
LJNZ = Long jump if word not 0							
	Label to register	R R R 1 0 0 0 0	0 1 0 0 0 0 0 0	disp-lo	disp-hi		
	Label to memory	0 0 0 1 0 A A 1	1 1 1 0 0 0 M M	offset if AA=01	disp-lo	disp-hi	
***JNZB** = Jump if byte not 0		0 0 0 0 1 A A 0	1 1 1 0 0 0 M M	offset if AA=01	disp-8		
LJNZB = Long jump if byte not 0		0 0 0 1 0 A A 0	1 1 1 0 0 0 M M	offset if AA=01	disp-lo	disp-hi	
***JMCE** = Jump if masked compare equal		0 0 0 0 1 A A 0	1 0 1 1 0 0 M M	offset if AA=01	disp-8		
LJMCE = Long jump if masked compare equal		0 0 0 1 0 A A 0	1 0 1 1 0 0 M M	offset if AA=01	disp-lo	disp-hi	
***JMCNE** = Jump if masked compare not equal		0 0 0 0 1 A A 0	1 0 1 1 0 1 M M	offset if AA=01	disp-8		
LJMCNE = Long jump if masked compare not equal		0 0 0 1 0 A A 0	1 0 1 1 0 1 M M	offset if AA=01	disp-lo	disp-hi	
***JBT** = Jump if bit is 1		B B B 0 1 A A 0	1 0 1 1 1 1 M M	offset if AA=01	disp-8		

*The ASM-89 Assembler will automatically generate the long form of a program transfer instruction when the target is known to be beyond the byte-displacement range.

Table 4-7 8089 Instruction Encoding (continued)

PROGRAM TRANSFER INSTRUCTIONS (Cont'd.)

Instruction	7 6 5 4 3 2 1 0	7 6 5 4 3 2 1 0	7 6 5 4 3 2 1 0	7 6 5 4 3 2 1 0	7 6 5 4 3 2 1 0	7 6 5 4 3 2 1 0
LJBT = Long jump if bit is 1	B B B 1 0 A A 0	1 0 1 1 1 1 M M	offset if AA=01	disp-lo	disp-hi	
***JNBT** = Jump if bit is not 1	B B B 0 1 A A 0	1 0 1 1 1 0 M M	offset if AA=01	disp-8		
LJNBT = Long jump if bit is not 1	B B B 1 0 A A 0	1 0 1 1 1 0 M M	offset if AA=01	disp-lo	disp-hi	

PROCESSOR CONTROL INSTRUCTIONS

Instruction	7 6 5 4 3 2 1 0	7 6 5 4 3 2 1 0	7 6 5 4 3 2 1 0	7 6 5 4 3 2 1 0	7 6 5 4 3 2 1 0
TSL = Test and set while locked	0 0 0 1 1 A A 0	1 0 0 1 0 1 M M	offset if AA=01	data-8	disp-8
WID = Set logical bus widths	1 S D* 0 0 0 0 0	0 0 0 0 0 0 0 0			
XFER = Enter DMA mode	0 1 1 0 0 0 0 0	0 0 0 0 0 0 0 0			
SINTR = Set interrupt service bit	0 1 0 0 0 0 0 0	0 0 0 0 0 0 0 0			
HLT = Halt channel program	0 0 1 0 0 0 0 0	0 1 0 0 1 0 0 0			
NOP = No operation	0 0 0 0 0 0 0 0	0 0 0 0 0 0 0 0			

*S=source width, D=destination width; 0=8 bits, 1=16 bits

*The ASM-89 Assembler will automatically generate the long form of a program transfer instruction when the target is known to be beyond the byte-displacement range.

4.3 DEVICE PIN ASSIGNMENTS

Figure 4-7 shows the 8089 IOP DIP pin assignments and Table 4-13 provides a complete function description of each device pin signal and correlates the description to the pin number and associated signal symbol.

4.4 OPERATING MODES

Communication between a CPU and the 8089 IOP occurs in two distinct modes: initialization and command. Initialization is typically performed when the system is powered-up or reset. The CPU initializes the IOP by preparing a series of linked message blocks in memory. On a signal from the CPU, the IOP reads these blocks and determines from them how the data buses are configured and how access to the buses is to be controlled.

After the initialization process is completed, the CPU directs all communications to either of the IOP's two channels. During normal operations the IOP actually appears to be two separate devices, channel 1 and channel 2. All CPU-to-channel communications centers on the channel control block (CB — see Figure 4-8). The CB is located in the CPU's memory space, and its address is passed to the IOP during initialization. Half of the control block is dedicated to each channel. Each channel maintains a BUSY flag to indicate whether it is in the midst of an operation or is available for a new command from the CPU. The CPU sets the channel command word (CCW) to indicate what kind of operation it wants the IOP to perform. There

Table 4-8 8089 Machine Instruction Decoding Guide

Identifier	Explanation
S	Logical width of source bus; 0=8, 1=16
D	Logical width of destination bus; 0=8, 1=16
PPP	Pointer register encoded in R/B/P field
RRR	Register encoded in R/B/P field
AA	AA (addressing mode) field
BBB	Bit select encoded in R/B/P field
offset-lo	Low-order byte of offset word in doubleword pointer
offset-hi	High-order byte of offset word in doubleword pointer
segment-lo	Low-order byte of segment word in doubleword pointer
segment-hi	High-order byte of segment word in doubleword pointer
data-8	8-bit immediate constant
data-lo	Low-order byte of 16-bit immediate constant
data-hi	High-order byte of 16-bit immediate constant
disp-8	8-bit signed displacement
disp-lo	Low-order byte of 16-bit signed displacement
disp-hi	High-order byte of 16-bit signed displacement
(offset)	Optional 8-bit offset used in offset addressing

Table 4-9 R/B/P Field Encoding

Code	Register	Bit	Pointer
000	GA	0	GA
001	GB	1	GB
010	GC	2	GC
011	BC	3	N/A
100	TP	4	TP
101	IX	5	N/A
110	CC	6	N/A
111	MC	7	N/A

are six different commands that allow the CPU to start or stop programs, remove interrupt requests, etc.

When the CPU desires a specific channel to run a program, it directs the channel to a parameter control block

Table 4-10 WB Field Encoding

Code	Interpretation
00	No displacement/data bytes
01	One displacement/data byte
10	Two displacement/data bytes
11	TSL instruction only

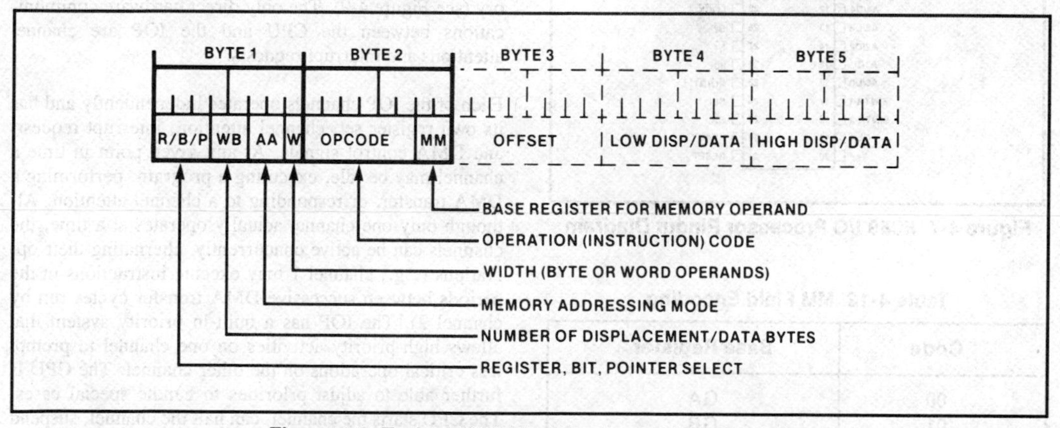

Figure 4-6 Typical 8089 Machine Instruction Format

Table 4-11 AA Field Encoding

Code	Interpretation
00	Base register only
01	Base register plus offset
10	Base register plus IX
11	Base register plus IX, auto-increment

(PB) and a task block (TB). (See Figure 4-8.) The PB is a parameter list that contains variable data for the channel program to use in carrying out its assignment. The PB may also contains space for variables (results) that the channel is to return to the CPU. Except for the first two words, the format and size of the PB are completely open and may be set up to exchange any type of information between the CPU and the channel program.

A task block (TB) is a sequence of 8089 instructions that perform an operation (i.e., a channel program). There are no restrictions on what a channel program can do. Its function may be as simple or as complex as a particular application requires.

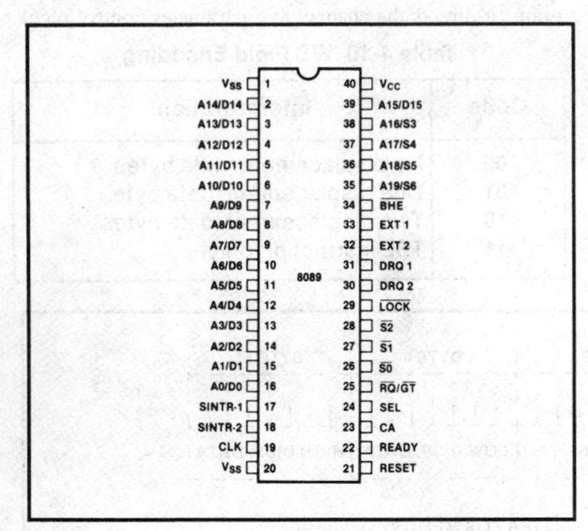

Figure 4-7 8089 I/O Processor Pinout Diagram

Table 4-12 MM Field Encoding

Code	Base Register
00	GA
01	GB
10	GC
11	PP

The CPU links the channel program (TB) to the parameter block (PB) before it starts the program (see Figure 4-8). This link is accomplished using standard 8086/88 double-word pointer variables where the lower-addressed word contains an offset and the higher-addresses word contains a segment base value. A system may have many different parameter and task blocks, but only one of each can be linked to a channel at any given time.

When the CPU has filled the CCW and linked the CB to a parameter block and task block, it issues a channel attention (CA). This is accomplished by activating the IOP's CA and SEL pins. The state of SEL on the falling edge of CA directs the channel attention to either channel 1 or channel 2. If the IOP is located in the CPU's I/O space, it will appear to the CPU as two consecutive I/O ports (one for each channel). At this time, an OUT instruction to the port functions as a CA. If the IOP is memory-mapped, the channels look like two memory locations and any memory reference instruction to these locations causes a channel attention.

An IOP channel attention is functionally similar to a CPU interrupt. When the channel recognizes the CA, it stops what it is doing (it will typically be idle) and examines the command in the CCW. If the channel is to start a program, it loads the addresses of the parameter and task blocks into internal registers, sets the BUSY flag and starts executing the channel program. After issuing the CA, the CPU is free to perform other functions. The IOP channel can perform its function in parallel with the CPU (subject to limitations imposed by bus configurations).

When the channel program is completed, the channel clears its BUSY flag in the CB to notify the CPU. The channel may also issue an interrupt request to the CPU.

Most communications between the CPU and IOP take place through "message areas" shared in common memory (see Figure 4-9). The only direct hardware communications between the CPU and the IOP are channel attentions and interrupt requests.

Each of the IOP channels operates independently and has its own register set, channel attention, interrupt request, and DMA control signals. At any given point in time a channel may be idle, executing a program, performing a DMA transfer, or responding to a channel attention. Although only one channel actually operates at a time, the channels can be active concurrently, alternating their operations (e.g., channel 1 may execute instructions in the periods between successive DMA transfer cycles run by channel 2). The IOP has a built-in priority system that allows high-priority activities on one channel to prempt less critical operations on the other channel. The CPU is further able to adjust priorities to handle special cases. The CPU starts the channel, can halt the channel, suspend channel operation, or cause the channel to resume suspended operations by placing different values in the CCW.

Table 4-13 8089 DIP Pin Assignments

Symbol	Type	Name and Function
A0–A15/ D0–D15	I/O	**Multiplexed Address and Data Bus:** The function of these lines are defined by the state of $\overline{S0}$, $\overline{S1}$ and $\overline{S2}$ lines. The pins are floated after reset and when the bus is not acquired. A8–A15 are stable on transfers to a physical 8-bit data bus (same bus as 8088), and are multiplexed with data on transfers to a 16-bit physical bus.
A16–A19/ S3–S6	O	**Address and Status:** Multiplexed most significant address lines and status information. The address lines are active only when addressing memory. Otherwise, the status lines are active and are encoded as shown below. The pins are floated after reset and when the bus is not acquired. **S6 S5 S4 S3** 1 1 0 0 DMA cycle on CH1 1 1 0 1 DMA cycle on CH2 1 1 1 0 Non-DMA cycle on CH1 1 1 1 1 Non-DMA cycle on CH2
$\overline{BHE}$	O	**Bus High Enable:** The Bus High Enable is used to enable data operations on the most significant half of the data bus (D8–D15). The signal is active low when a byte is to be transferred on the upper half of the data bus. The pin is floated after reset and when the bus is not acquired. $\overline{BHE}$ does not have to be latched.
$\overline{S0}$, $\overline{S1}$, $\overline{S2}$	O	**Status:** These are the status pins that define the IOP activity during any given cycle. They are encoded as shown below: **$\overline{S2}$ $\overline{S1}$ $\overline{S0}$** 0 0 0 Instruction fetch; I/O space 0 0 1 Data fetch; I/O space 0 1 0 Data store; I/O space 0 1 1 Not used 1 0 0 Instruction fetch; System Memory 1 0 1 Data fetch; System Memory 1 1 0 Data store; System Memroy 1 1 1 Passive The status lines are utilized by the bus controller and bus arbiter to generate all memory and I/O control signals. The signals change during T4 if a new cycle is to be entered while the return to passive state in T3 or T_W indicates the end of a cycle. The pins are floated after system reset and when the bus is not acquired.
READY	I	**Ready:** The ready signal received from the addressed device indicates that the device is ready for data transfer. The signal is active high and is synchronized by the 8284 clock generator.
$\overline{LOCK}$	O	**Lock:** The lock output signal indicates to the bus controller that the bus is needed for more than one contiguous cycle. It is set via the channel control register, and during the TSL instruction. The pin floats after reset and when the bus is not acquired. This output is active low.
RESET	I	**Reset:** The receipt of a reset signal causes the IOP to suspend all its activities and enter an idle state until a channel attention is received. The signal must be active for at least four clock cycles.
CLK	I	**Clock:** Clock provides all timing needed for internal IOP operation.
CA	I	**Channel Attention:** Gets the attention of the IOP. Upon the falling edge of this signal, the SEL input pin is examined to determine Master/Slave or CH1/CH2 information. This input is active high.
SEL	I	**Select:** The first CA received after system reset informs the IOP via the SEL line, whether it is a Master or Slave (0/1 for Master/Slave respectively) and starts the initialization sequence. During any other CA the SEL line signifies the selection of CH1/CH2. (0/1 respectively.)
DRQ1–2	I	**Data Request:** DMA request inputs which signal the IOP that a peripheral is ready to transfer/receive data using channels 1 or 2 respectively. The signals must be held active high until the appropriate fetch/stroke is initiated.
$\overline{RQ}/\overline{GT}$	I/O	**Request Grant:** Request Grant implements the communication dialogue required to arbitrate the use of the system bus (between IOP and CPU, LOCAL mode) or I/O bus when two IOPs share the same bus (REMOTE mode). The $\overline{RQ}/\overline{GT}$ signal is active low. An internal pull-up permits $\overline{RQ}/\overline{GT}$ to be left floating if not used.
SINTR1–2	O	**Signal Interrupt:** Signal Interrupt outputs from channels 1 and 2 respectively. The interrupts may be sent directly to the CPU or through the 8295A interrupt controller. They are used to indicate to the system the occurrence of user defined events.
EXT1–2	I	**External Terminate:** External terminate inputs for channels 1 and 2 respectively. The EXT signals will cause the termination of the current DMA transfer operation if the channel is so programmed by the channel control register. The signal must be held active high until termination is complete.
V_{CC}		**Voltage:** +5 volt power input.
V_{SS}		**Ground.**

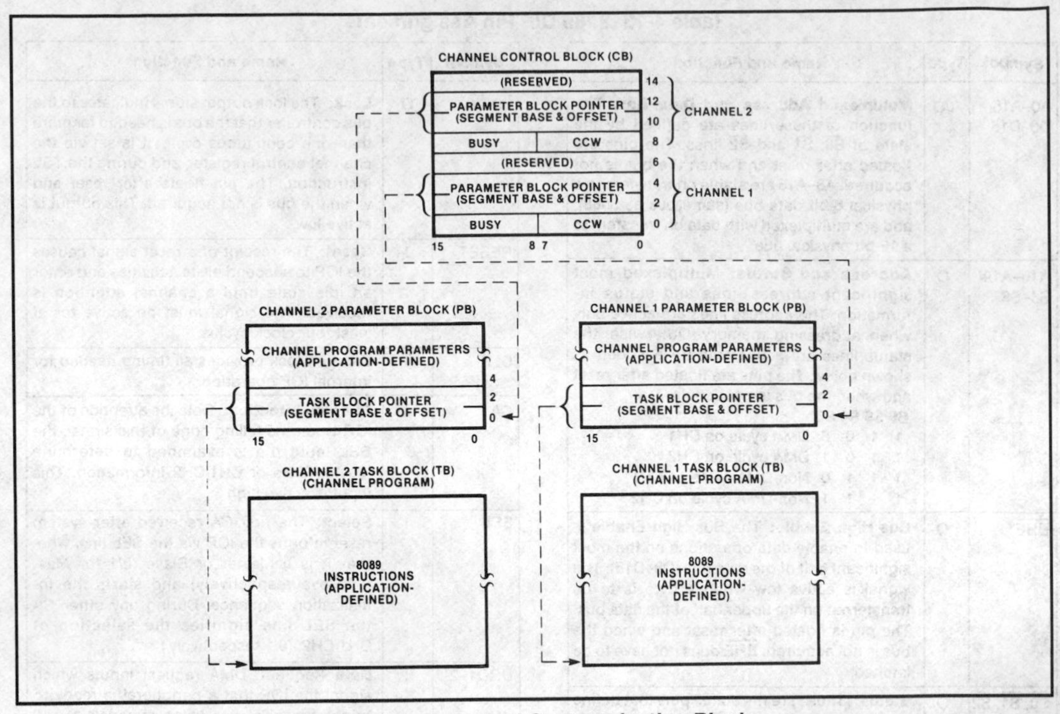

Figure 4-8 Command Communication Blocks

All channel programs (task blocks) are written in 8089 assembly language (ASM-89) using the 56 basic instructions available for these programs. The IOP instruction set contains general purpose instructions similar to those found in CPUs as well as instructions tailored especially for I/O operations (see paragraph 4.4.2 for details on these instructions). These instructions operate on bit, byte, word and doubleword (pointer) variable types. In addition, a 20-bit physical address type (not used by the 8086/88) can be manipulated. Data may be taken from registers, immediate constants and memory. Four memory addressing modes allow flexible access to both memory variables and I/O devices located anywhere in either the CPU's megabyte memory space or in the 8089's 64k I/O space. Data transfer, simple arithmetic, logical and address manipulation operations are available, as well as unconditional jump and call instructions that allow channel programs to link to each other. An individual bit may be set or cleared with a single instruction. Conditional jumps can test a bit and jump if it is set (or cleared), or can test a value and jump if it is zero (or non-zero). Other instructions are provided to initiate DMA transfers, a locked test-and-set semaphore operation and issue an interrupt request to the CPU.

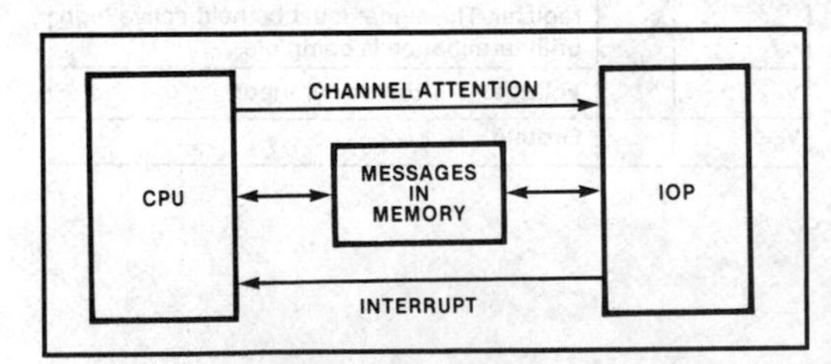

Figure 4-9 CPU/IOP Communications

4.4.1 Interfacing the 8089 to the 8086 and 80186

The 8089 IOP is functionally compatible with the iAPX 86, 88 family, and supports any combination of 8/16 bit buses. IOP hardware and communication architecture design provides simple mechanisms for system upgrade. Channel attention and interrupt lines handle the only direct communication between the IOP and CPU. The 8089 passes status information, parameters, and task programs through blocks of shared memory. This simplifies hardware interface and encourages structured programming (refer to Volume I of this User's Guide).

The 8089 can be used in one of two system configurations, local mode and remote mode. In the local mode the 8089 shares the system bus with an 8086/88 or 80186/188 CPU. In the remote mode the 8089 has exclusive access to

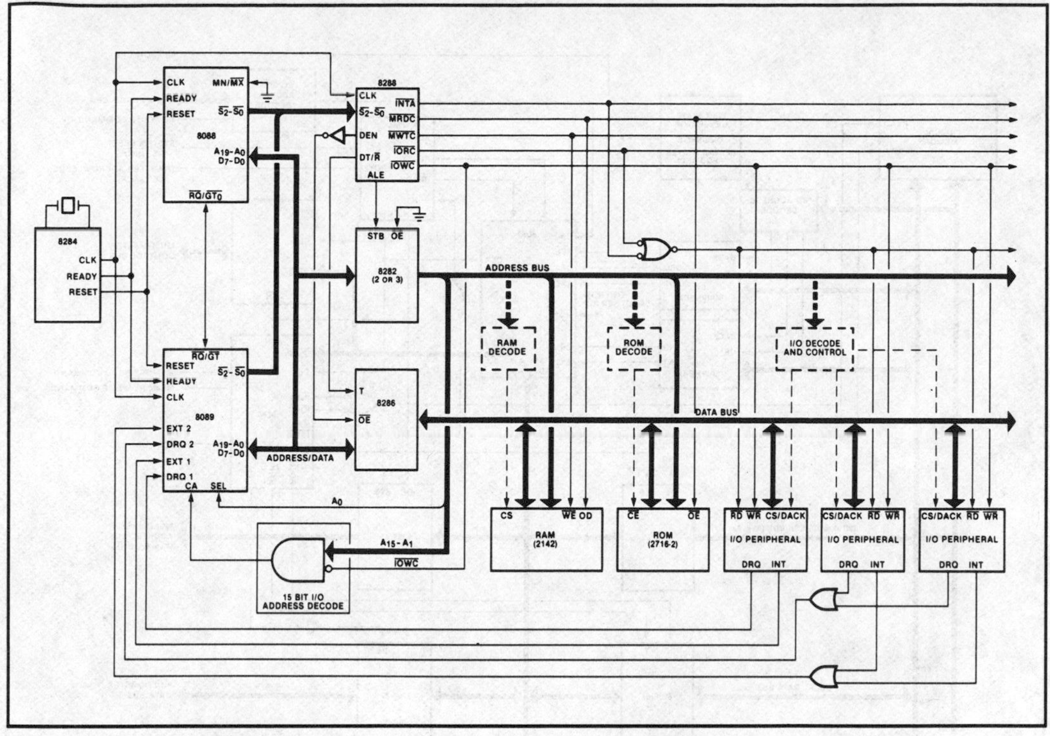

Figure 4-10 iAPX 86/11, 88/11 Configuration with 8089 in Local Mode

its own dedicated bus as well as access to the system Bus. In either mode, the 8089 can address a full megabyte of system memory and 64k bytes of its own I/O space.

LOCAL MODE

In the local mode, the 8089 acts as a slave to a maximum mode 8086 or 8088 CPU. In this configuration, the 8089 shares the system address latches, data transceivers and bus controller with the CPU (see Figure 4-10).

Since the IOP and CPU both share the system bus, either may have access to the bus at any one time. When one processor is using the bus, the other processor tri-states its address/data and control lines. Bus access between the IOP and CPU is determined through the request/grant function (refer to paragraph 4.6). To gain access to the bus, the IOP requests the bus from the CPU, the CPU grants the bus to the IOP, and the IOP relinquishes the bus to the CPU when it completes its operation.

NOTE

The CPU cannot request the bus from the IOP (the CPU is only capable of granting the bus and must wait for the IOP to release the bus).

Since the request/grant pulse exchange must be synchronized, both the CPU and IOP must be referenced to the same clock signal.

When the 8089 IOP is used in the local mode, it can be added to an 8086 or 8088 maximum mode configuration with little affect on component count (channel attention decoding logic used as required). It offers the benefits of intelligent DMA (scan/match, translate, variable termination conditions), modular programming in a full megabyte of memory address space and a set of optimized I/O instructions that are unavailable to the 8086 CPU. Since the system bus is shared in the local configuration, bus contention always exists between the CPU and IOP. Using the bus load limit field in the channel control word can help reduce IOP bus access during task block program execution (bus load limiting has no affect on DMA transfers). For I/O intensive systems, the design engineer should consider the remote mode.

REMOTE MODE

In the remote mode, the 8089 provides a multiprocessor system with true parallel processing. In this mode, the 8089 has a separate (local) bus and memory for I/O pe-

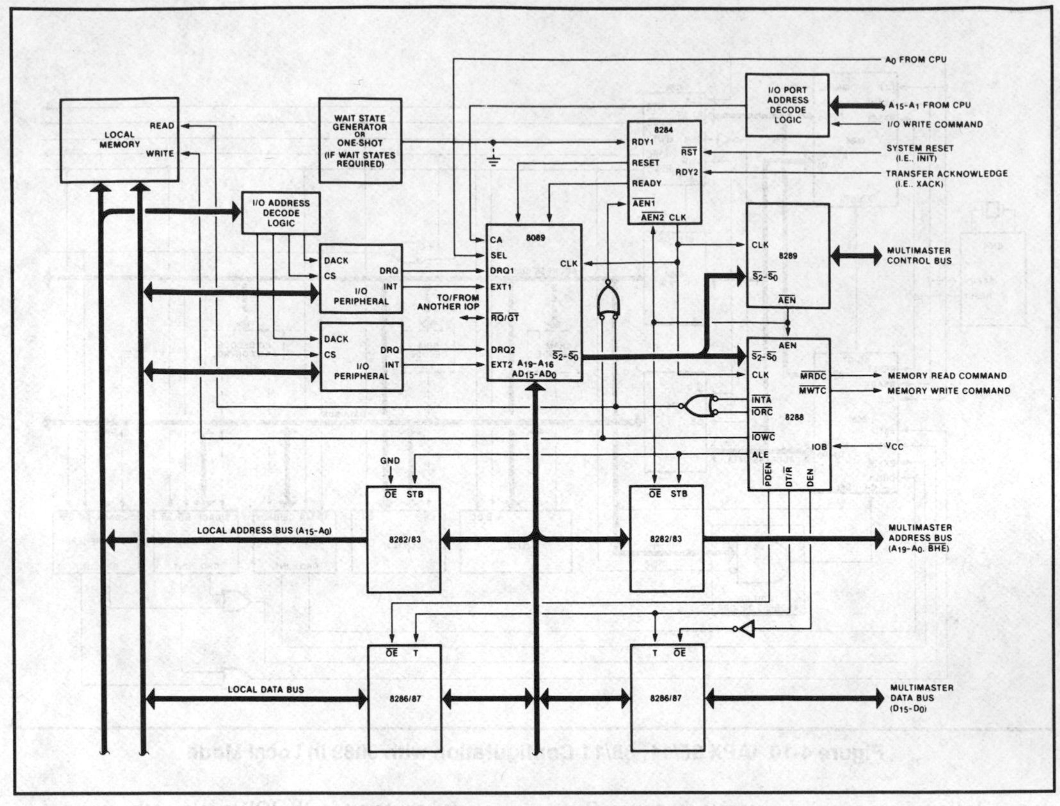

Figure 4-11 Typical 8089 Remote Configuration

ripheral communications, and the system bus is completely isolated from the I/O peripheral(s). In addition, I/O transfers between an I/O peripheral and the IOP's local memory can occur simultaneously with CPU operations on the system bus.

In a typical remote mode configuration, data transceivers and address latches (see Figure 4-11) separate the IOP's local bus from the system bus. An 8288 Bus Controller generates the bus control signals for both the local and system buses and governs the operation of the transceivers/latches. Also, an 8289 Bus Arbiter controls access to the system bus (each processor in the system would have an associated 8289 Bus Arbiter). To interface the 8089 to its local bus, another set of address latches is required (unless MCS-85 mutliplexed address components are used exclusively) and, depending on the bus loading demands, one (8-bit bus) or two (16-bit bus) data transceivers would be used.

The IOP's local bus is treated as up to 64k bytes of I/O space in the remote mode, and the system bus is treated as 1 megabyte of memory space. The 8288 Bus Controller's I/O command outputs control the local (I/O) bus, and its memory command outputs control the system (memory) bus. The 8289 Bus Arbiter, which is operated in its I/O peripheral bus mode, also decodes the 8289's status outputs (S2*-S0*). In this mode, the 8289 will not request the multi-master system bus when the IOP indicates an operation on its local bus. If the IOP's bus arbiter currently has access to the system bus, the CPU's arbiter (or any other arbiter in the system) can acquire use of the system bus at this time (a bus arbiter maintains bus access until another arbiter requests the bus).

4.4.2 IOP Initialization

IOP initialization is generally the responsibility of the host processor. The host processor prepares the communications data structure in shared memory (refer to Volume I of this User's Guide). Actual IOP initialization begins with activation of the IOP's RESET input. This input, which typically originates from an 8284A Clock Generator, must be held active for at least five clock cycles to allow the 8089's internal RESET sequence to be completed. Like the 8086 CPU, the RESET input to the IOP must be held active for at least 50 microseconds when power is first applied. When the reset interval is complete,

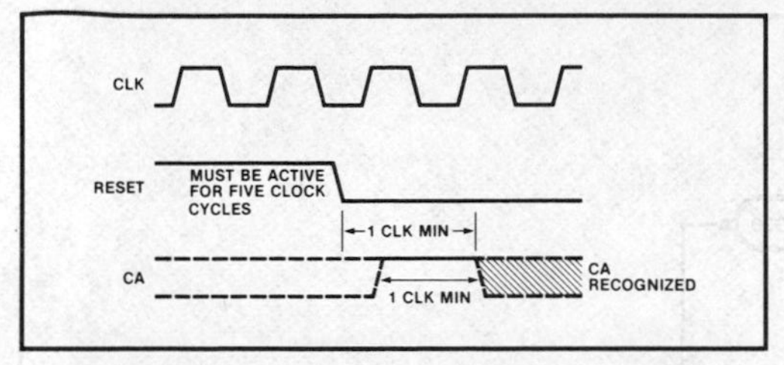

Figure 4-12 RESET-CA Initialization Timing

the host processor signals the IOP to begin its initialization sequence by activating the 8089's Channel Attention (CA) input. The 8089 does not recognize a pulse at its CA input until one clock cycle after the RESET input returns to an inactive level.

NOTE

The minimum width for a CA pulse does not occur prior to one clock. This pulse may go active prior to RESET returning to an inactive level provided that the negative-going, trailing-edge of the CA pulse does not occur prior to one clock cycle after RESET goes inactive (see Figure 4-12).

The 8089 samples the Select (SEL) input from the host, coincident with the trailing edge of the first CA pulse after RESET, to determine master/slave status for its request/grant circuits. If SEL is inactive (low), the 8089 is designated a "master". If SEL is active (high), the 8089 is designated a "slave". As a master, the 8089 assumes that it has the bus initially, and it will subsequently grant the bus to a requesting slave when the bus becomes available (i.e., the 8089 will respond to a "request" pulse on its RQ*/GT* line with a "grant" pulse). A single 8089 in the remote configuration (or one of two 8089s in a remote configuration) would be designated a master. As a slave, the 8089 can only request the bus from a master processor (i.e., the 8089 initiates the request/grant sequence by outputting a "request" pulse on its RQ*/GT* line). An 8089 that shares a bus with an 8086 (or one of two 8089s in a remote configuration) would be designated a slave.

NOTE

Since the 8086 CPU can grant the bus only in response to a request, whenever an 8086 and an 8089 share a common bus, the 8089 must be designated the slave. Also, when the RQ*/GT* line is not used (i.e., a single 8089 in the remote configuration), the 8089 must be designated a master.

The CA pulse input, in addition to determining master/slave status, causes the 8089 to begin execution of its internal ROM initialization sequence. The 8089 must have access to the system bus in order to perform this sequence, therefore, it immediately initiates a request/grant sequence (if designated a slave) and, if required, requests the bus through the 8289 Arbiter. If the 8089 is designated a master, it requests the bus through the 8289 Arbiter. When executing the initialization sequence, the 8089 first fetches the SYSBUS byte from location FFFF6H. The W bit (bit 0) of this byte specifies the physical bus width of the system bus. Depending on the bus width specified, the 8089 then fetches the address of the system configuration block (SCB) contained in locations FFFF8H through FFFFBH in either two bus cycles (16-bit bus, W bit equal 1) or four bus cycles (8-bit bus, W bit equal 0). The SCB offset segment address values fetched are combined into a 20-bit physical address that is stored in an internal register. The 8089 uses this address to fetch the system operation command (SOC) byte. SOC specifies both the request/ grant operational mode (R bit) and the physical width of the I/O bus (I bit — refer to Volume I of this User's Guide). After reading the SOC byte, the 8089 fetches the channel control block (CB) offset and segment address values. These values are combined into a 20-bit physical address that is stored in another internal register. To inform the host CPU that it has completed the initialization sequence, the 8089 clears the Channel 1 Busy flag in the channel control block by writing data byte "00" into the Busy flag byte.

After the IOP has been initialized, the system configuration block may be altered to initialize another IOP. When an IOP has been initialized, its channel control block, located in system memory, cannot be moved since the CB address, which is internally stored by the IOP during the initialization sequence, is automatically accessed on every subsequent CA pulse.

Generation of the CA and SEL inputs to the IOP are the responsibility of the host CPU. These signals typically result from the CPU's execution of an I/O write instruction to one of two adjacent I/O ports (I/O port addresses that only differ by A0). A simple decoding circuit that could be used to generate the CA and SEL signals is shown in Figure 4-13. By qualifying the CA output with IOWC*, the SEL output, since it is latched for the entire I/O bus cycle, is guaranteed to be stable on the trailing edge of the CA pulse.

4.4.3 Channel Commands

After initialization, any channel attention (CA) is interpreted as a command to channel 1 (SEL = low) or to channel 2 (SEL = high). Depending upon the activities of both channels, the CA may not be recognized immediately. However, the CA is latched so that it will be serviced as soon as priorities allow.

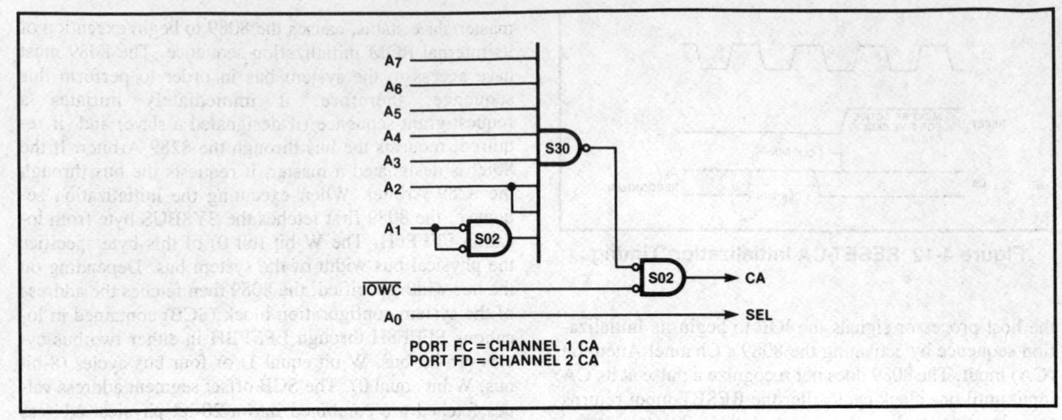

Figure 4-13 Channel Attention Decoding Circuit

The channel sets its BUSY flag in the CB to FFH when it recognizes the CA. This does not prevent the CPU from issuing another CA, but provides status information only. When the channel responds to a CA, it reads various control fields from system memory. The CPU must ensure that the appropriate fields are properly initialized before issuing the CA.

The channel reads its CCW from the CB after setting its BUSY flag. It examines the command field (see Figure 4-14) and executes the command encoded there by the CPU.

The channel's response to each type of command is shown in Figure 4-15. Note that if CF contains a reserved value (010 or 100), the channel's response is unpredictable.

The CPU can use the "update PSW" command to alter the bus load limit and priority bits in the PSW (see Figure 4-22) without otherwise affecting the channel. This command also allows the CPU to control interrupts originating in the channel.

The two "start program" commands differ only in their affect on the TP tag bit. If CF-001 is used, the channel sets the tag to 1 to indicate that the program resides in the I/O space. If CF-011 is used, the tag is cleared to 0, and the program is assumed to be in the system space. The channel converts the doubleword parameter block pointer to a 20-bit physical address and loads this into PP. It loads the doubleword task block (channel program) pointer into

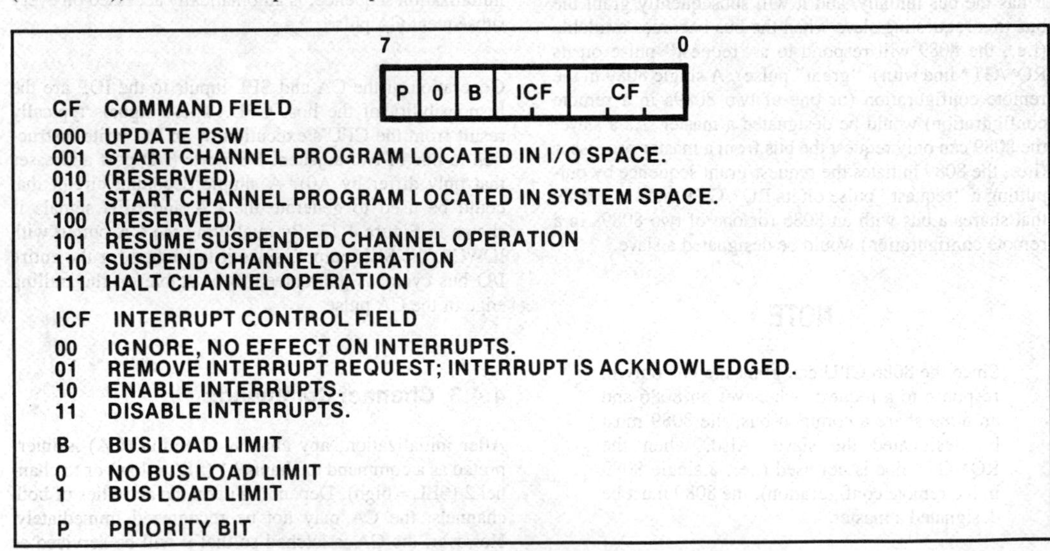

Figure 4-14 Channel Command Word Encoding

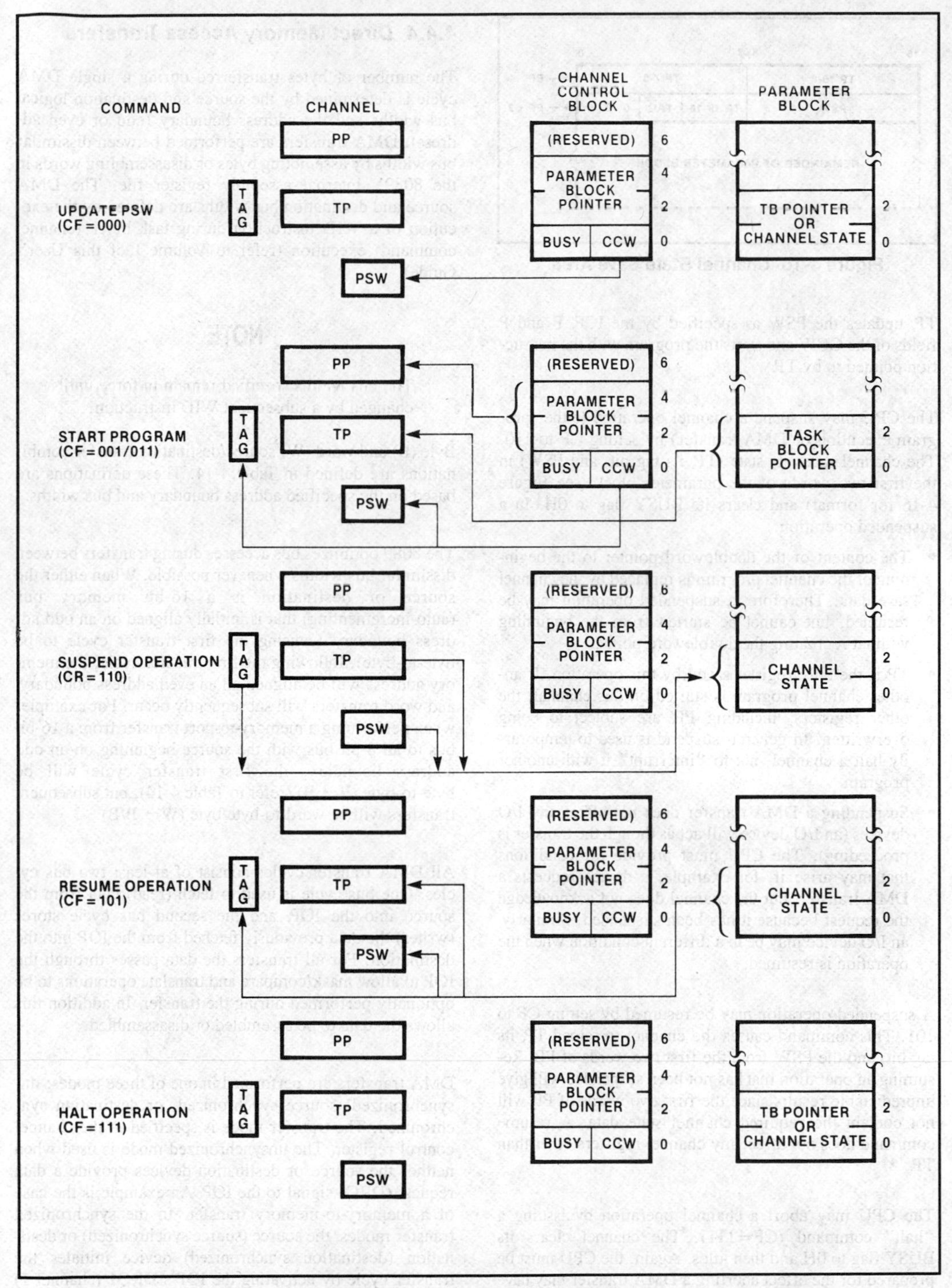

Figure 4-15 Channel Commands

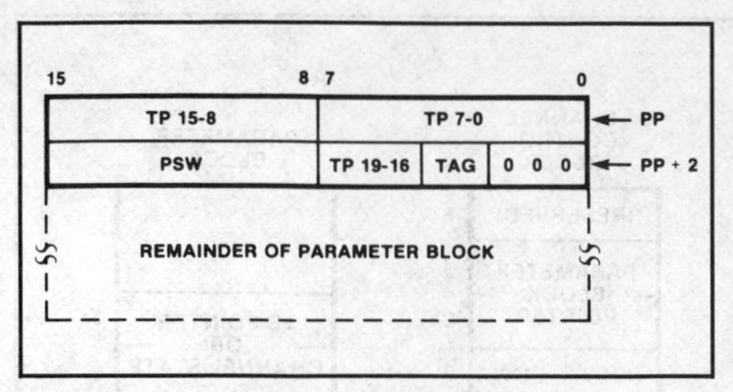

Figure 4-16 Channel State Save Area

TP, updates the PSW as specified by the ICF, B and P fields of the CCW and starts the program with the instruction pointed to by TP.

The CPU may suspend a channel operation (either program execution or DMA transfer) by setting CF to 110. The channel saves its state (TP, its tag bit, and PSW) in the first two words of the parameter block (see Figure 4-16 for format) and clears its BUSY flag to 0H. In a suspended operation:

- The content of the doubleword pointer to the beginning of the channel program is replaced by the channel save data. Therefore, a suspended operation may be resumed, but cannot be started from the beginning without recreating the doubleword pointer.
- TP is the only register saved by this operation. If another channel program is started on this channel, the other registers, including PP, are subject to being overwritten. In general, suspend is used to temporarily halt a channel, not to "interrupt" it with another program.
- Suspending a DMA transfer does not affect any I/O devices (an I/O device will act as though the transfer is proceeding). The CPU must provide for conditions that may arise if, for example, a device requests a DMA transfer, but the channel does not acknowledge the request because it has been suspended. Similarly, an I/O device may be in a different condition when the operation is resumed.

A suspended operation may be resumed by setting CF to 101. This command causes the channel to reload TP, its tag bit, and the PSW from the first two words of PB. Resuming an operation that has not been suspended will give unpredictable results since the first two words of PB will not contain the required channel state data. A resume command does not affect any channel registers other than TP.

The CPU may abort a channel operation by issuing a "halt" command (CF = 111). The channel clears its BUSY flag to 0H and then idles. Again, the CPU must be prepared for the effect aborting a DMA transfer may have on an I/O device.

4.4.4 Direct Memory Access Transfers

The number of bytes transferred during a single DMA cycle is determined by the source and destination logical bus widths and the address boundary (odd or even address). DMA transfers are performed between dissimilar bus widths by assembling bytes or disassembling words in the 8089's internal assembly register file. The DMA source and destination bus widths are defined by the execution of a WID instruction during task block (channel command) execution (refer to Volume I of this User's Guide).

NOTE

The bus widths specified remain in force until changed by a subsequent WID instruction.

Byte (B) and word (W) source/destination transfer combinations are defined in Table 4-14. These definations are based on the specified address boundary and bus widths.

The 8089 optimizes bus accesses during transfers between dissimilar bus widths whenever possible. When either the source or destination is a 16-bit memory bus (auto-incrementing) that is initially aligned on an odd address boundary (causing the first transfer cycle to be byte-to-byte), following the first transfer cycle, the memory address will be aligned on an even address boundary, and word transfers will subsequently occur. For example, when performing a memory-to-port transfer from a 16-bit bus to an 8-bit bus with the source beginning on an odd address boundary, the first transfer cycle will be byte-to-byte (B→ B) (refer to Table 4-14), but subsequent transfers will be word-to-byte/byte (W→ B/B).

All DMA transfer cycles consist of at least two bus cycles. One bus cycle is used to fetch (read) data from the source into the IOP, and the second bus cycle stores (writes) the data previously fetched from the IOP into the destination. For all transfers the data passes through the IOP to allow mask/compare and translate operations to be optionally performed during the transfer. In addition this allows the data to be assembled or disassembled.

DMA transfers are performed in one of three modes: unsynchronized, source synchronized, or destination synchronized. The transfer mode is specified in the channel control register. The unsynchronized mode is used when neither the source or destination devices provide a data request (DRQ) signal to the IOP. An example is the case of a memory-to-memory transfer. In the synchronized transfer modes, the source (source synchronized) or destination (destination synchronized) device initiates the transfer cycle by activating the IOP's DRQ1 (channel 1) or DRQ2 (channel 2) input.

Table 4-14 DMA Assembly Register Operation

Address Boundary (Source → Destination)	Logical Bus Width (Source → Destination)			
	8 → 8	8 → 16	16 → 8	16 → 16
Even → Even	B → B	B/B → W	W → B/B	W → W
Even → Odd	B → B	B → B	W → B/B	W → B/B
Odd → Even	B → B	B/B → W	B → B	B/B → W
Odd → Odd	B → B	B → B	B → B	B → B

The DRQ input is asynchronous and usually originates from an I/O device controller instead of a memory circuit. This input is latched on the positive transition of the clock (CLK) signal and must therefore remain active for more than one clock period (more than 200 nanoseconds when using a 5 MHz clock) in order to guarantee that it is recognized.

During T1 of the associated fetch bus cycle (source synchronized — see Figure 4-17) or the store bus cycle (destination synchronized — see Figure 4-18), the IOP outputs the port address of the I/O device. This address must be decoded by external circuits to generate the DMA acknowledge (DACK) signal to the I/O controller as the response to the controller's DMA request. An I/O controller typically uses DACK as a conditional input for the removal of DRQ. (After receipt of the DACK signal, most Intel peripheral controllers deactivate DRQ following receipt of the corresponding read or write signal.)

Table 4-15 defines the DMA transfer cycles in terms of the number of bus and clock cycles required.

DACK latency is defined as the time required for the 8089 to acknowledge a DMA request at its DRQ input, by outputting the device's corresponding port address. This response latency depends on a number of factors that include the transfer cycle being performed, activity on the other channel, memory address boundaries, wait states present in either bus cycle and bus arbitration times.

Generally, when the other channel is idle, the maximum DACK latency is five clock cycles (1 microsecond at 5 MHz), excluding wait states and bus arbitration times. An exception occurs when performing a word transfer to or from an odd memory address boundary. Since two store (source synchronized) or two fetch (destination synchronized) bus cycles are required to access memory, this operation has a maximum possible latency of nine clock cycles. When the other channel is performing DMA transfers to equal priority ("P" bits equal), interleaving occurs at bus cycle boundaries. Therefore, the maximum latency is either nine clock cycles when the other channel is performing a normal 4-clock fetch or store bus cycle, or twelve clock cycles when the other channel is performing the first fetch cycle of a memory-to-memory transfer. If the other channel is performing "chained" task block instruction execution of equal priority, maximum latency can be as high as 12 clock cycles (channel command instruction execution is interrupted at machine cycle boundaries which range from two to eight clock cycles).

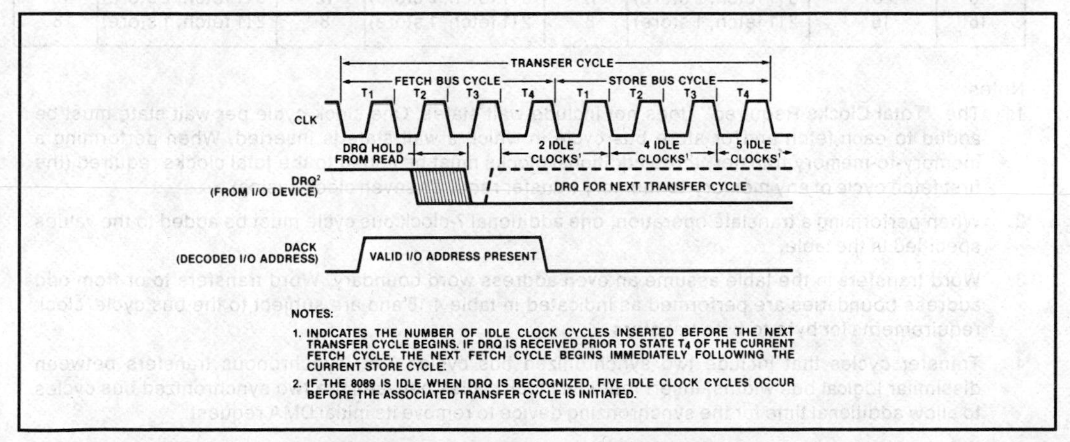

Figure 4-17 Source Synchronized Transfer Cycle

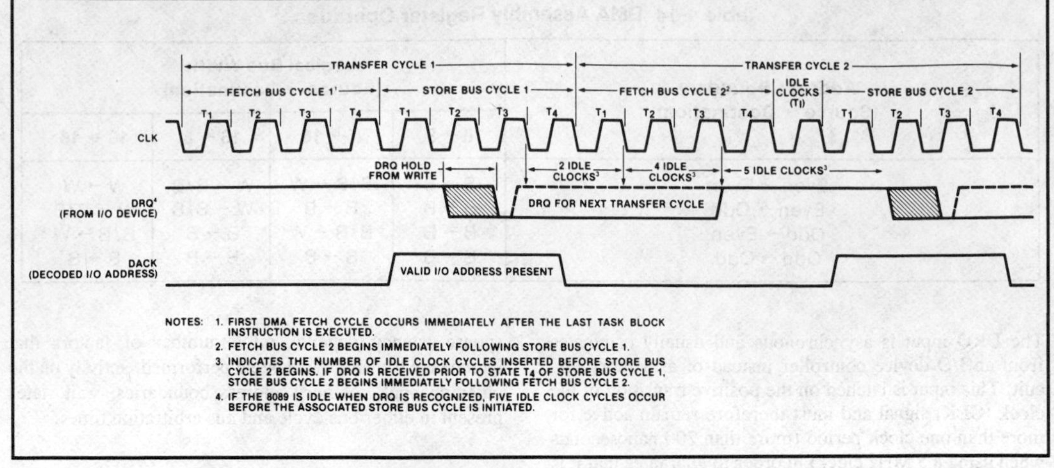

Figure 4-18 Destination Synchronized Transfer Cycle

4.4.5 DMA Termination

A channel can exit the DMA transfer mode (and return to task block execution) on any of the following terminate conditions (refer to Volume I of this User's Guide):

1. Single cycle transfer;
2. Byte count expired;
3. Mask/compare match or mismatch;
4. External event.

Table 4-15 DMA Transfer Cycles

Logical Bus Width		Transfer Mode					
		Unsynchronized		Source Synchronized		Destination Synchronized	
Source	Destination	Bus Cycles Required	Total[1] Clocks	Bus Cycles Required	Total[1] Clocks	Bus Cycles Required	Total[1] Clocks
8	8	2 (1 fetch, 1 store)	8[2]	2 (1 fetch, 1 store)	8[2]	2 (1 fetch, 1 store)	8[2]
8	16[3]	3 (2 fetch, 1 store)	12	3 (2 fetch, 1 store)	16[4]	3 (2 fetch, 1 store)	12
16[3]	8	3 (1 fetch, 2 store)	12	3 (1 fetch, 2 store)	12	3 (1 fetch, 2 store)	16[4]
16[3]	16[3]	2 (1 fetch, 1 store)	8	2 (1 fetch, 1 store)	8	2 (1 fetch, 1 store)	8

Notes:

1. The "Total Clocks Required" does not include wait states. One clock cycle per wait state must be added to each fetch and/or store bus cycle in which a wait state is inserted. When performing a memory-to-memory transfer, three additional clocks must be added to the total clocks required (the first fetch cycle of any memory-to-memory transfer requires seven clock cycles).
2. When performing a translate operation, one additional 7-clock bus cycle must be added to the values specified in the table.
3. Word transfers in the table assume an even address word boundary. Word transfers to or from odd address boundaries are performed as indicated in table 4-18 and are subject to the bus cycle/clock requirements for byte-to-byte transfers.
4. Transfer cycles that include two synchronized bus cycles (i.e., synchronous transfers between dissimilar logical bus widths) insert four idle clock cycles between the two synchronized bus cycles to allow additional time for the synchronzing device to remove its initial DMA request.

Individual fields in the channel control register specify the terminate conditions. More than one terminate condition can be specified for a transfer (e.g., a transfer can be terminated when a specific byte count is reached →or→ on the occurrence of an external event). When more than one terminate condition is possible, specified displacements (which are added to the task pointer register value) cause task block execution to resume at a unique entry point for each condition. Three re-entry points are available: TP, TP+4, and TP+8. The time interval between the occurrence of a terminate condition and the resumption of task block execution is 12 clock cycles for re-entry point TP and 15 clock cycles for re-entry points TP+4 and TP+8.

4.4.6 Peripheral Interfacing

When the 8089 interfaces a peripheral to an 8-bit physical data bus, only the lower half of the address/data lines (AD7-AD0) are used for the bidirectional data bus. The upper half of the address/data lines (AD15-AD8) are used to maintain address information for the entire bus cycle. With this bus configuration, only one octal latch is required since only the lower half of the address/data lines are time-multiplexed (unless the address bus requires the increased current drive capability and capacitive load immunity provided by the latch).

When a peripheral is interfaced to a 16-bit data bus, both the lower and upper halves of the address/data lines are time-multiplexed, and two octal latches are required. Note that unlike the 8086 CPU, the 8089 does not time-multiplex BHE*, this signal is valid for the entire bus cycle. Both 8-and 16-bit peripherals can be interfaced to a 16-bit bus. An 8-bit peripheral can be connected to either the upper or lower half of the bus. An 8-bit peripheral on the lower half of the bus must use an even source/destination address, and an 8-bit peripheral on the upper half of the bus must use an odd source/destination address. To take advantage of word transfers, a 16-bit peripheral must use an even source/destination address.

Command and parameter data is written to a peripheral device's command/status port (usually by using pointer register GC) to prepare the device for a DMA transfer. The additional task block instruction executed by the 8089 following execution of the XFER instruction (the XFER instruction causes the 8089 to enter the DMA mode) is used to access the command port of an I/O device. This I/O device immediately begins DMA operation on receipt of the last command (the 8271 Floppy Disk Controller begins its DMA transfer on receipt of the last command parameter). Since a translate DMA operation requires the use of all three pointer registers (GA and GB specify the source and destination address; GC specifies the base address of the translation table), when it is necessary to use the last task block instruction to start the device, command port access can be accomplished relative to one of the pointer registers or relative to the PP register. If the device's data port address (GA or GB) is below the device's command port address, either an offset or an indexed reference can be used to access the command port.

8089 DMA COMMUNICATION PROTOCOL

A peripheral's (or peripheral controller's) DMA communication protocol with the 8089 is as follows:

- The peripheral (when source or destination synchronized) initiates a DMA transfer cycle by activating the 8089's DRQ (DMA request) input.
- The 8089 acknowledges the request by placing the peripheral's assigned data port address on the bus during state T1 of the corresponding fetch (source synchronized) or store (destination synchronized) bus cycle. The peripheral is responsible for decoding this address as the DMA acknowledge (DACK) to its request.
- The data is transferred between the peripheral and the 8089 during the T2 through T4 state interval of the bus cycle. The peripheral must remove its DMA request during this interval.
- The peripheral, when ready, requests another DMA transfer cycle by again activating the DRQ input, and the above sequence repeats.
- The peripheral can, as an option, end the DMA transfer by activating the 8089's EXT (external terminate) input.

The 8089 supports multiple peripheral devices on a single channel if only one device is in the active transfer mode at any one time. To interface multiple devices, the DMA request (DRQ) lines are OR'ed together. The external terminate (EXT) lines are also OR'ed together. However, unique port addresses are assigned to each device so that an individual DMA acknowledge (DACK) returns to only the active device. DACK can be decoded using an Intel 8205 Binary Decoder or a ROM circuit.

NOTE

The 8089 can only determine which device has requested or terminated service by the context of the task block program.

Most peripheral devices interfaced to the 8089 use the decoded DMA acknowledge signal (DACK) as the chip select input. Peripheral devices that do not follow this convention must use DACK as a conditional input of chip select.

8089 NON-DMA INTERRUPTS

Most interrupts associated with the 8089 are DMA requests or external terminates, but non-DMA related interrupts can be supported. One technique that can be used for an 8089 configured in local mode (or when an 8086 and an 8089 are locally connected as a remote module) allows the CPU to accept the interrupt and then direct the 8089 to the interrupt service routine. Another technique allows the 8089 to poll the device to determine when an interrupt has occurred (most peripheral controllers have an interrupt pending bit in a status word). The 8089's bit test instructions are ideally suited for polling.

When configured in remote mode, non-DMA related interrupts can be supported by the 8089 with the addition of an Intel 8259A Programmable Interrupt Controller. Systems that require this type of interrupt structure would dedicate one of the 8089's channels to interrupt servicing. In this structure, the interrupt output from the 8259A connects directly to the channel's external terminate (EXT) input, and the channel's DRQ input is not used. The 8089 initially executes a task block program to perform a source-synchronized DMA transfer (with an external terminate) on the "interrupt" channel to "arm" the interrupt mechanism. Since the DRQ input is not used, when the channel enters the DMA transfer mode, the channel idles while waiting for the first DMA request (which never occurs). Since the interrupt channel is idle, the other channel operates at maximum throughput. When an interrupt occurs, the pseudo DMA transfer immediately terminates, and task block instruction execution resumes. The task block program would write a poll command to the 8259A's command port and then read the 8259A's data port to acknowledge the interrupt and to determine the device responsible for the interrupt (the device is identified by a 3-bit binary number in the associated data byte). The device number read would be used by the task block program as a vector into a jump table for the device's interrupt service routine. Pertinent interrupt data could be written into the associated parameter block for subsequent examination by the host processor. Since it uses the 8089's external terminate function, this interrupt mechanism provides an extremely fast interrupt response time.

When using dynamic RAM memory with the 8089, an Intel 8203 Dynamic RAM Controller can be used to simplify the interface and to perform the RAM refresh cycle. When maximum transfer rates are required, the RAM refresh cycle can be externally initiated by the 8089. By connecting the decoded DACK (DMA acknowledge) signal to the 8203's REFRQ (refresh request) input, the refresh cycle will occur coincident with the I/O device bus cycle and will not impose wait states in the memory bus cycle.

4.4.7 Status Lines

The IOP sends signals to external devices on the S0*-S2* status lines to indicate the type of bus cycle the processor is starting (see Table 4-16 for the signals output for each type of cycle). These status lines are connected to an 8288 Bus Controller. The bus controller decodes these lines and outputs the signals that control components attached

Table 4-16 Status Signals S0-S2

$\overline{S2}$	$\overline{S1}$	$\overline{S0}$	Type of Bus Cycle
0	0	0	Instruction fetch from I/O space
0	0	1	Data fetch from I/O space
0	1	0	Data store to I/O space
0	1	1	(not used)
1	0	0	Instruction fetch from system space
1	0	1	Data fetch from system space
1	1	0	Data store to system space
1	1	1	Passive; no bus cycle run

to the bus. In the remote configuration, an 8289 Bus Arbiter monitors the S0*-S2* status lines to determine when a system bus access is required.

Status lines S3 — S6 indicate if the bus cycle is DMA or non-DMA, and which channel is running the cycle (see Table 4-17). When the IOP is not running a bus cycle (e.g., it is idle or executing an internal cycle that does not use the bus), the status lines reflect the last bus cycle run.

4.5 BUS OPERATION

The 8089 uses the same bus structure as a maximum mode 8086 CPU. Bus cycles are performed only on demand to fetch an instruction during task block execution or to perform a data transfer. The bus cycle itself is identical to an 8086 CPU's bus cycle. Each cycle consists of four T-states and uses the same time-multiplexing technique for the address/data lines. The 8089 outputs the address (and ALE signal) during state T1 for either a read or write cycle (see Figures 4-19 and 4-20). Depending on the type of cycle indicated, the 8089 tri-states the address/data lines during state T2 for a read cycle (see Figure 4-19) or outputs data on these lines during a write cycle (see Figure 4-20). During state T3, the 8089 maintains write data or samples read data and then concludes the busy cycle in state T4.

Table 4-17 Status Signals S3-S6

S6	S5	S4	S3	Bus Cycle
1	1	0	0	DMA cycle on channel 1
1	1	0	1	DMA cycle on channel 2
1	1	1	0	Non-DMA cycle on channel 1
1	1	1	1	Non-DMA cycle on channel 2

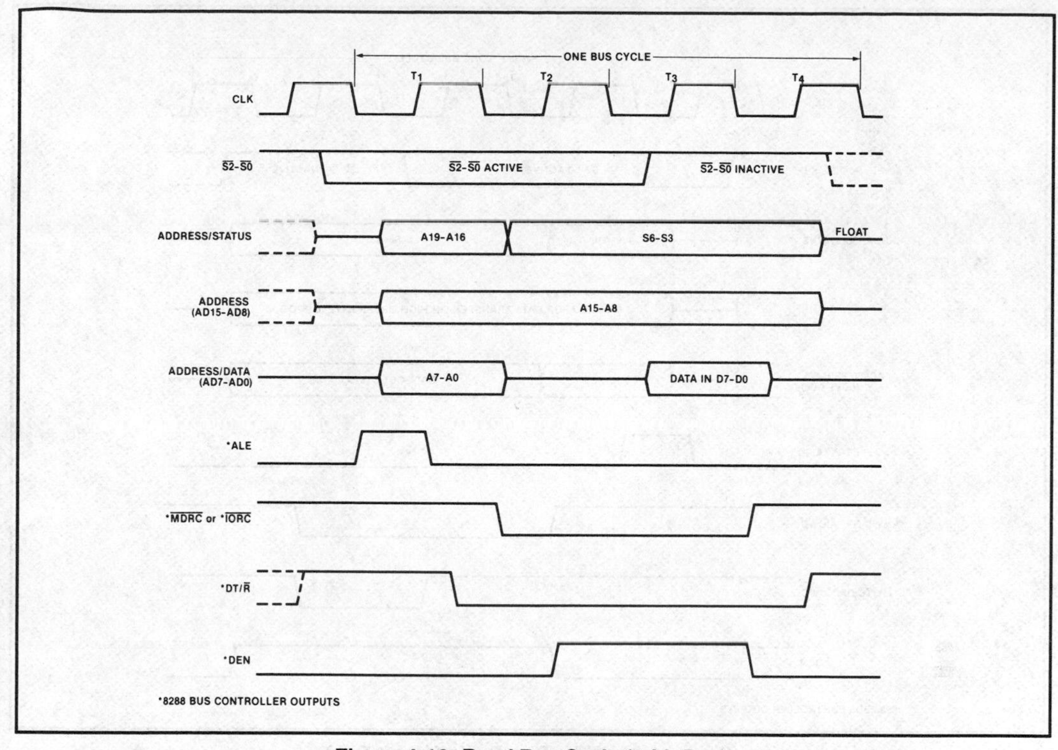

Figure 4-19 Read Bus Cycle (8-bit Bus)

The 8089 can transfer data to or from both 8-bit and 16-bit buses. Therefore, when an 8-bit physical bus is specified during the initialization sequence, the IOP maintains the address present on the AD15 through AD8 address/data lines for the entire bus cycle (see Figure 4-19). Unless added drive capability is required, the associated address latch can be eliminated. An 8-bit data bus is compatible with the 8088 CPU and with the MCS-85 multiplexed address peripherals (8155, 8185, etc.).

8089 operation is identical to the 8086 CPU with respect to the use of the low-and high-order halves of the data bus. Table 4-18 defines the data bus use for the various combinations of bus width and address boundaries.

Status lines S2* through S0* define the bus cycle to be performed. These status lines are used by an 8288 Bus Controller to generate all memory and I/O command control signals (refer to Table 4-19 for signal decoding).

Since the 8288 Bus Controller decodes an input status value of zero as an interrupt acknowledge bus cycle, the bus controller's INTA* output must be OR'ed with its IORC* output to permit fetching of task block instructions from local 8089 memory (remote configuration) or system I/O space (local and remote configurations).

Status lines S2* through S0* become active in state T4 if a subsequent bus cycle is to be performed. The 8089 sets these lines inactive (all high) in the state immediately prior to state T4 of the current bus cycle (state T3 or Tw) and tri-states the lines when the 8089 does not have access to the bus.

Status lines S6 through S3 are multiplexed with the high-order address bits (A19-A16) and, accordingly, become valid in state T2 of the bus cycle. These status lines reflect the type of bus cycle being performed on the corresponding channel (Table 4-20).

Status lines S6 and S5 are always high on the 8089. Since these lines are not both high on the other processors in the 8086 family (S6 is always low on the 8086 CPU), these status lines can be used as a "signature" in a multiprocessor system to identify the type of processor performing the bus cycle.

The 8089 includes the same provisions for insertion of wait states (Tw) as the 8086 CPU. Wait states are inserted in a bus cycle when the associated memory or I/O device cannot respond within an allotted time interval or in the remote mode when the 8089 must wait for access to the system bus. An 8284A Clock Generator/ Driver controls insertion of wait states. When required, wait states are

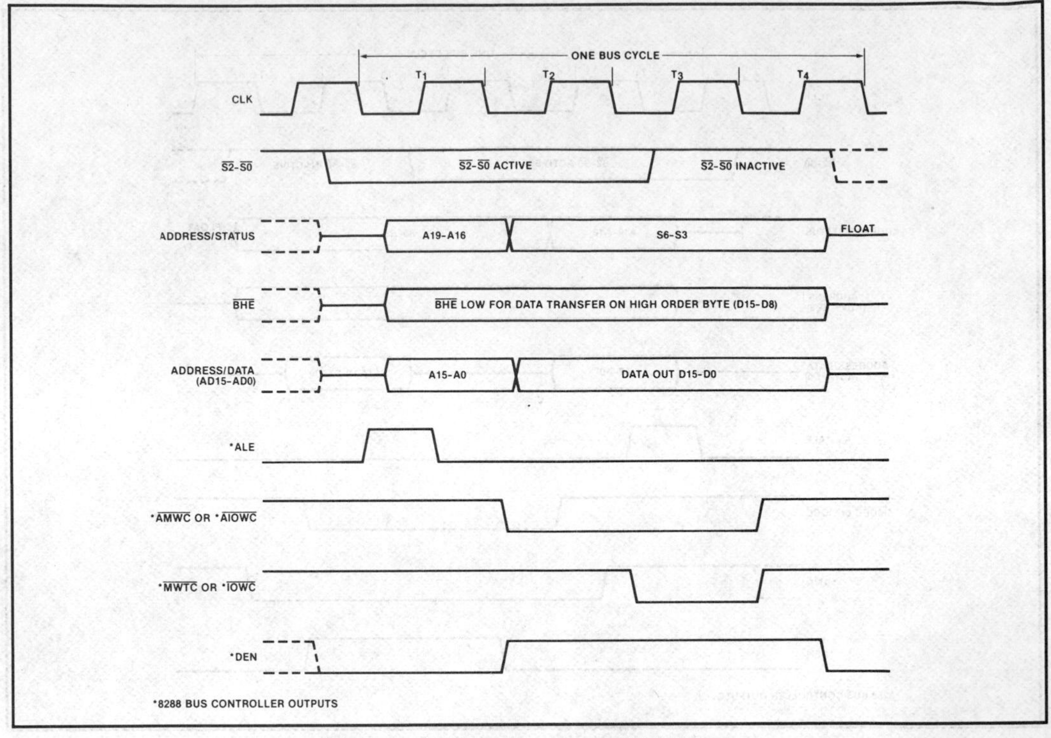

Figure 4-20 Write Bus Cycle (16-bit Bus)

inserted between states T3 and T4. Deactivating one of the 8284A's RDY inputs, RDY1 or RDY2, actually inserts the wait states. When enabled by the corresponding AEN1* or AEN2* input, either RDY1 or RDY2 can be directly deactivated by a memory or I/O device to extend the 8089's bus cycle (i.e., addressed device is not ready to present or accept data). The 8284A's READY output (synchronized to the CLK signal) connects directly to the 8089's READY input. When the addressed device requires one or more wait states to be inserted into a bus cycle (see Figure 4-21), it deactivates the 8284A's RDY input prior to the end of state T2. The READY output from the 8284A subsequently deactivates at the end of state T2, causing the 8089 to insert wait state T3. To exit the wait state, the device activates the 8284A's RDY input, causing the 8089 READY input to go active on the next clock cycle. This allows the 8089 to enter state T4.

Periods of inactivity, or idle states (TI) can occur between bus cycles. These idle states result from the execution of a "long" instruction or the loss of the bus to another processor during task block instruction execution. Additionally, the 8089 can experience idle states when it is in the DMA mode and it is waiting for a DMA request from the addressed I/O device, or when the bus load limit (BLL) function is enabled for a channel performing task block instruction execution and the other channel is idle.

4.6 BUS EXCHANGE MECHANISM

The 8089 shares the multiprocessing facilities that are common to the iAPX 86 family of processors. It has on-chip logic for arbitrating the use of the local bus with a CPU or other IOP. System bus arbitration is delegated to an 8289 Bus Arbiter.

The 8089's test and set while locked instruction (TSL) enables it to share a resource, such as a buffer, with other processors by means of semaphore. In addition, the 8089 can lock the system bus for the duration of a DMA transfer to ensure that the transfer completes without interference from other processors on the bus.

In the remote configuration, the 8089 is electrically compatible with Intel's MULTIBUS multimaster bus design. Therefore, the power and convience of 8089 I/O processing can be used in 8085-or 8086-based systems that implement the MULTIBUS protocol or a subset of it. In addition, the IOP can access other iSBC board products such as memory and communications controllers.

Table 4-18 Data Bus Usage

Logical Bus Width[1]	Address Boundary	Physical Bus Width[2]		
		8	16	
			Byte Transfer	Word Transfer
8	Even	AD7-AD0 = DATA ($\overline{\text{BHE}}$ not used)	AD7-AD0 = DATA ($\overline{\text{BHE}}$ high)	N/A
8	Odd	AD7-AD0 = DATA ($\overline{\text{BHE}}$ not used)	AD15-AD8 = DATA ($\overline{\text{BHE}}$ low)	N/A
16	Even	Illegal	AD7-AD0 = DATA ($\overline{\text{BHE}}$ high)	AD15-AD0 = DATA ($\overline{\text{BHE}}$ low)
16	Odd	Illegal	AD15-AD8 = DATA ($\overline{\text{BHE}}$ low)	N/A[3]

Notes:

1. Logical bus width is specified by the WID instruction prior to the DMA transfer.
2. Physical bus width is specified when the 8089 is initialized.
3. A word transfer to or from an odd boundary is performed as two byte transfers. The first byte transferred is the low-order byte on the high-order data bus (AD15-AD8), and the second byte is the high-order byte on the low-order data bus (AD7-AD0). The 8089 automatically assembles the two bytes in their proper order.

Table 4-19 Bus Cycle Decoding

$\overline{\text{S2}}$	$\overline{\text{S1}}$	$\overline{\text{S0}}$	Bus Cycle Indicated	Bus Controller Command Output
0	0	0	Instruction fetch from I/O space	$\overline{\text{INTA}}$
0	0	1	Data read from I/O space	$\overline{\text{IORC}}$
0	1	0	Data write to I/O space	$\overline{\text{IOWC}}$, $\overline{\text{AIOWC}}$
0	1	1	Not used	None
1	0	0	Instruction fetch from system memory	$\overline{\text{MRDC}}$
1	0	1	Data read from system memory	$\overline{\text{MRDC}}$
1	1	0	Data write to system memory	$\overline{\text{MWTC}}$, $\overline{\text{AMWC}}$
1	1	1	Passive	None

(Status Output: $\overline{\text{S2}}$, $\overline{\text{S1}}$, $\overline{\text{S0}}$)

Table 4-20 Type of Cycle Decoding

S4	S3	Type of Cycle
0	0	DMA on Channel 1
0	1	DMA on Channel 2
1	0	Non-DMA on Channel 1
1	1	Non-DMA on Channel 2

(Status Output: S4, S3)

4.6.1 Bus Arbitration

The 8089 shares its system bus with a CPU, and may also share its I/O bus with an IOP or another CPU. Only one processor at a time may drive a bus. When two (or more) processors want to use a shared bus, the system must provide an arbitration mechanism that will grant the bus to one of the processors. The following paragraphs describe the 8089 bus arbitration facilities and their applicability to different IOP configurations.

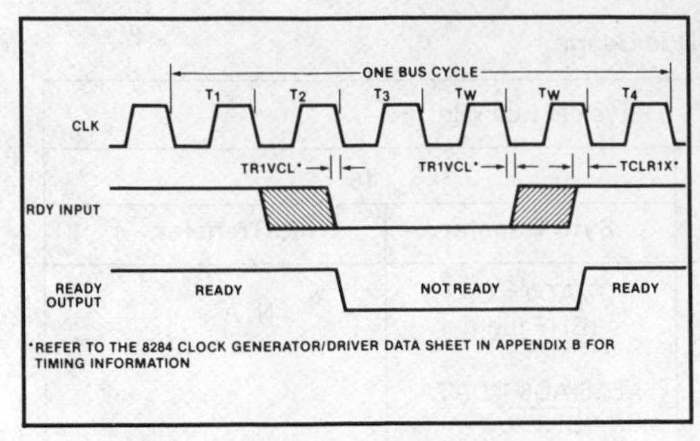

Figure 4-21 Wait State Timing

REQUEST/GRANT LINE

When an 8089 is directly connected to another 8089, an 8086 or an 8088, the RQ*/GT* (request/grant) lines built into all of these processors are used to arbitrate the use of a local bus. In the local mode, RQ*/GT* is used to control access to both the system and the I/O bus.

The CPU's request/grant lines (RQ*/GT0* and RQ*/GT1*) operate as follows:

1. An external processor sends a pulse to the CPU to request use of the bus;
2. The CPU finishes its current bus cycle, if one is in progress, and sends a pulse to the processor to indicate that it has been granted the bus; and
3. When the external processor is finished with the bus, it sends a final pulse to the CPU, to indicate that it is releasing the bus.

The 8089's request/grant circuit can operate in two modes. The mode is selected when the IOP is initialized (see paragraph 4.4.2). Mode 0 is compatible with the 8086/8088 request/grant circuit and must be specified when the 8089's RQ*/GT* line is connected to RQ*/GT0* or RQ*/GT1* of one of those CPU's. Mode 0 *may* be specified when RQ*/GT* of one 8089 is tied to the RQ*/GT* of another 8089. When mode 0 is used with a CPU, the CPU is designated the master, and the IOP is designated a slave. When mode 0 is used with another IOP, one IOP is the master, and the other is the slave. Master/slave designation also is made at initialization time as discussed in paragraph 4.4.2. The master has the bus when the system is initialized and keeps the bus until it is requested by the slave. When the slave requests the bus, the master grants it if the master is idle. In this sense, the CPU becomes idle at the end of current bus cycle. An IOP master, on the other hand, does not become idle until both channels have halted program execution or are waiting for DMA requests. Once granted the bus, the slave (always an IOP) uses it until both channels are idle, and then releases it to the master. In mode 0, the master has no way of requesting the slave to return the bus.

Mode 1 operation may only be used to arbitrate use of a private I/O bus between two IOP's. In this instance, one IOP is designated the master, and the other is designated the slave. However, the only difference between a master and a slave running in Mode 1 is that the master has the bus at initialization time. Both processors may request the bus from each other at any time. The processor that has the bus will grant it to the requestor as soon as one of the following occurs:

1. An unchained channel program instruction is completed, or
2. A channel goes idle due to a program halt or the completion of a synchronized transfer cycle (the channel waits for a DMA request).

Execution of a chained channel program, a DMA termination sequence, a channel attention sequence, or a synchronized DMA transfer (i.e., a high-priority operation) on either channel prevents the IOP from granting the bus to the requesting IOP.

The handshaking sequence in Mode 1 is:

1. The requesting processor pulses once on RQ*/GT*;
2. The processor with the bus grants it by pulsing once; and
3. If the processor granting the bus wants it back immediately (for example, to fetch the next instruction), it will pulse RQ*/GT* again, two clocks after the grant pulse.

The fundamental difference between the two request/grant circuit modes is the frequency with which the bus can be switched between the two processors when both are active. In mode 0, the processor that has the bus will tend to keep it for relatively long periods if it is executing a channel program. Mode 1 in effect places unchained channel programs at a lower priority since the processor will give up the bus at the end of the next instruction. Therefore, when both processors are running channel programs or synchronized DMA, they will share the bus more or less equally. When a processor changes to what would typically be considered a high-priority activity such as chained program execution or DMA termination, it will generally be able to obtain the bus quickly and keep the bus for the duration of the more critical activity.

8289 BUS ARBITER

When an IOP is configured remotely, an 8289 Bus Arbiter is used to control the IOP's access to the shared system bus (the CPU also has its own 8289). In a remote cluster of two IOP's and a CPU, one 8289 control access to the system bus for both processors in the cluster. The 8289 has several operating modes. When used with an 8089, the 8289 is usually strapped in its IOB (I/O Peripheral Bus) mode.

Table 4-21 Bus Arbitration Requirements and Options

IOP	Local		Remote		Remote With Local CPU	
	Master/ Slave	$\overline{RQ}/\overline{GT}$ Mode	Master/ Slave	$\overline{RQ}/\overline{GT}$ Mode	Master/ Slave	$\overline{RQ}/\overline{GT}$ Mode
IOP1	Slave	0	Master	0 or 1	Slave	0
IOP2	Slave	0	Slave	Same as Master	N/A	N/A

The 8289 monitor's the IOP's status lines. When the status lines indicate the IOP needs a cycle on the system bus, and the IOP does not presently have the bus, the 8289 activates a bus request signal. This signal, along with the bus request lines of the other 8289's on the same bus, can be routed to an external priority-resolving circuit. At the end of the current bus cycle, this circuit grants the bus to the requesting 8289 with the highest priority. Several different prioritizing techniques may be used. In a typical system, an IOP would have higher bus priority than a CPU. If the 8289 does not obtain the bus for its processor, it makes the bus appear "not ready" as if a slow memory were being accessed. The processor's clock generator responds to the "not ready" condition by inserting wait states into the IOP's bus cycle. This will extend the cycle until the bus is acquired.

BUS ARBITRATION FOR IOP CONFIGURATIONS

When the CPU initializes an IOP, it must inform the IOP whether it is a master or a slave, and which request/grant mode is to be used. Refer to paragraph 4.4.2 for a description of how the information is communicated at initialization time.

In the local configuration (see Table 4-21 for a summarization of bus arbitration requirements and options by IOP configuration), all bus arbitration is performed by the request/grant lines without additional hardware. One IOP may be connected to each of the CPU's RQ*/GT* lines. The IOP connected to RQ*/GT0* will obtain the bus if both processors make simultaneous requests.

Since a single IOP in a remote configuration does not use RQ*/GT*, its mode may be set to 0 or 1 without affect. The single remote IOP, however, must be initialized as a master. If two remote IOP's share an I/O bus, one must be a master and the other a slave. Both must be initialized to use the same request/grant mode. Normally, mode 1 will be selected for its improved responsiveness, and the designation of master will be arbitrary. If one IOP must have the I/O bus when the system comes up, it should be initialized as the master.

When a remote IOP shares its I/O bus with a local CPU, it must be a slave and must use request/grant mode 0.

4.6.2 Bus Load Limit

A locally configured IOP effectively has higher bus priority than the CPU since the CPU will grant the bus upon request from the IOP. In this instance, one or two local IOP's can potentially monopolize the bus at the expense of the CPU. Of course, if the IOP activities are time-critical, this is exactly what should happen. On the other hand, there may be low-priority channel programs that have less demanding performance requirements.

In these cases, the CPU sets a CCW bit called bus load limit to constrain the channel's use of the bus during normal (unchained) channel program execution. When this bit is set, the channel decrements a 7-bit counter from 7F (127) to 0H with each instruction executed. Since the counter is decremented once per clock period, the channel waits a minimum of 128 clock cycles before it executes the next instruction. By forcing the execution time of all instructions to 128 clocks, the use of the bus is reduced to between 3 and 25 percent of the available bus cycles.

Setting the bus load limit effectively enables a CPU to slow the execution of a normal channel program, freeing up bus cycles. This is useful in local configurations, but may also be effective in remote configurations, particularly when channel programs are executed from system memory. Bus load limit has no effect on chained channel programs, DMA transfers, DMA termination, or channel attention sequences.

4.6.3 Bus Lock

The 8089 has a LOCK* (bus lock) signal, like the 8086/88 and 80186/188, which can be activated by software. The LOCK* output is normally connected to the LOCK* input of the 8289 Bus Arbiter. When LOCK* is active, the bus arbiter will not release the bus to another processor regardless of its priority. A channel automatically locks the bus during execution of the test and set while locked (TSL) instruction and may lock the bus for the duration of a DMA transfer.

If bit 9 of the CC register is set, the 8089 activates its LOCK* output during a DMA transfer on that channel. If the transfer is synchronized, LOCK* is active from the time that the first DRQ is recognized. If the transfer is unsynchronized, LOCK* is active throughout the entire transfer (there are no idle periods in an unsynchronized transfer). LOCK* goes inactive when the channel begins the DMA termination sequence.

A locked transfer ensures that the transfer will be completed in the shortest possible time and that the transferring channel has exclusive use of the bus. Once the channel obtains the bus and starts a locked transfer, the channel, in effect, becomes the highest-priority processor on that bus.

The 8089 test and set while locked instruction (TSL) can be used to implement a semaphore. The instruction activates LOCK* and inspects the value of a byte in memory. If the value of the byte is 0H, it is changed (set) to a value specified in the instruction and the following instruction is executed. If the byte does not contain 0H, control is transferred to another location specified in the instruction. The byte is locked from the time the byte is read until it is either written or control is transferred to ensure that another processor does not access the variable after TSL has read it, but before it has updated it (i.e., between bus cycles). The following line of code will repeatedly test a semaphore pointed to by GA until it is found to contain zero:

```
TEST_FLAG: TSL [GA],0FFH,TEST_FLAG
```

When the semaphore is found to be zero, it is set to FFH and the program continues with the next instruction.

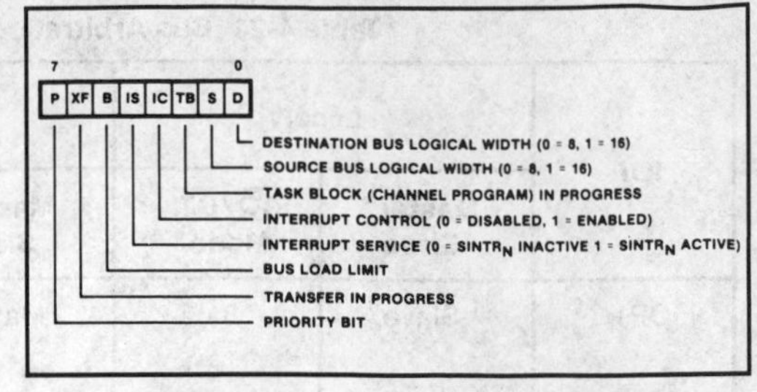

Figure 4-22 Program Status Word

4.7 INTERRUPTS

Each channel has a separate system interrupt line (SINTR1 and SINTR2). A channel program may generate a CPU interrupt request by executing a SINTR instruction. Whether this instruction actually activates the SINTR line, however, depends upon the state of the interrupt bit (bit 3 of the PSW — see Figure 4-22). If this bit is set, interrupts from the channel are enabled, and execution of the SINTR instruction activates SINTR. If the interrupt control bit is cleared, the SINTR instruction has no effect and interrupts from the channel are disabled.

The CPU can alter a channel's interrupt control bit by sending any command to the channel with the value of ICF (interrupt control field) in the CCW set to 10 (enable) or 11 (disable). Therefore, the CPU can prevent interrupts from either channel.

Once activated, SINTR remains active until the CPU sends a channel command with ICF set to 01 (interrupt acknowledge). When the channel receives this command, it clears the interrupt service bit in the PSW (see Figure 4-22) and removes the interrupt request. Disabling interrupts also clears the interrupt service bit and lowers SINTR.

80130 Operating System Firmware

5

CHAPTER 5
80130 OPERATING SYSTEM FIRMWARE

5.1 GENERAL INFORMATION

The 80130 is a component that is designed to work in conjunction with the 8086, the 8088, the 80186, and the 80188 microprocessors. When the 80130 is combined with the iAPX 86/10 (8086) microprocessor, the pair of components is called the iAPX 86/30 Operating System Processor. When the 80130 is combined with the iAPX 88/10 (8088) microprocessor, the pair of components is called the iAPX 88/30 Operating System Processor. In order to simplify nomenclature, this chapter uses the term *OSP* to refer to either pair of components. You can add the 8087 Numeric Processor Extension (NPX) to either pair of components.

5.2 80130 ARCHITECTURE

The 80130 component, shown in Figure 5-1, is internally divided into a number of independent units. The Operating System Unit (OSU) provides the kernel control store, while the Control Unit contains hardware facilities that support it. Also included in the OSU are the Operating System Timers, which are used by the OSP for scheduling and timing intervals, the Programmable Interrupt Controller (PIC), which provides seven independent interrupt lines and one line for the system timer, and User-Programmable Baud Rate Generator for input into a USART.

5.3 DEVICE PIN ASSIGNMENTS

The 80130 device pin assignments are listed with the appropriate description in Table 5-1. The device pin assignments are shown in Figure 5-2.

5.4 OPERATING SYSTEM PRIMITIVES SUMMARY

This section contains the calling sequences and other information about the OSP primitives. The primitives are listed in alphabetical order in Table 5-2. the information for each primitive is organized into the following categories:

1. Primitive
2. A description of the effects of the primitive.
3. The condition codes that can result from using the primitive.

PL/M-86 and iOSP 86 data types, such as BYTE, WORD, SELECTOR, and TOKEN are used in this section. They are always capitalized and their definitions can be found in Table 5-3. In addition, Table 5-4 lists the mnemonic codes for both unavoidable and avoidable exceptions along with the numeric values assigned to each mnemonic exceptor. If your compiler supports the SELECTOR data type, a TOKEN can be declared literally either SELECTOR or WORD. The word "token" in lower case refers to a value that the iOSP 86 Processor assigns to an object. The OSP returns this value to a TOKEN (the data type) when it creates the object.

5.5 INTERFACING WITH THE 8086/88

The iAPX 86/30 and iAPX 88/30 are two-chip microprocessors offering general-purpose CPU (8086) instructions combined with real-time operating system support. The iAPX 86/30 consists of an iAPX 86/10 (16-bit 8086 CPU) and an Operating System Firmware (OSF) component (80130). The 88/30 consists of the OSF and an iAPX 88/10 (8-bit 8088 CPU). The 80130 resides on the CPU local multiplexed bus (Figure 5-3). The main processor is always configured for maximum mode operation. The 80130 automatically selects between its 88/30 and 86/30 operating modes. The 80130 used in the 86/30 configuration, as shown in Figure 5-3 (or similar 88/30 configuration), operates at both 5 and 8 Mhz without requiring processor wait states.

5.5.1 Programming The 80130 OSP's Onchip Peripherals

During normal 8086/8088 and 80186/80188 system operation the 80130's primitives control the onchip programmable interrupt controller (PIC) and timers. During this operation, to ensure proper system operation, the applications software should not control the onchip peripherals. There are, however, a few special cases when direct control of the PIC and timers is required. One case occurs during initial hardware debugging when the systems software is not desired or is not available. Another case is when writing diagnostic software, either self-diagnostic code or board/ system test software.

The information necessary to program the 80130's PIC and timers in these special cases is provided in the following paragraphs. The operation and programming of the PIC's is similar to the 8259A programmable interrupt controller and the operation and programming of the three timers are similar to the 8254 programmable

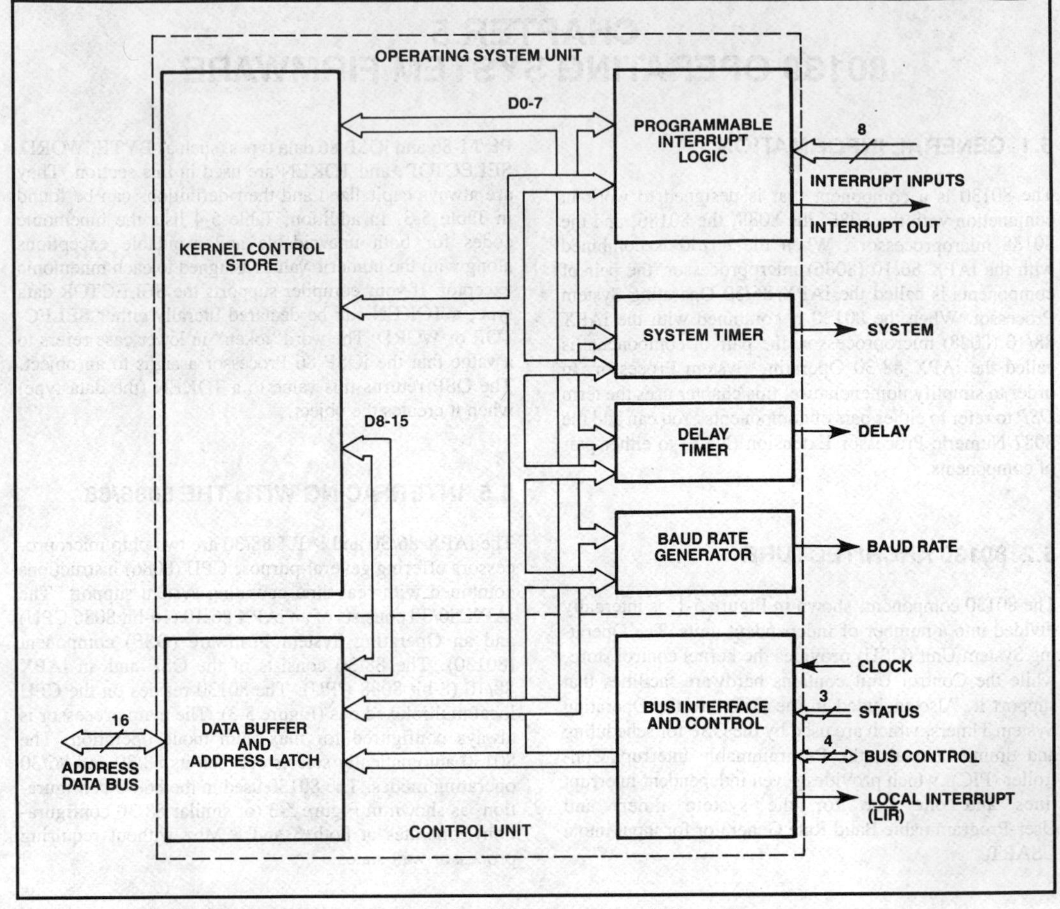

Figure 5-1 80130 Simplified Functional Block Diagram

interval timer. For additional operation and programming information for the onchip peripherals refer to the data sheets for the 80130, 8259A, and 8254 devices.

PROGRAMMABLE INTERRUPT CONTROLLER (PIC)

PIC Commands

The PIC accepts two types of command words from the CPU:

a. Initialization Command Words (ICW's): Before normal operation can begin, the PIC must be initialized with a sequence of 3, 4, 5 or 6 bytes.

b. Operation Command Words OCW: These are command words sent to the PIC for various forms of operation, such as interrupt masking, end of interrupt, and interrupt status.

The OCW's can be sent to the PIC anytime after initialization.

Initialization Command Word 1 (ICW1)

Whenever a command word is sent to address 0H with IOCS/ = 0 and D4 = 1 with a write I/O port bus cycle (S2/ – S0/ = 010), the data is interpreted as Initialization Command Word 1. ICW1 starts the initialization during which the following automatically occurs:

a. The edge sense circuits are reset, which means that following initialization an interrupt request (IR) input must make a low-to-high transition to

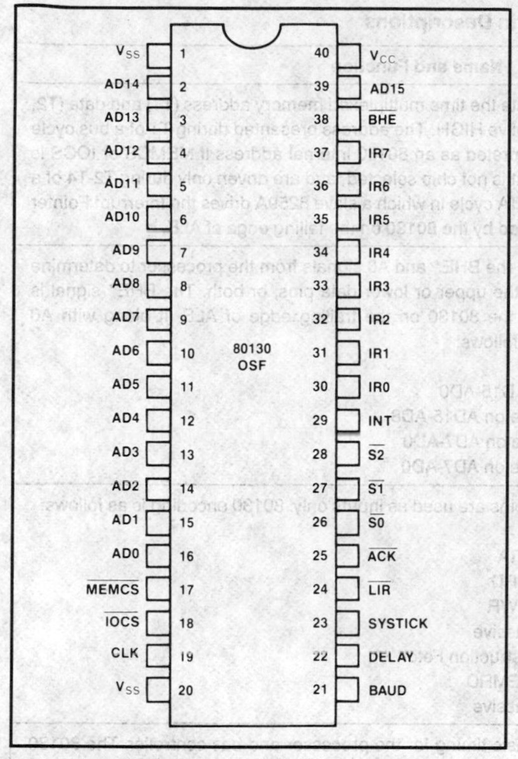

Figure 5-2 80130 OSP Pinout Diagram

generate an interrupt unless the IR input is programmed as a level sensitive input in which case a high level will generate the interrupt.

b. The interrupt mask register is cleared.

c. Status read is set to interrupt request register.

d. All interrupts will be acknowledged with LIR/ = 1 unless ICW6 is sent.

Sending ICW1, ICW2, and ICW4 is the minimum amount of programming needed by the PIC. ICW1 specifies whether the remaining control words (ICW3, ICW5, and ICW6) will be sent. Once ICW1 has been sent, the following writes to I/O address 02H from the base I/O address must be the sequence of ICW2, ICW3, ICW4, ICW5 and ICW6 (with the exception of ICW3, ICW5, and ICW6 if not specified in ICW1). The PIC is ready to accept interrupts after the last ICW is sent.

Bits 7-6 = 00:	Unused but set to 0
Bit 5 = 0:	All inputs are non-local (LIR/ = 1) and ICW6 is not read
= 1:	ICW6 is read to specify local/non-local inputs
Bit 4 = 1:	Indicates ICW1
Bits 3-2 = 00:	Edge triggered interrupts; ICW5 is not read
= 10:	Level triggered interrupts; ICW5 is not read
= × 1:	ICW5 is read to specify interrupt triggering
Bit 1 = 0:	One or more 8259A slaves are connected to IR inputs
= 1:	No 8259A slaves are connected to IR inputs
Bit 0 = 1:	ICW4 is read.

Initialization Command Word 2 (ICW2)

ICW2 contains bits 7-3 of the 8-bit vector that is sent to the CPU during the second interrupt acknowledge cycle. The remaining 3 bits, 2-0 are generated by the PIC depending on the interrupt request input being serviced. ICW2 is sent to I/O address 02H with IOCS/ = 0. Bits 7-3 contain the five most significant bits of an 8-bit interrupt type number. Bits 2-0 are unused and may be any value.

Initialization Command Word 3 (ICW3)

ICW3 is sent only when there are one or more 8259A slaves in the system and is sent to I/O address 02H with

Table 5-1 80130 Pin Descriptions

Symbol	Type	Name and Function
AD15-AD0	I/O	Address Data: These pins constitute the time multiplexed memory address (T1) and data (T2, T3, Tw, T4) bus. These lines are active HIGH. The address presented during T1 of a bus cycle will be latched internally and interpreted as an 80130 internal address if MEMCS or IOCS is active. These pins float whenever it is not chip selected, and are driven only during T2-T4 of a read or INTA cycle and T1 of an INTA cycle in which a slave 8259A drives the Interrupt Pointer during T2-T4. AD0-AD15 are latched by the 80130 on the falling edge of ALE.
BHE*/S7	I	Bus High Enable: The 80130 uses the BHE* and A0 signals from the processor to determine whether to respond with data on the upper or lower data pins, or both. The BHE* signal is active LOW. BHE* is latched by the 80130 on the trailing edge of ALE. It along with A0 controls the 80130 output data as follows: BHE* A0 0 0 Word on AD15-AD0 0 1 Upper byte on AD15-AD8 1 0 Lower byte on AD7-AD0 1 1 Upper byte on AD7-AD0
S2*,S1*,S0*	I	Status: For the 80130, the status pins are used as inputs only. 80130 encoding is as follows: S2 S1 S0 0 0 0 INTA 0 0 1 IORD 0 1 0 IOWR 0 1 1 Passive 1 0 0 Instruction Fetch 1 0 1 MEMRD 1 1 X Passive
CLK	I	The system clock provides the basic timing for the processor and bus controller. The 80130 uses the system clock as an input to the SYSTICK and BAUD timers and to synchronize operation with the host CPU.
INT	O	INT is HIGH whenever a valid interrupt request is asserted. It is normally used to interrupt the CPU by connecting it to INTR.
IR7-IR0	I	Interrupt Requests: An interrupt request can be generated by raising an IR input (LOW to HIGH) and holding it until it is acknowledged.
ACK*	0	Acknowledge: This pin is LOW whenever an 80130 resource is being accessed. It is also LOW during the first and second INTA cycles if the 80130 is supplying the interrupt vector information. This signaling can be used as a bus-ready acknowledgement and/or bus transceiver control.
MEMCS*	I	Memory Chip Select: This input must be driven LOW when a kernel primitive is being fetched by the CPU. AD13-AD0 are used to select the instruction.
IOCS*	I	Input/Output Chip Select: When this input is LOW, during an IORD or IOWR cycle, the 80130's kernel primitives are accessing the appropriate peripheral function was specified by the table on the following page. BHE* A3* A2* A1* A0* 0 X X X X Passive X X X X 1 Passive X 0 1 X X Passive 1 0 0 0 0 Interrupt Controller 1 0 0 1 0 Interrupt Controller 1 1 0 0 0 Systick Timer 1 1 0 1 0 Delay Counter 1 1 1 0 0 Baud Rate Timer 1 1 1 1 0 Timer Control

Table 5-1 80130 Pin Descriptions (continued)

Symbol	Type	Name and Function
LIR*	O	Local Bus Interrupt Request: This signal is LOW when the interrupt request is for a non-slave input or slave input programmed as being a local slave.
Vcc		Power: Vcc is the +5V supply pin.
Vss		Ground: Vss is the ground pin.
SYSTICK	O	System Clock Tick: Timer 0 Output. Operating System Clock Reference. SYSTICK is normally wired to IR2 to implement operating system timing interrupt.
DELAY	O	Delay Timer: Output of timer 1. Reserved by Intel for future use.
BAUD	O	Baud Rate Generator: 8254 Mode 3-compatible output. Output of 80130 timer 2.
GND		Ground: GND is the ground pin.

IOCS/ = 0. Bit 7 is the specification bit for IR7, bit for IR6, . . ., and bit 0 for IR0. If no 8258A slave is connected to an IR, the specification bit is 0. If a slave is connected, the specification bit is 0. If a slave is connected, the specification bit is 1.

Initialization Command Word 4 (ICW4)

ICW4 is always reguired and selects either the normally fully nested mode or the special fully nested mode. ICW4 is sent to I/O address 02H with IOCS/ – 0.

Bits 7-5 = 000: Unused but set to 0
Bit 4 = 0: Normal fully nested mode
= 1: Special fully nested mode
Bit 3 = 1: Buffered mode
Bit 2 = 1: Master Interrupt controller
Bit 1 = 0: Normal end of interrupt (EOI)
Bit 0 = 1: 8086 mode

Initialization Command Word 5 (ICW5)

ICW5 is sent only if specified in ICW1 and individually selects edge or level triggering for each IR input. ICW5 is sent to I/O address 02H with IOCS/ = 0. Bit 7 is the specification bit for IR7, bit 6 for IR6, . . ., and bit 0 for IR0. For edge triggering the specification bit is 0 and for level triggering the specification bit is 1.

Initialization Command Word 6 (ICW6)

ICW6 is sent if specified in ICW1 and selects IR inputs as being either local of non-local. During an interrupt acknowledge cycle, the LIR/ output is driven to zero in response to a local IR input (non-slave input or slave on local bus) or driven to 1 in response to a non-local IR input (slave on system bus). The LIR/ outputs can be used in multimaster systems to control the 8289 Bus Arbiter's SYSB/RESW input. ICW6 is sent to I/O address 02H with IOCS/ = 0. Bit 7 is the specification bit for IR7, bit 6 for IR6, bit 5 for IR5, . . ., and bit 0 for IR0. For non-local IR input, the specification bit is 0 and for a local IR input, the specification bit is 1.

Operation Command Word 1 (OCW1)

OCW1 sets and clears the mask bits in the Interrupt Mask Register (IMR) and is sent to I/O address 02H with IOCS/ = 0. Bit 7 is the specification bit for IR7, bit 6 for IR6, bit 5 for IR5, . . ., and bit 0 for IR0. To enable interrupts on an IR input, the specification bit is 0. To mask or inhibit interrupts on an IR input, the specification bit 1. Masking an IR input does not affect the operation of the other IR inputs.

Operation Command Word 2 (OCW2)

OCW2 is used to send an end of interrupt (EOI) command to the PIC which resets an in-service bit in the In-service Register (ISR). OCW2 is sent to I/O address 0H with IOCS/ = 0.

Bits 7-5 = 011: Specific end of interrupt
Bits 4-3 = 00: Indicates OCW2
Bits 2-1 = 000: End of Interrupt on IR0
= 001: End of Interrupt on IR1
= 010: End of Interrupt on IR2
= 011: End of Interrupt on IR3
= 100: End of Interrupt on IR4
= 101: End of Interrupt on IR5
= 110: End of Interrupt on IR6
= 111: End of Interrupt on IR7

Operation Command Word 3 (OCW3)

OCW3 is used to read two of the PIC's internal registers: Interrupt Request Register (IRR) and In-service Register (ISR). IRR is an 8-bit register that indicates which IR inputs are waiting to be acknowledged. ISR is an 8-bit

Table 5-2 OSP Primitives

Primitive	Description	Condition Codes
ACCEPT$CONTROL	Requests immediate access to data protected by a region.	E$OK E$BUSY E$EXIST E$TYPE
CREATE$JOB	Creates a job containing a single task.	E$OK E$EXIST E$LIMIT E$MEM E$PARAM
CREATE$MAILBOX	Creates a mailbox.	E$OK E$LIMIT E$MEM
CREATE$REGION	Creates a region.	E$OK E$LIMIT E$MEM
CREATE$SEGMENT	Creates a segment.	E$OK E$LIMIT E$MEM
CREATE$TASK	Creates a task.	E$OK E$LIMIT E$MEM E$PARAM
DELETE$MAILBOX	Deletes a mailbox.	E$OK E$EXIST E$TYPE
DELETE$REGION	Deletes a region.	E$OK E$CONTEXT E$EXIST E$TYPE
DELETE$SEGMENT	Deletes a segment.	E$OK E$EXIST E$TYPE
DELETE$TASK	Deletes a task.	E$OK E$CONTEXT E$EXIST E$TYPE
DISABLE	Disables an interrupt line.	E$OK E$CONTEXT E$PARAM
DISABLE$DELETION	Makes an object immune to ordinary deletion.	E$OK E$EXIST E$LIMIT
ENABLE	Enables an interrupt line.	E$OK E$CONTEXT E$PARAM
ENABLE$DELETION	Enables the deletion of objects that have deletion disabled.	E$OK E$CONTEXT E$EXIST
ENTER$INTERRUPT	Used by interrupt handlers to load a previously specified segment base address into the register.	E$OK E$CONTEXT E$PARAM DS

Table 5-2 OSP Primitives (continued)

Primitive	Description	Condition Codes
EXIT$INTERRUPT	Used by interrupt handlers when they don't invoke interrupt tasks. This primitive sends an end-of-interrupt signal to the hardware.	E$OK E$CONTEXT E$PARAM
GET$EXCEPTION$HANDLER	Returns information about the calling task's exception handler.	E$OK
GET$LEVEL	Returns the number of the highest priority interrupt line being serviced.	E$OK
GET$TASK$TOKENS	Returns the token requested by the calling task.	E$OK E$PARAM
GET$TYPE	Returns the encoded type of an object.	E$OK E$EXIST
RECEIVE$CONTROL	Allows the calling task to gain access to data protected by a region.	E$OK E$CONTEXT E$EXIST E$TYPE
RECEIVE$MESSAGE	Queues the calling task at a mailbox, where it can wait for an object token to be returned.	E$OK E$EXIST E$TIME E$TYPE
RESET$INTERRUPT	Cancels the assignment of an interrupt handler to an interrupt line.	E$OK E$CONTEXT E$PARAM
RESUME$TASK	Decreases by one the suspension depth of a task.	E$OK E$CONTEXT E$EXIST E$STATE E$TYPE
SEND$CONTROL	Allows a task to surrender access to data protected by a region.	E$OK E$CONTEXT
SEND$MESSAGE	Sends an object token to a mailbox.	E$OK E$EXIST E$MEM E$TYPE
SET$EXCEPTION$HANDLER	Assigns an exception handler to the calling task.	E$OK E$PARAM
SET$INTERRUPT	Assigns an interrupt handler to an interrupt line and, optionally, makes the calling task the interrupt task for the line.	E$OK E$CONTEXT E$PARAM
SETOSEXTENSION	Either enters the address of an entry (or function) procedure in the Interrupt Vector Table or it deletes such an entry.	E$OK E$CONTEXT E$PARAM
SET$PRIORITY	Change the priority of a task.	E$OK E$CONTEXT E$EXIST E$LIMIT E$TYPE
SIGNAL$EXCEPTION	Invoked by extensions of the OS Processor to signal the occurrence of an exceptional condition.	E$OK

Table 5-2 OSP Primitives (continued)

Primitive	Description	Condition Codes
SIGNAL$INTERRUPT	Used by an interrupt handler to activate an interrupt task.	E$OK E$CONTEXT E$INTERRUPT-SATURATION E$INTERRUPT-OVERFLOW E$LIMIT E$PARAM
SLEEP	Puts the calling task to sleep.	E$OK E$PARAM
SUSPEND$TASK	Increases by one the suspension depth of a task.	E$OK E$CONTEXT E$EXIST E$LIMIT E$TYPE
WAIT$INTERRUPT	Used by an interrupt task to signal its readiness to service an interrupt.	E$OK E$CONTEXT E$PARAM

register that indicates which IR inputs are being serviced. Upon receiving an EOI command, the specified bit in the ISR is reset. OCW3 is sent to I/O address 0H (with IOCS/ = 0) and during the subsequent read from I/O address 0H, the PIC sends the contents of the specified register to the CPU. It is not necessary to send an OCW3 for each read register operation provided that the same register is being read as the previous read register operation. The PIC remembers whether IRR or ISR was previously selected by OCW3.

Bits 7-5 = xxx: Unused and may be any value
Bits 4-3 = 01: Indicates OCW3
Bits 2-1 = xx: Unused and may be any value

Bit0 = 0: Read Interrupt Request Register
= 1: Read In-service Register.

Reading the Interrupt Mask Register (IMR)

The IMR is an 8-bit register that indicates which IR inputs are masked (interrupts are inhibited). IMR is read by reading from I/O address 02H with IOCS/ = 0.

Differences between 80130 and 8259A

The 80130 PIC does not provide:

Table 5-3 Data Types

Data Type	Definition
BYTE	An unsigned, 8-bit, binary number.
WORD	An unsigned, two-byte, binary number.
INTEGER	A signed, two-byte, binary number that is stored in two's complement form.
BASE	A word whose value represents a 16-byte boundary which defines a 64K-byte segment.
OFFSET	A word whose value represents the distance from the base of a segment.
TOKEN	A word or selector whose value identifies an object. A token can be declared literally a WORD or SELECTOR depending upon your needs.
POINTER	Two words containing the base of a segment and an offset, in the reverse order.
STRING	A sequence of consecutive bytes. The first byte contains the number (not to exceed 12) of bytes that follow it in the string.
SELECTOR	A word that is useful when used as the base portion of a 32-bit address (in the form base: offset) whose offset is zero.

Table 5-4 Mnemonic Codes for Exceptions

Mnemonic Codes for Unavoidable Exceptions

E$OK	Exception Code Value = 0 the operation was successful
E$TIME	Exception Code Value = 1 the specified time limit expired before completion of the operations was possible
E$MEM	Exception Code Value = 2 insufficient nucleus memory is available to satisfy the request
E$BUSY	Exception Code Value = 3 specified region is currently busy
E$LIMIT	Exception Code Value = 4 attempted violation of a job, semaphore, or system limit
E$CONTEXT	Exception Code Value = 5 the primitive was called in an illegal context (e.g., call to enable for an already enabled interrupt)
E$EXIST	Exception Code Value = 6 a token argument does not currently refer to any object; note that the object could have been deleted at any time by its owner
E$STATE	Exception Code Value = 7 attempted illegal state transition by a task
ENOTCONFIGURED	Exception Code Value = 8 the primitive called is not configured in this system
E$INTERRUPT$SATURATION	Exception Code Value = 9 The interrupt task on the requested level has reached its user specified saturation point for interrupt service requests. No further interrupts will be allowed on the level until the interrupt task executes a WAIT$INTERRUPT. (This error is only returned, in line, to interrupt handlers.)
E$INTERRUPT$OVERFLOW	Exception Code Value = 10 The interrupt task on the requested level previously reached its saturation point and caused an E$INTERRUPT$SATURATION condition. It subsequently executed an ENABLE allowing further interrupts to come in and has received another SIGNAL$INTERRUPTcall, bringing it over its specified saturation point for interrupt service requests. (This error is only returned, in line, to interrupt handlers).

Mnemonic Codes for Avoidable Exceptions

E$ZERO$DIVIDE	Exception Code Value = 8000H divide by zero interrupt occurred
E$OVERFLOW	Exception Code Value = 8001H overflow interrupt occurred
E$TYPE	Exception Code Value = 8002H a token argument referred to an object tha was not of required type
E$BOUNDS	Exception Code Value = 8003H an offset argument is out of segment bounds
E$PARAM	Exception Code Value = 8004H a (non-token,non-offset) argument has an illegal value
EBADCALL	Exception Code Value = 8005H an entry code for which there is no corresponding primitive was passed
E$ARRAY$BOUNDS = 8006H	Hardware or Language has detected an array overflow
ENDPERROR	Exception Code Value = 8007H an 8087 (Numeric data Processor) error has been detected; (the 8087 status information is contained in a parameter to the exception handler)

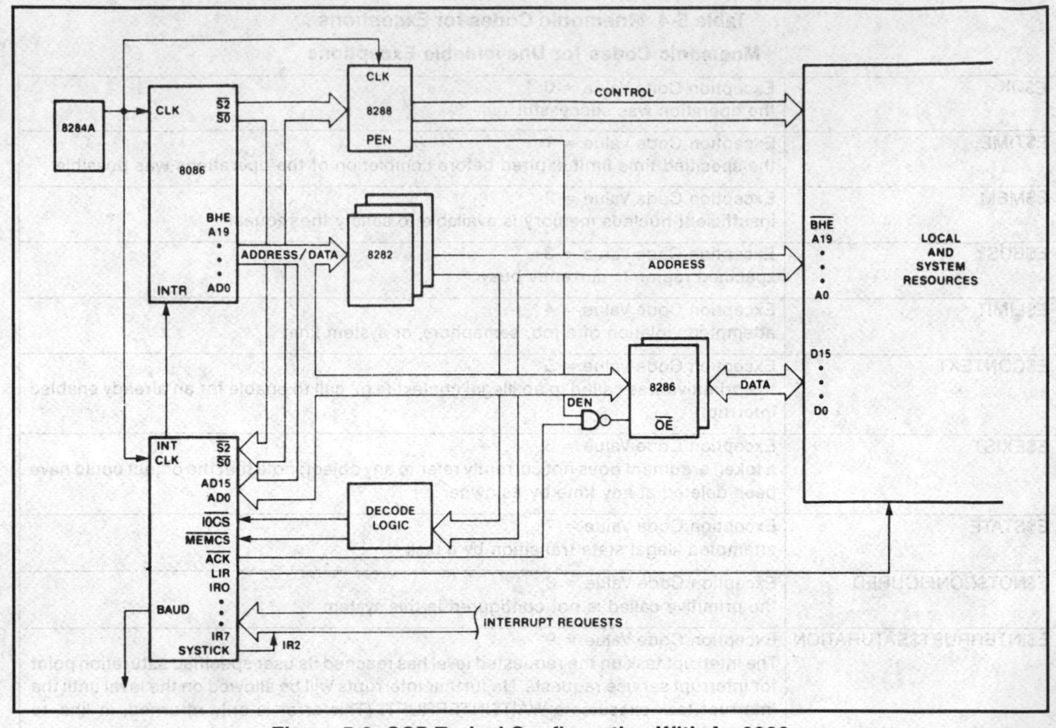

Figure 5-3 OSP Typical Configuration With An 8086

- 8080 and 8085 mode of operation;
- Slave mode of operation;
- Automatic EOI;
- Non-specific EOI;
- Rotating or programmed priorities;
- Polling;
- Special mask mode.

The 80130 PIC does provide:

- Individual IR input selection of edge or level triggering;
- Local or non-local identification for each IR input.

PROGRAMMABLE TIMERS

The 80130 contains three programmable timers, each with 16-bits of resolution. Each timer has a fixed mode of operation needed by the iRMX 86 nucleus. Timer 0 operates only in the 8284 compatible rate generator mode (mode 2). Timer 1 operates only in the 8254 compatible interrupt on terminal count mode (mode 0). Timer 2 operates only in the 8254 compatible square wave generator mode (mode3). Each timer is programmable by sending the appropriate control word followed by the least significant byte of the count value and then the most significant byte.

The 80130 timers are connected to the lower half of the data bus and are addressed at even addresses. The timers are read as two successive bytes, with the least significant byte always followed by the most significant byte. The most significant byte is always latched on a read operation and remains latched until operation is complete. The OSP uses configuration information to perform all necessary initialization of the timers.

The Baud Rate generator is compatible with the 8254 Programmable Interval Timer in squarewave mode 3. Its output, BAUD, is initially high and remains high until the count register is loaded with a count. The first falling edge of the clock after the count register is loaded causes the transfer of the internal counter to the count register. The output stays high for N/2 (or (N+1)/2 if N is odd) counts and then goes low for N/2 (or (N−1)/2 if N is odd) counts. The output returns to the high state when the falling edge of the input clock is detected during the final count for the output in low state. At this time, the contents of the count register are transferred to the internal

Table 5-5 Baud Rate Counter Values (16X)

Baud Rate	8 Mhz Count Value	5 Mhz Count Value
300	1667	1042
600	833	521
1200	417	260
2400	208	130
4800	104	65
9600	52	33

counter. The whole process is then repeated. Baud rate count values for 5 and 8 Mhz input are shown in Table 5-5.

The baud rate generator's count register is at location 0CH (12 decimal), relative to the beginning of the 80130's I/O (designated OSF in the following example). The timer control word is located at relative address, 0EH (14 decimal). The I/O space chip select must be lower (IOCS = 0) in order to access the OSU timers. Timers 0 and 1 are assigned exclusively to the iOSP processor and should not be programmed by any direct commands.

Programming is performed automatically during the 80130 Configuration Process.

The baud rate generator can be programmed. The baud rate generator command byte is 0B6H (read/write baud rate delay value). The following example sets the baud rate to 9600. Table 5-5 shows that a count value of 52 corresponds to 9600 baud at 8 Mhz. OSF represents the base address of the 80130 I/O space.

```
MOV AL,0B6H        ;Prepare to write delay to timer 3
OUT OSF + 14,AL    ;control word
MOV AX, 52
OUT OSF + 12,AL    ;Least significant byte written
                   first
XCHG AL,AH
OUT OSF + 12,AL    ;Most significant byte written af-
                   ter.
```

Initializing the Timers

The 80130 timers are initialized by sending initialization words to the control word register at I/O address 0EH with IOCS/ = 0. Due to fixed operation of the counters, each counter has only one possible initialization word. This initialization word must be sent prior to sending the two bytes of the count value. The initialization words and the meaning of the encoding is as follows:

Timer	Initialization Word
0	00110100B
1	01110000B
2	10110110B

```
Bits 7-6 = 00:    Select timer 0
         = 01:    Select timer 1
         = 10:    Select timer 2
Bits 5-4 = 11:    Least significant byte first then most
                  significant byte
Bits 3-1 = 000:   Mode 0 (timer 1 only)
         = 010:   Mode 2 (timer 0 only)
         = 011:   Mode 3 (timer 2 only)
Bit    0 =   0:   Binary count mode.
```

After each initialization word is sent, the 16-bit count value is sent to the appropriate timer port, least significant bit first and then most significant bit. The timer ports for timers 0, 1, and 2 are located at I/O addresses 08H, 0AH, and 0CH with IOCS/ = 0, respectively.

Reading the Count Value

The count value of each counter is read by sending a latch command to the control word register at I/O address 0EH (with IOCS/ = 0) and then reading the count value bytes from the appropriate timer port, least significant byte first and then the most significant byte. The timer ports for timers 0, 1, and 2 are located at I/O addresses 08H, 0AH, and 0CH with IOCS/ = 0, respectively. The latch command does not stop the timer counting but stores the current count value to insure accurate reading of both bytes.

Timer	Latch Command
0	00000000B
1	01000000B
2	10000000B

Differences Between 80130 Timers and 8253/8254

The 80130 timers do not provide:

- Programmable modes for each timer;
- Gate inputs;
- Programmable Read/Write modes;
- BCD count mode;
- Read-Back command (8254 only)

The 80130 timers do provide:

- 8 MHz operation;
- TO output internally connected to T1 clock input.

5.6 OSP MEMORY USAGE

The following lists the amount of memory the OSP requires for object creation and memory borrowing. The OSP obtains this memory from the calling task's job memory pool when creating the specified object. The OSP uses the following amounts of memory when it creates objects:

Object	Number or 16-Byte Paragraphs Required by the OSP
job	3 + object directory + 1 per entry in the object directory
task	5 + 6 (if the task uses the 8087 NPX) + stacksize/16 (if the OSP allocates the stack)
mailbox	2 + ((size of high-performance queue)/4) − 1
region	2
segment	1 + segmentsize/16

When a job borrows memory from its parent, the OSP uses three 16-byte paragraphs in addition to the amount it uses for object creation. The OSP obtains this memory from the parent job.

The OSP needs:

760H bytes + (10H * the number of Root Object Directory (ROD) entries)

for operating system free space. The OSP uses different amounts of memory, depending upon whether you include parameter validation or not.

- With parameter validation — 6.8k.
- Without parameter vaildation — 5.5k.

5.7 INTERRUPT CONTROLLER

The 80130 Programmable Interrupt Controller, or PIC, is another integral unit of the 80130 component. The OSP initializes the PIC according to user-supplied configuration information.

The PIC logic portion of the 80130 component provides eight input pins for eight separately-vectored priority interrupts. However, one of these pins is reserved for the system timing function. Up to seven external 8259A slave interrupt controllers can be used to expand the total number of OSP external interrupts to as many as 56. The default OSP configuration expects INT2 to be connected to the SYSTICK output.

The 80130 component provides two ways of sensing an active interrupt request:

1) a level-sensitive input
2) an edge-sensitive input

The OSP initializes each interrupt pin to be either edge-or level-sensitive based on user-supplied configuration information.

5.7.1 Level-Triggered Mode

When an IR input pin (IR0 through IR7) of the 80130 PIC is in the level-triggered mode, the 80130 PIC recognizes any active (high) level as an interrupt request. If the IR input remains active after the EXIT$INTERRUPT primitive has been executed, another interrupt request is generated. This will be recognized only if the processor INT pin is enabled. Unless repetitious interrupt generation is desired, the IR input must be brought to an inactive state before the EXIT$INTERRUPT primitive has been executed. However, it must not go inactive so soon that it violates necessary timing requirements. The request on the IR input must remain until after the falling edge of the first INTA pulse. If the request on any IR input becomes inactive before the first INTA pulse, the 80130 PIC responds as if IR7 was active. If this is a possibility in the design, the IR7 default feature can be used as a safeguard. The IR7 routine is used as a "clean-up routine", which rechecks the status of the PIC or merely returns program execution to its pre-interrupt location.

Depending upon the particular design and application, the level-triggered mode has the following advantages.

1) It allows repetitious interrupt generation. This is useful in cases when service routine needs to be executed continually until the IR input goes inactive.
2) It allows a number of interrupting devices to use the same IR input pin. This cannot be done in the edge-triggered mode. Note that when multiple devices use the same IR input pin, the actual requesting device has to be ascertained by the interrupt handler.

5.7.2 Edge-Triggered Mode

When an IR input pin (IR0 through IR7) of the 80130 PIC is in the edge-triggered mode, it only recognizes interrupts that are generated by an inactive (low) to active (high) transition. The edge-triggered mode incorporates an edge-lockout method of operation. This means that, after acknowledgement of a request, the high level of the IR input will not generate further interrupts until another low-to-high transition occurs. Thus, after acknowledgement, the request does not have to be removed quickly, as might be the case in the level-triggered mode. Before another interrupt can be generated, the IR input must be returned to the inactive state.

The edge-triggered mode, the request on the IR input must remain active until after the falling edge of the first INTA pulse for that particular interrupt. Because of the way the edge-triggered mode functions, it is more convenient to use a positive level with a negative pulse to trigger the IR requests. With this type of input, the trailing edge of the pulse causes the interrupt, the maintained positive level meets the necessary timing requirements (by remaining high until after the interrupt is acknowledged.) Note that the IR/ default feature mentioned in the level-triggered mode section also works for the edge-triggered mode.

Depending upon the particular design and application, the edge-triggered mode has the following advantages:

1) Because of its edge-triggered operation, it is best used in those applications where repetitious interrupt generation isn't desired.
2) It is very useful in systems where the interrupt request is a pulse (which should be in the form of a negative pulse to the on-chip PIC).
3) It simplifies your design considerations, because the duration of the interrupt request at a positive level is usually not a factor.

5.7.3 Local Interrupt Requests

In addition to standard PIC functions, the 80130 PIC unit provides an output signal (LIR/) for local bus interrupt requests. During an interrupt acknowledge cycle, this signal indicates whether the interrupt request is from a non-slave input or a slave on the local bus (LIR/ = 0), or from a slave on the system bus (LIR/ = 1).

The OSP programs each IR input pin (IR0 through IR7) to produce LIR/ = 0 or LIR/ = 1 according to user-supplied configuration information. This signal can be used in multimaster systems to control the 8289 Bus Arbiter's SYSB/RESB input and minimizes the number of system bus accesses.

5.7.4 Interrupt Sequence

The OSP interrupt sequence is as follows:

1. One or more of the interrupts is set by a low-to-high transition on edge-sensitive IR inputs or by a high input on level-sensitive IR inputs.
2. The 80130 component evaluates these requests, and sends an INT to the CPU, if appropriate.
3. The CPU acknowledges the INT by responding with an interrupt acknowledge cycle that is encoded in S2/-S0/.
4. Upon receiving the first interrupt acknowledge from the CPU, the 80130 component sets the highest priority interrupt and resets the corresponding edge-detect latch. The 80130 does not drive the address/data bus during this bus cycle but does acknowledge the cycle by setting ACK/ to 0 and LIR/ to the level of the IR input being acknowledged.
5. The CPU then initiates a second interrupt acknowledge cycle. During T1, the 80130 component either supplies the cascade address of the interrupting 8259A slave on AD10-AD8 or releases an 8-bit pointer onto the local bus to be read by the CPU. If the 80130 does supply the pointer, the ACK/ will be low for the cycle. This cycle also has the value LIR/ for the IR input being acknowledged.
6. The in-service register (ISR) bit in the on-chip PIC remains set until either the EXIT INTERRUPT or the SIGNAL INTERRUPT primitive is called by the INterrupt Handler to complete interrupt processing.

5.8 TIMING

System timing analysis typically presents the most difficult part of digital hardware design, although timing for the 80130 is fairly simple. By design the 80130 is compatible with the timing of the host processor. Since the 80130 interfaces directly with the CPU pins, traditional setup, hold, and access times no longer matter.

Two areas of concern must be taken into consideration when analyzing the timing for most OSP systems. Both of these areas relate to the user generated chip-select signals. Figure 5-4 illustrates the relevant timing signals of a standard 8086 four-state Read cycle (memory or I/O), along with the timing responses of the 80130. I/O Write cycle timing is the same. (Full timing diagrams may be found in the respective data sheets.)

The first area of concern is that MEMCS* and IOCS* must be active early in a memory or I/O cycle if the 80130 is to respond during T_3. In each case, the chip-select signals must be active T_{CSCL} before the end of state T_2. Assuming wait states are not desired, addresses generated by the CPU must propagate through the address latches and be decoded during T_1 or T_2.

By convention, T_{CLAV} is the delay from the start of of T_1 until address information is valid on the CPU pins; T_{IVOV} is the propagation delay through an 8282 latch; and T_{CSCL} is the 80130 chip-select logic propagation delay, after the latch outputs are stable. The sum of these four delays must be less than two system clock cycles, reduced by the clock transition time.

$$T_{CLAV} + T_{IVOV} + T_{OVCS} + T_{CSCL} \leq T_{CLCL} + T_{CLCL}$$
$$T_{OVCS} \leq T_{CLCL} + T_{CLCL} - T_{CLAV} - T_{IVOV} - T_{CSCL}$$
$$\leq 125 + 125 - 60 - 30 - 20 \text{ (nsec.)}$$
$$\leq 140 \text{ nsec.}$$

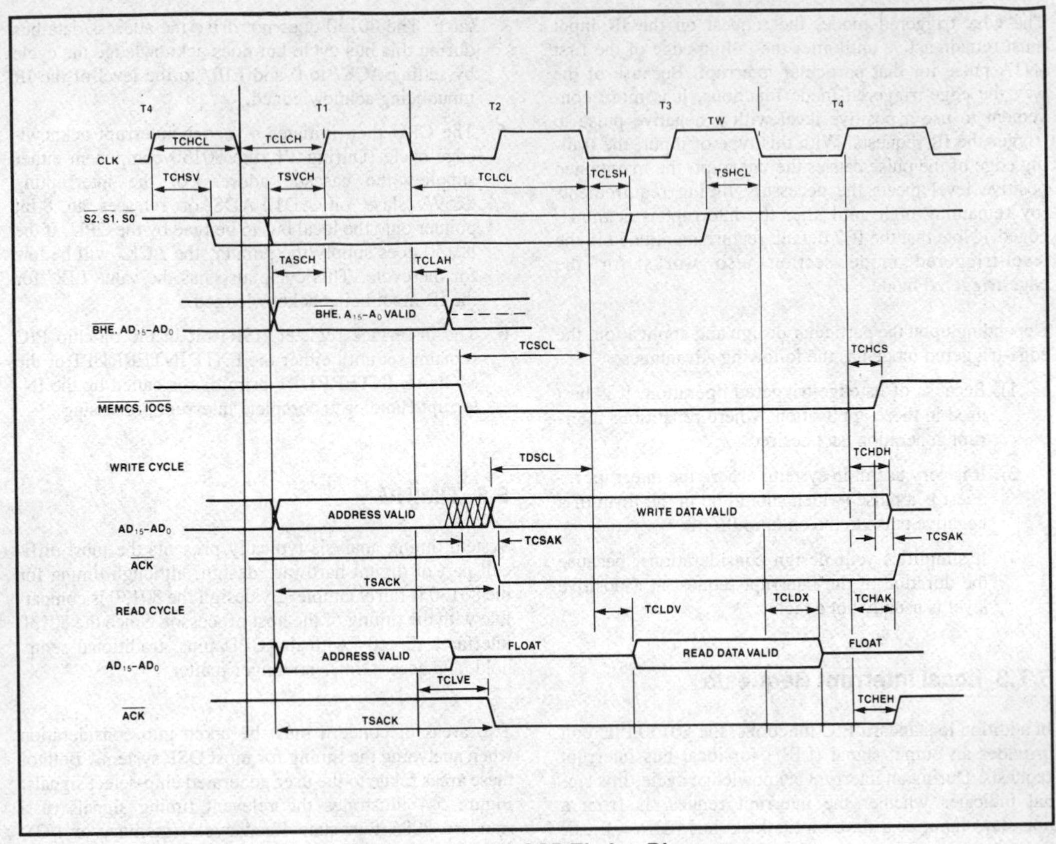

Figure 5-4 80130 OSP Timing Diagram

The propagation delay numbers used in the preceding equation are worst-case values from the appropriate data sheets. The CPU is an 8086-2 operating at 8 MHz. This means the address decode logic must produce stable CS outputs within 140 nanoseconds. Using standard, low power Schottky TTL, it will typically not take longer than 140 nsec. to decode 6 program or 12 I/O address bits. Even if these timing specifications are not met the 80130 will work fine, although performance would be degraded some because wait states would be needed until the chip-select signal became active.

The second point of concern relates to ready signal timing. The 80130's acknowledge output signal, ACK*, can be used to control the CPU's ready signal. For this case, the chip-select signal must be active early in a memory or I/O cycle to allow activation of ACK* early enough to prevent wait states. There are two schemes for implementing ready signals; "normally ready" and "normally not ready". (For more details, refer to AP-67, "8086 System Design.") Chip-select timing is more critical in some "normally not ready" systems.

In a "normally not ready" design, acknowledge signals are generated when each resource is accessed. The individual acknowledgements are combined to form a system-wide ready signal which is synchronized by the 8284A clock generator via the RDY and AEN inputs. The 8284A can be strapped to accept asynchronous ready signals (asynchronous operation) or to accept synchronous ready signals (synchronous operation). Synchronous 8284A operation provides more time for address latch propagation and chip-select decoding. In addition, inverting ACK off chip produces an active-high ready signal compatible with the 8284A RDY inputs, which have shorter set-up requirements than AEN inputs. (Also, a NAND gate used like this can combine ACK with the active-low acknowledge signals from other parts of the system.) Based on these assumptions, the time available for address latch propagation and chip-select decoding at 8 MHz is:

$$T_{CLAV} + T_{OVCS} + T_{CSAK} + R_{R1VCL} \leq T_{CLCL} + T_{CLCL}$$
$$T_{OVCS} \leq 2\,T_{CLCL} - T_{CLAV} - T_{CSAK} - T_{R1VCL}$$
$$\leq 250 - 60 - 110 - 35$$
$$\leq 45 \text{ nsec.}$$

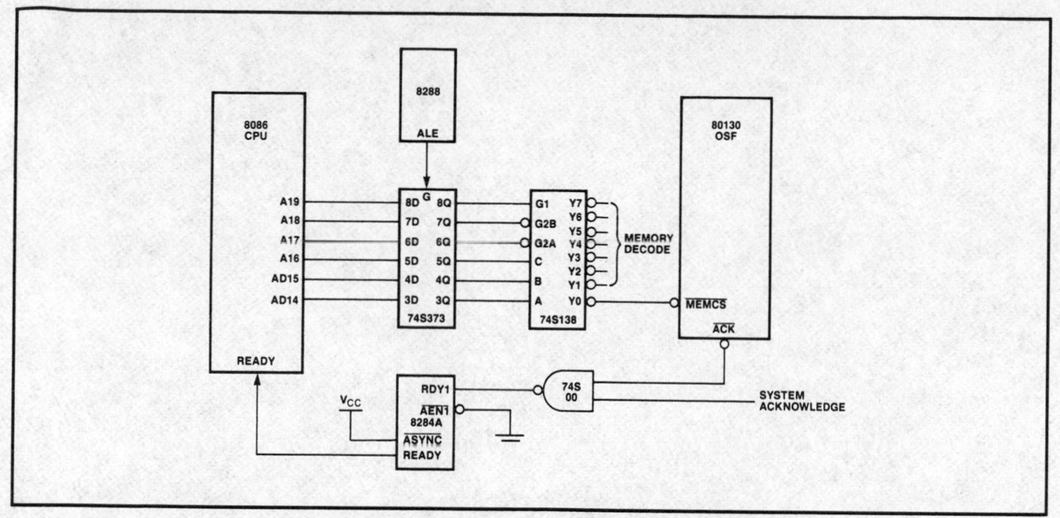

Figure 5-5 High-Speed Address Decoding Circuit

A typical circuit (see Figure 5-5) which uses Schottky TTL components leaves approximately 15 nanoseconds to produce MEMCS* from the high order address bits, more than enough for the 74S138 one-of-eight decoders. This type of circuit allows a minimum of time to fully decode the I/O bits. Also, a 12-input NAND gate on AD15-AD4 could be used. This introduces only a single propagation delay, but forces the I/O register to start at 0FFF0H. Incomplete decoding is also allowable; it is safe to drive IOCS* with the (latched) AD15 signal directly, provided all other ports in the system are disabled when this bit is low. In this case, the effective address of the I/O block (which must be specified during the system configuration step) could be 0000H, or any other multiple of 16 between 0000H and 7FF0H.

The OSP will still operate even if the memory or I/O decoding is slow. The acknowledge signal returned to the host CPU would just be delayed accordingly, so unnecessary wait states would be inserted in the access cycle, but the 80130 would not malfunction. The OSP seldom accesses resources in its own I/O space. Even if slow decode logic were to insert several wait states into every I/O cycle, the overall effect on system performance would be insignificant.

The designer must exercise caution, though, if the 8284A is strapped for synchronous operation. In this case, external circuits must guarantee that ready-input transitions do not violate the latch set-up requirements. Also, the chip-select signal must not remain low so long after the address changes that the 80130 could respond to a non-80130 access cycle.

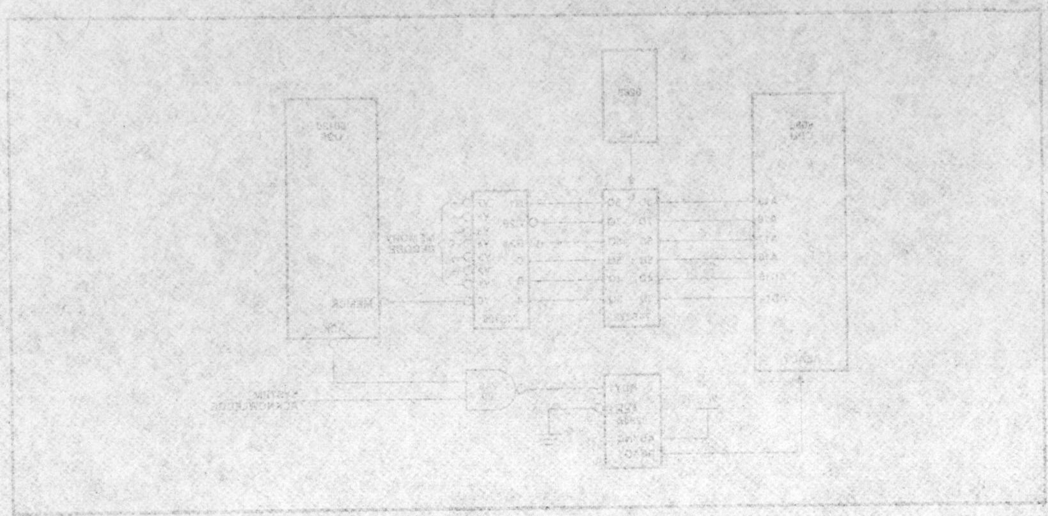

Index

INDEX